PLANT
SYNONYMS

21,000 plant name
changes simplified

Karen Platt

Black Tulip Publishing

This edition of Plant Synonyms is dedicated to my son.

British Library Cataloguing in publication Data.
A catalogue record of this book is available from the British Library.

ISBN   0 9545764 54

© Karen Platt 2006

Published by
Black Tulip Publishing
35 Longfield Rd
Crookes
Sheffield
S10 1QW

www.karenplatt.co.uk
www.blackplants.co.uk

Cover Design: Joshua Coventry

CONTENTS

Aralia japonica became Fatsia japonica

Rudbeckia purpurea became Echinacea purpurea

Aquilegia vulgaris 'William Guiness' is often also sold as 'Magpie'

Meconopsis betonicifolia was M. baileyi

Epipremnun aureum was known as Scindapus

Chrysanthemums are one of the more confusing Genera

Preface

Six years ago, I wrote Plant Names A-Z- a guide to using the correct plant names. The book covered synonyms, common names, plant families, meanings of latin epithets as well as a horticultural dictionary.

However, the book was originally written to guide readers through the muddle of plant names and the prolific use of synonyms encountered when I compiled five editions of the Seed Search.

Now the first edition of Plant Names A-Z is out of print, I have decided to split it into several volumes under different titles; each one treating each section in depth.

As the Synonyms are the most important aspect in my opinion, I have made a start with these. The other books in the series will follow to join the Reference series of books I have written. Plants are explored in the series of Colour books.

Why synonyms? I found that many plant name changes are ignored in the industry and I encountered many seeds listed under two names, sometimes with different descriptions. On one memorable occasion, I found one company selling the same plant under three names. In the name of fairness, I thought it right that I should produce a book so that no-one bought the same plant inadvertently more than once, no matter how many names it should be sold under. I believe I have achieved my aim, this book includes over 21,000 synonyms and their correct current botanical names as opposed to just 8,000 in the original edition.

If by my efforts, I can clear up some of the confusion that surrounds plant names. then I shall have achieved my aim. Life should be simple without unnecessary complications. I trust you will find Plant Synonyms a comprehensive and accurate reference work.

Every supplier has a duty to the consumer to ensure that plants are correctly labelled. I hope that this book makes the task easier.

The Scourge of Plant Names

Many people are afraid of botanical names, they are afraid of opening their mouths for fear of pronouncing them incorrectly.

Any name is a means of identification. Those who correct us at every step when we endeavour to pronounce unspeakable names, should be smiled upon politely, and we should proceed as before. You could also ask these know-it-alls when they last conversed with a Roman in fluent latin. There is, or should be no need for embarrasment. Just remember, someone who laughs at a person who is trying their best, is not really a very nice person. And above all, remember latin is a dead language.

Many latin words are easy to pronounce, many others are the exact opposite. The point is that the listener understands which plant is being spoken about; not that the speaker pronounces the name perfectly. Of course, one has to take his or her hat off to the person who has managed to get their tongue around each and every word of latin-this is undoubtedly a triumph. However, the triumphant should never force their achievements down the throats or ears of others less accomplished. Speak and thou shall be heard - be grateful you do not need to learn the grammar!

Common names widely differ from area to area, so with this in mind, it is the best course not to put anyone off pronouncing botanical names. The latter are not merely latin either, there is a smattering of Greek. Yes, I know the joke, it's all Greek to me.

Tips for Pronunciation

Basically one says it as it is written, with few exceptions
if an epithet ends in ii - only one i is heard
g and c are hard sounds as in gap and cap
ch as in chorus
qu as in kw
x as ks
e usually ay as in they, but in et, est, sed it is pronounced as in bet
ps is pronounced as s

In two-syllable words, the stress is on the first syllable
In longer words, the stress usually falls on the penultimate syllable.

For me, as a linguist, it has to sound right. I would rather say Abies (ABees) than (AB-ee-ayes).

There is a good pronunciation guide with sound by Fine Gardening, the American magazine. Unfortunately, or fortunately for me, they need this book as some of their plant names are sadly out of date.

So, if I don't believe that pronunciation is the be all and end all, why do I get so hot under the collar about the current botanical plant name? Read on...

Best advice of all is to say it with conviction, even if it is your own interpretation of it.

Nomenclature

Nomenclature and taxonomy are the dirty names of horticulture. There are rules to follow. In this book I have endeavoured to follow the Rules of Nomenclature set out in the International Code of Botanical Nomenclature 1994 (ICBN) and the International Code of Nomenclature for Cultivated Plants 1995 (ICNP).

Under the rules it is stated that no cultivar name may bear a Latin generic name. Viola 'Gazania' would be invalid because Gazania is a Latin generic name.
Also English Names cannot be latinized. Since 1959, the Code has not allowed wholly or partly Latin names to be used as cultivar names.

Seed strains are unstable and are not usually granted cultivar status. However, there are more and more instances of one particular seed company raising named cultivars. A cultivar is defined by the Code as 'distinct, uniform and stable'. Many seed strains bear the word group as in Acer palmatum Atropurpurea Group.

Plant names originating in a foreign language should remain as such and should not be translated.

Hyphenation is permitted for two separate words such as novi-belgii but not for compounded forms such as albo-striata which should be written as albostriata.

Botanical names often have the author of the name written after. Where a plant has been named by two or more authors, the first name bears precedence.

Why Plants Names Change

Big Business

What do you do if you are a big company and you want a plant that another company is selling under Plant Breeders Rights? What do you do if a little guy will not let you have the plant you want to mass produce? Some companies just take the plant and change the name. We then have two plants being sold under two or more different names. Not only is the public being fooled, but the poor plant breeder is fiddled out of breeder's rights. It happens and unfortunately it will probably happen more in the future. Horticulture is being invaded by guys in expensive suits, with smart haircuts; the ones who will take you out for dinner and wine and dine you at the company's expense. They are no better than second hand car salesmen; I know from experience. This is not to say that all big plant companies behave in this unscrupulous way, some still have standards.

The Botanists

Everyone likes to blame the botanists. However, science has progressed and discoveries are unearthed that enable botanists to reclassify plants. Hence plants change their names legally. Unfortunately, this leads to much confusion, because the new names are not always accepted within the industry or they leak onto plant labels very slowly. This gives rise to plants being sold under different names.
Botanists are doing a useful job, it is for the industry to take this on board and to avoid confusion by adopting new plant names as quickly as possible.

The Naming of Names

Botanical plant names

A group of plants is defined by the word genus. Within a genus there exists at least one species. In the binomial system devised by Linnaeus, the first half of the name is the genus, the second half is the species. The gender of the species must agree with that of the genus, therefore we find that the specific epithets have different endings.

Cultivars appear in quotation marks and species can be subdivided into subspecies- noting a marked difference from the type; varietas when the difference is not so marked and forma when the difference is only in one characteristic.

The genus name is always written with a capital letter, the species in lower case:
Abies procera

Cultivar names begin with a capital letter and are in single quotation marks:
Abies procera 'Prostrata'
Abies cephalonica 'Meyer's Dwarf'

Avoiding the Pitfalls

Some of the most common errors are in giving cultivar status to subspecies. The use of alba and variegata is widely misused. Another trap is the misspelling of names. Watch out for caerulea and coerulea, thibetica and tibetica, nepaulensis and napaulensis, niponicum and nipponicum.

Another particular favourite of one major seed supplier is to list the synonym as the current botanical name and vice versa. Very misleading and confusing.

How To Use This Book

The text is arranged alphabetically for synonyms- these are the names we should no longer be using. The current botanical name is given in the right hand column.

Where the genus remains the same, the name has been abbreviated to the initial letter. In some instances, where the name is particularly long, other parts of the name have been abbreviated. It should be easy from the preceeding names to work out the abbreviated name. If you should encounter any problem with this, do write or call and I shall be happy to clarify the name.

Not all authors agree, some differences are noted and I have tried to only include accepted plant name changes.

Disclaimer

As the compiler and editor, I have taken every care to compile this work. However, with many thousands of records, errors and omissions can sometimes occur. The editor, compiler and publisher cannot be held responsible in any way, for any consequences arising from any such errors. I would be grateful to know of any errors so that they may be amended in subsequent editons.

Abbreviations

h	of gardens
f	forma
Gr.	Group
mis.	misapplied
ssp	subspecies
unv	unverified
v	varietas

SYNONYMS

Synonym	Current Name	Synonym	Current Name
Abelia chinensis h.	A. x grandiflora	Abies fortunei -A.Murr.	Keteleeria fortunei
Abelia rupestris -Lindley	A. chinensis	Abies georgei -Orr	A. forrestii v georgei
Abelia rupestris grandiflora	A. x grandiflora	Abies glehnii -F.Schmidt	Picea glehnii
Abelia rupestris h.	A. x grandiflora	Abies gmelinii -Rupr.	Larix gmelinii
Abelia x grandiflora 'Aurea'	A. x grand. 'Gold Spot'	Abies heterophylla	Tsuga heterophylla
Abelia x grandiflora 'Gold Strike'	A. x grand. 'Gold Spot'	Abies hirtella	A. religiosa
Abelia x grandiflora 'Goldsport'	A. x grand. 'Gold Spot'	Abies hispanica	A. pinsapo
Abelia x grandiflora 'Variegata'	A. x g. 'Francis Mason'	Abies hudsonia	A. balsamea
Abelia zanderi	A. dielsii	Abies jezoensis -Sieb. & Zucc.	Picea jezoensis
Abelicea hirta	Zelkova serrata	Abies kamschatica -Rupr.	Larix gmelinii v
Abies alba 'Pendula Compacta'	A. alba 'Pendula'		japonica -(Reg.) Pilger
Abies alba v acutifolia	A. borisii-regis	Abies khutrow -Loud.	Picea smithiana
Abies alba v nebrodensis	A. nebrodensis	Abies koreana 'Aurea'	A. koreana 'Flava'
Abies amabilis 'Procumbens'	A. am. 'Spreading Star'	Abies k. 'Horstmann's Silberlocke'	A. koreana
Abies americana	Tsuga canadensis		'Silberlocke'
Abies apollinis Link.	A. cephalonica v	Abies koreana 'Prostrata'	A. koreana 'Prostrate
	apollinis (Link) Beissn.		Beauty'
Abies arizonica -Merriam	A. lasiocarpa v	Abies lasiocarpa 'Compacta'	A. lasiocarpa
	arizonica		'Arizonica Compacta'
Abies arizonica 'Compacta'	A. lasiocarpa	Abies ledebourii -Rupr.	Larix sibirica -Ledeb.
	'Arizonica Compacta'	Abies leptolepis -Sieb. & Zucc.	Larix kaempferi
Abies balsamea f hudsonia	A. balsamea	Abies likiangensis -Franch.	Picea likiangensis Abies
Abies balsamea ssp lasiocarpa	A. lasiocarpa	likiangensis v balfouriana	Picea balfouriana
Abies balsamea v fallax	A. lasiocarpa	Abies likiangensis v purpurea	Picea purpurea -Mast.
Abies balsamea v phanerolepis	A. balsamea	Abies lowiana -(Gord). A.Murr.	A. concolor v lowiana
Abies beissneriana -Rehd. & Wils	A. chensiensis	Abies magnifica 'Nana'	A. magnifica 'Prostrata'
Abies bicolor -Maxim.	Picea alcockiana -Carr.	Abies mariana -Mill.	Picea mariana
Abies bifida	A. firma	Abies mariesii v kawakamii -Hayata	A. kawakamii
Abies brachyphylla -Maxim.	A. homolepis	Abies marocana	A. pinsapo v marocana
Abies brachyphylla dwarf	A. homolepis 'Prostrata'	Abies menziesii -Lindl.	Picea sitchensis
Abies brachytyla -Franch.	Picea brachytyla	Abies menziesii -Mirbel.	Pseudotsuga menziesii
Abies canadensis -Mill.	Picea glauca	Abies momi	A. firma
Abies cephalonica 'Nana'	A. cephalonica	Abies mucronata -Raf.	Pseudotsuga menziesii
	'Meyer's Dwarf'	Abies nobilis -(D.Don) Lindl.	A. procera -Rehd.
Abies chinensis	Tsuga chinensis	Abies nordmanniana 'Aurea Nana'	A. n. 'Golden Spreader'
Abies concolor 'Candicans'	A. concolor 'Argentea'	Abies pardei	A. alba
Abies concolor 'Glauca Compacta'	A. concolor 'Compacta'	Abies parryana h.	Picea pungens-Engelm.
Abies concolor 'Glauca'	A. c. Violacea Group	Abies pectinata -DC.	A. alba
Abies concolor 'Hillier Broom'	A. c. 'Hillier's Dwarf'	Abies picea -Mill.	Picea abies
A. delavayi v delavayi 'Nana Headfort'	A. fargesii 'Headfort'	Abies pindrow v brevifolia	A. gamblei -Hickel
Abies delavayi v del. Fabri Group	A. fabri	Abies pindrow v intermedia	A. spectabilis v interm.
Abies delavayi v fabri	A. fabri	Abies procera 'Compacta'	A. p. 'Glauca Prostrata'
Abies del. v faxoniana -Rehd. & Wils.	A. fargesii	Abies procera 'Prostrata'	A. p. 'Glauca Prostrata'
Abies del. v faxoniana -Rehd & Wills.	A. faxoniana	Abies sibirica v nephrolepis -Tratv.	A. nephrolepis
Abies delavayi v forrestii	A. delavayi v smithii	Abies sikokiana	A. veitchii
Abies del. v forrestii C.C.Rogers	A. forrestii	Abies smithiana	Picea smithiana
Abies del. v georgei -(Orr) Melville	A. forrestii v georgei	Abies subalpina -Engelm.	A. lasiocarpa Abies
Abies douglasii -(Lindl.) Carr.	Pseudotsuga menziesii	subalpina v fallax -Engelm.	A. lasiocarpa
Abies eichleri	A. veitchii	Abies sutchuenensis	A. fargesii
Abies engelmannii -Parry	Picea engelmannii	Abies veitchii v reflexa	A. veitchii
Abies ernestii -Rehd.	A. recurvata v ernestii	Abies v. v sachalinensis -Schmidt	A. sachalinensis
Abies excelsior	A. grandis	Abies venusta	A. pectinata
Abies fargesii v sutchuensis Franch.	A. sutchuensis	Abies venusta -(Dougl). K. Koch	A. bracteata
Abies faxoniana -Rehd. & Wils.	A. fargesii	Abies webbiana -Lindl.	A. spectabilis
Abies forrestii	A. delavayi v smithii	Abies webbiana v brevifolia	A. spectabilis v brevif.

Synonym	Current Name	Synonym	Current Name
Abies webbiana v pindrow	A. pindrow -Royle	Acacia aulacocarpa v macrocarpa	A. disparrima
Abroba viridiflora	A. tenuifolia	Acacia australis	A. calyculata
Abromeitiella chlorantha	A. brevifolia	Acacia axillaris v axillaris	A. axillaris
Abronia arenaria	A. latifolia	Acacia axillaris v macrophylla	A. riceana
Abronia exalata	A. turbinata	Acacia ayersiana v latifolia	A. ayersiana
Abronia orbiculata	A. turbinata	Acacia baileyana v aurea	A. baileyana
Absinthium frigida	Artemisia frigida	Acacia bancroftii	A. bancroftiorum
Abutilon 'Louise de Marignac'	A. 'Louis Marignac'	Acacia basaltica	Archidendropsis
Abutilon 'Margherita Manns'	A. ochsenii		basaltica
Abutilon abutilon -(L.) Rusb.	A. theophrasti	Acacia benthamii v angustior	A. applanata
Abutilon avicennae	A. theophrasti	Acacia bidentata v pubescens	A. bidentata
Abutilon esculentum	A. purpurascens	Acacia bidwillii v bidwillii	A. bidwillii
Abutilon globosum	A. x hybridum	Acacia bidwillii v major	A. valida
Abutilon striatum h.	A. pictum	Acacia bidwillii v polytricha	A. bidwillii
Abutilon vexillarium -Morr.	A. megapotamicum	Acacia biflora v aurea	A. chrysocephala
Abutilon x hybridum 'Savitzii'	A. 'Savitzii'	Acacia binervata - Dehn.	A. verniciflua -Cunn.
Acacia 'Veitchiana'	Acacia Exeter Hybrid	Acacia binervosa	A. bivenosa
Acacia abietina	A. linifolia	Acacia bivenosa ssp wayi	A. bivenosa
Acacia accola	A. adunca	Acacia bivenosa v borealis	A. bivenosa
Acacia acicularis	A. brownii	Acacia boorabbinensis	A. coolgardiensis
Acacia aciphylla v leptostachys	A. sessiilispica	Acacia botrycephala	A. terminalis
Acacia acuminata v ciliata	A. ac. ssp acuminata	Acacia brachybotrya f glabra	A. brachybotrya
Acacia acuminata v glaucescens	A. yorkrakinensis ssp acrita	Acacia brachybotrya f glaucophylla	A. brachybotrya
		Acacia brachybotrya v spilleriana	A. spilleriana
Acacia acutifolia	A. myrtifolia	Acacia brevifolia (F.Muell.) Benth.	A. lazaridis
Acacia aff bidentata	A. aristulata	Acacia brevifolia G. Don	A. buxifolia
Acacia aff dictyoneura	A. awestoniana	Acacia brownei	A. brownii
Acacia aff pusilla	A. rhamphophylla	Acacia browniana v brevifolia	A. browniana
Acacia aff wilhelmiana	A. brachypoda	Acacia bruncioides ssp gordonii	A. gordonii
Acacia aff yassalii	A. leptalea	Acacia buxifolia v decora	A. decora
Acacia alata v genuina	A. alata	Acacia buxifolia v neglecta	A. buxifolia
Acacia alata v glabrata	A. alata	Acacia buxifolia v subvelutina	A. kybeanensis
Acacia anceps v angustifolia	A. anceps	Acacia calamifolia v euthycarpa	A. calamifolia
Acacia aneura v ayersiana	A. ayersiana	Acacia calamifolia v wilhelmiana	A. wilhelmiana
Acacia aneura v brachystachya	A. brachystachya	Acacia calamistrata	A. extensa
Acacia aneura v latifolia	A. aneura v argentea	Acacia calligera	A. wickhamii ssp
Acacia aneura v latifolia	A. ayersiana		parviphyllodinea
Acacia aneura v stenocarpa	A. brachystachya	Acacia celsiana	A. anceps
Acacia angustifolia	A. floribunda	Acacia chordophylla	A. rigens
Acacia apiculata	A. subcaerulea	Acacia chrysobotrya	A. spectabilis
Acacia arceuthos	A. brownii	Acacia cibaria	A. brachystachya
Acacia armata	A. paradoxa	Acacia ciliata	A. browniana
Acacia armata v angustifolia	A. paradoxa	Acacia ciliata	A. luteola
Acacia armata v longipedunculata	A. paradoxa	Acacia ciliata v brevifolia	A. browniana
Acacia armata v microphylla	A. paradoxa	Acacia ciliata v intermedia	A. browniana v interm.
Acacia armata v ornithophora	A. paradoxa	Acacia cinerascens	A. binervia
Acacia armata v pendula	A. paradoxa	Acacia curvicarpa	A. acradenia
Acacia armata v plana	A. paradoxa	Acacia cyanophylla	A. saligna
Acacia armata v typica	A. paradoxa	Acacia decurrens v dealbata	A. dealbata -Link.
Acacia armata v undulata	A. paradoxa	Acacia densifolia	A. aspera
Acacia arundelliana	A. oshanesii	Acacia dictyocarpa	A. brachybotrya
Acacia aspera v densifolia	A. aspera	Acacia diphylla	A. blakei ssp diphylla
Acacia astringens	A. falciformis	Acacia diptera	A. applanata
Acacia aulacocarpa	A. aulacocarpa	Acacia diptera v angustior	A. applanata
Acacia aulacocarpa v fruticosa	A. aulacocarpa	Acacia diptera v eriocarpa	A. applanata

11

Synonym	Current Name	Synonym	Current Name
Acacia dolabriformis	Daviesia incrassata ssp incrassata		laevigata
		Acaena adscendens h.	A. magellanica ssp magellanica
Acacia doratoxylon v angustifolia	A. caroleae		
Acacia drewiana ssp pungens	A. anarthros	Acaena adscendens Margery Fish	A. affinis
Acacia elliptica	A. bivenosa	Acaena anserinifolia h.	A. novae-zelandiae
Acacia endlicheri	A. browniana v endl.	Acaena caerulea	A. caesiiglauca
Acacia erythrocephala	A. aspera	Acaena glaucophylla	A. magellanica ssp magellanica
Acacia euthycarpa	A. calamifolia		
Acacia galioides f denudata	A. asperulacea	Acaena microphylla 'Glauca'	A. caesiiglauca
Acacia galioides f hirsutiuscula	A. asperulacea	Acaena microphylla 'Inermis'	A. inermis
Acacia galioides lycopodiifolia	A. asperulacea	Acaena microphylla Copper Carpet	A. microphylla 'Kupferteppich'
Acacia glaucescens	A. anceps		
Acacia harveyi	A. aestivalis	Acaena pallida 'Pewter'	A. saccaticupula 'Blue Haze'
Acacia hispidissima -DC.	A. pulchella -R.Br.		
Acacia homomalla	A. binervia	Acaena profundeincisa	A. anserinifolia -Druce
Acacia hunteriana	A. boormanii	Acaena sanguisorbae -Linnaeus	A. anserinifolia -Druce
Acacia julibrissin	Albizia julibrissin	Acaena viridior	A. anserinifolia -Druce
Acacia juniperina	A. ulicifolia	Acalypha amentacea ssp wilkesiana	A. wilkesiana
Acacia juniperina v brownei	A. brownii	Acalypha chinensis	A. australis
Acacia latrobei	A. acinacea	Acalypha godseffiana	A. wilkesiana
Acacia leiophylla v microcephala	A. chamaeleon	Acalypha pauciflora	A. australis
Acacia leptoclada v polyphylla	A. bidwillii	Acalypha pendula	A. reptans
Acacia leptoneura v pungens	A. acellerata	Acalypha tricolor	A. wilkesiana
Acacia leucadendron	A. binervia	Acalypha virgata	A. australis
Acacia muelleri	A. anceps	Acalypha wilkesiana 'Godseffiana'	A. wilkesiana
Acacia myrtifolia f celastrifolia	A. celastrifolia	Acanthocalycium aurantiacum	Echinopsis thionantha
Acacia neglecta	A. buxifolia	Acanthocalycium violaceum	Echinopsis spiniflora
Acacia obliqua	A. acinacea	Acanthocalyx	Morina
Acacia podalyriifolia v caleyi	A. caleyi	Acantholimon androsaceum	A. ulicinum
Acacia polybotrya h.	A. glaucocarpa	Acantholimon pinnardii	A. acerosum
Acacia porphyrochila	A. camptoclada	Acanthopanax	Eleutherococcus
Acacia pterigoidea	A. anceps	Acanthopanax diversifolium -Hemsl.	Pseudopanax davidii
Acacia pugioniformis	A. brownii	Acanthopanax henryi	Eleutherococcus henryi -Oliver
Acacia pulchella v subsessilis	A. amputata		
Acacia pulverulenta	A. calamifolia	Acanthopanax pentaphyllus	Eleutherococcus sieboldianus
Acacia pumila	A. bynoeana		
Acacia rotundifolia	A. acinacea	Acanthopanax ricinifolius	Eleutherococcus sieboldianus
Acacia sclerophylla v lissophylla	A. ancistrophylla v lis.		
Acacia sentis	A. victoriae	Acanthopanax sciadophylloides	Eleutherococcus sciad.
Acacia smallii	A. farnesiana	Acanthopanax senticosus	Eleutherococcus sent.
Acacia stowardii	A. chamaeleon	Acanthopanax sessiliflorus	Eleutherococcus sess.
Acacia strigosa	A. aspera	Acanthopanax sieboldianus	Eleutherococcus sieboldianus
Acacia strigosa	A. browniana		
Acacia strigosa v intermedia	A. browniana v interm.	Acanthopanax simonii	Eleutherococcus sim.
Acacia tetragonocarpa v scabra	A. aemula ssp aemula	Acanthopanax spinosus	Eleutherococcus sieboldianus
Acacia triangularis	A. biflora		
Acacia ulicifolia v brownei	A. brownii	Acanthopanax spinosus h.	Eleutherococcus sieboldianus
Acacia umbrosa	A. binervata		
Acacia uncinata	A. calamifolia	Acanthopanax ternatus Rehd.	Eleutherococcus wardii
Acacia uniglandosa	A. alata		
Acaena 'Pewter'	A. saccaticupula 'Blue Haze'	Acanthophoenix crinita	A. rubra
		Acanthus balcanicus	A. hungaricus
Acaena 'Purple Carpet'	A. microphylla 'Kupferteppich'	Acanthus latifolius	A. mollis Latifolius Gr.
		Acanthus longifolius	A. hungaricus
Acaena adscendens -Vahl	A. magellanica ssp	Acanthus mollis 'Fielding Gold'	A. m. 'Hollard's Gold'

12

Synonym	Current Name	Synonym	Current Name
Acanthus mollis 'Jefalba'	A. mollis Latifolius Group 'Rue Ledan'	Acer hersii	A. grosseri v hersii
		Acer heterolobum	A. campestre -L.
Acanthus spinosissimus	A. spinosus Spinosissimus Group	Acer heterophyllum -Willd.	A. sempervirens -L.
		Acer heterotomum	A. campestre -L.
Acer 'Dissectum'	A. palmatum v dissectum	Acer insigne -Boiss.	A. velutinum -Boiss.
		Acer italum -Lauth.	A. opalus -Mill.
Acer 'Silver Vein'	A. x conspicuum 'Silver Vein'	Acer japonicum 'Aureum'	A. shirasawanum 'Aureum'
Acer acutilobum	A. campestre	Acer japonicum 'Ezo-no-momiji'	A. shirasawanum 'Ezo-no-momiji'
Acer affine not Hoffman	A. campestre		
Acer ambiguum -Dipp.	A. mono f ambiguum	Acer japonicum 'Filicifolium'	A. jap. 'Aconitifolium'
Acer austriacum	A. campestre	Acer japonicum 'Laciniatum'	A. jap. 'Aconitifolium'
Acer austriacum f trifidum	A. campestre	Acer japonicum 'Ogurayama'	A. shirasawanum 'Ogurayama'
Acer bedoi	A. campestre		
Acer brevilobum h.	A. nipponicum -Hara	Acer japonicum f microphyllum	A. shirasawanum 'Microphyllum'
Acer buergerianum 'Integrifolium'	A. buergerianum 'Subintegrum'		
		Acer kawakamii	A. caudatifolium
Acer caesium ssp giraldii	A. giraldii	Acer laetum - C.A.Mey.	A. cappadocicum
Acer campbellii ssp sinense	A. sinense	Acer laevigatum h. not Wall.	A. campestre -L.
Acer campbellii ssp wilsonii	A. wilsonii	Acer laxiflorum -some not Pax	A. maximowiczii -Pax
Acer campestre ssp leiocarpum	A. campestre	Acer laxiflorum v longilobum -Rehd.	A. taronense
Acer campestre ssp marsicum	A. campestre	Acer leucoderme -Small	A. saccharum ssp leu.
Acer campestre v austriacum	A. campestre	Acer lobelii -Bunge	A. turkestanicum
Acer campestre v hebecarpum	A. campestre	Acer lobelii v. dieckii - Pax	A. x dieckii -Pax
Acer campestre v tauricum	A. campestre	Acer macrocarpon	A. campestre
Acer capillipes v morifolium	A. morifolium	Acer mayrii -Schwer.	A. mono v mayrii
Acer cappadocicum ssp lobelii	A. cappadocicum	Acer microcarpon	A. campestre
Acer cappadocicum v cultratum	A. cappadocicum	Acer molle	A. campestre
Acer cappadocicum v indicum	A. cappadocicum	Acer mono	A. pictum
Acer cappadocicum v mono	A. pictum	Acer mono v tricuspis	A. cappadocicum ssp sinicum v tricaudatum
Acer catalpifolium	A. longipes ssp catalp.		
Acer caudatum -Wall. ex Rehd.	A. ukurunduense caud.	Acer morrisonense	A. caudatifolium
Acer caudatum -Wall. in part	A. acuminatum	Acer neapolitanum -Ten.	A. opalus v tomentosum
Acer cinnamomifolium	A. coriaceifolium		
Acer cissifolium ssp henryi	A. henryi	Acer neglectum	A. x zoeschense
Acer collinum	A. campestre	Acer negundo 'Argenteovariegatum'	A. neg. 'Variegatum'
Acer creticum -L.	A. sempervirens -L.	Acer negundo 'Elegantissimum'	A. negundo 'Elegans'
Acer cultratum	A. cappadocicum	Acer nigrum	A. saccharinum ssp nigrum
Acer cultratum -Wall.	A. cappadocicum v cul.		
Acer dasycarpum -Ehrh.	A. saccharinum L.	Acer nikoense	A. maximowiczianum
Acer davidii 'Silver Vein'	A. x conspicuum 'Silver Vein'	Acer nikoense v griseum -Franch.	A. griseum
		Acer oblongum v biauritum	A. paxii -Franch.
Acer drummondii -Hook. & Arn.	A. rubrum v drummon.	Acer obtusatum -Willd.	A. opalus v obtusatum
Acer eriocarpum -Michx.	A. saccharinum -L.	Acer opalus v neapolitanum -Ten.	A. opalus v tomentosum
Acer eriocarpum -not Michx.	A. campestre -L.		
Acer erythrocarpum	A. campestre -L.	Acer opulifolium -Vill.	A. opalus -Mill.
Acer flabellatum	A. campbellii ssp flabel.	Acer opulifolium v tomentosum	A. opalus v tomentosum
Acer flabellatum v yunnanense	A. campbelli v yunna.		
Acer fulvescens	A. longipes	Acer orientale -auct.	A. sempervirens -L.
Acer ginnala	A. tataricum ssp ginn.	Acer orthopteron	A. campestre
Acer ginnala v semenovii	A. tataricum ssp seme.	Acer palmatisectum	A. campestre
Acer globosum	A. platanoides 'Globosum'	Acer palmatum 'Akaji-nishiki'	A. truncatum 'Ajaki-nishiki'
Acer grandidentatum	A. saccharum ssp grandidentatum	Acer palmatum 'Aoshime-no-uchi'	A. palmatum 'Shinobugaoka'

Synonym	Current Name	Synonym	Current
A. palmatum 'Beni-shigitatsusawa'	A. palmatum 'Aka Shigitatsusawa'		'Atropurpureum'
Acer palmatum 'Bonfire'	A. truncatum 'Ajaki-nishiki'	Acer polycarpon	A. campestre
		Acer polymorphum -Sieb. & Zucc.	A. palmatum -Thunb.
Acer palmatum 'Carminium'	A. palmatum 'Corallinum'	Acer praecox	A. campestre
		Acer pseudoplatanus 'Leopoldii' mis.	A. pseudoplatanus f variegatum
Acer palmatum 'Chishio Improved'	A. palmatum 'Shishio'		
Acer palmatum 'Chishio'	A. palmatum 'Shishio'	Acer ps. 'Spaethii' misapplied	A. pseudoplatanus 'Atropurpureum'
Acer palmatum 'Effegi'	A. palmatum 'Fireglow'		
Acer palmatum 'Ever Red'	A. p. v dissectum 'Dissectum Nigrum'	Acer pulverulentum	A. campestre
		Acer quinquelobatum	A. campestre
Acer palmatum 'Frederici Guglielmi'	A. p. v diss. 'Dissectum Variegatum'	Acer quinquelobum -K.Koch.	A. divergens -Pax.
		Acer regelii	A. pentapotamicum
A.p.'Heptalobum Elegans Purpureum'	A. palmatum 'Hessei'	Acer rubrum 'Scarsen'	A. r. 'Scarlet Sentinel'
Acer palmatum 'Junihitoe'	A. shirasawanum 'Junihitoe'	Acer rubrum v pycnanthum	A. pycnantheum
		Acer rufinerve 'Albolimbatum'	A. ruf. 'Hatsuyuki'
Acer palmatum 'Little Princess'	A. p. 'Mapi-no-machihime'	Acer rufinerve 'Albomarginatum'	A. ruf. 'Hatsuyuki'
		Acer rufinerve f albolimbatum	A. ruf. 'Hatsuyuki'
		Acer rugelii -Pax	A. saccharum v rugelii
Acer palmatum 'Mikasayama'	A. jap. 'Mikasa-yama'	Acer saccharinum -Wangenh.	A. saccharum -Marsh.
Acer p. 'Nomurishidare' misapplied	A. p. v dissectum 'Shojo-shidare'	Acer saccharinum 'Elegans'	A. x freemanii 'Elegant'
		Acer saccharinum 'Fastigiatum'	A. sacc. f pyramidale
Acer palmatum 'Pine Bark Maple'	A. p. 'Nishiki-gawa'	Acer saccharinum 'Pyramidale'	A. sacc. f pyramidale
Acer palmatum 'Reticulatum'	A. palmatum 'Shigitatsu-sawa'	Acer saccharinum 'Wieri'	A. saccharinum 'Laciniatum Wieri'
Acer palmatum 'Ribesifolium'	A. palmatum 'Shishigashira'	A. saccharinum Laciniatum Group	A. sacc. f laciniatum
		Acer saccharum 'Columnare'	A. sa. 'Newton Sentry'
Acer palmatum 'Roseomarginatum'	A. palmatum 'Kagiri-nishiki'	Acer saccharum 'Monumentale'	A. saccharum 'Temple's Upright'
Acer palmatum 'Rough Bark Maple'	A. palmatum 'Arakawa'	Acer saccharum ssp barbatum	A. sac. ssp floridanum
Acer palmatum 'Scolopendrifolium'	A. p. 'Linearilobum'	Acer semenovii -Reg. & Herd.	A. tataricum ssp sem.
Acer palmatum 'Senkaki'	A. p. 'Sango-kaku'	Acer septemlobum -Thunb.	Kalopanax septemlobus
Acer p. 'Septemlobum Elegans'	A. palmatum 'Heptalobum Elegans'	Acer sikkimense (unv)	A. hookeri
		Acer sikkimense ssp metcalfii	A. metcalfii
Acer p. 'Septemlobum Purpureum'	A. palmatum 'Hessei'	Acer stachyophyllum	A. tetramerum
Acer palmatum 'Sessilifolium' dwarf	A. p. 'Hagoromo'	Acer striatum -Duroi	A. pensylvanicum
Acer palmatum 'Sessilifolium' tall	A. p. 'Koshimino'	Acer suberosum	A. campestre
Acer palmatum 'Wou-nishiki'	A. palmatum 'O-nishiki'	Acer sylvestre	A. campestre
Acer papilio -King	A. caudatum	Acer syriacum	A. obtusifolium
Acer parviflorum -Franch. & Sav.	A. nipponicum -Hara	Acer tauschianum	A. campestre
Acer pectinatum 'Sirene'	A. forrestii 'Sirene'	A.tegmentosum ssp glaucorufinerve	A. rufinerve
Acer pectinatum 'Sparkling'	A. forrestii 'Sparkling'	Acer tenellum -Pax	A. mono v tricuspis
Acer pectinatum ssp forrestii	A. forrestii	Acer tetramerum	A. stachyophyllum
Acer pectinatum ssp laxiflorum	A. laxiflorum	Acer tomentosum v serotinum	A. campestre
Acer pictum colchicum h.	A. cappadocicum	Acer trattinickii	A. campestre
Acer platanoides 'Dissectum'	A. plat. 'Palmatifidum'	Acer trifidum - Hook. & Arn.	A. buergerianum -Miq.
Acer platanoides 'Fastigiatum'	A. pseudop. 'Erectum'	Acer trilobum -nom inv.	A. campestre
Acer platanoides 'Lorbergii'	A. plat. 'Palmatifidum'	Acer ukurunduense -Trautv. & Mey.	A. caudatum v ukuru.
Acer platanoides 'Parkway'	A. plat 'Columnarbroad'	Acer urophyllum -Maxim.	A. maximowiczii -Pax
Acer plat. 'Purpureum Spaethii' h.	A. pseudoplatanus 'Atropurpureum'	Acer vanvolxemii -Mast.	A. velutinum v vanvolxemii
Acer platanoides 'Spaethii' h.	A. pseudoplatanus 'Atropurpureum'		A. sterculiaceum
		Acer villosum	A. thomsonii -Miq.
Acer platanoides f purpureum	A. ps. 'Atropurpureum'	Acer villosum v thomsonii	
Acer platanoides integrilobum -Zab.	A. x dieckii -Pax	Acer vulgare	A. campestre
Acer platanoides Purpureum Group	A. pseudoplatanus	Acer wondracekii	A. campestre
		Acer x conspicuum 'Silver Cardinal'	A. 'Silver Cardinal'

Synonym	Current Name	Synonym	Current Name
Aceranthus sagittatus	Epimedium sagittatum	Achimenes coccinea	A. erecta
Aceriphyllum	Mukdenia	Achimenes ehrenbergii	Eucodonia ehrenbergii
Acetosa acetosella	Rumex acetosella	Achimenes longiflora 'Alba'	A. 'Jaureguia Maxima'
Acetosa angustata	Rumex acetosa	Achimenes pulchella	A. erecta
Acetosa pratensis	Rumex acetosa	Achimenes Snow White	A. 'Schneewittchen'
Acetosella	Rumex	Achiote	Bixa orellana
Achasma megalocheilos	A. macrocheilos	Achnatherum	Stipa
Achillea 'Great Expectations'	A. 'Hoffnung'	Achyranthes bidentata japonica	A. japonica
Achillea 'King Edward'	A. x lewisii 'King Edward'	Acidanthera	Gladiolus
		Acidanthera bicolor	Gladiolus callianthus
Achillea 'Peter Davis'	Hippolytia herderi	Acidanthera bicolor v murieliae	Gladiolus callianthus
Achillea 'Salmon Beauty'	A. 'Lachsschonheit'	Acidanthera murieliae	Gladiolus callianthus
Achillea 'Sandstone'	A. 'Wesersandstein'	Acinos acinos	Acinos arvensis
Achillea 'Sulphur Flowers'	A. 'Schwefelblute'	Acinos forminii	Acinos rotundifolius
Achillea 'The Beacon'	A. 'Fanal'	Acinos graveolens	Acinos rotundifolius
Achillea alpina	A. sibirica	Acinos schizodontos	Acinos arvensis
Achillea Appleblossom	A. 'Apfelblute'	Acinos thymoides	Acinos arvensis
Achillea argentea -Lamark	Tanacetum argenteum	Aciphylla latifolia	Anisotome latifolia
Achillea argentea misapplied	A. clavennae	Acnistus australis	Dunalia australis
Achillea argentea misapplied	A. umbellata	Acokanthera spectabilis	A. oblongifolia
Achillea aurea	A. chrysocoma	Aconitum anglicum	A. napellus ssp napellus Anglicum Group
Achillea decolorans	A. ageratum		
Achillea eupatorium	A. filipendulina	Aconitum autumnale -Reichenbach	A. fischeri
Achillea Flowers of Sulphur	A. 'Schwefelblute'	Aconitum cilicicum	Eranthis hyemalis
Achillea gerberi	A. ptarmica		Cilicica Group
Achillea grandifolia misapplied	Tanacetum macrophyllum	Aconitum compactum	A. napellus ssp vulgare
		Aconitum compactum 'Carneum'	A. napellus ssp vulgare 'Carneum'
Achillea herba-rota	A. erba-rotta		
Achillea huteri	A. 'Huteri'	Aconitum faurei	A. japonicum
Achillea ircutiana	A. ptarmica	Aconitum fischeri misapplied	A. carmichaelii
Achillea lanulosa	A. millefolium	Aconitum fortunei misapplied	A. carmichaelii
A. millefolium 'Lavender Beauty'	A. millefolium 'Lilac Beauty'	Aconitum hyemale	Eranthis hyemalis
		Aconitum lamarckii	A. lycoctonum ssp neapolitanum
Achillea mongolica	A. sibirica		
Achillea monocephala	A. brachyphylla	Aconitum napellus 'Albiflorus'	A. napellus ssp vulgare 'Albidum'
Achillea moschata	A. erba-rotta ssp mos.		
Achillea multiflora	A. sibirica	Aconitum napellus 'Bicolor'	A. x cammarum 'Bicolor'
Achillea ptarmica 'Innocence'	A. ptarmica 'Unschuld'		
Achillea ptarmica 'Schneeball'	A. p. 'Boule de Neige'	Aconitum napellus 'Carneum'	A. napellus ssp vulgare 'Carneum'
Achillea ptarmica 'Stephanie Cohen'	A. sibirica 'Stephanie Cohen'		
		Aconitum neapolitanum	A. lycoctonum ssp nea.
Achillea ptarmica 'The Pearl' seed raised not clonal		Aconitum orientale h.	A. lycoctonum ssp vulparia
	A. p. The Pearl Group		
Achillea pumila	A. distans ssp tanacetifolia	Aconitum pyrenaicum	A. lycoctonum ssp nea.
		Aconitum ranunculifolius	A. lycoctonum ssp nea.
Achillea pyrenaica	A. ptarmica	Aconitum septentrionale	A. lycoctonum ssp lyc.
Achillea serbica	A. ageratifolia	Aconitum septentrionale 'Ivorine'	A. 'Ivorine'
Achillea serrata h.	A. ageratum	Aconitum stoerkianum	A. x cammarum 'Bicolor'
Achillea speciosa	A. ptarmica		
Achillea sylvestris	A. ptarmica	Aconitum volubile h.	A. hemsleyanum
Achillea tomentosa 'Maynard's Gold'	A. tomentosa 'Aurea'	Aconitum vulparia	A. lycoctonum ssp vul.
Achillea umbellata 'Weston'	A. x kolbiana 'Weston'	Aconitum x arendsii	A. carmichaelii 'Arendsii'
Achillea x wilczekii	A. 'Wilczekii'		
Achimenes 'Shirley Fireglow'	A. 'Harveyi'	Aconitum x bicolor	A. x cammarum 'Bicolor'
Achimenes bella	Eucodonia verticillata		

Synonym	Current Name	Synonym	Current Name
Aconitum x tubergenii	Eranthis hyemalis Tubergenii Group	Adenium micranthum	A. obesum
		Adenium multiflorum	A. obesum
Aconogonon	Persicaria	Adenium speciosum	A. obesum
Acorus elatus	A. calamus	Adenocarpus anagyrus -Spreng.	A. viscosus
Acorus odoratus	A. calamus	Adenocarpus frankenioides -Chois.	A. viscosus
Acorus undulatus	A. calamus	Adenophora 'Afterglow'	Campanula rapunculoi.
Acorus vulgaris	A. calamus		'Afterglow'
Acosta stoebe	Centaurea stoebe-L.	Adenophora chinensis	A. sinensis
Acrocentron scabiosa	Centaurea scabiosa -L.	Adenophora communis	A. liliifolia
Acrocladium	Calliergon	Adenophora farreri	A. confusa
Acroclinium	Rhodanthe	Adenophora latifolia h.	A. pereskiifolia
Acroclinium roseum	Rhodanthe chloro cephala ssp roseum	Adenophora liliiflora	A. liliifolia
		Adenophora nipponica	A. nikoensis v stenophylla
Acrostichum alpinum	Woodsia alpina		
Acrostichum areolatum	Woodwardia areolata	Adenophora polymorpha	A. nikoensis
Acrostichum lingua	Pyrrosia lingua	Adenophora polymorpha tashiroi	A. tashiroi
Acrostichum platyneuron	Asplenium platyneuron	Adenophora suaveolens	A. liliifolia
Acrostichum ruta-muraria	Asplenium r-muraria	Adenophora takedai	A. takedae
Acrostichum septentrionale -L.	Asplenium septentrion.	Adenophora tetraphylla	A. triphylla
Acrostichum thelypteris	Thelypteris palustris	Adenostyles alpina	Cacalia hastata
Actaea alba	A. pachypoda	Adhatoda duvernoia	Justicia adhatoda
Actaea americana v alba	A. pachypoda	Adhatoda vasica	Justicia adhatoda
Actaea americana v rubra	A. rubra	Adiantum affine	A. capillus-veneris
Actaea arguta	A. rubra	Adiantum americanum	A. pedatum
Actaea arguta eburnea	A. rubra	Adiantum boreale	A. aleuticum
Actaea arguta v pauciflora	A. rubra	Adiantum capillus	A. capillus-veneris
Actaea aspenifolia	A. rubra	Adiantum capillus-veneris 'Mairisii'	A. x mairisii
Actaea brachypetala v alba	A. pachypoda	A. capillus-veneris v modestum	A. capillus-veneris
Actaea brachypetala v rubra	A. rubra	A. capillus-veneris v prostratum	A. capillus-veneris
Actaea brachypoda -sensu	A. pachypoda	Adiantum capillus-veneris v rimicola	A. capillus-veneris
Actaea caudata	A. rubra	Adiantum cuneatum	A. raddianum
Actaea eburnea	A. rubra	Adiantum modestum	A. capillus-veneris
Actaea neglecta	A. rubra f neglecta	Adiantum pedatum 'Japonicum'	A. aleuticum 'Japonicum'
Actaea nigra	A. spicata		
Actaea rubra alba	A. rubra f neglecta	Adiantum pedatum 'Roseum'	A. al. 'Japonicum'
Actaea rubra arguta	A. rubra f neglecta	Adiantum pedatum Asiatic form	A. al. 'Japonicum'
Actaea rubra v dissecta	A. rubra f neglecta	Adiantum pedatum ssp calderi -Cody	A. aleuticum
Actaea spicata v alba	A. spicata	Adiantum pedatum v aleuticum	A. aleuticum
Actaea spicata v rubra	A. rubra	Adiantum pedatum v minus	A. al. 'Subpumilum'
Actinella scaposa	Tetraneuris scaposa	Adiantum pedatum v subpumilum	A. al. 'Subpumilum'
Actinidia arguta v rufa	A. rufa	A. pedatum v subpumilum f minimum	A. aleuticum
Actinidia callosa v henryi -Maxim.	A. henryi	Adiantum raddianum 'Fragrans'	A. r. 'Fragrantissimum'
Actinidia chinensis h.	A. deliciosa	Adiantum raddianum 'Gracilis'	A. r. 'Gracillimum'
Actinidia cordifolia	A. arguta	Adiantum rimicola	A. capillus-veneris
Actinidia megalocarpa	A. arguta	Adiantum scandens	Lygodium japonicum
Actinidia platyphylla	A. arguta	Adiantum venustum v monochlamys	A. venustum
Actinomeris alternifolia	Verbesina alternifolia	Adlumia cirrhosa	A. fungosa
Adelia acuminata -Michx.	Forestiera acuminata	Adnaria resinosa	Gaylussacia baccata
Adelia ligustrina -Michx.	Forestiera ligustrina	Adonidia merrillii	Veitchia merrillii
Adelia neomexicana	Forestiera neomexic.	Adonis amurensis 'Plena'	A. multiflora 'Sandanzaki'
Adelocaryum	Lindelofia		
Adelonema	Homalomena	Adonis amurensis 'Pleniflora'	A. m. 'Sandanzaki'
Adenia buchananii	A. digitata	Adromischus claviolius	A. cooperi
Adenium arabicum	A. obesum	Adyseton alyssoides	Alyssum alyssoides
Adenium coetanum	A. obesum	Adyseton halimifolium	Lobularia maritima

Synonym	Current Name	Synonym	Current Name
Adyseton maritimum	Lobularia maritima	Aesculus x plantierensis -Andre	A. x carnea -Hayne
Adyseton saxatile	Aurinia saxatilis	Aesculus x rubicunda -Loisel.	A. x carnea -Hayne
Aechmea caerulea	A. lueddemanniana	Aethionema graecum	A. saxatile
Aechmea marmorata	Quesnelia marmorata	Aethionema jucundum	A. coridifolium
Aegle sepiaria -DC.	Poncirus trifoliata	Aethionema pulchellum	A. grandiflorum
Aeollanthus graveolens	A. gamwelliae		Pulchellum Group
Aeonium bertoletianum	A. tabuliforme	Aetopteron aculeatum	Polystichum aculeatum
Aeonium exsul	A. canariense	Aetopteron munitum	Polystichum munitum
Aeonium subplanum	A. can. v subplanum	Aetopteron polyblepharon	Polyst. polyblepharum
Aeonium x domesticum	Aichryson x domest.	Afrorhaphidophora	Rhaphidophora
Aerides japonica	Sedirea japonica	Agapanthus Danube	A. 'Donau'
Aeschynanthus 'Hillbrandii'	A. hildebrandii	Agapanthus giganteus	A. praecox ssp
Aeschynanthus lobbianus	A. radicans		maximus
Aeschynanthus marmoratus	A. longicaulis	Agapanthus orientalis	A. pr. ssp orientalis
Aeschynanthus parvifolius	A. radicans	Agapanthus Palmer's hybrids	A. Headbourne hybrids
Aeschyn. radicans v lobbianus	A. radicans	Agapanthus umbellatus -L'Herit.	A. africanus
Aeschynanthus splendens	A. speciosus	Agapanthus umbellatus -Redoute	A. pr. ssp orientalis
Aeschynanthus zebrinus	A. longicaulis	A. umbellatus 'White Dwarf'	A. umbellatus white
Aesculus arguta	A. glabra v arguta		dwarf hybrids
Aesculus asplenifolia h. ex Loud.	A. hippocastanum -L.	Agapanthus umbellatus maximus	A. pr. ssp maximus
Aesculus castanea -Gilib.	A. hippocastanum -L.	Agapanthus weillighii	A. inapertus
Aesculus dupontii -Sarg.	A. x woerlitzensis	Agapetes macrantha	A. variegata v macran.
Aesculus flava v purpurascens	A. x hybrida -DC.	Agapetes rugosa	A. incurvata
Aesculus flava x pavia	A. x hybrida -DC.	Agapetes rugosa x serpens	A. 'Ludgvan Cross'
Aesculus floribunda h. ex Dippel	A. x carnea -Hayne	Agastache anethiodora	A. foeniculum
Aesculus georgiana	A. sylvatica	Agastache anisata	A. foeniculum
Aesculus glabra v sargentii -Rehd.	A. glabra v arguta	Agastache mexicana 'Rosea'	A. cana
Aesculus glaucescens	A. x neglecta	Agathaea	Felicia
Aesculus heterophylla h. ex Handl.	A. hippocastanum -L.	Agathaea coelestis	Felicia amelloides
A. hippocastanum 'Flore Pleno'	A. hip. 'Baumannii'	Agathosma serratifolia	A. crenulata
Aesculus hippocastanum 'Globosa'	A. hippocastanum	Agave affinis -Trelease	A. sobria -T.Brandegee
	'Umbraculifera'	Agave altissima	A. americana
Aesculus hippocastanum 'Pumila'	A. hipp. 'Digitata'	Agave angustissima -Engelm.	A. geminiflora
Aesculus hippocastanum f laciniata	A. hipp. 'Laciniata'	Agave asperrima -Jacobi	A. scabra -Salm-Dyck
Aesculus lucida h. ex Handl.	A. flava -Soland.	Agave atrovirens v sigmatophyla	A. salmiana
Aesculus lutea Wangenh.	A. flava -Soland.	Agave avellanidens	A. sebastiana
Aesculus macrostachya -Michx.	A. parviflora -Walt.	Agave botteri -Baker	A. celsii -J.Hook.
Aesculus memmingeri h. ex K.Koch	A. hippocastanum -L.	Agave bouchei -Jacobi	A. celsii -J.Hook.
Aesculus mississippiensis	A. x bushii	Agave caeciliana -Berger	A. scabra -Salm-Dyck
Aesculus octandra -Marsh	A. flava -Soland.	Agave carchariodonta -Pampanini	A. xylonacantha
Aesculus octandra v hybrida	A. x hybrida -DC.	Agave carminis -Trelease	A. sobria -T.Brandegee
Aesculus octandra v purpurascens	A. x hybrida -DC.	Agave carol-schmidtii -Berger	A. seemanniana -Jacobi
Aesculus pallida -Willd.	A. glabra f pallida	Agave cernua -Berger	A. attenuata
Aesculus pavia 'Penduliflora'	A. x mutabilis	Agave cerulata	A. sobria
	'Penduliflora'	Agave chihuahuana -Trelease	A. parryi -Engelm.
Aesculus procera -Salis.	A. hippocastanum -L.	Agave coarctata	A. mitriformis
Aesculus rubicunda - Loisel.	A. x carnea	Agave cochlearis -Jacobi	A. salmiana
Aesculus septenata -Stokes	A. hippocastanum -L.	Agave complicata	A. americana -L.
Aesculus spectabilis h. ex Dippel	A. x carnea -Hayne	Agave consideranti -Carr.	A. victoriae-reginae
Aesculus splendens	A. pavia	Agave consociata -Trelease	A. deserti -Engelm.
Aesculus versicolor - Wend.	A. x hybrida	Agave couesii -Engelm. ex Trelease	A. parryi v parryi
Aesculus x lyonii h.	A. x hybrida	Agave dentiens	A. deserti
Aesculus x mississippiensis	A. x bushii	Agave disceptata -Drummond	A. schidigera -Lemaire
Aesculus x mutabilis 'Rosea Nana'	A. pavia 'Rosea Nana'	Agave echinoides -Jacobi in part	A. striata -Zuccarini
Aesculus x neglecta v georgiana	A. sylvatica	Agave eduardii -Trelease	A. vilmoriniana -Berger

Synonym	Current Name	Synonym	Current Name
Agave elongata -Jacobi	A. angustifolia	Agave recurva -Zuccarini	A. striata -Zuccarini
Agave excelsa -Baker	A. angustifolia	Agave regeliana -Jacobi	A. desmettiana
Agave felina -Trelease	A. americana -L.	Agave repanda -Trelease	A. chrysantha -Peebles
Agave ferdinandi-regis -Berger	A. scabra x victoriae-reginae	Agave roezliana -Baker	A. ghiesbreghtii
		Agave saundersii -J.Hook.	A. potatorum
Agave filamentosa -Salm-Dyck	A. filifera -Salm-Dyck	Agave scaphoidea	A. utahensis
Agave filamentosa v filamentosa	A. filifera -Salm-Dyck	Agave scaphoidea	A. utahensis -Engelm.
Agave foetida -L.	Furcraea foetida	Agave scolymus -Karwinsky	A. potatorum -Zucc.
Agave franceschiana -Trelease	A. weberi	Agave slevenii -I.M.Johnston	A. sobria -T.Brandegee
Agave gigantea	Furcraea foetida	Agave striata v stricta -Baker	A. stricta -Salm-Dyck
Agave glaucescens -J.Hook.	A. attenuata	Agave subtilis -Trelease	A. tequilana -Weber
Agave gracilispina -Engelm.	A. americana -L.	Agave subzonata -Trelease	A. americana -L.
Agave guatemalensis -Berger	A. seemanniana -Jacobi	Agave sullivani -Trelease	A. fourcroydes
Agave hartmannii	A. parviflora	Agave todaroi -Baker	A. marmorata -Roezl.
Agave haseloffii -Jacobi	A. celsii -J.Hook.	Agave tortispina -Trelease	A. seemanniana -Jacobi
Agave haynaldii v utahensis	A. utahensis -Engelm.	Agave univittata -Haworth	A. lophantha v univitt.
Agave heteracantha -Zuccarini	A. lophantha -Schiede	Agave utahensis v discreta -Jones	A. utahensis -Engelm.
Agave heteracantha h.	A. lechugilla -Torr.	Agave vestita	A. schidigera
Agave houghii h. ex Trelease	A. vilmoriniana -Berger	Agave vestita -S.Watson	A. schidigera -Lemaire
Agave huachucensis -Baker	A. parryi v huachucen.	Agave vittata -Regel	A. lophantha -Schiede
Agave huehueteca -Stand. & Stey.	A. ghiesbreghtii	Agave wislizenii -Engelm.	A. parrasana -Berger
Agave hystrix	A. stricta	Agave x wrightii -Drummond	A. schidigera -Lemaire
A. ixtli -Karwinsky ex Salm-Dyck	A. angustifolia	Agave yacquiana -Trelease	A. angustifolia
Agave jacquiniana -Schultes	A. angustifolia	Agave zapupa -Trelease	A. angustifolia
Agave kochii -Jacobi	A. xylonacantha	Agave zonata -Trelease	A. americana -L.
Agave laxiflora -Baker	A. decipiens -Baker	Ageratina	Eupatorium
Agave lehmanni -Jacobi	A. salmiana	Ageratina adenophera	Eup. adenopherum
Agave mayoensis -Gentry	A. vilmoriniana -Berger	Ageratina altissima	Eup. rugosum
Agave melliflua -Trelease	A. americana -L.	Ageratina ligustrina	Eup. ligustrinum -DC.
Agave mezortillo h.	A. lophantha -Schiede	Ageratum mexicanum	A. houstonianum
Agave micracantha -Salm-Dyck	A. celsii -J.Hook.	Aglaonema 'Pewter'	A. 'Malay Beauty'
Agave miradorensis -Jacobi	A. desmettiana - Jacobi	Aglaonema marantifolium v tricolor	A. commutatum 'Tricolor'
Agave mitis	A. celsii -J.Hook.		
Agave mitriformis -Jacobi	A. salmiana	Aglaonema roebelinii	A. crispum
Agave multilineata -Baker	A. lechugilla -Torr.	Agnostus	Stenocarpus
Agave nelsonii	A. deserti	Agonis abnormalis	Leptospermum brachyandrum
Agave newberryi -Engelm.	A. utahensis -Engelm.		
Agave nichelsii -R.Gosselin	A. victoriae-reginae	Agonis scortechiniana	Lept. speciosum
Agave orcuttiana -Trelease	A. shawii -Engelm.	Agonis speciosa	Lept. speciosum
Agave pachyacantha -Trelease	A. shawii -Engelm.	Agoseris scorzonerifolia	A. glauca v dasycephala
Agave pacifica -Trelease	A. angustifolia		
Agave palmaris -Trelease	A. tequilana -Weber	Agrimonia canescens	A. eupatoria -L.
Agave palmeri v chrysantha	A. chrysantha -Peebles	Agrimonia elata	A. eupatoria -L.
Agave parryi v couesii	A. parryi v parryi	Agrimonia eupatoria ssp officinalis	A. eupatoria -L.
Agave patonii -Trelease	A. parryi -Engelm.	Agrimonia minor	A. eupatoria -L.
Agave pedrosana -Trelease	A. tequilana -Weber	Agrimonia odorata -Miller	A. repens
Agave picta	A. americana	Agrimonia officinalis	A. eupatoria -L.
Agave poselgeri -Salm-Dyck	A. lechugilla -Torr.	Agrimonia officinarum	A. eupatoria -L.
Agave prainiana -Berger	A. angustifolia	Agrimonia sulcata	A. eupatoria -L.
Agave pres-mulae -Trelease	A. tequilana -Weber	Agrimonia vulgaris	A. eupatoria -L.
Agave pringlei -Engelm. ex Baker	A. deserti -Engelm.	Agropyron alaskanum	Elymus alaskanus
Agave pruinosa -Leaire ex Jacobi	A. attenuata	Agropyron altissimum	Elymus repens
Agave pseudotequilana -Trelease	A. tequilana -Weber	Agropyron caldesii	Elymus repens
Agave purpusorum -Berger	A. ghiesbreghtii	Agropyron collinum	Elymus repens
Agave rasconensis -Trelease	A. americana -L.	Agropyron firmum	Elymus repens

Synonym	Current Name	Synonym	Current Name
Agropyron glaucum	Elymus hispidus		lophantha
Agropyron glaucum	Elymus repens	Albizia lophantha	Paras. lophantha
Agropyron junceum	Elymus repens	Albizzia	Albizia
Agropyron lanceolatum	Elymus lanceolatus	Albonia peregrina	Ailanthus altissima
Agropyron leersianum	Elymus repens	Albuca minor	A. canadensis
Agropyron magellanicum	Elymus magellanicus	Alchemilla 'Mr. Polland's Variety'	A. venosa
Agropyron multiflorum	Elymus repens	Alchemilla arvensis	Aphanes arvensis
Agropyron pubiflorum	Elymus magellanicus	Alchemilla hoppeana h.	A. plicatula
Agropyron reichenbachianum	Elymus repens	Alchemilla pedata	A. abyssinica
Agropyron repens	Elymus repens	Alchemilla splendens misapplied	A. x fulgens
Agropyron sachalinense	Elymus repens	Alchemilla vulgaris h.	A. xanthochlora
Agropyron scabrum	Elymus scabrus	Aleurites triloba	A. moluccana
Agropyron subulatum	Elymus repens	Aleuritopteris argentea	Cheilanthes argentea
Agropyron vaillantianum	Elymus repens	Alisma natans	Luronium natans
Agrostemma coeli-rosa	Silene coeli-rosa	Alisma parviflorum	A. plantago-aquatica v
Agrostemma coronaria	Lychnis coronaria		parviflorum
Agrostemma flos-jovis	Lychnis flos-jovis	A. plantago-aq. ssp subcordatum	A. pl.-aq. v parviflorum
A. githago 'Purple Queen'	A. g. 'Milas Cerise'	Alisma ranunculoides	Baldellia ranunculoides
Agrostemma githago 'Rose Queen'	A. githago 'Milas'	Alisma subcordatum	A. pl.-aq. v parviflorum
Agrostis calamagrostis	Stipa calamagrostis	Alitubus pyrenaicus	Achillea ptarmica
Agrostis effusa	Milium effusum	Allamanda neriifolia	A. schottii
Agrostis heterolepis	Sporolobus heterolepis	Allamanda violacea	A. blanchettii
Agrostis karsensis	A. stolonifera	Allantodia aemula	Dryopteris aemula
Agrostis latifolia	Cinna latifolia	Allardia glabra	A. tridactylites
Agrostis mexicanus	Muhlenbergia mexicana	Allemanda	Allamanda
		Alliaria officinalis	A. petiolata
Agrostis tenuis (unv)	A. capillaris	Allium 'Hair'	A. vineale 'Hair'
Ailanthus cacodendron	A. altissima	Allium 'Summer Beauty'	A. senescens ssp montanum
Ailanthus flavescens -Carr.	Toona sinensis		
Ailanthus giraldii	A. altissima	Allium 'Violet Beauty'	A. stipitatum 'Violet Beauty'
Ailanthus glandulosa -Desf.	A. altissima		
Ailanthus peregrina	A. altissima	Allium aflatunense h.	A. holllandicum
Ailanthus procera	A. altissima	Allium albidum	A. denudatum
Ailanthus rhodoptera	A. altissima	Allium albopilosum	A. cristophii
Ailanthus sutchuensis -Dode	A. altissima v sutchu.	Allium amabile	A. mairei v amabile
Ailanthus vilmoriniana	A. altissima	Allium ambiguum	A. roseum v carneum
Aira caespitosa	Deschampsia cespitosa	Allium angustitepalum	A. jesdianum ssp ang.
Aira flexuosa	Deschampsia flexuosa	Allium azureum	A. caeruleum
Ajuga alpina	A. genevensis	Allium beesianum h.	A. cyaneum
Ajuga brockbankii	A. 'Brockbankii'	Allium blandum	A. carolinianum
Ajuga genevensis 'Brockbankii'	A. 'Brockbankii'	Allium breweri	A. falicifolium
Ajuga genevensis 'Crispa'	A. pyramidalis 'Metallica Crispa'	Allium bulgaricum	Nectaroscordum siculum ssp bulgar.
Ajuga grandiflora	A. australis	Allium caeruleum azureum	A. caeruleum
Ajuga metallica h.	A. pyramidalis	Allium callumischon	A. callimischon
Ajuga reptans 'Argentea'	A. reptans 'Variegata'	Allium cernuum 'Major'	A. cernuum 'Hidcote'
Ajuga reptans 'Jumbo'	A. r. 'Jungle Beauty'	Allium christophii	A. cristophii
Ajuga reptans 'Macrophylla'	A. r. 'Catlin's Giant'	Allium cirrhosum	A. carinatum ssp pulchellum
Ajuga reptans 'Mahogany'	A. reptans 'Braunherz'		
Ajuga reptans 'Purpurea'	A. r. 'Atropurpurea'	Allium controversum	A.sativum
Ajuga reptans 'Rainbow'	A. reptans 'Multicolor'	Allium cowanii	A. neapolitanum
Ajuga reptans 'Tricolor'	A. reptans 'Multicolor'		Cownaii Group
Akebia lobata -Decne.	A. trifoliata	Allium dioscoridis	Nectaroscordum sicul.
Alaternus	Rhamnus	Allium dioscoridis	Nectaroscordum sic. ssp bulgaricum
Albizia distachya	Paraserianthes		

Synonym	Current Name	Synonym	Current Name
Allium elatum	A. macleanii	Alnus acuminata	A. jorullensis
Allium farreri	A. cyathophorum v far.	Alnus alnobetula -K.Koch	A. viridis -(Chaix) DC.
Allium flavum 'Glaucum'	A. flavum 'Blue Leaf'	Alnus alnus	A. glutinosa
Allium flavum 'Minus'	A. fl. ssp fl. v minus	Alnus barbata -C.A.Mey	A. glutinosa v barbata
Allium glaucum	A. senescens ssp montanum v glaucum	Alnus brembana -Rota	A. viridis v pumila
		Alnus crispa	A. viridis ssp crispa
Allium griffithianum	A. rubellum	Alnus firma v multinervis	A. pendula -Matsum.
Allium haemosticum	A. callimischon ssp haemostichum	Alnus firma v sieboldiana -Matsum.	A. sieboldiana
		Alnus firma v yasha	A. firma -Sieb. & Zucc.
Allium jajlae	A. rotundum ssp jajlae	Alnus fruticosa	A. viridis ssp fruticosa
A. jesdianum 'Michael Hoog'	A. rosenbachianum 'Michael Hoog'	Alnus glutinosa 'Fastigiata'	A. glut. 'Pyramidalis'
		Alnus glutinosa v incisa -Willd.	A. glutinosa f incisa
Allium kansuense	A. sikkimense	Alnus incana 'Acuminata'	A. incana 'Laciniata'
Allium komarovianum	A. thunbergii	Alnus incana 'Ramulis Coccineis'	A. incana 'Aurea'
Allium montanum	A. senescens ssp mon.	Alnus incana v americana	A. rugosa
Allium multibulbosum	A. nigrum	Alnus incana v hirsuta -Spach	A. hirsuta
Allium murrayanum	A. acuminatum	Alnus incana v sibirica -Spach	A. hirsuta v sibirica
Allium murrayanum h.	A. unifolium	Alnus oregona -Nutt	A. rubra -Bong.
A. narcissiflorum missapplied	A. insubricum	Alnus rotundifolia	A. glutinosa
Allium neriniflorum	Caloscordum nerinifl.	Alnus rubra 'Pinnatifida'	A. rubra f pinnatisecta
Allium nuttallii	A. drummondii	Alnus serrulata	A. rugosa
Allium odorum -Linnaeus	A. ramosum -Linnaeus	Alnus sinuata	A. sinuata v viridis
Allium ostrowskianum	A. oreophilum	Alnus sitchensis -Sarg.	A. sinuata v viridis
Allium oviflorum	A. macranthum	Alnus tinctoria -Sarg.	A. hirsuta
Allium pedemontanum	A. narcissiflorum	Alnus viridis v brembana	A. viridis v pumila
Allium polyphyllum	A. carolinianum	Alnus viridis v parvifolia -Reg.	A. viridis v pumila
Allium pulchellum	A. carinatum ssp pulc.	Alnus viridis v sibirica -Reg.	A. maximowiczii
Allium purdomii	A. cyaneum	Alnus vulgaris	A. glutinosa
A. pyrenaicum misapplied	A. angulosum	Alnus yasha -Matsum.	A. firma
Allium ramosum	A. obliquum	Alocasia 'Quilted Dreams'	A. guttata v imperialis
A. rosenbachianum misapplied	A. hollandicum	Alocasia 'Vic Santos'	A. 'Corozon'
A. roseum 'Grandiflorum'	A. roseum v bulbiferum	Alocasia indica v metallica h.	A. plumbea
Allium scorodoprasum ssp jajlae	A. rotundum ssp jajlae	Alocasia lowii v veitchii	A. veitchii
Allium senescens 'Glaucum'	A. senescens ssp mon tanum v glaucum	Alocasia nigra	A. plumbea 'Nigra'
		Alocasia picta	A. veitchii
Allium senescens v calcareum	A. senescens ssp mon.	Alocasia whinkii	A. 'Uhinkii'
Allium sibiricum	A. schoenoprasum	Alocasiophyllum	Cercestis
Allium sibthorpianum	A. paniculatum	Aloe arabica	A. vera
Allium siculum	Nectaroscordum sicu.	Aloe atherstonei	A. pluridens
Allium siculum dioscoridis	Nectaroscordum sicu lum ssp bulgaricum	Aloe ausana	A. variegata
		Aloe barbadensis	A. vera
Allium strictum Ledeb.	A. szovitsii	Aloe ellenbergeri	A. aristata
Allium strictum Schrad.	A. lineare	Aloe ferox v xanthostachys (unv)	A. spectabilis
Allium tibeticum	A. sikkimense	Aloe galpinii	A. ferox
Allium violaceum	A. carinatum	Aloe indica	A. vera
Allium yunnanense	A. mairei v amabile	Aloe paniculata	A. striata
Allocasuarina campestris ssp camp.	A. campestris	Aloe perfoliata v arborescens	A. arborescens
A. campestris ssp eriochlamys	A. eriochlamys	Aloe platyphylla	A. zebrina
A. campestris ssp grossa	A. eriochl. ssp grossa	Aloe prolifera	A. brevifolia
Allocasuarina robusta	A. mackliniana ssp xerophila	Aloe punctata	A. variegata
		Aloe pycnantha (unv)	A. rupestris
Allosorus atropurpureus	Pellaea atropurpurea	Aloe socotrina	A. ferox
Allosorus crispus	Cryptogramma crispa	Aloe supralaevis	A. ferox
Allostelites arvense	Equisetum arvense -L.	Aloe xanthocantha	A. mitriformis
Allostelites sylvaticum	Equisetum sylvaticum	Aloe yuccifolia -Gary	Hesperaloe parviflora

Synonym	Current Name	Synonym	Current Name
Aloinella haworthioides	Aloe haworthioides	Alyssum halimifolium	Lobularia maritima
Alomia pinetorum	Ageratum houstonianum	Alyssum jonasianum	Lobularia maritima
		Alyssum lagascae	A. purpureum
Alonsoa albiflora h.	A. acutifolia candida	Alyssum lapeyrousianum	Ptilotrichum lapeyrou.
Alonsoa caulialata	A. meridionalis	Alyssum longicaule	Ptilotrichum long.
Alonsoa grandiflora	A. warscewiczii	Alyssum maritimum	Lobularia maritima
Alonsoa linifolia	A. linearis	Alyssum mildeanum	A. stribrnyi
Alonsoa myrtifolia	A. acutifolia	Alyssum minimum	Lobularia maritima
Alonsoa warscewiczii pale form	A. warscewiczii 'Peachy-keen'	Alyssum montanum Mountain Gold	A. montanum 'Berggold'
		Alyssum ovirense	A. wulfenianum
Alopecurus alpinus ssp glaucus	A. borealis ssp glaucus	Alyssum petraeum	Aurinia petraea
Alopecurus pallescens	A. geniculatus	Alyssum podolicum	Schivereckia podolica
A. palustris ssp geniculatus	A. geniculatus	Alyssum reverchonii	Ptilotrichum reverch.
Alophia lahue	Herbertia lahue	Alyssum rochellii	A. wulfenianum
Aloysia citriodora -Ortega ex Pers.	A. triphylla	Alyssum rupestre	Ptilotrichum rupestre
Alpinia magnifica	Nicolaia elatior	Alyssum saxatile	Aurinia saxatilis
Alpinia nutans h.	A. zerumbet	Alyssum trichostachyum	A. repens
Alpinia sanderae h.	A. vittata	Alyssum utriculatum	Alyssoides utriculata
Alpinia speciosa	A. zerumbet	Alyssum vesicaria	Coluteocarpus vesicarius
Alsine laricifolia	Minuartia laricifolia		
Alsine verna	Minuartia verna	Amana	Tulipa
Alsobia	Episcia	Amaracas	Origanum
Alsobia dianthiflora	Episcia dianthiflora	Amaranthus albus v pubescens	A. albus
Alsophila	Cyathea	Amaranthus dussii	A. caudatus
Alsophila australis h.	Cyathea cooperi	Amaranthus gracilentus	A. albus
Alsophila brevipinna	Cyathea brevipinna	Amaranthus graecizans	A. albus
A. leichhardtiana v woollsiana	Cyathea woollsiana	Amaranthus mantegazzianus	A. caudatus
Alsophila macarthurii	Cyathea leichhardtiana	Amaranthus pubescens	A. albus
Alsophila robertsiana	Cyathea robertsiana	Amaryllis belladonna 'Pallida'	A. belladonna 'Elata'
Alsophila tricolor	Cyathea dealbata	Amaryllis belladonna 'Parkeri Alba'	x Amarygia parkeri 'Alba'
Alstroemeria 'Orchid'	A. 'Walter Fleming'		
Alstroemeria 'Regina'	A. 'Victoria'	Amaryllis ornata	Crinum latifolium v zeylanicum
Alstroemeria 'Stacova'	A. 'Margaret'		
Alstroemeria 'Stadoran'	A. 'Beatrix'	Amaryllis reginae	Hippeastrum reginae
Alstroemeria aurantiaca	A. aurea	Amblyopetalum caeruleum	Tweedia caerulea
Alstroemeria gayana	A. pelegrina	Ambrina botrys	Chenopodium botrys
Alstroemeria kingii	A. versicolor	Amdromeda caerulea -L.	Phyllodoce caerulea
Alstroemeria psittacina variegated	A. ps. 'Royal Star'	Amelanchier canadensis -many authors not (L.) Med.	
Alstroemeria pulchella -Sims	A. psittacina		A. arborea
Alstroemeria violacea	A. paupercula	A. canadensis -many authors not Mespilus canadensis -L.	
Alternanthera amoena	A. ficoidea v amoena		A. laevis -Wieg.
Alternanthera versicolor	A. ficoidea 'Versicolor'	Amelanchier canadensis h.	A. lamarckii
Althaea frutex h.	Hibiscus syriacus -L.	Amelanchier canadensis v alnifolia	A. alnifolia
Althaea rosea	Alcea rosea	Amelanchier canadensis v japonica	A. asiatica
Althaea rugosostellulata	Alcea rugosa	A. canadensis v oblongifolia	A. canadensis
Alyssum 'Snow Carpet'	A. 'Carpet of Snow'	Amelanchier cusickii -Fern.	A. alnifolia v cusickii
Alyssum amamum	A. sphacioticum	Amelanchier florida	A. alnifolia v semiintegrifolia
Alyssum arduinii	Aurinia saxatilis		
Alyssum argenteum h.	A. murale	Amelanchier lamarckii 'Rubescens'	A. x grandiflora 'Rubescens'
Alyssum bornmuelleri	Schivereckia bornm.		
Alyssum corymbosum	Aurinia corymbosa	Amelanchier lucida	A. canadensis
Alyssum deltoideum	Aubrieta deltoidea	Amelanchier mucronata	A. humilis
Alyssum diffusum	A. montanum	Amelanchier oblongifolia -Roem.	A. canadensis
Alyssum edulenteum	Aurinia petraea	A. oblongifolia v micropetala	A. arborea
Alyssum gemonense	Aurinia petraea	Amelanchier oligocarpa -Roem.	A. bartramiana

Synonym	Current Name	Synonym	Current Name
Amelanchier ovalis -Lam.	A. x spicata	Ampelopsis latifolia	Parthenocissus quinquefolia
Amelanchier oxyodon -Koehne	A. alnifolia v semiintegrifolia	Ampelopsis micans -Rehd.	Ampelopsis bodinieri
Amelanchier prunifolia -Greene	A. utahensis -Koehne	Ampelopsis muralis	Parthenocissus quinquefolia
Amelanchier pumila	A. alnifolia v pumila		
Amelanchier purpusii -Koehne	A. utahensis -Koehne	Ampelopsis pubescens	Parthenocissus quinq.
Amelanchier racemosa -Lindl.	Exochorda racemosa	Ampelopsis quinquefolia h. in part	Parth. inserta
Amelanchier rotundifolia	A. ovalis -Med.	A. quinquefolia v engelmannii -Rehd.	Parthenocissus quinquefolia v engelmannii
Amelanchier rotundifolia -Roem.	A. sanguinea		
Amelanchier rubescens -Greene	A. utahensis -Koehne	Ampelopsis quinquefolia v vitacea	Parthenocissus inser.
A. sanguinea f grandiflora -Wieg.	A. sang. v grandiflora	Ampelopsis sempervirens h.	Cissus striata
Amelanchier sanguinea v alnifolia	A. alnifolia	Ampelopsis tricuspidata	Parthenocissus tricus.
Amelanchier sanguinea v gaspensis	A. gaspensis	Ampelopsis tricuspidata 'Veitchii'	Parthenocissus tricuspidata 'Veitchii'
Amelanchier stolonifera v lucida	A. canadensis		
Amelanchier vulgaris -Moench	A. rotundifolia	Ampelopsis watsoniana -Wils.	A. chaffanjonii
Amelanchier vulgaris -Moench	A. ovalis -Med.	Amphicome	Incarvillea
Amelanchier vulgaris v cretica	A. ovalis v cretica	Amphiraphis albescens -DC.	Aster albescens
Amelanchier vulgaris v integrifolia	A. ovalis v integrifolia	Amsonia salicifolia	A. tabernaemontana v salicifolia
Amellus diffusus -Forst.	Chiliotrichium diffusum		
Amellus speciosus	Callistephus chinensis	Amygdalus	Prunus
Amesia latifolia	Epipactis helleborine	Amygdalus communis -L.	Prunus dulcis
Amesium ruta-muraria -(L.) Newman	Asplenium ruta-mur.	Amygdalus hybrida -Poit. & Turpin	Prun. x amygdopersica
Ammi copticum	Trachyspermum ammi	Amygdalus nana -L.	Prunus tenella
Ammogeton scorzonerifolia	A. glauca v dasycephala	Anacampseros intermedia	A. telephiastrum
		Anacampseros varians	A. telephiastrum
Ammyrsine prostrata -Loud.	Leiophyllum buxifolium v prostratum	Anacharis canadensis	Elodea canadensis
		Anacharis densa	Egeria densa
Amomophyllum	Spathiphyllum	Anacharis linearis	Elodea canadensis
Amomum cardamomum	A. compactum	Anacharis nuttallii	Elodea nuttallii
Amomum magnificum	Nicolaia elatior	Anacyclus depressus	A. pyrethrum v depr.
Amorpha brachycarpa	A. canescens	Anadendron -Schott	Anadendrum -Schott
Amorpha microphylla -Pursh	A. nana -Nutt.	Anadenia hakeoides	Hakea undulata
Ampelodesmos tenax	A. mauritanicus	Anagallis breweri	A. monellii ssp linifolia
Ampelopsis bipinnata -Michx.	Ampelopsis arborea	Anagallis caerulea	A. arvensis v caerulea
Ampelopsis brevipedunculata	A. glandulosa v brevipedunculata	Anagallis collina	A. monellii
		Anagallis fruticosa	A. monellii ssp linifolia
A. brevipedunculata 'Citrulloides'	Ampelopsis glandulosa v brevip. f citrulloides	Anagallis grandiflora	A. monellii ssp linifolia
		Anagallis linifolia	A. monellii ssp linifolia
Ampelopsis engelmannii -Spaeth	Parthenocissus quinquefolia v engelmannii	Anagallis phillipsii	A. monellii ssp linifolia
		Anagallis willmoriana	A. monellii ssp linifolia
Ampelopsis glandulosa	A. brevipedunculata	Anandendron	Anadendrum
A. gl. v brevipedunculata 'Tricolor'	A. gl. v brevipeduncul. 'Elegans'	Anaphalis angustifolia	A. margaritacea
		Anaphalis cinnamomea	A. margaritacea v cin.
A.gl. v brevipedunculata 'Variegata'	A. glandulosa v brevipedunculata 'Elegans'	Anaphalis margaritacea New Snow	A. marg. 'Neuschnee'
		Anaphalis nubigena	A. nepalensis v monocephala
Ampelopsis graebneri	Parthenocissus quinq.	Anaphalis occidentalis	A. margaritacea
Ampelopsis hederacea -(Ehrh.) DC.	Parthenocissus quinq.	Anaphalis subalpina	A. margaritacea
Ampelopsis henryana	Parthenocissus henr.	A. triplinervis 'Sulphur Light'	Helichrysum 'Schwefellicht'
Ampelopsis heterophylla	A. glandulosa v heter.		
A. heterophylla v amurensis	A. glandulosa v brevipedunculata	A. triplinervis Summer Snow	A. tr. 'Sommerschnee'
		Anaphalis triplinervis v intermedia	A. nepalensis
Ampelopsis himalayana -Royle	Parthenocissus himal.	Anaphalis yedoensis	A. margaritacea v yed.
Ampelopsis hirsuta	Parthenocissus quinquefolia	Anarmodium -Schott	Dracunculus -Mill.
Ampelopsis inserta -Kerner	Parthenocissus inser.	Anchistea virginica	Woodwardia virginica

Synonym	Current Name	Synonym	Current Name
Anchusa angustissima	A. leptophylla ssp incana	Andromeda nikoensis -Maxim.	Enkianthus subsessilis
		Andromeda ovalifolia -Wall.	Lyonia ovalifolia
Anchusa arvensis ssp occidentalis	A. arvensis	Andromeda polifolia 'Compacta Alba'	A. polifolia 'Alba'
Anchusa caespitosa	A. cespitosa -Lamarck	A. polifolia ssp glaucophylla	A. glaucophylla
Anchusa caespitosa h.	A. leptophylla ssp incana	Andromeda polifolia v latifolia -Ait.	A. glaucophylla v latif.
		Andromeda populifolia -Lam.	Agarista populifolia
Anchusa italica	A. azurea	Andromeda prostrata -Cav.	Gaultheria myrsinoides
Anchusa italica v azurea	A. azurea	Andromeda racemosa -L.	Leucothoe racemosa
Anchusa laxiflora	Borago pygmaea	Andromeda recurva -Buckl.	Leucothoe recurva
Anchusa myosotidiflora	Brunnera macrophylla	Andromeda rosmarinifolia	A. glaucophylla
Anchusa sempervirens	Pentaglottis semperv.	Andromeda rupestris -L. f.	Gaultheria rupestris
Ancistrocactus	Sclerocactus	Andromeda spicata -Wats.	Leucothoe racemosa
Ancistrocactus crassihamatus	Sclerocactus uncina tus v crassihamatus	Andromeda stelleriana -Pall.	Cassiope stelleriana
		Andromeda subsessilis -Miq.	Enkianthus subsessilis
Ancistrocactus megarhizus	Sclerocactus scheeri	Andromeda tetragona -L.	Cassiope tetragona
Ancistrocactus scheeri	Sclerocactus scheeri	A. tetragona ssp saximontana	Cassiope tetragona v saximontana
Ancistrocactus uncinatus	Sclerocactus uncinat.		
Andromeda acuminata -Ait.	Leucothoe populifolia -	Andromeda walteri	Leucothoe fontanesiana
Andromeda adenothrix -Miq.	Gaultheria adenothrix -	Andromycia -A.Rich	Asterostigma
Andromeda americana h.	A. glaucophylla	Andropogon furcatus	A. gerardii
Andromeda angustifolia	Chamaedaphne calyculata	Andropogon ischaemum	Bothriochloa isch.
		Andropogon provincialis	A. gerardii
Andromeda arborea -L.	Oxydendrum arboreum	Andropogon scoparius	Schizachyrium scoparium
Andromeda axillaris -Lam.	Leucothoe axillaris -		
Andromeda baccata -Wangenh.	Gaylussacia baccata -	Andropogon sorghum	Sorghum bicolor
Andromeda bryantha -L.	Bryanthus gmelinii	Andropogon tennesseensis	A. gerardii
Andromeda calyculata -L.	Chamaedaphne calyc.	Androsace acaulis	A. septentrionalis
Andromeda campanulata -Miq.	Enkianthus campanulatus	Androsace aizoon coccinea	A. bulleyana
		Androsace aizoon himalaica	A. himalaica
Andromeda canadensis	A. glaucophylla	Androsace arachnoidea	A. villosa v arachn.
Andromeda canescens -Small	A. glauc. v latifolia	Androsace argentea	A. vandellii
Andromeda catesbaei - Walt.	Leucothoe axillaris	Androsace brevis	A. charpentieri
Andromeda chinensis	Vaccinium bracteatum	Androsace carnea v halleri	A. carnea ssp rosea
Andromeda ciliicalyx -Miq.	Menziesia ciliicalyx	Androsace caucasica	A. raddeana
Andromeda coerulea -L.	Phyllodoce caerulea	Androsace chumbyi	A. sarmentosa 'Chumbyi'
Andromeda coriacea -Ait.	Lyonia lucida		
Andromeda crispa	Chamaedaphne calyculata	Androsace coccinea	A. bulleyana
		Androsace gaudinii	A. x heeri
Andromeda cupressina -Hook.	Cassiope mertensiana	Androsace glacialis	A. alpina
Andromeda daboecia	Daboecia cantabrica	Androsace halleri	A. carnea ssp rosea
Andromeda elliptica -Sieb. & Zucc.	Lyonia ovalifolia v ellip.	Androsace imbricata	A. vandellii
Andromeda empetrifolia -Lam.	Gaultheria pumila	Androsace jacquemontii	A. villosa v jacquem.
Andromeda eriophylla -Pers.	Gaultheria eriophylla -	Androsace laggeri	A. carnea v laggeri
Andromeda fastigiata -Wall.	Cassiope fastigiata	Androsace limprichtii	A. sarmentosa v watkinsii
Andromeda floribunda	Pieris floribunda		
Andromeda fontanesiana -Steud.	Leucothoe walteri	Androsace microphylla	A. mucronifolia -Watt
Andromeda formosa -Wall.	Pieris formosa	Androsace mollis	A. sarmentosa v yunnanensis
Andromeda hypnoides -L.	Cassiope hypnoides		
Andromeda japonica -Thunb.	Pieris japonica	Androsace mucronifolia h.	A. sempervivoides
Andromeda lanceolata -Wall.	Lyonia ovalifolia v lanc.	Androsace pacheri	A. wulfeniana
Andromeda lucida -Lam.	Lyonia lucida	Androsace primuloides -Duby	A. studiosorum
Andromeda lycopodioides -Pall.	Cassiope lycopodioides	Androsace primuloides h.	A. sarmentosa
Andromeda mariana -L.	Lyonia mariana	Androsace reverchonii	A. carnea
Andromeda mertensiana -Bong.	Cassiope mertensiana	Androsace salicifolia	A. lactiflora
Andromeda nana -Maxim.	Pieris nana	Androsace sarmentosa 'Chumbyi'	A. studiosorum

Synonym	Current Name	Synonym	Current Name
	'Chumbyi'	Anemone multifida misapplied red	A. x lesseri
A. sarmentosa 'Salmon's Variety'	A. studiosorum	Anemone nemerosa 'Currey's Pink'	A. nem. 'Lismore Pink'
	'Salmon's Variety'	A. nemerosa 'Dr. Lowe's Variety'	A. n. 'Leeds' Variety'
Androsace sarmentosa misapplied	A. studiosorum	Anemone nemerosa 'Plena'	A. nem. 'Flore Pleno'
A.sarmentosa v yunnanensis -Kunth	A. mollis	Anemone nemerosa v bastardii	A. nemerosa
A. sarm. v yunnanensis misapplied	A. studiosorum	Anemone nemerosa v grandiflora	A. nemerosa
Androsace tschuktschorum	A. ochotensis	Anemone nemerosa v quinquaefolia	A. nemerosa
Androsace vitaliana	Vitaliana primuliflora	Anemone nemerosa v tenuifolia	A. nemerosa
Androsace watkinsii	A. sarmentosa v wat.	A. nemerosa x ranunculoides	A. x lipsiensis
Androsace yunnanense	A. sarmentosa v yun.	Anemone nigricans	Pulsatilla pratensis
Androsaemum officinale -All.	Hypericum	Anemone nobilis	Hepatica nobilis
	androsaemum -L.	Anemone nobilis obtusa	Hepatica americana
Androsaemum xylosteifolium	Hypericum xylosteif.	Anemone nobilis rhodantha	Hepatica americana
Androstephium violaceum	A. caeruleum	Anemone nudicaulis	Ranunculus lapponicus
Andryala lanata	Hieracium lanatum	Anemone nuttalliana -DC.	Pulsatilla patens v
Anemone 'Bressingham Glow'	A. hupehensis v japoni		multifida
	ca 'Bressingham Glow'	Anemone occidentalis	Pulsatilla occidentalis
Anemone aconitifolia -Michx.	A. narcissiflora	Anemone parviflora v grandifolia	A. parviflora
Anemone acultiloba	Hepatica acutiloba	Anemone parviflora	Pulsatilla patens
Anemone acutipetala	Pulsatilla pratensis	Anemone patens	Pulsatilla patens
Anemone alpina	Pulsatilla alpina	Anemone pedata	A. nemerosa
Anemone americana	Hepatica americana	Anemone pennsylvanica	A. canadensis
Anemone angulosa	Hepatica transsilvanica	Anemone pentaphylla	A. nemerosa
Anemone baicalensis	A. flaccida	Anemone praecox	Hepatica nobilis
Anemone biarmiensis	A. narcissiflora ssp	Anemone pratensis	Pulsatilla pratensis
	biarmiensis	Anemone pulsatilla	Pulsatilla vulgaris
Anemone bogenhardiana	Pulsatilla vulgaris	A. ranunculoides 'Flore Pleno'	A. ran. 'Pleniflora'
Anemone borealis	A. parviflora	Anemone riparia	A. virginiana v alba
Anemone cernua	Pulsatilla cernua	Anemone siuzevii	A. stolonifera
Anemone collina	Pulsatila vulgaris	Anemone soyensis	A. flaccida
A. coronaria De Caen Group 'His Excellency'		Anemone stellata	A. hortensis
	A. coronaria De Caen	Anemone stellata v heldreichii	A. hortensis ssp held.
	Group 'Hollandia'	Anemone sulphurea	Pulsatilla alpina ssp
A. cor. De Caen Group 'The Bride'	A. cor. De Caen Group		apiifolia
	'Die Braut'	Anemone sylvestris 'Flore Pleno'	A. syl. 'Elise Fellmann'
A. dichotoma ssp pennsylvanica	A. canadensis	Anemone thalictroides	Anemonella thalictr.
Anemone fasciculata	A. narcissiflora	Anemone tomentosa 'Robustissima'	A. x hybrida
Anemone globosa	A. multifida		'Robustissima'
Anemone groenlandica	Coptis trifolia	Anemone triloba v americana	Hepatica americana
Anemone halleri	Pulsatilla halleri	Anemone vahlii	A. richardsonii
Anemone hepatica	Hepatica nobilis	Anemone vernalis	Pulsatilla vernalis
Anemone hupehensis 'Crispa'	A. x hybrida 'Lady	Anemone vitifolia 'Robustissima'	A. x hybrida
	Gilmour' Wolley-Dod		'Robustissima'
A. hupehensis 'September Charm'	A. x hybrida	Anemone vitifolia misapplied	A. tomentosa
	'September Charm'	Anemone wockeana	A. ranunculoides
Anemone hupehensis Pink Shell	A. hupehensis	Anemone wolfgangiana -Bess.	Pulsatilla patens v
	'Rosenschale'		multifida
A. hup. v japonica Prince Henry	A. hupehensis v japoni	Anemone x elegans	A. x hybrida
	ca 'Prinz Heinrich'	Anemone x hybrida 'Alba' h. in U.K.	A. x hybrida 'Honorine
Anemone janczewskii	Pulsatilla vulgaris		Jobert'
Anemone japonica	A. hupehensis	Anemone x hybrida 'Alba' h. in U.K.	A. x hybrida 'Honorine
Anemone japonica	A. x hybrida		Jobert'
Anemone laevigata	A. flaccida	A. x hybrida 'Alba' h. in U.S.A.	A. x hybrida 'Lady
Anemone magellanica h.	A. multifida		Ardilaun'
Anemone montana	Pulsatilla montana	A. x hybrida 'Albert Schweitzer'	A. x hybrida 'Elegans'
		Anemone x hybrida 'Bowles' Pink'	A. x hupehensis

24

Synonym	Current Name	Synonym	Current Name
	'Bowles' Pink'	Angelica montana	A. sylvestris
Anemone x hybrida 'Bowles' Pink'	A. hup. 'Bowles' Pink'	Angelica officinalis	A. archangelica
A. x hybrida 'Bressingham Glow'	A. x hup. v japonica	Angelica paludapifolium	Levisticum officinale
	'Bressingham Glow'	Angelica polymorpha sinensis	A. polymorpha
A. x hybrida 'Bressingham Glow'	A. hup. v japonica	Angelica refracta	A. genuflexa
	'Bressingham Glow'	Angelica sinensis	A. polymorpha sinensis
Anemone x hybrida 'Lady Gilmour'	A. x hyb 'Margarete'	Angelica sinuata	A. polymorpha
Anemone x hybrida 'Max Vogel'	A. x hybrida 'Elegans'	Angophora angustata	A. bakeri
Anemone x hybrida 'Monterosa'	A. x hyb 'Margarete'	Angophora bakeri ssp bakeri	A. bakeri
Anemone x hybrida 'Pamina'	A. hup. v japonica	Angophora bakeri ssp crassifolia	A. crassifolia
	'Pamina'	Angophora cordifolia	A. hispida
Anemone x hybrida 'Prinz Heinrich'	A. hup. v japonica	Angophora costata ssp costata	A. costata
	'Prinz Heinrich'	Angophora costata ssp euryphylla	A. euryphylla
Anemone x hybrida 'Rotkappchen'	A. hup. v japonica	Angophora costata ssp leiocarpa	A. leiocarpa
	'Rotkappchen'	Angophora floribunda v floribunda	A. floribunda
Anemone x hybrida 'Tourbillon'	A. x hybrida	Angophora florida	A. floribunda
	'Whirlwind'	Angophora intermedia	A. floribunda
Anemone x hybrida 'White Giant'	A. x hybrida 'Geante	A. intermedia v melanoxyon	A. melanoxylon
	des Blanches'	Angophora intermedia v woodsiana	A. woodsiana
Anemone x hybrida 'White Queen'	A. x hybrida 'Geante	Angophora lanceolata	A. costata
	des Blanches'	Angophora lanceolata v angustifolia	A. bakeri
Anemone x hybrida 'Wirbelwind'	A. x hybrida	Angophora lanceolata v hispida	A. costata
	'Whirlwind'	Anguloa virginalis	A. uniflora
Anemone x hybrida Prince Henry	A. hup. v japonica	Anhalonium retusum	Ariocarpus retusus
	'Prinz Heinrich'	Anhalonium trigonum	Ariocarpus trigonus
Anemone x hybrida Queen Charlotte	A. x hybrida 'Konigin	Anil	Indigofera
	Charlotte'	Anisantha rigida	Bromus rigidus
Anemone x hybrida Tourbillon	A. x hybrida	Anisantha tectorum	Bromus tectorum
	'Whirlwind'	Anisodontea huegelii	Alyogyne huegelii
Anemone x intermedia	A. x lipsiensis	A. x hypomadara misapplied	A. capensis
Anemone x seemannii	A. x lipsiensis	Anisodontea x hypomandarum	A. x hypomadara
Anemonella thalict. 'Schoaf's Double'	A. thalictroides 'Oscar	Anisotome gingidium	Angelica sylvestris
	Schoaf'		(A. montana -
A. thalictroides 'Schoaf's Pink'	A. thal. 'Oscar Schoaf'		(J.R.&G.Forst) Ckn.
Anemonidium canadense	Anemone canadensis	Anisum odoratum	Pimpinella anisum
Anemonidium nemorosum	A. nemerosa	Anisum officinarum	Pimpinella anisum
Anemonidium richardsonii	A. richardsonii	Anisum vulgare	Pimpinella anisum
Anepsias -Schott	Rhodospatha -Poepp.	Anneliesia candida	Miltonia candida
Anethum arvense	A. graveolens	Annona triloba -L.	Asimina triloba
Anethum benevolens	A. graveolens	Anoda ochsenii -(Phil.) Phil.	Abutilon ochsenii
Anethum dulce	Foeniculum vulgare	Anogra	Oenothera
Anethum foeniculum	Foeniculum vulgare	Anoiganthus	Cyrtanthus
Anethum minus	Foeniculum vulgare	Anoiganthus luteus	Cyrtanthus breviflorus
Anethum panmorium	Foeniculum vulgare	Anomalesia	Gladiolus
Anethum piperitum	Foeniculum vulgare	Anomatheca cruenta	A. laxa
Anethum rupestre	Foeniculum vulgare	Anonymus aquatica -Walt.	Planera aquatica
Anethum sowa	A. graveolens	Antennaria aprica	A. parvifolia
Angelica cartilaginomarginata	A. crucifolia	Antennaria candida	A. diocia 'Minima'
Angelica cryptotaeniifolia	A. gigas	Antennaria cinnamomea v angustior	Anaphalis
Angelica curtisii	A. triquinata		margaritacea
Angelica gingidium	A. sylvestris (A.monta	Antennaria dioica 'Aprica'	A. parvifolia
	na (J.R.&G.Forst)Ckn.	Antennaria dioica tomentosa	A. dioica v hyperborea
Angelica jaluana	A. animala	Antennaria dioica v rosea	A. microphylla
Angelica kiusiana	A. japonica	Antennaria hyperborea	A. dioica v hyperborea
Angelica levisticum	Levisticum officinale	Antennaria leontopodium	Leontopodium alpinum

Synonym	Current Name	Synonym	Current Name
Antennaria macrophylla h.	A. microphylla	Antirrhinum grandiflorum	A. majus ssp majus
Antennaria margaritacea	Anaphalis margaritacea	Antirrhinum italicum -Mill.	A. majus ssp majus
A. margaritacea v subalpina	Anaphalis margaritacea	Antirrhinum lianria	Linaria vulgaris
Antennaria parvifolia v rosea	A. microphylla	Antirrhinum murale	A. majus ssp majus
Antennaria tomentosa	A. dioica	Antirrhinum purpureum	Linaria purpurea
Anthelia -Schott	Epipremnum -Schott	Antirrhinum vulgare	A. majus ssp majus
A. 'Grallagh Gold' orange-yellow	A. 'Beauty of Grallagh'	Antommarchia	Correa
Anthemis ageratifolia	A. ageratifolia	Apactis japonica	Xylosma japonica
Anthemis agrestis	A. arvensis	Apargia autumnalis	Leontodon autumnalis
Anthemis aizoon	Achillea ageratifolia ssp aizoon	Apargia pratensis	Leontodon autumnalis
		Apatemone -Schott	Schismatoglottis
Anthemis arvensis v agrestis	A. arvensis	Apera arundinacea	Calamagrostis arund.
Anthemis biebersteiniana	A. marschalliana	Aphanichilus stauntonii	Elsholtzia stauntonii
Anthemis biebersteinii	A. marschalliana	Aphelandra fascinator	A. aurantiaca
Anthemis frutescens	Argyranthemum frut.	Aphyllarum -S.Moore	Caladium -Vent.
Anthemis macedonica	A. cretica ssp cretica	Apios apios	A. americana
Anthemis montana	A. cretica ssp cretica	Apios tuberosa	A. americana
Anthemis nobilis	Chamaemelum nobile	Apiospermum -Klit.	Pistia -L.
Anthemis rudolphiana	A. marschalliana	Apium ammi -(Crantz)	Ammi majus
Anthemis styriaca	A. carpatica	Apium ammi -not Crantz	Cyclospermum
Anthemis tinctoria 'Grallagh Gold'	A. 'Grallagh Gold'		leptophyllum
A. tinctoria 'Pride of Grallagh'	A. 'Pride of Grallagh'	Apium anisum	Pimpinella anisum
Anthericum algeriense	A. liliago v major	Apium australe	A. graveolens
Anthericum graminifolium h.	A. ramosum	Apium australe v latisectum	A. graveolens
Anthericum hookeri	Bulbinella hookeri	Apium carvi	Carum carvi
Anthericum liliago 'Major'	A. liliago v major	Apium celleri	A. graveolens
Anthericum liliastrum	Paradisea liliastrum	Apium crispum	Petroselinum crispum
Anthericum racemosum	A. ramosum	Apium dulce	A. graveolens v dulce
Anthericum ramosum plumosum	Trichopetalum plum.	Apium insulare	A. graveolens
Anthericum yedoense	Alectorurus yedoensis	Apium laetum	Petroselinum crispum
Antholyza coccinea	Crocosmia paniculata	Apium latifolium	Petroselinum crispum
Antholyza crocosmioides	Crocosmia latifolia	Apium leptophyllum	Cyclospermum lept.
Antholyza floribunda	Chasmanthe floribunda	Apium lusitanicum	A. graveolens
Antholyza paniculata	Crocosmia paniculata	Apium maritimum	A. graveolens
Anthriscus anatolica	A. sylvestris	Apium palustre	A. graveolens
Anthriscus longirostris	A. cerefolium	Apium petroselinum	Petroselinum crispum
Anthriscus macrocarpa	A. sylvestris	Apium podagraria	Aegopodium podagr.
A. sylvestris ssp nemerosa	A. sylvestris	Apium prostratum ssp phillipii	A. prostratum Poron-gurup Range Group
Anthriscus yunnanensis	A. sylvestris		
Anthurium andraeanum 'Rose'	A. x ferrierense 'Roseum'	Apium prostratum v filiforme	A. filiforme
		Apium rapaceum	A. graveolems v rap.
Anthurium cordatum	A. leuconeurum	Apium saxifragum	Pimpinella saxifraga
Anthurium x cultorum	A. x ferrierense	Apium sisarum	Sium sisarum
Anthurium x rothschildianum	A. 'Rothschildianum'	Apium vulgare	A. graveolens
Anthyllis alpestris	A. vulneraria	Aplopappus	Haplopappus
Anthyllis cuneata	Lespedeza cuneata	Aplotaxis circioides	Cirsium arvense
Anthyllis erinacea -L.	Erinacea anthyllis	Aplotaxis roylei	Saussurea roylei
Anthyllis hermanniae 'Compacta'	A. hermanniae 'Minor'	Apoballis -Schott	Schismatoglottis
Anthyllis jacquinii	A. montana	Apocynum sibiricum	A. cannabinum
Anthyllis serpeniticola	A. vulveraria	Aponogeton krausseanus	A. desertorum
Anticlea elegans	Zigadenus elegans	Aporocactus conzattii	A. martianus
Antigramma rhizophylla	Asplenium rhizophyllum	Aporocactus mallisonii	x Aporoheliocereus smithii
Antirrhinum asarina	Asarina procumbens		
Antirrhinum genistifolium	Linaria genistifolia	Aprica arachnoides	Haworthia arachnoidea
Antirrhinum glutinosum	A. hispanicum ssp hisp.	Aquifolium ilex	Ilex aquifolium

Synonym	Current Name	Synonym	Current Name
Aquifolium spinosum	Ilex aquifolium	Aquilegia vulgaris 'Dove'	A. (Songbird) 'Dove'
Aquifolium vulgare	Ilex aquifolium	Aquilegia vulgaris 'Gold Finch'	A. (Songb.) 'Goldfinch'
Aquilaria adoxoides	Semiaquilegia adox.	Aquilegia vulgaris 'Magpie'	A. vulgaris 'William
Aquilaria agallocha	A. malaccensis		Guiness'
Aquilegia 'Firewheel'	A. vulgaris v stellata	Aquilegia vulgaris 'Pink Spurless'	A. vul. v stellata pink
	'Firewheel'	Aquilegia vulgaris 'Red Star'	A. (Star) 'Red Star'
A. 'Lavender and White' (Songbird)	A. 'Nuthatch'	Aquilegia vulgaris 'Robin'	A. (Songbird) 'Robin'
Aquilegia 'Magpie'	A. vulgaris 'William	Aquilegia vulgaris 'White Spurless'	A. vul. v stellata white
	Guiness'	Aquilegia vulgaris 'White Star'	A. (Star) 'White Star'
Aquilegia 'Mrs Scott-Elliot'	A. Mrs Scott-Elliot	Aquilegia vulgaris clematiflora	A. vulgaris v stellata
	Hybrids	Aquilegia vulgaris Munstead White	A. vulgaris 'Nivea'
Aquilegia 'Roman Bronze'	Aquilegia x Semi-	Aquilegia vulgaris Olympica Group	A. olympica
	aquil. 'Roman Bronze'	A. vulgaris variegated foliage	A. vulgaris
Aquilegia akitensis h.	A. flabellata		Vervaeneana Group
Aquilegia akitensis h.	A. flabellata v pumila	Arabidium	Arabis
Aquilegia alpina 'Hensol Harebell'	A. 'Hensol Harebell'	Arabidium alpestre	Arabis alpina ssp alp.
Aquilegia amaliae	A. ottonis ssp amaliae	Arabis accedens	A. hirsuta
Aquilegia aragonensis	A. pyrenaica	Arabis albida	A. alpina ssp caucasica
Aquilegia arctica	A. formosa	Arabis alliaria	Alliatia petiolata
Aquilegia atropurpurea	A. buergeriana	Arabis alpestris	A. ciliata v hirsuta
Aquilegia aurea misapplied	A. vulgaris golden-lvd	Arabis alpina ssp caucasica 'Plena'	A. alpina ssp caucasica
Aquilegia australis	A. canadensis		'Flore Pleno'
Aquilegia baicalensis	A.vul. BaicalensisGroup	A. alpina ssp caucasica Snowcap	A. alpina ssp caucasica
Aquilegia buergeriana v oxysepala	A. oxysepala		'Schneehaube'
Aquilegia canadensis flavescens	A. flavescens	Arabis billardieri	A. caucasica
Aquilegia cazorlensis	A. pyrenaica ssp caz.	A. blepharophylla Spring Charm	A. blepharophylla
Aquilegia chrysantha v chaplinei	A. chaplinei		'Fruhlingszauber'
Aquilegia clematiflora	A. vulgaris v stellata	Arabis canadensis	Diplotaxis muralis
Aquilegia coccinea	A. canadensis	Arabis carduchorum	Draba gigas
Aquilegia ecalcarata	Semiaquil. ecalcarata	Arabis caucasica	A. alpina ssp caucasica
Aquilegia eminens	A. canadensis v emin.	Arabis caucasica 'Flore Pleno'	A. alpina ssp caucasica
Aquilegia flabellata 'Nana Alba'	A. flab. v pumila f alba		'Flore Pleno'
Aquilegia flaviflora	A. canadensis v flav.	Arabis caucasica 'Rosabella'	A. x arendsii
Aquilegia glauca	A. fragrans		'Rosabella'
Aquilegia helenae	A. caerulea	Arabis crantziana	Arabidopsis thaliana
Aquilegia hinckleyana	A. chrysantha v hinck.	Arabis douglasii	Cardamine douglasii
Aquilegia hirsutissima	A. viscosa ssp hirsut.	A. ferdinandi-coburgi 'Variegata'	A. procurrens
Aquilegia japonica	A. flabellata v pumila		'Variegata'
Aquilegia jucunda	A. glandulosa jucunda	Arabis glabra	Turritis glabra
Aquilegia macrantha	A. micrantha	Arabis hirsuta	Turritis hirsuta
Aquilegia montana	A. alpina	Arabis muralis	A. collina
Aquilegia nevadensis	A. vulgaris ssp nevad.	Arabis muralis	Arabidopsis thaliana
Aquilegia nigricans	A. atrata	Arabis nutans	A. pumila
Aquilegia phoenicantha	A. canadensis	Arabis perfoliata	Turritis glabra
Aquilegia reuteri	A. bertolonii	Arabis petiolata	Alliaria petiolata
Aquilegia rubicunda	A. barnebeyi	Arabis petraea	Cardaminopsis
Aquilegia scopulorum 'Perplexus'	A. scop. ssp perplexus	Arabis praecox	A. procurrens
Aquilegia Snow Queen	A. 'Schneekonigin'	Arabis pubicalyx	Arabidopsis thaliana
Aquilegia stellata	A. vulgaris v stellata	Arabis ramosa	Arabidopsis thaliana
A. Vervaeneana Group 'Woodside'	A. vulgaris	Arabis rhomboidea	Cardamine bulbosa
	Vervaeneana Group	Arabis rosea	A. collina ssp rosea
A. viridiflora 'Chocolate Soldier'	A. viridiflora	Arabis Snow Cap	A. alpina ssp caucasica
Aquilegia vulgaris 'Aureovariegata'	A. vulgaris		'Schneehaube'
	Vervaeneana Group	Arabis soyeri ssp jacquinii	A. soyeri ssp coriacea
Aquilegia vulgaris 'Blue Star'	A. (Series) 'Blue Star'	Arabis stellulata	A. pumila

Synonym	Current Name	Synonym	Current Name
Arabis stricta	A. scabra	Arctium edule	A. lappa
Arabis suecica	Arabidopsis suecica	Arctium glabrescens	A. minus
Arabis thaliana	Arabidopsis thaliana	Arctium intermedium	A. minus
Arachniodes aristata variegata	A. simpicior	Arctium lappa ssp majus	A. lappa
Aralia canescens -Sieb. & Zucc.	A. elata -(Miq.) Seem.	Arctium lappa v minus	A. minus
Aralia chinensis misapplied	A. elata	Arctium lappa v tomentosa	A. tomentosum
Aralia chinensis v mandschurica	A. elata (Miq.) Seem.	Arctium leiospermum	A. lappa
Aralia cordata sachalinensis	A. schmidtii	Arctium macrosperma	A. minus
Aralia elata 'Albomarginata'	A. elata 'Variegata'	Arctium majus	A. lappa
Aralia elegantissima	Schefflera elegant.	Arctium nemorosum	A. minus
Aralia japonica -Thunb.	Fatsia japonica	Arctostaphylos adenotricha	A. uva-ursi
Aralia papyrifer	Tetrapanax payrifer	Arctostaphylos alpina -(L.) Spreng.	Arctous alpina
Aralia pentaphylla	Eleutherococcus sieboldianus	A. nummularia v myrtifolia	A. myrtifolia -Parry
		Arctostaphylos officinalis	A. uva-ursi
Aralia quinquefolia	Panax quinquefolium	Arctostaphylos procumbens	A. uva-ursi
Aralia racemosa sachalinensis	A. schmidtii	Arctostaphylos pungens manzanita	A. manzanita
Aralia sieboldii -de Vriese	Fatsia japonica	Arctostaphylos tomentosa	A. columbiana
Aralia spinosa v canescens	A. elata -(Miq.) Seem.	A. uva-ursi 'Snow Camp'	A.x media 'Snow Camp'
Aralia spinosa v elata	A. elata -(Miq.) Seem.	Arctotis stoechadifolia	A. venusta
Aralia stipulata	A. chinensis	Arctous alpinus	Arctostaphylos alpinus
Aralia trifolia	Panax trifolia	Ardisia crenulata	A. crenata
Araucaria cookii	A. columnaris	Areca lutescens	Dypsis lutescens
Araucaria excelsa h.	A. heterophylla	Arecastrum	Syagrus
Araucaria imbricata -Pavon	A. araucana	Arecastrum romanzoffianum	Syagrus romanzoffiana
Araujia hortorum	A. sericifera	Aregelia	Neoregelia
Araujia sericofera -Brot.	A. sericifera	Aregelia carolinae	Neoregelia carolinae
Arborvitae	Thuja	Arenaria alfacarensis	A. lithops
Arbutus alpina -L.	Arctous alpinus	Arenaria alpicola	A. serpyllifolia
Arbutus buxifolia	Arctostaphylos uva-ursi	Arenaria arduinii	Minuartia graminifolia
		Arenaria banatica	A. setacea
Arbutus filiformis	Gaultheria hispidula	Arenaria breviflora	A. serpyllifolia
Arbutus furens -Hook.	Gaultheria insana	Arenaria buxifolia	Moehringia lateriflora
Arbutus glandulosa	Arctostaphylos gland.	Arenaria caespitosa	Minuartia verna ssp caespitosa
Arbutus leucocarpa	Gaulltheria pumila leu.		
Arbutus mucronata -L.f.	Gaultheria mucronata	Arenaria campestris	Spergularia rubra
Arbutus procera -Douglas	A. menziesii -Pursh	Arenaria capitata	A. aggregata
Arbutus pumila -L.f.	Gaultheria pumila	Arenaria ciliata v humifusa	A. humifusa
Arbutus tomentosa -Pursh	Arcostaphylos tomen.	Arenaria cylindrocarpa	A. humifusa
Arbutus ursina -L.	Arcostap. uva-ursi	Arenaria decussata	A. tetraquetra
Arbutus uva-ursi -L.	Arcostap. uva-ursi	Arenaria densa	A. gracilis
Arbutus x hybrida -Ker-Gawler	A. x andrachnoides	Arenaria filifolia	A. graminifolia
Arbutus xalapensis	A. texana	Arenaria franklinii	A. hookeri
Arceuthobium minutum	A. pusillum	Arenaria laricifolia	Minuartia laricifolia
Arceuthobium oxycedri	A. pusillum	Arenaria leteriflora	Moehringia lateriflora
Arceuthos drupacea	Juniperus drupacea	Arenaria lloydii	A. serpyllifolia
Archangelica atropurpurea	Angelica atropurpurea	Arenaria magellanica	Colobanthus quitensis
Archangelica gmelini	Coelopleurum gmelini	Arenaria musciformis	A. polytrichoides
Archangelica keiskei	Angelica keiskei	Arenaria obtusiloba	Minuartia obtusiloba
Archangelica officinalis	Angelica archangelica	Arenaria parnassica	Minuartia stellata
Archiclematis alternata	Clematis alternata	Arenaria patula	A. serpyllifolia
Arcterica	Pieris	Arenaria pinifolia	Minuartia circassica
Arcterica nana -(Maxim.) Makino	Pieris nana	Arenaria pulvinata	A. lithops
Arcterica oxycoccoides	Pieris nana	Arenaria recurva	Minuartia recurva
Arctiodracon -A.Gray	Lysichiton -Schott	Arenaria rubra	Spergularia rubra
Arctium chaorum	A. lappa	Arenaria sphaerocarpa	A. serpyllifolia

Synonym	Current Name	Synonym	Current Name
Arenaria tetraquetra v granatensis	A. tetraq. ssp amabilis	Arisaema onoticum	A. lobatum
Arenaria varia	A. serpyllifolia	Arisaema praecox	A. ringens
Arenaria verna	Minuartia verna	Arisaema purpureogalatum	A. franchetianum
Arenaria viscida	A. serpyllifolia	Arisaema ringens misapplied	A. amurense ssp
Arenaria wallichiana	A. serpyllifolia		robustum
Arequipa hempeliana	Oreocereus hemp.	Arisaema robustum	A. am. ssp robustum
Aretia	Douglasia	Arisaema sieboldii	A. ringens
Argemone alba	A. albiflora	Arisaema stewardsonii	A. triphyllum
Argemone ochroleuca	A. mexicana	Arisaema stewardsonii -Brit.	A. triphyllum ssp trip.
Argemone polyanthemos	A. albiflora	Arisaema triphyllum -not L.	A. ringens
Argentina anserina	Potentilla anserina	Arisaema verrucosum	A. griffithii
Argentina argentea	Potentilla anserina	Arisaema verrucosum v utile	A. utile
Argorips alba	Salix alba	Arisaron -Adans.	Arisaema -Mart.
Argussiera rhamnoides	Hippophae rhamnoides	Aristea thyrsiflora	A. major
Argyranthemum 'Apricot Surprise'	A. 'Peach Cheeks'	Aristolochia altissima -Desf.	A. sempervirens (some
Argyranthemum 'Cheek's Peach'	A. 'Peach Cheeks'		authors, not all)
Argyranthemum 'Chelsea Girl'	A. gracile 'Chelsea Girl'	Aristolochia durior -Rehd. not Hill.	A. macrophylla -Lam.
Argyranthemum 'Flamingo'	Rhodanthemum	Aristolochia elegans	A. littoralis
	gayanum	Aristolochia gigas	A. grandiflora
A. 'Jamaica Snowstorm'	A. 'Snow Storm'	Aristolochia heterophylla	A. kaempferi f heterop.
Argyranthemum 'Mini-snowflake'	A. 'Blizzard'	Aristolochia nipponica	A. contorta
Argyranthemum 'Nevada Cream'	A. 'Qinta White'	Aristolochia recurvilabra	A. debilis
Argyranthemum 'Pink Delight'	A. 'Petite Pink'	Aristolochia ringens -Link & Otto	A. labiata
Argyranthemum 'Royal Haze'	A. foeniculaceum 'Royal	Aristolochia sipho -L'Herit.	A. macrophylla -Lam.
	Haze' -Webb	Aristotelia macqui -L'Herit.	A. chilensis
Argyranthemum 'Silver Queen'	A. foeniculaceum mis.	Aristotelia racemosa	A. serrata
A. 'Snowflake' misapplied	A. 'Mrs. F. Sander'	Arjona tuberosa	A. patagonica
A.m Boston Yellow daisy	A. callichrysum	Armeniaca brigantina	Prunus brigantina
A. callichrysum Yellow Star	A. callichr. 'Etoile d'Or'	Armeniaca dasycarpa	Prunus x dasycarpa
Argyranthemum canariense h.	A. frutescens ssp	Armeniaca manshurica	Prunus madschurica
	canariae	Armeniaca mume	Prunus mume
A. foeniculaceum misapplied pink	A. 'Petite Pink'	Armeniaca sibirica	Prunus sibirica
Argyranthemum mawii	Rhodanthemum	Armeniaca vulgaris -Lam.	Prunus armeniaca -L.
	gayanum	Armeria arenaria	A. alliacea
Argyranthemum ochroleucum	A. maderense	Armeria atrosanguinea	A. pseudarmeria
Argyreia speciosa	A. nervosa	Armeria caespitosa	A. juniperifolia
Argyrocytisus	Cytisus	Armeria cespitosa	A. juniperifolia
Argyrocytisus battandieri	Cytisus battandieri	Armeria corsica	A. maritima 'Corsica'
Argyroderma aureum	A. delaetti	Armeria drummondii	Phlox drummondii
Argyroderma blandum	A. delaetti	Armeria elongata	A. maritima
Argyroderma brevipes	A. fissum	Armeria juncea	A. girardii
Argyroderma schlechteri	A. pearsonii	Armeria latifolia	A. pseudarmeria
Aria japonica	Sorbus japonica	Armeria laucheana	A. maritima
Aria nivea	Sorbus aria		'Laucheana'
Arisacontis -Schott	Cytrosperma -Griff.	Armeria maritima Dusseldorf Pride	A. maritima
Arisaema acuminatum -Sm.	A. triphyllum ssp trip.		'Dusseldorfer Stolz'
Arisaema angustatum v serratum	A. serratum	Armeria maritima ssp alpina	A. alpina
Arisaema atrorubens	A. triphyllum v atror.	Armeria patagonica	Armeria maritima
Arisaema biauriculatum	A. wattii	Armeria pilosa	Phlox pilosa
Arisaema cornutum	A. jacquemontii	Armeria plantaginea	A. alliacea
Arisaema curvatum	A. tortuosum	Armeria setacea	A. girardii
Arisaema exile	A. jacquemontii	Armeria vulgaris	A. maritima
Arisaema helleborifolium	A. tortuosum	Armeria wilkommii	A. humilis ssp humilis
Arisaema japonicum	A. serratum	Armoracia armoracia	A. rusticana
Arisaema ochraceum	A. nepenthoides	Armoracia lapathifolia	A. rusticana

Synonym	Current Name	Synonym	Current Name
Armoracia sativa	A. rusticana	Artemisia assoana	A. caucasica
Arnebia echioides	A. pulchra	Artemisia balsamita	A. pontica -L.
Arnebia longiflora	A. pulchra	Artemisia biennis v diffusa	A. biennis -Willd.
Arnica alpina	A. angustifolia ssp alp.	Artemisia caerulescens	Seriphidium caerul.
Arnica attenuata	A. angustifolia ssp ang.	Artemisia camphorata	A. alba
Arnica bernardina	A. chamissonis -Less.	Artemisia cana	Seriphidium canum
Arnica chamissonis Schmidt	A. sachaliensis	Artemisia canariensis	A. thuscula
Arnica chionopappa	A. lonchophylla	Artemisia canescens -Willdenow	A. armeniaca
Arnica foliosa	A. chamissonis -Less.	Artemisia canescens h.	A. alba 'Canescens'
Arnica gaspensis	A. lonchophylla	Artemisia chamomilla	A. annua -L.
Arnica hardinae	A. cordifolia	Artemisia cretacea	Seriphidium nutans
Arnica humilis	A. cordifolia	Artemisia discolor	A. michauxiana
Arnica japonica	Ligularia japonica	A. douglasiana 'Valerie Finnis'	A. ludoviciana 'Valerie Finnis'
Arnica montana v angustifolia	A. angustifolia ssp ang.		
Arnica oporina -Forst. f.	Olearia oporina	Artemisia dracunculoides	A. dracunculus
Arnica paniculata	A. cordifolia	Artemisia dubia	A. indica
Arnica plantaginea	A. angustifolia ssp ang.	Artemisia dubia -Wall.	A. lancea -Vance
Arnica sornborgeri	A. angustifolia ssp ang.	Artemisia dubia orientalis	A. indica
Arnica whitneyi	A. cordifolia	Artemisia elatior	A. tilesii
Arnoglossum atriplicifolium	Cacalia atriplicifolia	Artemisia feddei	A. lancea -Vance
Arnopogon dalechampii	Urospermum dalech.	Artemisia ferganensis	Seriphidium ferganense
Arodendron -Werth	Typhonodorum -Schott		
Arodes -Kuntze	Zantedeschia -Spreng.	Artemisia fragrans Willd.	Seriphidium fragrans
Aroides -Heist.	Calla -L.	Artemisia frigida v gmelinianum	A. frigida
Aron -Adans.	Arum -L.	Artemisia frigida v williamsae	A. frigida
Aronia 'Brilliantissima'	A. x prunifolia 'Brilliant'	Artemisia genipii	A. spicata
		Artemisia glauca	A. dracunculus
Aronia 'Floribunda' -Spach	Aronia prunifolia	Artemisia glutinosa	A. campestris
Aronia alnifolia	Amelanchier alnifolia	Artemisia gnaphalodes	A. ludoviciana
Aronia arbutifolia 'Brilliant'	A. x prun. 'Brilliant'	Artemisia gracilis	A. scoparia
Aronia asiatica -Sieb. & Zucc.	Amelanchier asiatica	Artemisia hookeriana	A. tilesii
Aronia bartramiana	Amelanchier bartram.	Artemisia hultenii	A. tilesii
Aronia canadensis	Amelanchier canaden.	Artemisia indica maximowiczii	A. princeps
Aronia floribunda - Spach	A. x prunifolia	Artemisia iwayomogi	A. gmelinii
Aronia melanocarpa 'Brilliant'	A. x prun. 'Brilliant'	Artemisia kitadakensis 'Guizhou'	A. lactiflora Guizhou Group
Aronicum	Doronicum		
Arorangi	Olearia macrodonta	Artemisia lactiflora 'Variegata'	A. vulgaris 'Variegata'
Arosma -Raf.	Philodendron -Schott	Artemisia lactiflora dark from	A. lact. Guizhou Group
Arrabidaea magnifica	Saritaea magnifica	Artemisia lactiflora purpurea	A. lact. Guizhou Group
Arracacia esculenta	A. xanthorrhiza	Artemisia lanata -Willdenow	A. caucasica
Arrhenatherum bulbosum	A. elatius ssp bulbos.	Artemisia lavandulaefolia	A. lancea -Vance
A. elatius 'Bulbosum Variegatum'	A. elatius ssp bulbosum 'Variegatum'	Artemisia laxa	A. umbelliformis
		Artemisia leptophylla	Dendranthema nubigenum
Artemisia absinthium v insipida	A. absinthium		
Artemisia albula	A. ludoviciana ssp alb.	Artemisia ludoviciana ssp albula	A. ludoviciana ssp mexicana v albula
Artemisia albula	A. ludoviciana ssp mexicana v albula		
		Artemisia ludoviciana v latifolia	A. ludoviciana ssp ludoviciana v latiloba
Artemisia altaica	A. pontica -L.		
Artemisia apiacea	A. caruifolia	Artemisia maritima	Seriphidium maritimum
Artemisia arborea	A. arborescens	Artemisia mexicana	A. lud. ssp mexicana
A. arborescens 'Brass Band'	A. 'Powis Castle'	Artemisia microcephala	A. ludoviciana ssp mexicana v albula
Artemisia arbuscula	Seriphidium novum		
Artemisia argentea h.	A. arborescens	Artemisia mutellina	A. umbelliformis
Artemisia aromatica	A. dracunculus	Artemisia nova	Seriphidium novum
Artemisia asiatica	A. indica	Artemisia nutans	Seriphidium nutans

Synonym	Current Name	Synonym	Current Name
Artemisia opulenta	A. vulgaria	Arum sanctum	A. palaestinum
Artemisia palmeri -A Gray	Seriphidium palmeri	Arum serratum	Arisaema serratum
Artemisia palmeri h.	A. ludoviciana	Arum ternatum	Pinellia ternata
Artemisia pedemontana	A. caucasica	Arum tortuosum	Arisaema tortuosum
Artemisia procera	A. abrotanum	Arum triphyllum	Arisaema triphyllum
Artemisia purshiana	A. ludoviciana	Arum virginicum	Peltandra virginica
Artemisia sacrorum	A. gmelinii	A. dioicus Child of Two Worlds	A. d. 'Zweiweltenkind'
Artemisia selengensis	A. vulgaria	Aruncus plumosus	A. dioicus
Artemisia sieberi sp Guiz 137	A. lact. Guizhou Group	Aruncus sylvestris	A. dioicus
Artemisia splendens misapplied	A. alba 'Canescens'	Aruncus vulgaris	A. dioicus
Artemisia stelleriana 'Mori'	A. stelleriana 'Boughton Silver'	Arundinaria 'Wang Tsai'	Bambusa multiplex 'Floribunda'
Artemisia stelleriana 'Prostrata'	A. s. 'Boughton Silver'	Arundinaria amabilis	Pseudosasa amabilis
A. stelleriana 'Silver Brocade'	A. s. 'Boughton Silver'	Arundinaria anceps	Yushania anceps
Artemisia subintegra	A. japonica	Arundinaria angustifolia	Pleioblastus chino f angustifolius
Artemisia thunbergiana	A. caruifolia		
Artemisia tridentata	Seriphidium tridentatum	Arundinaria aristata -Gamble	Thamnocalamus aristatus
Artemisia trifida	Seriph. tripartitum	Arundinaria auricoma	Pleioblas. viridistriatus
Artemisia tripartita	Seriph. tripartitum	Arundinaria chino	Pleioblastus chino
Artemisia unalaskensis	A. tilesii	Arundinaria chrysantha -Mitf.	Sasa chrysantha
Artemisia vallesiaca	Seriph. vallesiacum	Arundinaria disticha	Pleioblastus pygmaeus 'Distichus'
Artemisia villarsii	A. baumgartenii		
Artemisia vulgaris 'Canescens'	A. alba 'Canescens'	Arundinaria falcata -Nees	Drepanostachyum falcatum
Artemisia vulgaris indica	A. indica		
Arthropodium cirrhatum	A. cirratum	Arundinaria falconeri	Himalayacalamus falconeri
Arthropodium millefoliatum	A. milleflorum		
Arthropodium paniculatum	A. milleflorum	Arundinaria fargesii	Bashania fargesii
Arthropodium pendulum	A. milleflorum	Arundinaria fastuosa -(Mitf.) Mak.	Semiarundinaria fastuosa
Arthropodium reflexum	A. candidum		
Arthrostygma	Petrophile	Arundinaria fortunei -Riviere	Pleioblastus variegatus
Artocarpus communis	A. altilis	Arundinaria fortunei v viridis h.	Pleioblastus humilis
Artocarpus incisus	A. altilis	Arundinaria funghomii	Schizostachyum fungh.
Arum atrorubens	Arisaema triphyllum ssp triphyllum	Arundinaria graminea	Pleioblastus gramineus
		Arundinaria hindsii -Munro	Pleioblastus hindsii h.
Arum conophalloides	A. rupicola v rupicola	Arundinaria hindsii graminea	Pleioblastus gramineus
Arum cornutum	Sauromatum venosum	Arundinaria hindsii v graminea	Pleioblastus gramineus
Arum corsicum pictum	A. pictum	Arundinaria hookeriana -Munro	Himalayacalamus hookerianus
Arum costatum	Arisaema costatum		
Arum detruncatum v detruncatum	A. rupicola v rupicola	Arundinaria hookeriana misapplied	Hiamalayacalamus falconeri 'Damarapa'
Arum dioscoridis v leipoldtii	A. dioscoridis v diosc.		
Arum dioscoridis v smithii	A. dioscoridis v dios.	Arundinaria humilis -Mitf.	Pleioblastus humilis
Arum dracontium	Arisaema dracontium	Arundinaria japonica -Sieb. & Zucc.	Pseudosasa japonica
Arum dracunculus	Dracunculus vulgaris	Arundinaria jaunsarensis Y	ushania anceps
Arum flavum	Arisaema flavum	Arundinaria kokantsik -Kurz	Chimonobambusa marmorea
Arum hygrophilum -Boiss.	A. dioscoridis		
Arum italicum 'Pictum'	A. italicum ssp italicum 'Marmoratum'	Arundinaria kurilensis	Sasa kurilensis
		Arundinaria latifolia	Indocalamus latifolius
Arum neglectum	A. italicum	Arundinaria laydeckeri -Bean	Pleioblastus chino 'Laydeckeri'
Arum nickelii	A. concinnatum		
Arum orientale ssp besserianum	A. besserianum	Arundinaria macrosperma -Michx.	A. gigantea
Arum petteri h.	A. nigrum	Arundinaria macrosperma v tecta	A. gigantea Arundinaria
Arum pictum 'Taff's Form'	A. italicum ssp italicum 'White Winter'	maling	Yushania maling
		Arundinaria marmorea	Chimonobambusa mar.
Arum ringens	Arisaema ringens	Arundinaria murieliae	Fargesia murieliae

Synonym	Current Name	Synonym	Current Name
Arundinaria narihira	Semiarundinaria fastuosa	Asarina lophantha	Lophospermum scandens
Arundinaria nitida -Mitf.	Fargesia nitida	Asarina lophospermum	Loph. scandens
Arundinaria nobilis -Mitf.	Himalayacalamus falconeri	Asarina orontium	Misopates
		Asarina purpusii	Maurandya purpusii
Arundinaria oedogonata	Clavinodum oedogonatum	Asarina scandens	Maurandya scandens
		Asarum acuminatum	A. canadense
Arundinaria palmata	Sasa palmata	Asarum blumei -not Duch.	A. nipponicum
Arundinaria pumila -Mitf.	Pleioblastus argen teostriatus f pumilus	Asarum canadense reflexum	A. reflexum
		Asarum canadense v acuminatum	A. canadense
Arundinaria pygmaea	Pleioblastus pygmaeus	Asarum grandiflorum	A. arifolium
Arundinaria quadrangularis quad.	Chimonobambusa	Asarum marmoratum	A. hartwegii
		Asarum reflexum	A. canadense
Arundinaria racemosa	Yushania maling	Asarum reflexum v ambiguum	A. canadense
Arundinaria ragamowskii	Sasa ragamowskii	Asarum rubrocinctum	A. canadense
Arundinaria ragamowskii	Indocalamus tessellatus	Asclepias apocinum	A. syriaca
		Asclepias bicknellii	A. exaltata
Arundinaria simonii	Pleioblastus simonii	Asclepias cornuti	A. syriaca
Arundinaria simonii v chino	Pleioblastus chino	Asclepias cornuttii	A. syriaca
Arundinaria spathiflora -Trin.	Thamnocalamus spathiflorus	Asclepias decumbens	A. tuberosa
		Asclepias fasciculata	A. fascicularis
Arundinaria tessellata	Thamnocalamus tessellatus	Asclepias fremonttii	A. eriocarpa
		Asclepias fruticosa	Gomphocarpus fruticosus
Arundinaria tootsik -Makino	Sinobambusa tootsik		
Arundinaria vagans -Gamble	Sasaella ramosa	Asclepias intemedia	A. syriaca
Arundinaria variabilis -H.de Lehaie	Pleioblastus pumilus	Asclepias kansana	A. syriaca
A. variegata -(Miq.) Makino	Pleioblastus variegatus	Asclepias nivea	A. exaltata
A. veitchii -(Carr). N.E.Brown	Sasa veitchii	Asclepias nivea v curassavica	A. exaltata
A. viridistriata -(Reg.) Makino	Pleioblastus viridistriatus	Asclepias nuttalliana	A. ovalifolia
		Asclepias physocarpa	Gomph. physocarpus
Arundo altissima	Phragmites australis	Asclepias phytolaccoides	A. exaltata
Arundo ampelodesmos	Ampelodesmos mauritanicus	Asclepias pubescens	A. syriaca
		Asclepias pubigera	A. syriaca
Arundo australis	Phragmites australis	Asclepias ramosa	A. syriaca
Arundo bicolor	Ampelod. mauritanicus	Asclepias tenacissima	Marsdenia tenacissima
Arundo colorata -Ait.	Phalaris arundinacea	Ascyrum hypericoides	Hypericum hyperic.
Arundo conspicua	Chionochloa conspicua	Aspalathus contaminatus	A. linearis
Arundo conspicua fulvida	Cortaderia fulvida	Asparagus 'Myers'	A. densiflorus 'Meyersii'
Arundo donax 'Variegata'	A. donax v versicolor		
Arundo festucoides	Ampelo. mauritanicus	Asparagus falcatus	A. cochinchinensis
Arundo gigantea -Walt.	Arundinaria gigantea	Asparagus graminifolus	Liriope graminifolia
Arundo graeca	Phragmites australis	Asparagus horridus	A. stipularis
Arundo mauritanica	Amp. mauritanicus	Asparagus insularis	A. cochinchinensis
Arundo maxima	A. donax -L.	Asparagus lucidus	A. cochinchinensis
Arundo occidentalis	Phragmites australis	Asparagus meyeri	A. dens. 'Meyersii'
Arundo phragmites	Phragmites australis	Asparagus meyersii	A. dens. 'Meyersii'
Arundo tecta -Walt.	Arundinaria gigantea	Asparagus parviflorus	A. schoberioides
Arundo tenax	Amp. mauritanicus	Asparagus plumosus	A. setaceus
Asarina 'Victoria Falls'	Maurandya 'Victoria Falls'	Asparagus rigidulus	A. schoberioides
		Asparagus sieboldii	A. schoberioides
Asarina antirrhiniflora	Maurandella antirrhin.	Asparagus sprengeri	A. d. Sprengeri Group
Asarina barclayana	Maurandya barclayana	Asparagus wrightii	A. schoberioides
Asarina erubescens	Lophospermum erub.	Asperella oryzoides	Leersia oryzoides
Asarina hispanica	Antirrhinum hispanicum	Asperula aristata ssp thessala	A. sintenisii
		Asperula athoa h.	A. suberosa

Synonym	Current Name	Synonym	Current Name
Asperula azurea	A. orientalis	Aspidium munitum v nudatum	Polystichum imbricans
Asperula lilaciflora v caespitosa	A. lilaciflora ssp lilac.	Aspidium obtusatum	Woodsia obtusa
Asperula montana	A. cyanchica	Aspidium palustre	Thelypteris palustris
Asperula nitida ssp puberula	A. sintenisii	Aspidium phegopteris	Phegopteris connectilis
Asperula odorata	Galium odoratum	Aspidium polyblepharum	Polystichum polyblep.
Asperula suberosa misapplied	A. arcadiensis	Aspidium proliferum	Polystichum proliferum
Asphodeline lutea Yellow Candle	A. lutea 'Gelbkerze'	Aspidium pseudofilix-mas	Dryopteris pseudof-m
Asphodelus brevicaulis	Asphodeline brevic.	Aspidium punctilobulum -Sw.	Dennstaedtia
Asphodelus cerasiferus	A. ramosus		punctilobula
Asphodelus lusitanicus	A. ramosus	Aspidium radicans -Sieb.	Polystichum proliferum
Asphodelus luteus	Asphodeline lutea	Aspidium rigidum v remotum	Dryopteris x remota
Asphodelus macrocarpus	A. albus	Aspidium sieboldii	Dryopteris sieboldii
Asphodelus microcarpus	A. aestivus	Aspidium spinulosum	D. carthusiana
Asphodelus ramosus	A. aestivus	Aspidium tenerum	Lastreopsis calantha
Asphodelus tenuifolius	A. fistulosus	Aspidium thelypteris	Thelypteris palustris
Aspidistra lurida	A. elatior	Aspidium transitorium	Dryopteris tokyoensis
Aspidium aculeatum	Polystichum aculeatum	Aspidium truncatum v keffordii	Christella
Aspidium aculeatum	Polys. polyblepharum		subpubescens
Aspidium aculeatum ssp lobatum	Polystichum aculeatum	Aspidium tsus-simense	Polystich. tsussimense
Aspidium aemulum	Dryopteris aemula	Asplenium acrostichoides	Deparia acrostichoides
Aspidium alpestre	Athyrium alpestre	Asplenium alternans	A. dalhousieae
Aspidium aristatum v simplicius	Arachnoides simplicior	Asplenium andrewsii	A. adiantum-nigrum
Aspidium braunii	Polystichum braunii	Asplenium atropurpureum	Pellaea atropurpureum
Aspidium calcareum	Gymnocarpium	Asplenium chihuahuense	A. adiantum-nigrum
	robertianum	Asplenium commixtum	Athyrium vidalii
Aspidium callipteris	Dryopt. carthusiana	Asplenium cryptolepis -Fernald	A. ruta-muraria
Aspidium capense	Lastreopsis calantha	Asplenium cryptolepis v ohionis	A. ruta-muraria
Aspidium caryotideum	Cyrtomium caryotid.	Asplenium dubiosum	A. adiantum-nigrum
Aspidium championii	Dryopteris championii	Asplenium ebenum -Ait.	A. platyneuron
Aspidium clintoniana	Dryopteris clintoniana	Asplenium filix-femina	Athyrium filix-femina
Aspidium coriaceum	Lastreopsis calantha	Asplenium furcatum -Thunberg	A. aethiopicum
Aspidium cristatum	Dryopteris cristata	Asplenium intermedium	A. viride
Aspidium cristatum v clintonianum	Dryopteris clintoniana	Asplenium japonicum	Deparia japonica
Aspidium cycadinum	Dryopteris cycadina	Asplenium leptophyllum	A. ruta-muraria
Aspidium decompositum	Lastreopsis calantha	Asplenium matthiola	A. ruta-muraria
Aspidium dilatatum	Dryopteris dilatata	Asplenium multicaule	A. ruta-muraria
Aspidium dryopteris	Gymnocarpium dryop.	Asplenium murale	A. ruta-muraria
Aspidium erythrosorum	Dryopt. erythrosora	Asplenium muraria	A. ruta-muraria
Aspidium falcatum	Cyrtomium falcatum	Asplenium murorum	A. ruta-muraria
Aspidium falcatum v fortunei	Cyrtomium fortunei	Asplenium niponicum	Athyrium niponicum
Aspidium falcatum v macrophyllum	Cyrt. macrophyllum	Asplenium otophorum -Miq.	Athyrium otophorum
Aspidium filix-mas	Dryopteris filix-mas	A. platyneuron v baccalum-rubrum	A. platyneuron
Aspidium filix-mas v marginale	Dryopteris marginale	A. platyneuron v incisum	A. platyneuron
Aspidium formosanum	Dryopteris formosana	Asplenium polypodioides	A. platyneuron
Aspidium goldianum	Dryopt. erythrosora	Asplenium pycnocarpon	Diplazium pycnocarpon
Aspidium hispidum	Lastreopsis hispida	Asplenium ramosum	A. viride
Aspidium lancastriense	Dryopteris cristata	Asplenium robinsonii	A. australasicum f rob.
Aspidium lonchitis	Polystichum lonchitis	A. ruta-muraria cryptolepis	A. ruta-muraria
Aspidium molle f keffordii	Christella	Asplenium trichomanes-ramosum	A. viride
	subpubescens	Asplenium trichomanoides	A. platyneuron
Aspidium montanum	Oreopteris	Asplenium umbrosum	A. viride
	limbosperma	Asplenium uropteron	Athyrium niponicum
Aspidium munitum	Polystichum aculeatum	Asplenium vidalii	Athyrium vidalii
Aspidium munitum	Polystichum munitum	Asplenium vogesiacum	A. viride
Aspidium munitum v imbricans	Polystichum imbricans	Asplenium zoliense	A. ruta-muraria

33

Synonym	Current Name	Synonym	Current Name
Astelia chathamica 'Silver Spear'	A. chathamica	Aster hispidus -Thunb.	Heteropappus hispidus
Astelia cockaynei	A. nervosa	Aster hispidus isochaeta	A. kantoensis
Astelia cunninghamii	A. solandri	Aster hybridus luteus	x Solidaster luteus
Astelia graminifolia	Collospermum microspermum	Aster hygrophilus	Olearia hygrophila
		Aster ibericus	A. amellus
Astelia nervosa montana	A. nervosa	Aster laterifolius 'Snow Flurry'	A. e. f p. 'Snow Flurry'
Astelia nervosa v chathamica	A. chathamica	Aster likiangensis	A. asteroides
Aster 'Connecticut Snow Flurry'	A. ericoides f prostratus 'Snow Flurry'	Aster linosyris 'Goldilocks'	A. linosyris
		Aster liratus -Sims	Olearia lirata
Aster 'Fanny's Fall'	A. oblongifolius 'Fanny's Fall'	Aster mongolicus	Kalimeris mongolica
		Aster mooneyi	Olearia mooneyi
Aster 'Snow Flurry'	A. e. f p. 'Snow Flurry'	Aster myrsinoides -Labill.	Olearia myrsinoides
Aster acris	A. sedifolius	Aster natalensis	Felicia rosulata
Aster ageratoides	A. trinervius ssp ager.	A. novae-angliae 'Alma Potschke'	A. n-a. 'Andenken an Alma Potschke'
Aster alpinus 'Dark Beauty'	A. alp. 'Dunkle Schone'		
Aster alpinus v himalaicus	A. himalaicus	Aster novae-angliae Autumn Snow	A. n-a. 'Herbstschnee'
Aster altaicus -non Willd.	A. kantoensis	A. novae-angliae September Ruby	A. novae-angliae 'Septemberrubin'
Aster amelloides	Felicia amelloides		
Aster amellus Empress	A. amellus 'Glucksfund'	Aster novi-belgii 'Christina'	A. novi-belgii 'Kristina'
Aster amellus Pink Zenith	A. am. 'Rosa Erfullung'	Aster novi-belgii 'Climax Albus'	A. 'White Climax'
Aster amellus Violet Queen	A. amellus 'Veilchenkonigin'	Aster novi-belgii 'Rector'	A. n-belgii 'The Rector'
		Aster novi-belgii Antwerp Pearl	A. novi-belgii 'Antwerpse Parel'
Aster amygdalinus	A. umbellatus		
Aster argophyllus -Labill.	Olearia argophylla	Aster novi-belgii Silver Carpet	A. novi-belgii 'Silberteppich'
Aster asper	A. bakerianus		
Aster ballii	Olearia ballii	Aster novi-belgii Snow Cushion	A. novi-belgii 'Schneekissen'
Aster bellis	Bellis perennis		
Aster bessarabicus	A. amellus	Aster Octoberlight	A. 'Oktoberlicht'
Aster cabulicus -Lindl.	A. albescens	Aster oliganthemus	Olearia oliganthema
Aster cantoniensis	Kalimeris pinnatifida	Aster paniculatus	A. lanceolatus
Aster capensis	Felicia amelloides	Aster pappei	Felicia amoena
Aster capensis 'Variegatus'	Felicia am. variegated	Aster petiolatus	Felicia petiolata
Aster chinensis	Callistephus chinensis	Aster phlogopappa -Labill.	Olearia phlogopappa
Aster coelestis	Felicia amelloides	Aster pseudoamellus	A. amellus
Aster collinus	A. amellus	Aster pulchellus	A. alpigenus
Aster cordifolius 'Little Carlow'	A. 'Little Carlow' (cordifolius hybrid)	Aster purdomii	A. flaccidus
		Aster ramulosus -Labill.	Olearia ramulosa
Aster cordifolius 'Little Dorrit'	A. 'Little Dorrit' (cordifolius hybrid)	Aster rotundifolius 'Variegatus'	Felicia am. variegated
		Aster scandens	A. carolinianus
Aster cordifolius 'Photograph'	A. 'Photograph'	Aster scepusiensis	A. amellus
Aster corymbosus	A. divaricatus	Aster sedifolius 'Snow Flurries'	A. e. f p. 'Snow Flurry'
Aster diffusus	A. lateriflorus	Aster stellulatus -Labill.	Olearia stellulata
Aster divaricatus Raiche form	A. div. 'Eastern Star'	Aster subcaeruleus	A. tongolensis
Aster elegans	A. amellus	Aster tibeticus	A. flaccidus
Aster ensifolius	Inula ensifolia	Aster tinctorius	A. amellus
Aster ericoides 'Hon. Vicary Gibbs'	A. 'Hon. Vicary Gibbs' (ericoides hybrid)	Aster tongolensis Summer Greeting	A. t. 'Sommergruss'
		Aster tradescantii misapplied	A. pilosus v demotus
Aster ericoides 'Monte Cassino'	A. pilosus v pringlei 'Monte Cassino'	Aster vimineus -Lamarck	A. lateriflorus
		Aster vimineus 'Delight'	A. lateriflorus 'Delight'
Aster fastigiatus -Ledeb.	A. hauptii	Aster vimineus 'Ptarmicoides'	A. ptarmicoides
Aster frostii -F.v.Muell.	Olearia frostii	Aster x frikartii Wonder of Stafa	A.x f. 'Wunder von Stafa'
Aster furfuraceus -A.Rich.	Olearia furfuracea		
Aster glandulosus -Labill.	Olearia glandulosa	Asterago luteus	x Solidaster luteus
Aster hesperius	A. lanceolatus	Asteriscus 'Gold Coin'	Pallensis maritima
Aster hispidus -Lam.	A. puniceus	Asteriscus maritimus	Pallensis maritima

34

Synonym	Current Name	Synonym	Current Name
Asterochiton pygmaeus	Thomasia pygmaea	Astragalus australis	A. aboriginorum
Asteromoea mongolica	Kalimerus mongolica	Astragalus bicuspis	A. multiceps
Asteromoea pinnatifida	Kalimerus pinnatifida	Astragalus carolinianus	A. canadensis
Astilbe 'Bridal Veil'	A. 'Brautschleier'	Astragalus caryocarpus	A. crassicarpus
Astilbe 'Bronze Elegans'	A. 'Bronce Elegans' (simplicifolia hybrid)	Astragalus ceramicus	A. pictus
		Astragalus crassicaulis	Caragana nubigena
Astilbe 'Crimson Feather'	A. 'Gloria Purpurea'	Astragalus deflexus	Oxytropis deflexa
Astilbe 'Drayton Glory'	A. x rosea 'Peach Blossom'	Astragalus gerardianus -Graham	Caragana gerardiana
		Astragalus hypoglottis	A. danicus
Astilbe 'Gladstone' (x arendsii)	A. 'W.E.Gladstone'	Astragalus larkyaensis	Caragana nubigena
Astilbe 'Glow'	A. 'Glut'	Astragalus mexicanus	A. crassicarpus
Astilbe 'Gnom'	A. x crispa 'Gnom'	Astragalus mongholicus	A. membranaceus v m.
Astilbe 'Perkeo'	A. x crispa 'Perkeo'	Astragalus multiflorus	A. tenellus
Astilbe 'Supeba'	A. chinensis v taquetii 'Superba'	Astragalus nubigenus	Caragana nubigena
		A. penduliflorus membranaceus	A. membranaceus
A.chinensis v taquetii Purple Lance	A. chinensis taquetii 'Purpurlanze'	Astragalus succulentus	A. crassicarpus
		Astragalus tragacantha h.	A. massiliensis
Astilbe Cologne	A. 'Koln'	Astragalus virgultulus	A. agrestis
Astilbe davidii	A. chinensis v davidii	Astrantia biebersteinii	A. major
Astilbe Diamond	A. 'Diamant'	Astrantia carinthiaca	A. major
Astilbe Fire	A. 'Feuer'	Astrantia carniolica 'Variegata'	A. major 'Sunningdale Variegated'
Astilbe glaberrima saxosa	A. 'Saxosa'		
Astilbe Hyacinth	A. 'Hyazinth'	Astrantia carniolica major A. major	
Astilbe japonica v terrestris	A. glaberrima	Astrantia carniolica v rubra	A. major 'Rubra'
Astilbe Ostrich Plume	A. 'Straussenfeder' (thunbergii hybrid)	Astrantia helleborifolia misapplied	A. maxima
		Astrantia major 'Variegata'	A. major 'Sunningdale Variegated'
Astilbe Pink Pearl (x arendsii)	A. 'Rosa Perle' (x a)		
Astilbe pumila	A. chinensis v pumila	Astrantia major carinthiaca	A. m. ssp involucrata
Astilbe Red Light	A. 'Rotlicht'	A.m. ssp involucrata 'Margery Fish'	A. m. ssp inv. 'Shaggy'
Astilbe Salmon Queen	A. 'Lachskonigin'	Astrantia rubra	A. major 'Rubra'
Astilbe simplicifolia 'Gnome'	A. x crispa 'Gnom'	Astrantia trifida	A. major
A. simplicifolia Bronze Elegance	A. 'Bronce Elegans' (simplicifolia hybrid)	Asystasia bella	Mackaya bella
		Asystasia violacea	A. gangetica
Astilbe White Gloria	A. 'Weisse Gloria' (x a)	Atelophragma alpinum	Astragalus alpinus
Astilbe x arendsii 'Cherry Ripe'	A. x arendsii 'Feuer'	Athamantha	Athamantha
Astilbe x arendsii 'Drayton Glory'	A. x rosea 'Peach Blossom'	Athamantha chinense	Conioselinum chinense
		Athamantha matthioli	A. turbith
Astilbe x arendsii Bridal Veil	A. x a. 'Brautschleier'	Atherurus -Blume	Pinellia -Ten.
Astilbe x arendsii Diamond	A. x arendsii 'Diamant'	Athrotaxis doniana -Gordon	A. laxifolia -Hook.
Astilbe x arendsii Fire	A. x arendsii 'Feuer'	Athrotaxis gunneana	A. selaginoides
Astilbe x arendsii Glow	A. x arendsii 'Glut'	Athyriopsis japonica	Deparia japonica
Astilbe x arendsii Hyacinth	A. x arendsii 'Hyazinth'	Athyrium acrostichoides	Deparia acrostichoides
Astilbe x arendsii Pink Pearl	A. x a. 'Rosa Perle'	Athyrium alpestre ssp americanum	Athyrium alpestre
Astilbe x arendsii Red Light	A. x arendsii 'Rotlicht'	Athyrium alpestre v gaspense	Athyrium alpestre
Astilbe x arendsii Salmon Queen	A. x a. 'Lachskonigin'	Athyrium americanum	Athyrium alpestre
Astracantha adscendens	Astragalus adscendens	Athyrium asplenoides	A. filix-femina
Astracantha echinus	Astragalus echinus	Athyrium crenatum	Diplazium sibiricum
Astracantha elymaiticus	Astragalus globiflorus	Athyrium distentifolium	Athyrium alpestre
Astracantha florulenta	Astragalus florulentus	A. distentifolium v americanum	Athyrium alpestre
Astracantha globiflora	Astragalus globiflorus	Athyrium fangustun -Willd.	A. filix-femina
Astracantha gummifera	Astragalus gummifer	Athyrium filix-femina v asplenoides	A. filix-femina
Astracantha kurdica	Astragalus kurdicus	Athyrium filix-femina v michauxii	A. filix-femina
Astracantha leiocladus	Astragalus leiocladus	A. filix-femina Victoriae Group	A. filix-femina
Astracantha microcephala	Astrag. microcephalus		Cruciatum Group
Astracantha strobilifera	Astrag. strobiliferus	Athyrium glabrescens	A. vidalii

Synonym	Current Name	Synonym	Current Name
Athyrium glabrum	A. vidalii	Atriplex latifolia	A. prostrata
Athyrium goeringianum	A. niponicum	Atriplex leptocarpa f armata	A. leptocarpa
Athyrium goeringianum 'Pictum'	A. niponicum v pictum	Atriplex leptocarpa f gracilis	A. leptocarpa
Athyrium japonicum	Deparia japonica	Atriplex leptocarpa v inermis	A. leptocarpa
Athyrium michauxii	A. filix-femina	Atriplex leptocarpa v minor	A. sturtii
Athyrium niponicum 'Pictum'	A. niponicum v pictum	Atriplex leptocarpa v turbinata	A. turbinata
Athyrium niponicum f metallicum	A. niponicum v pictum	Atriplex limbiata v sexifida	A. limbiata
Athyrium nipponicum	A. niponicum	Atriplex lindleyi ssp conduplicata	A. conduplicata
Athyrium proliferum	Diplazium proliferum	Atriplex marina	A. littoralis
Athyrium pycnocarpon	Diplazium pycnocarpon	Atriplex microcarpa	A. infrequens
Athyrium Red Stem	A. filix-femina 'Rotstiel'	Atriplex microsperma	A. prostrata
Athyrium rigescens -Mak.	A. otophorum	Atriplex moquiniana	A. paludosa ssp moq.
Athyrium sibiricum	Diplazium sibiricum	Atriplex neurivalvis	A. semibaccata
Athyrium thelypterioides	Deparia acrostichoides	Atriplex nummularia ssp omissa	A. nummularia
Athyrium uropteron	A. niponicum	Atriplex paludosa v appendiculata	A. vesicaria ssp appen.
Atimeta -Schott	Rhodospatha -Poepp.	Atriplex paludosa v cordivalvis	A. pal. ssp cordata
Atractylis lancea	Atractylodes lancea	Atriplex patula v gunnii	A. australasica
Atractylis ovata	Atractylodes lancea	Atriplex patula v serratifolia	A. australasica
Atractylodes chinensis	A. lancea	Atriplex portulacoides -L.	Halimione portulac.
Atractylodes ovata	A. lancea	Atriplex procumbens	A. patula
Atragene	Clematis	Atriplex prostrata	A. pumilio
Atragene alpina -L.	Clematis alpina	Atriplex prostrata v microcarpa	A. infrequens
Atragene americana -Sims	Clematis occidentalis	Atriplex pterocarpa	A. holocarpa
Atragene sibirica -L.	Clematis alpina ssp alp	Atriplex reniformis	A. paludosa ssp
Atraphaxis latifolia -Koehne	A. muschetowii		cordata
Atriplex acutibractea whyallensis	A. acutib. ssp acutib.	Atriplex ruderalis	A. prostrata
A. angulata v campanulatiformis	A. angulata	Atriplex sackii	A. prostrata
Atriplex angustifolia	A. patula	Atriplex salicina	A. littoralis
Atriplex arenaria	A. mucronata	Atriplex salina	A. patula
Atriplex australasica	A. patula	Atriplex semibaccata v biformis	A. semibaccata
Atriplex babingtonii	A. glabriuscula	Atriplex semibaccata v gracilis	A. semibaccata
Atriplex botrys	Chenopodium botrys	Atriplex semibaccata v microcarpa	A. infrequens
Atriplex bracteosa	A. serenana	Atriplex serrata	A. littoralis
Atriplex campanulata v adnata	A. eichleri	Atriplex spongiivalvis	A. acutibractea ssp
A.campanulata v multiappendiculata	A. eardleyae		karoniensis
Atriplex campestris	A. patula	Atriplex subspicata	A. dioica
Atriplex chrystallina	A. billardierei	Atriplex triangularis	A. prostrata
Atriplex cinerea f appendiculata	A. cinerea	Atriplex virgata	A. patula
Atriplex cinerea ssp humilis	A. humilis	Atropa acuminata	A. belladonna
Atriplex cinerea v typica	A. cinerea	Atropa caucasica	A. belladonna
Atriplex decumbens	A. pumilio	Atropa komarovii	A. belladonna
Atriplex deltoidea	A. hastata	Atropa lethalis	A. belladonna
Atriplex erecta	A. patula	Atropa mandragora	Mandragora
Atriplex expansa	A. argentea expansa		officinarum
Atriplex fasciculiflora	A. acutibractea ssp	Atropa pallida	A. belladonna
	karoniensis	Atylus	Isopogon
Atriplex flagellaris	A. semibaccata	Atylus -Steud.	Petrophile
Atriplex gardneri aptera	A. nuttallii	Aubrieta 'Carnival'	A. 'Hartswood Purple'
Atriplex halimoides	A. linleyi	Aubrieta 'Golden King'	A. 'Aureovariegata'
Atriplex halimoides v deplanata	A. codonocarpa	Aubrieta 'Hemswell Purity'	A. 'Snow Maiden'
Atriplex hastata v salina	A. prostrata	Aubrieta 'Schofield's Double'	A. 'Bob Saunders'
Atriplex hochreutineri	A. quadrivalvata v	Aubrieta albomarginata	A. 'Argenteovariegata'
	quadrivalvata	Aubrieta Blaue Schonheit	A. 'Blue Beauty'
Atriplex hymenotheca v minor	A. vesicaria ssp minor	Aubrieta graeca	A. deltoidea
Atriplex jonesii	A. confertifolia	Aubrieta integrifolia	A. deltoidea

Synonym	Current Name	Synonym	Current Name
Aubrieta intermedia	A. deltoidea	Azalea indica -Sims	Rhododendron simsii
Aubrieta libanotica	A. columnae macrostyla	Azalea kiusiana	Rhodo. kiusianum
Aubrieta scardica ssp scardica	A. gracilis ssp scard.	Azalea mollis -(Sieb & Zucc). Andre	Rhododendron molle ssp japonicum
Aubrieta Spring Charm	A. 'Fruhlingszauber'	Azalea mollis -Blume	Rhododendron molle
A. x cultorum 'Albomarginata'	A. 'Argenteovariegata'	Azalea nipponica	Rhodo. nipponicum
Aucuba japonica 'Crotonoides'	A. jap. 'Crotonifolia'	Azalea oblongifolia -Small	Rhodo. oblongifolium
Aucuba japonica 'Fructuluteo'	A. jap. 'Fructu-albo'	Azalea occidentalis -Torr. & Gray	Rhodo. occidentale
Aucuba japonica 'Maculata'	A. japonica 'Variegata'	Azalea oldhamii -(Maxim). Mast	Rhododendron oldhamii
Aucuba japonica 'Sulphurea'	A. japonica 'Sulphurea Marginata'	Azalea pilosa -Michx.	Menziesia pilosa
		Azalea pontica	Rhododendron luteum
Aulospermum longipes	Cymopterus longipes	Azalea pontica -L.	Rhododendron luteum
Aulospermum purpureum	Cymopterus purpureus	Azalea procumbens -L.	Loiseleuria procumb.
Aurinia Gold Ball	A. saxatilis 'Goldkugel'	Azalea prunifolia -Small	Rhodo. prunifolium
Avena byzantina	A. sativa	Azalea reticulata -K.Koch	Rhodo. reticulatum
Avena candida	Helictotrichon sempervirens	Azalea rosea -Loisel.	Rhododendron roseum
		Azalea rosiflora	Rhododendron indicum 'Balsaminiflorum'
Avena chinensis	A. sativa		
Avena cinerea	A. sativa	Azalea schlippenbachii	Rhodo. schlippenbachii
Avena diffusa	A. sativa	Azalea serpyllifolia -A.Gray	Rhodo. serpyllifolium
Avena disperma	A. sativa	Azalea viscosa -L.	Rhodo. viscosum
Avena distans	A. sativa	Azara brownae -Phil.	A. integrifolia v brownae
Avena flava	A. sativa	Azara dentata 'Variegata'	A. integ. 'Variegata'
Avena fusca	A. sativa	Azara gillesii -Hook & Arn.	A. petiolaris
Avena georgica	A. sativa	Azolla caroliniana	A. mexicana
Avena grandis	A. sativa	Azolla caroliniana -Willd.	A. filiculoides
Avena heteromalla	A. sativa	Azorella glebaria -A Gray	Bolax gummifera
Avena hyemalis	A. sativa	Azorella glebaria misapplied	A. trifurcata
Avena nigra	A. fatua	Azorella gummifera	Bolax gummifera
Avena nodipilosa	A. sativa	Azorella nivalis	A. trifurcata
Avena orientalis	A. sativa	Azureocereus	Browningia
Avena patens	A. fatua	Azureocereus hertlingianus	Brownin. hertlingiana
Avena persarum	A. sativa	Babiana caerulescens	B. plicata
Avena petermannii	A. fatua	Babiana disticha	B. plicata
Avena pseudosativa	A. sativa	Babiana reflexa	B. plicata
Avena racemosa	A. sativa	Baccharis salicifolia	B. viminea
Avena rubra	A. sativa	Bacopa 'Snowflake'	Sutera cordata 'Snowflake'
Avena sativa v fatua	A. fatua		
Avena sempervirens	Helictotrichon semper.	Bactyrilobium -(Willd.) Willd.	Cassia -L.
Avena sterilis ssp fatua	A. fatua	Baeckea behrii	Babingtonia behrii
Avena tatarica	A. sativa	Baeckea crenatifolia	Babingtonia crenulata
Avena thellungii	A. sativa	Baeckea densifolia	Babingtonia densifolia
Avena trabutiana	A. sativa	Baeckea fascicularis	Babingtonia densifolia
Avena trisperma	A. sativa	Baeckea intertropica	Astartea intratropica
Avena vilis	A. fatua	Baeckea jucunda	Babingtonia jucunda
Avenula	Helictotrichon	Baeckea nova-anglica	Babingtonia densifolia
Axyris ceratioides -L.	Eurotia ceratioides	Baeckea obtusifolia	Babingtonia virgata
Ayapana	Eupatorium	Baeckea parvula v latifolia	Babingtonia virgata
Azalea albrechtii -(Maxim). Kuntze	Rhododendron luteum	Baeckea phylicoides	Kunzea ericoides
Azalea amagiana -Mak.	Rhodo. amagianum	Baeckea squarrulosa	Babingtonia squarrul.
Azalea arborescens -Pursh	Rhodo. arborescens	Baeckea virgata	Babingtonia virgata
Azalea atlantica -Ashe	Rhodo. atlanticum	Baeckea virgata v parvula	Babingtonia bidwillii
Azalea calendulacea -Michx.	Rhodo. calendulaceum	Baeckia	Baeckea
Azalea canescens -Michx.	Rhodo. canescens	Bahia lanata	Eriophyllum lanatum
Azalea indica -L.	Rhododendron indicum	Baillonia juncea	Diostea juncea

Synonym	Current Name	Synonym	Current Name
Baldingera arundinacea	Phalaris arundinacea	Bambusa ruscifolia	Shibataea kumasasa
Baldingera colorata	Phalaris arundinacea	Bambusa senanensis	Sasa senanensis
Balisma -M.Lag.	Arisarum -Mill.	Bambusa simonii -Carr.	Pleioblastus simonii
Ballota nigra 'Archer's Variety'	B. nigra 'Archer's Variegated'	Bambusa tootsik h.	Sinobambusa tootsik
		Bambusa variegata -Miq.	Pleioblastus variegatus
Ballota nigra 'Variegata'	B. nigra 'Archer's Variegated'	Bambusa veitchii -Carr.	Sasa veitchii
		Bambusa vilmorinii	Pleioblastus chino f angustifolius
Ballota spinosa -Link.	B. frutescens		
Balsamina foeminea	Impatiens giorgii	Bambusa viridi-glaucescens -Carr.	Phyllostachys viridiglaucescens
Balsamita	Tanacetum		
Balsamita major	Tanacetum balsamita	Bambusa viridistrata -Reg.	Pleioblastus auricomus
Balsamorhiza hirsuta	B. hookeri	Bambusa viridistriata -Regel.	Pleioblastus simonii
Bambusa albostriata	Pleioblastus simonii	Banksia alpina	Pimelea alpina
Bambusa angustifolia	Pl. chino f angustifolius	Banksia ammocharis	Pimelea ammocharis
Bambusa argentea	B. multiplex	Banksia angustifolia	Pimelea angustifolia
Bambusa aurea -h. ex Carr.	Phyllostachys aurea	Banksia aquifolium	B. ilicifolia
Bambusa borealis	Sasa borealis	Banksia aspleniifolia	B. oblongifolia
Bambusa castilloni -Marliac	Phyllostachys bambu soides 'Castillonis'	Banksia barbigera	B. goodii
		Banksia bowmannii	Pim. leptospermoides
Bambusa chino -Franch. & Sav.	Pleioblastus chino	Banksia caleyi v sinuosa	B. caleyi
Bambusa disticha -Mitf.	Pleioblastus pygmaeus v distichus	Banksia compar	B. integrifolia ssp com.
		Banksia cunninghamii (unv)	Banksia spinulosa v cunninghamii
Bambusa fastuosa -Mitf.	Semiarundinaria fastuosa	Banksia dactyloides	Hakea dactyloides
Bambusa flexuosa -Carr.	Phyllostachys flexuosa	Banksia depressa	B. marginata
Bambusa fortunei aurea h.	Pleioblastus auricomus	Banksia depressa v subintegra	B. marginata
Bambusa glaucescens	B. multiplex	Banksia dolichostyla	B. sphaerocarpa v dol.
Bambusa gracilis	Drepanostachyum falcatum	Banksia elatior	B. aemula
		Banksia ericifolia v ericifolia	B. ericifolia ssp ericif.
Bambusa kumasasa	Shibataea kumasasa	Banksia fagifolia	B. robura
Bambusa kurilensis	Sasa kurilensis	Banksia ferrea	B. marginata
Bambusa marmorea -Mitf.	Chimonobambusa mar.	Banksia gardneri v brevidentata	B. brevidentata
Bambusa metake -Sieb.	Pseudosasa japonica	Banksia gardneri v hiemalis	B. hiemalis
Bambusa metallica -Mirtford	Sasa palmata	Banksia glauca	B. integrifolia ssp int.
Bambusa mitis h.	Phyllostachys edulis	Banksia gunnii	B. marginata
B. multiplex 'Chinese Goddess'	B. multiplex v riviereorum	Banksia ilicifolia v integrifolia	B. ilicifolia
		Banksia insularis	B. marginata
Bambusa multiplex 'Elegans'	B. mult. 'Floribunda'	Banksia integrifolia ssp aquilonia	B. aquilonia
Bambusa multiplex 'Fernleaf'	B. mult. 'Floribunda'	Banksia integrifolia ssp oblongifolia	B. oblongifolia
Bambusa multiplex 'Wang Tsai'	B. mult. 'Floribunda'	Banksia integrifolia v major	B. glauca
Bambusa nagashina h.	Pleioblastus humilis	Banksia integrifolia v typica	B. glauca
Bambusa nana h.	Pleioblastus pygmaeus v distichus	Banksia latifolia v minor	B. oblongifolia
		Banksia ledifolia	B. spinulosa v cunninghamii
Bambusa nigra -Lodd.	Phyllostachys nigra		
Bambusa nipponica	Sasa nipponica	Banksia leptospermoides	Pimelea leptosperm.
Bambusa oldhamii	Sinocalamus oldhamii	Banksia littoralis v seminuda	B. seminuda
Bambusa palmata -Burb.	Sasa palmata	Banksia macrophylla	B. robur
Bambusa puberula -Miq.	Phyllostachys nigra v henonis -(Mitf) Rendle	Banksia marcescens	B. marginata
		Banksia nervosa	Pimelea nervosa
Bambusa pubescens	Dendrocalamus strictus	Banksia oleifolia	Hakea dactyloides
		Banksia pinifolia	B. leptophylla
Bambusa pumila h.	Pleioblastus pumilus	Banksia procumbens	B. dentata
Bambusa pygmaea h.	Sasaella ramosa	Banksia prostrata	B. gardneri
Bambusa quadrangularis -Fenzi	Chimonobambusa quadrangularis	Banksia prostrata -J.R.&G.Forst.	Protea prostrata
		Banksia purpurea	B. coccinea

Synonym	Current Name	Synonym	Current Name
B. sphaerocarpa v glabrescens	B. incana	Beauverdia	Leucocoryne
Banksia sphaerocarpa v major	B. leptophylla	Begonia 'Can-can'	B. 'Herzog von Sagan'
Banksia sphaerocarpa v pinifolia	B. leptophylla	Begonia 'Corallina de Lucerna'	B. 'Lucerna'
Banksia spicata	B. glauca	Begonia 'Elaine's Baby'	B. 'Elaine Wilkerson'
Banksia spicata	Banksia integrifolia	Begonia 'Fire Flush'	B. 'Bettina Rothschild'
Banksia spicata	Pimelea spicata	Begonia 'Flaming Queen'	B. 'Feuerkonigin'
Banksia tenuifolia -Salisb.	Hakea sericea	Begonia 'Iron Cross'	B. masoniana
Baptisia exaltata	B. australis 'Exaltata'	Begonia 'Lucerna'	B. x corallina 'Lucerna'
Baptisia lactea	B. alba v macrophylla	Begonia 'Rosea'	B. foliosa v miniata
Baptisia leucantha	B. alba v macrophylla		'Rosea'
Baptisia leucophaea	B. bracteata v leuc.	Begonia 'Ruhrtal'	B. 'Merry Christmas'
Baptisia pendula	B. alba	Begonia 'Silver'	B. pustulata 'Argentea'
Baptisia villosa	B. bracteata v leuc.	Begonia acerifolia	B. vitifolia
Barbacenia elegans	Talbotia elegans	Begonia angularis	B. stipulacea
Barbarea americana	B. orthoceras	Begonia argyrostigma	B. maculata
Barbarea arcuata	B. vulgaris	Begonia compta	B. stipulacea
Barbarea australis	B. vulgaris	Begonia dietrichiana	B. echinosepala
Barbarea barbarea	B. vulgaris		'Dietrichiana'
Barbarea cochlearifolia	B. orthoceras	Begonia discolor	B. grandis ssp
Barbarea hirsuta	B. vulgaris		evansiana
Barbarea hondoensis	B. orthoceras	Begonia disticha	B. stipulacea
Barbarea iberica	B. vulgaris	Begonia echinata	B. picta
Barbarea kayseri	B. vulgaris	Begonia erosa	B. picta
Barbarea lyrata	B. vulgaris	Begonia evansiana	B. grandis evansiana
Barbarea lyrifolium	B. vulgaris	Begonia feastii 'Helix'	B. x erythrophylla
Barbarea macrophylla	B. vulgaris		'Helix'
Barbarea patens	B. orthoceras	Begonia fuchsioides 'Rosea'	B. foliosa v miniata
Barbarea praecox	B. verna		'Rosea'
Barbarea rivularis -not Loret	B. vulgaris	Begonia glaucophylla	B. radicans
Barbarea silvestris	B. vulgaris	Begonia grandis	B. gr. ssp evansiana
Barbarea stolonifera	B. vulgaris	Begonia griffithii	B. annulata
Barbarea stricta -not Andrz.	B. orthoceras	Begonia haageana	B. scharffii
Barbarea taurica	B. vulgaris	Begonia incana	B. peltata
Barbarea vulgaris v orthoceras	B. orthoceras	Begonia incarnata 'Metallica'	B. metallica
Barleria suberecta	Dicliptera suberecta	Begonia laciniata	B. palmata
Barosma betulina	Agathosma betulina	Begonia limmingheana	B. radicans
Barosma crenulata	Agathosma crenulata	Begonia martiana	B. gracilis v martiana
Barosma pulchella	Agathosma pulchella	Begonia nigramarga	B. bowerae v nigram.
Barringtonia speciosa (unv)	B. asiatica	Begonia procumbens	B. radicans
Bartlettina	Eupatorium	Begonia sceptrum	B. aconitifolia
Bartlettina sordida	Eupatorium sordidum	Begonia semperflorens h.	B. Semperflorens
Bartonia aurea	Mentzelia lindleyi		Cultorum Group
Bartsia acuminata	Castilleja	Begonia x carrierei	B. Semp. Cultorum Gr.
	setentrionalis	Begonia zebrina	B. stipulacea
Bartsia coccinea	Castilleja coccinea	Belamcanda punctata	B. chinensis
Bartsia pallida	Cast. setentrionalis	Belharnosia	Sanguinaria
Basella rubra	B. alba	Belladonna baccifera	Atropa belladonna
Bauera juncea	Tetratheca juncea	Bellevalia pycnantha h.	B. paradoxa
Bauhinia alba	B. variegata	Bellis alpina	B. perennis -L.
Bauhinia punctata	B. galpinii	Bellis caerulescens	B. rot. 'Caerulescens'
Bauhinia purpurea h.	B. variegata	Bellis Hen and Chickens	B. perennis 'Prolifera'
Baumea	Machaerina	Bellis hortensis -Mill.	B. perennis -L.
Beaucarnea inermis	Nolina recurvata	Bellis hybrida -Ten.	B. perennis -L.
Beaucarnea longifolia -Baker	Nolina longifolia	Bellis integrifolia -not Michx.	B. perennis -L.
Beaucarnea recurvata -Lemaire	Nolina recurvata	Bellis perennis 'Lipstick'	B. p. 'Habanera White

Synonym	Current Name	Synonym	Current Name
	with Red Tips'	Berberis congestiflora v hakeoides	B. hakeoides
Bellis perennis 'Single Blue'	B. rotundifolia	B. coriacea -Brandis, not St.Hill	B. glaucocarpa -Stapf
	'Caerulescens'	Berberis coryi	B. wilsoniae v
Bellium rotundifolium	B. minutum		subcaulialata
Beloperone	Justicia	Berberis darwinii 'Nana'	B. x stenophylla 'Nana'
Beloperone guttata	Justicia brandegeeana	Berberis darwinii 'Prostrata'	B. x stenophylla
Belvisia ruta-muraia	Justicia brandegeeana		'Prostrata'
Benincasa cerifera	B. hispida	Berberis dictyophylla 'Albicaulis'	B. dictyophylla
Benthamia capitata -(Wall.) Nakai.	Cornus capitata -Wall.	Berberis diversifolia	Mahonia aquifolium
Benthamia florida -Spach	Cornus florida	Berberis dulcis - Sweet	B. buxifolia - Lam.
Benthamia fragifera -Lind.	Cornus capitata -Wall.	Berberis dulcis 'Nana'	B. buxifolia 'Pygmaea'
Benthamia japonica -Sieb & Zucc.	Cornus kousa -Hance	Berberis erythroclada	B. concinna
Benthamia kousa	Cornus kousa	Berberis fascicularis -(DC.) Sims	Mahonia pinnata
Benthamidia capitata - (Wall.) Hara	Cornus capitata -Wall.	Berberis formosana	B. kawakamii
Benthamidia florida -Spach	Cornus florida -L.	Berberis fortunei -Lindl.	Mahonia fortunei
Benthamidia japonica	Cornus kousa -Hance	Berberis fremontii -Torr.	Mahonia fremontii
Benthamidia nuttallii	Cornus nuttallii	Berberis gagnepainii 'Purpurea'	B. x interposita
Benzoin aestivale -Nees	Lindera benzoin		'Wallich's Purple'
Benzoin cercidifolium	Lindera obtusiloba	Berberis gagnepainii h.	B. gagnepainii v
Benzoin grandifolium -Rehd.	Lindera megaphylla		lanceifolia
Benzoin obtusilobum	Lindera obtusiloba	Berberis geraldii -Veitch	B. aggregata -Schneid.
Benzoin odoriferum -Nees	Lindera benzoin	Berberis glumacea -Spreng.	Mahonia nervosa
Benzoin praecox -Sieb. & Zucc.	Lindera praecox	Berberis gracilipes	Mahonia gracilipes
Benzoin umbellatum -Kuntze	Lindera umbellata	Berberis haematocarpa -Wooton	Mahonia haematocarpa
Berberis 'Chenault'	B. x hybridogagnepainii	Berberis hookeri v candidula	B. candidula
	'Chenaultii'	Berberis hookeri v latifolia	B. manipurana
Berberis 'Chenaultii'	B. x hybridogagnepainii	Berberis hypoleuca h.	B. candidula -Schneid.
	'Chenaultii'	Berberis ilicifolia h. not Forst.	x Mahoberberis
Berberis 'Little Favourite'	B.thunb.f atropurpurea		neubertii
	'Atropurpurea Nana'	Berberis incrassata	B. insignis ssp incras.
Berberis 'Unique'	B. orthobotrys v	Berberis insignis v tongolensis	B. insignis - Hook
	canescens	Berberis irwinii	B. x stenophylla
B. acuminata - Stapf, not Franch.	B. gagnepainii Schneid.		'Irwinii'
B. acuminata - Veitch, not Franch.	B. veitchii -Schneid.	Berberis japonica -(Thunb.) R.Br.	Mahonia japonica
B. aggregata v prattii	B. prattii -Schneid.	Berberis kawakamii v formosana	B. kawakamii
Berberis aggregata v recurvata	B. prattii -Schneid.	Berberis knightii	B. manipurana
Berberis angulizans -Massias	B. canadensis -Mill.	Berberis leptoclada -Diels	B. amoena - Dunn
Berberis approximata - Sprague	B. dictyophylla v app.	Berberis levis	B. atrocarpa
Berberis aquifolium -Pursh	Mahonia aquifolium	Berberis ludlowii v capillaris	B. capillaris -Ahrendt
Berberis aquifolium 'Fascicularis'	Mahonia x wagneri	Berberis maximowiczii -Reg.	B. thunbergii v maxim.
	'Pinnacle'	Berberis montana v chillanensis	B. chillanensis
Berberis aristata -Parker	B. glaucocarpa	Berberis nana -Greene	Mahonia repens
Berberis aristata v coriaria	Berberis coriaria	Berberis napalensis	Mahonia napaulensis
B. aristata v floribunda -(G.Don) Hook. f. & Thoms. in part		Berberis nervosa -Nutt.	Mahonia nervosa
	Berberis coriaria	Berberis neubertii -Baumann	x Mahob. neubertii
Berberis aristata v micrantha -Hook.f. & Thoms. in part		Berberis nevinii -A.Gray	Mahonia nevinii
	B. sikkimensis	Berberis Park Jewel	B. x media 'Parkjuweel'
Berberis bealei -Fort.	Mahonia japonica	Berberis pinnata -Lag.	Mahonia pinnata
	Bealei Group	Berberis polyantha h.	B. prattii
Berberis brevipedunculata -Bean	B. prattii	Berberis pumila -Greene	Mahonia pinnata
Berberis buxifolia 'Nana' h.	B. buxifolia 'Pygmaea'	Berberis Red Jewel	B. x media 'Red Jewel'
Berberis buxifolia v nana h	B. buxifolia 'Pygmaea'	Berberis repens -Lindl.	Mahonia repens
Berberis candidula 'Jytte'	B. 'Jytte'	Berberis sanguinea h.	B. panlanensis
Berberis caroli v hoanghensis	B. vernae -Schneid.	Berberis schiedeana -Schlecht.	Mahonia trifolia
Berberis chitria v sikkimensis	B. sikkimensis	Berberis sinensis -DC. in part	B. chinensis -Poir.

Synonym	Current Name	Synonym	Current Name
Berberis sinensis DC. in part	B. poiretii -Schneid.	Bergenia crassifolia 'Orbicularis'	B. x schmidtii
Berberis stapfiana -Schneid.	B. wilsoniae v stapf.	Bergenia delavayi	B. purpurascens v del.
Berberis stenophylla	B. soulieana -Schneid.	Bergenia ligulata	B. ciliata
Berberis subcauliata -Schneid.	B. wilsoniae v subc.	Bergenia milesii	B. stracheyi
Berberis swaseyi	Mahonia swaseyi	Bergenia Morning Red	B. 'Morgenrote'
B. thunb. 'Atropurpurea Superba'	B. x ottawensis f purpurea 'Superba'	Bergenia purpurascens 'Ballawley'	B. 'Ballawley'
		Bergenia Silverlight	B. 'Silberlicht'
B. thunbergii 'Crimsom Pygmy'	B.thunb.f atropurpurea 'Atropurpurea Nana'	Bergenia Snow Queen	B. 'Schneekonigin'
		Bergenia stracheyi 'Alba'	B. strach. Alba Group
Berberis thunbergii 'Green Mantle'	B. thunbergii 'Kelleriis'	Bergenia stracheyi f alba	B. strach. Alba Group
Berberis thunbergii 'Green Marble'	B. thunbergii 'Kelleriis'	Bergenia Winter Fairy Tales	B. 'Wintermarchen'
Berberis thunbergii 'Silver Mile'	B. x ottawensis 'Silver Mile'	Berula pusilla	B. erecta
		Beta cicla	B. vulgaris cicla
B. thunbergii Atropurpurea Group	B. thunbergii f atrop.	Beta maritima	B. vulgaris maritima
Berberis thunbergii dawsonii	B. thunbergii 'Minor'	Betonica	Stachys
Berberis thunbergii v glabra	B. lecomtei	Betonica grandiflora	Stachys macrantha
Berberis trifoliolata -Moricand	Mahonia trifoliolata	Betonica officinalis	Stachys officinalis
Berberis vulgaris v amurensis -Reg.	B. amurensis -Rupr.	Betula 'Inverleith'	B. utilis v jacquemontii 'Inverleith'
Berberis vulgaris v brachybotrys	B. orthobotrys		
Berberis wallichiana - Hook	B. hookeri -Lem.	Betula 'Jermyns'	B. utilis v jacquemontii 'Jermyns'
Berberis wallichiana -Hook. not DC.	B. hookeri -Lem.		
Berberis wallichiana v hypoleuca h.	B. candidula -Schneid.	Betula acuminata	B. alnoides
Berberis wallichiana v pallida -Bois	B. candidula -Schneid.	Betula alaskana -not Lesq.	B. neoalaskana
Berberis wilsoniae 'Marianne'	B. wilsoniae 'Graciella'	Betula alba -L.	B. pendula -Roth
Berberis x irwinii -Byhouwer	B. x stenophylla 'Irwinii'	Betula alba ssp glutinosa	Alnus glutinosa
		Betula alba ssp mandschurica -Reg.	B. platyphylla
B. x irwinii 'Corallina Compacta'	B. x stenophylla 'Corallina Compacta'	B. a. ssp occidentalis v commutata	B. papyrifera v comm.
		B. alba ssp papyrifera v humilis	B. neoalaskana
Berberis x irwinii 'Corallina'	B. x stenophylla 'Corallina'	Betula alba v humilis	B. neoalaskana
		Betula alba v japonica -Miq.	B. mandschurica v jap.
Berberis x irwinii 'Gracilis Nana'	B. x stenophylla 'Gracilis Nana'	Betula alba v pendula -Ait.	B. pendula -Roth
		Betula alleghaniensis v fallax	B. alleghanensis
Berberis x irwinii 'Gracilis'	B. x st. 'Gracilis'	Betula alnoides v cylindrostachya	B. cylindrostachya
Berberis x irwinii 'Picturata'	B. x st. 'Picturata'	Betula alnoides v pyrifolia -Burk.	B. luminifera -Winkler
Berberis x media Park Jewel	B. x media 'Parkjuweel'	Betula alnus v incana -L.	Alnus incana
Berberis x media Park Juwel	B. x media 'Parkjuweel'	Betula bhojpattra - Wall.	B. utilis -D.Don
Berberis x ottawensis 'Purpurea'	B. x ottaw. f purpurea	Betula bhojpattra v jacquemontii	B. utilis v jacquemontii
Berberis x rubrostilla	B. 'Rubrostilla'	Betula bhojpattra v sinensis -Fran.	B. albosinensis -Burk.
B. x stenophylla 'Cornish Cream'	B. x st. 'Lemon Queen'	Betula borealis	B. pumila
B. x stenophylla 'Cream Showers'	B. x st. 'Lemon Queen'	Betula caerulea-grandis -Blanch.	B. x caerulea
Berberis xanthoxylum h.	B. manipurana	Betula carpinifolia	B. lenta
Berchemia axilliflora	B. lineata	Betula celtiberica	B. pubescens ssp celt.
Berchemia edgeworthii	B. lineata	Betula coerulea v blanchardii -Sarg.	B. x caerulea
Berchemia nana	B. lineata	Betula coerulea v grandis -Blanch.	B. x caerulea
Berchemia volubilis -(L.f.) DC.	B. scandens -(Hill.)	Betula coriacea - Gunn.	B. pubescens ssp carpatica
Bergenia 'Ballawley' seed-raised	B. Ballawley hybrids		
Bergenia 'Delbees'	B. 'Ballawley'	Betula costata h.	B. ermanii 'Grayswood Hill'
Bergenia 'Evening Glow'	B. 'Abendglut'		
Bergenia 'Lambrook'	B. 'Margery Fish'	Betula crispa	Alnus viridis crispa
Bergenia acanthifolia	B. x spathulata	Betula delavayi v forrestii -W.W.Sm.	B. forrestii
Bergenia beesiana	B. purpurascens	Betula ermannii v subcordata	B. ermannii
Bergenia Bell Tower	B. 'Glockenturm'	Betula exalata -S. Moore	B. chinensis -Maxim.
Bergenia bifolia	B. crassifolia	Betula fontinalis -Sarg.	B. occidentalis -Hook.
Bergenia ciliata f ligulata	B. pacumbis	Betula fruticosa	B. humilis
Bergenia ciliata x crassifolia	B. x schmidtii	Betula glandulifera	B. pumila

Synonym	Current Name	Synonym	Current Name
Betula glandulosa v glandulifera	B. pumila	Bidens filamentosa	B. cernua -L.
Betula glutinosa -L.	Alnus glutinosa	Bidens glaucescens	B. cernua -L.
Betula gmelinii	B. ovalifolia	Bidens gracilenta	B. cernua -L.
Betula incisa	B. ermanii	Bidens heterophylla -Ortega	B. aurea
Betula jacquemontii -Spach	B. utilis v jacquemontii	Bidens humilis	B. triplinervia v
Betula japonica -(Miq.) Winkler	B. mandschurica v jap.		macrantha
Betula japonica v szechuanica	B. platyphylla v szec.	Bidens kelloggii	B. cernua -L.
Betula kamtschatica	B. humilis	Bidens leptopoda	B. cernua -L.
Betula lutea -Michx.	B. alleghaniensis -Britt.	Bidens lonchophylla	B. cernua -L.
Betula lutea v fallax	B. alleghanensis	Bidens macounii	B. cernua -L.
Betula lyalliana -Bean	B. papyrifera v	Bidens minima	B. cernua -L.
	commutata	Bidens prionophylla	B. cernua -L.
Betula mandschurica -(Reg.) Nakai	B. platyphylla -Sukat.	Bidens quadriaristata v dentata	B. cernua -L.
Betula mandschurica v szechuanica	B. szechuanica	Bifora loureiri	Coriandrum sativum
Betula megrelica	B. medwedewii	Bigelowia douglasii -A.Gray	Chrysothamnus
Betula occidentalis -Sarg. not Hook.	B. papyrifera v comm.		viscidiflors
Betula oycowiensis -Besser	B. pendula f oycow.	B. graveolens -(Nutt.) A.Gray	Chrysothamnus
Betula papyracea -Ait.	B. papyrifera -Marsh.		graveolens
Betula papyrifera ssp humilis	B. neoalaskana	Bignonia callistegioides	Clytostoma callisteg.
Betula papyrifera v kenaica	B. kenaica	Bignonia capensis	Tecoma capensis
Betula papyrifera v neoalaskana	B. neoalaskana	Bignonia catalpa	Catalpa bignonioides
B. pendula 'Dalecarlica' misapplied	B. pendula 'Laciniata'	Bignonia cherere	Distictis buccinatoria
Betula pendula f crispa	B. pendula 'Laciniata'	Bignonia chinensis -Lam.	Campsis grandiflora
Betula pendula v japonica -Rehd.	B. mandschurica v jap.	Bignonia grandiflora -Thunb.	Campsis grandiflora
Betula platyphylla v japonica	B. mandschurica v jap.	Bignonia jasminoides	Pandorea jasminoides
Betula platyphylla v kamtschatica	B. mandschurica v jap.	Bignonia lindleyana	Clytostoma calysteg.
Betula platyphylla v rockii	B. rockii	Bignonia longiflora 'Alba'	B. long. 'Fructualbo'
Betula platyphylla v szechuanica	B. szechuanica	Bignonia pandorana	Pandorea pandorana
Betula pubescens ssp carpatica	B. pubescens v	Bignonia radicans -L.	Campsis radicans
	glabrata	Bignonia speciosa	Clytostoma callisteg.
Betula pubescens v murithii	B. pubescens v glabr.	Bignonia stans	Tecoma stans
Betula pumila v glandulifera -Reg.	B. glandulifera	Bignonia tomentosa -Thunb.	Paulownia tomentosa
Betula resinifera -Britton	B. neoalaskana	Bignonia unguis-cati	Macfadyena ung.-cati
Betula rubra -Michx.	B. nigra -L.	Bignonia venusta	Pyrostegia venusta
Betula serrulata	Alnus serrulata	Bilderdyckia aubertii	Fallopia baldschuanica
Betula shikokiana	B. ermanii	Bilderdyckia baldschuanica	Fallopia baldschuanica
Betula subcordata -Rydb.	B. papyrifera v subc.	Bilderdykia	Fallopia
Betula tatewakiana	B. ovalifolia	Billbergia rhodocyanea	Aechmea fasciata
Betula tauschii -(Reg).	B. platyphylla v japon.	Billbergia saundersii	B. chlorosticta
Betula ulmifolia -Sieb. & Zucc.	B. grossa	Billbergia sphacelata	Greigia sphacelata
Betula utilis v sinensis	B. albosinensis -Burk.	Biota orientalis -(L). Endl.	Platycladus orientalis
Betula verrucosa -Ehrh.	B. pendula -Roth	Biscutella megalocarpa	Megacarpaea megaloc.
Betula verrucosa v japonica -Henry	B. mandschurica v jap.	Bistorta	Persicaria
Betula verrucosa v laciniata	B. pendula 'Laciniata'	Bistorta affine	Persicaria affinis
Betula verrucosa v platyphylla	B. platyphylla	Bistorta amplexicaulis	Persicaria amplexic.
Betula viridis -Chaix	Alnus viridis	Bistorta macrophylla	Persicaria macrophyl.
Betula wilsonii -Bean	B. potaninii -Batal.	Bistorta major	Persicaria bistorta
Betula-Alnus maritima -Marsh.	Alnus maritima	Bistorta milletii	Persicaria milletii
Bidens acuta	B. tripartita	Bistorta vacciniifolia	Persicaria vaccin.
Bidens atrosanguinea	Cosmos atrosanguin.	Blackiella macropterocarpa	Atriplex macropteroc.
Bidens comosa	B. tripartita	Bladhia japonica -Thunb.	Ardisia japonica
Bidens connata	B. tripartita	Bladhia sieboldii	Ardisia sieboldii
Bidens cusickii	B. cernua -L.	Blandfordia flammea	B. grandiflora
Bidens dentata	B. cernua -L.	Blattaria vulgaris	Verbascum blattaria
Bidens elliptica	B. cernua -L.	Blechnum acuminatum	B. norfolkianum

Synonym	Current Name	Synonym	Current Name
Blechnum aggregatum	B. chambersii	Boltonia incisa	Kalimeris incisa
Blechnum alpinum	B. penna-marina ssp alpinum	Boltonia latisquama	B. asteroides v lat.
		Bomarea hirtella	B. edulis
Blechnum capense v scabrum	B. camfieldii	Bomarea kalbreyeri h.	B. caldasii
Blechnum capense v vestitum	B. wattsii	Bomarea pubigera h.	B. andimarcana
B. cartilagineum v appendiculatum	B. cartilagineum	Bombax malabaricum	B. ceiba
B. cartilagineum v cartilagineum	B. cartilagineum	Bombax pentandra	Ceiba pentandra
Blechnum cartilagineum v normale	B. cartilagineum	Bongardia rauwolfia	B. chrysogonum
Blechnum cartilagineum v tropicum	B. cartilagineum	Bonifazia quezalteca	Disocactus quezaltecus
Blechnum cordatum	B. chilense	Bontia denticulata	Eremophila denticulata
Blechnum lanceolatum	B. norfolkianum	Bontia viscida	Eremophila viscida
B. lanceolatum v norfolkianum	B. norfolkianum	Borago laxiflora	B. pygmaea
Blechnum magellanicum misapplied	B. chilense	Borago orientalis	Trachystemon orient.
Blechnum minus ssp scabrum	B. camfieldii	Borbonia pinifolia	Aspalanthus linearis
Blechnum nigropaleacum	B. whelanii	Boretta cantabrica	Daboecia cantabrica
Blechnum nudum	B. norfolkianum	Boretta daboecia	Daboecia cantabrica
Blechnum occidentale nanum	B. glandulosum	Boronia affinis	B. lanuginosa
Blechnum patersonii v elongatum	B. patersonii ssp queenslandicum	Boronia anemonifolia	B. fraseri
		Boronia anemonifolia v anethifolia	B. bipinnata
Blechnum spicant incisum	B. spicant 'Rickard's Serrate'	Boronia anemonifolia v dentigera	B. anemonifolia
		Boronia arborescens	Zieria arborescens
Blechnum striatum	B. indicum	Boronia artemisiifolia	B. lanuginosa
Blechnum tabulare misapplied	B. chilense	Boronia artemisiifolia v wilsonii	B. wilsonii
Blepharipappus glandulosus	Layia glandulosa	Boronia bipinnata v pubescens	B. occidentalis
Blepharipappus platyglossus	Layia platyglossa	Boronia calophylla	B. ternata v glabrifolia
Bletia hyacinthina	Bletilla striata	Boronia candollei	B. alata
Bletilla hyacinthina	B. striata	Boronia chironiifolia	B. denticulata
Bletilla striata alba	B. striata v japonica f gebina	B. coerulescens v glabrescens	B. coerulescens ssp coerulescens
Blitum capitatum	Chenopodium capitatum	B. coerulescens v pubescens	B. coer. ssp coerules.
		Boronia colorata	B. parviflora
Blitum chenopodioides	Monolepis nuttalliana	Boronia crenulata v gracilis	B. crenulata ssp cren.
Blitum hastatum	Chenopodium overi	Boronia elatior	B. molloyae
Blitum nuttallianum	Monolepis nuttalliana	Boronia fasciculifolia	B. scabra ssp scabra
Blitum rubrum	Chenopodium rubrum	Boronia fastigiata v tenuior	B. fastigiata ssp ten.
Bloomeria crocea aurea	B. aurea	Boronia flexuosa	B. dichotoma
Bobartia spathacea	B. indica	Boronia granulata	Zieria furfuracea ssp furfuracea
Bocconia	Macleaya		
Bocconia cordata	Macleaya cordata	Boronia haloragoides	B. crenulata ssp pubescens
Bocconia microcarpa	Macleaya microcarpa		
Boehmeria japonica	B. longispica	Boronia hirsuta	Zieria pilosa
Boehmeria macrostachya	B. macrophylla	Boronia hispida	B. nana v pubescens
Boehmeria malabrica	B. glomerulifera	Boronia humilis	B. crassifolia
Boehmeria nivea nipononivea	B. nipononivea	Boronia hypericifolia	B. denticulata
Boehmeria paraspicata	B. spicata	Boronia hyssopifolia	B. nana v hyssopifolia
Boehmeria platphylla tricuspis	B. tricuspis	Boronia inornata ssp leptophylla	B. leptophylla
Boehmeria platyphylla	B. macrophylla	Boronia integrifolia	B. dichotoma
Boehmeria tenacissima	B. nivea	Boronia laevigata	Zieria laevigata
Boehmeria tricuspis unicuspis	B. spicata	Boronia laniflora	B. juncea ssp laniflora
Boerhavia coccinea	B. diffusa	Boronia laniflora v macrantha	B. juncea ssp laniflora
Boerhavia repens	B. diffusa	Boronia lanuginosa v brevicalyx	B. oxyantha v brevical.
Bolax glebaria	Azorella trifurcata	Boronia ledifolia v glabra	B. glabra
Boldu boldus	Peumus boldus	Boronia ledifolia v normalis	B. ledifolia
Boltonia cantoniensis	Kalimeris pinnatifida	Boronia ledifolia v repanda	B. repanda
Boltonia glastifolia	B. asteroides	Boronia ledifolia v rosmariniifolia	B. rosmariniifolia

43

Synonym	Current Name	Synonym	Current Name
Boronia ledifolia v rubiginosa	B. rubiginosa	Boronia viminea v latifolia	B. crenulata ssp vim.
Boronia ledifolia v triphylla	B. ledifolia	Boronia whitei	B. ledifolia
Boronia ledophylla	B. ledifolia	Borya acuminata -(Michx.) Willd.	Forestiera acuminata
Boronia leptophylla	B. inornata ssp lept.	Borya distichophylla -Nutt.	Buckleya distichophylla
Boronia machardiana	B. crenulata ssp viminea	Borya ligustrina -(Michx.) Willd.	Forestiera ligustrina
		Borzicactus	Oreocereus
Boronia macra	B. spathulata	Borzicactus leucotrichus	Oreoc. hempelianus
Boronia minutiflora	Zieria minut. ssp min.	Boschniakia hookeri	Orobanche tuberosa
Boronia multicaulis	B. crassifolia	Boswellia carteri	B. sacra
Boronia palaefolia	B. falcifolia	Bothriochilus	Coelia
Boronia palustris	B. parviflora	Bothriochilus bellus	Coelia bella
Boronia paradoxa	B. ledifolia	Bothriochloa caucasica	B. bladhii
Boronia pilonema	B. parviflora	Botryanthus aucheri	Muscari aucheri
Boronia pilosa v floribunda	B. pilosa ssp pilosa	Botrychium cicutarium	B. australe
Boronia pilosa v laricifolia	B. pilosa ssp pilosa	Botrychium cuneatum	B. dissecrtum
Boronia pinnata v alba	B. pinnata	Botrychium ternatum	B. australe
Boronia pinnata v gunnii	B. gunnii	Botrychium virginianum	B. australe
Boronia pinnata v muelleri	B. muelleri	Botryopleuron axillare	Veronicastrum axillare
Boronia pinnata v pilosa	B. pilosa	Botryostege bracteata	Tripetaleia bracteata
Boronia polygalifolia v pubescens	B. nana v pubesccens	Bougainvillea 'Ailsa Lambe'	B. 'Mary Palmer' (Spectoperuviana Gr)
Boronia polygalifolia v robusta	B. rigens		
Boronia polygalifolia v trifoliata	B. nana	Bougainvillea 'Apple Blossom'	B. 'Elizabeth Doxey'
Boronia polygalifolia v trifoliata	B. nana v nana	Bougainvillea 'Audrey Grey'	B. 'Elizabeth Doxey'
Boronia pubescens	B. nana v pubescens	Bougainvillea 'Aussie Gold'	B. 'Carson's Gold'
Boronia repanda v alba	B. repanda	Bougainvillea 'Brasiliensis'	B. spectabilis 'Lateritia'
Boronia rosmariniifolia v albiflora	B. ledifolia		
Boronia ruppii	B. rubiginosa	Bougainvillea 'Bridal Bouquet'	B. 'Cherry Blossom'
Boronia semifertilis	B. molloyae	Bougainvillea 'Brilliant' misapplied	B. x buttiana 'Raspberry Ice'
Boronia spathulata v elatior	B. dichotoma		
Boronia spathulata v ramosa	B. spathulata	Bougainvillea 'California Gold'	B. x buttiana 'Enid Lancaster'
Boronia spinescens	B. coerulescens ssp spinescens		
		B. 'Crimson Lake' misapplied	B.x buttiana 'Mrs. Butt'
Boronia subcoerulea	B. ramosa ssp anethifolia	Bougainvillea 'Dauphine'	B. 'Los Banos Beauty'
		Bougainvillea 'Delicate'	B. 'Blondie'
Boronia tenuifolia	B. crenulata ssp viminea	Bougainvillea 'Doctor David Barry'	B. glabra 'Doctor David Barry'
Boronia tenuior	B. fastigiata ssp ten.	Bougainvillea 'Double Yellow'	B. 'Carson's Gold'
Boronia ternata v glabrifolia	B. calophylla	Bougainvillea 'Durban'	B. glabra 'Jane Snook'
Boronia tetandra v floribunda	B. pilosa ssp pilosa	Bougainvillea 'Enchantment'	B. 'Mary Palmer's Enchantment'
Boronia tetandra v grandifolia	B. gunnii		
Boronia tetandra v laricifolia	B. pilosa ssp pilosa	Bougainvillea 'Fair Lady'	B. 'Blondie'
Boronia tetandra v terminiflora	B. pilosa ssp pilosa	Bougainvillea 'Flamingo Pink'	B. 'Chiang Mai Beauty'
Boronia tetrandra v grandifolia	B. gunnii	Bougainvillea 'Golden Dubloon'	B. x buttiana 'Roseville's Delight'
Boronia tetrandra v pilosa	B. pilosa		
Boronia thymifolia	B. scabra ssp scabra	Bougainvillea 'Golden Glow'	B. x buttiana 'Enid Lancaster'
Boronia triphylla	B. ledifolia		
Boronia triphylla v flore-plena	B. ledifolia	Bougainvillea 'Golden Maclean'	B. x buttiana 'Golden Maclean'
Boronia triphylla v latifolia	B. ledifolia		
Boronia variabilis	B. anemonifolia ssp variabilis	Bougainvillea 'Harlequin'	B. 'Thimma' (Spectoperuviana Gr)
Boronia veronicea	Zieria veronicea	Bougainvillea 'Harrissii'	B. glabra 'Harrissii'
Boronia vilhelmii	B. alata	Bougainvillea 'Hawaiian Gold'	B. x butt. 'Golden Glow'
Boronia viminea	B. crenulata ssp vim.	Bougainvillea 'Hawaiian Scarlet'	B. 'San Diego Red'
Boronia viminea v gracilis	B. crenulata v angustifolia	Bougainvillea 'Helen Johnson'	B. 'Temple Fire'
		Bougainvillea 'Hugh Evans'	B. 'Blondie'

Synonym	Current Name	Synonym	Current Name
Bougainvillea 'Indian Flame'	B. 'Partha'	Bougainvillea 'Snow Cap'	B. 'Mary Palmer' (Spectoperuviana Gr)
Bougainvillea 'Jamaica Red'	B.x butt. 'Jamaica Red'		
Bougainvillea 'Jane Snook'	B. glabra 'Jane Snook'	Bougainvillea 'Tango'	B. x b. 'Miss Manila'
Bougainvillea 'Kauai Royal'	B. 'Elizabeth Angus'	Bougainvillea 'Temple Fire'	B. 'Closeburn'
Bougainvillea 'Klong Fire'	B. x buttiana 'Mahara'	Bougainvillea 'Thai Gold'	B. x buttiana 'Roseville's Delight'
Bougainvillea 'Lady Mary Baring'	B. x buttiana 'Lady Mary Baring'	Bougainvillea 'Tropical Rainbow'	B. 'Raspberry Ice'
Bougainvillea 'Lemmer's Special'	B. 'Partha'	Bougainvillea 'Variegata'	B. glabra 'Harrissii'
Bougainvillea 'Limberlost Beauty'	B. 'Cherry Blossom'	Bougainvillea 'Vicky'	B. 'Thimma' (Spectoperuviana Gr)
B. 'Lord Willingdon' misapplied	B. 'Torch Glow'		
Bougainvillea 'Magnifica Traillii'	B. glabra 'Magnifica'	B. glabra 'Jennifer Fernie'	B. 'Jennifer Fernie'
Bougainvillea 'Magnifica'	B. glabra 'Magnifica'	Bougainvillea glabra 'Variegata'	B. glabra 'Harrissii'
Bougainvillea 'Mahara Double Red'	B. x buttiana 'Mahara'	Bougainvillea Surprise	B. 'Mary Palmer' (Spectoperuviana Gr)
Bougainvillea 'Mahara Off-white'	B. 'Cherry Blossom'		
Bougainvillea 'Mahara Orange'	B. x buttiana 'Roseville's Delight'	Boussingaultia	Anredera
		Boussingaultia baselloides -Hook	Anredera cordifolia
Bougainvillea 'Mahara Pink'	B. 'Los Banos Beauty'	Bouteloua oligostachya	B. gracilis
Bougainvillea 'Mahara White'	B. 'Cherry Blossom'	Bouvardia humboldtii	B. longiflora
Bougainvillea 'Mahatma Gandhi'	B. 'Mrs H.C.Buck' (Spectoperuviana Gr)	Bouvardia triphylla	B. ternifolia
		Bowkeria triphylla h.	B.gerardiana -Harvey
Bougainvillea 'Manila Magic Red'	B. x buttiana 'Mahara'	Boykinia elata	B. occidentalis
Bougainvillea 'Mardi Gras'	B. x butt. 'Mardi Gras'	Boykinia heucheriformis	B. jamesii
Bougainvillea 'Mini-Thai'	B. 'Torch Glow'	Boykinia tellimoides	Peltoboykinia tellim.
Bougainvillea 'Mrs Butt Variegated'	B. x buttiana 'Mrs Butt Variegated'	Brachiaria obtusa	Panicum obtusum
		Brachychilum	Hedychium
Bougainvillea 'Mrs Butt'	B. x buttiana 'Mrs Butt'	Brachychiton acericifolius v gregorii	B. gregorii
Bougainvillea 'Mrs Helen McLean'	B. x but. 'Mrs McLean'	Brachychiton australis v incanus	B. incanus
Bougainvillea 'Mrs McLean'	B. x but. 'Mrs McLean'	Brachychiton diversifolius	B. populneus
Bougainvillea 'Orange Glow'	B. Camarillo Fiesta (spectabilis hybrid)	Brachychiton luridus	B. discolor
		Brachychiton paradoxus v discolor	B. discolor
Bougainvillea 'Orange King'	B. x b. 'Louise Wathen'	Brachychiton paradoxus v luridus	B. discolor
Bougainvillea 'Pagoda Pink'	B. 'Los Banos Beauty'	B. populneus v occidentalis	B. gregorii
Bougainvillea 'Penelope'	B. 'Mary Palmer's Enchantment'	Brachychiton ramiflorus	B. paradoxus
		Brachycome	Brachyscome
Bougainvillea 'Pink Champagne'	B. 'Los Banos Beauty'	Brachyglottis 'Sunshine Variegated'	B. 'Moira Reid' Dunedin Group
Bougainvillea 'Pixie'	B. 'Torch Glow'		
Bougainvillea 'Poultonii Special'	B. x buttiana 'Poulton's Special'	Brachyscome alpina -P. Morris	B. tenuiscapa
		Brachyscome billardieri -Benth.	B. ciliaris
Bougainvillea 'Poultonii'	B. x buttiana 'Poultonii'	Brachyscome billardieri -Cass.	B. aculeata
Bougainvillea 'Pride of Singapore'	B. glabra 'Pride of Singapore'	Brachyscome calocarpa	B. dentata
		Brachyscome cardiocarpa v alpina	B. tadgellii
Bougainvillea 'Princess Mahara'	B. x buttiana 'Mahara'	B. ciliaris v brachyglossa	B. ciliaris
Bougainvillea 'Purple King'	B. x b. 'Texas Dawn'	Brachyscome ciliaris v glandulosa	B. ciliaris
Bougainvillea 'Rainbow Gold'	B. x b. 'Rainbow Gold'	Brachyscome ciliaris v robusta	B. rigidula
Bougainvillea 'Raspberry Ice' (v)	B. x buttiana 'Raspberry Ice'	Brachyscome ciliaris v subintegra	B. ciliaris
		Brachyscome collina	B. perpusilla
Bougainvillea 'Robyn's Glory'	B. x b. 'Texas Dawn'	Brachyscome coongiensis	B. rara
Bougainvillea 'Rosenka'	B. x buttiana 'Rosenka'	B. decipiens v pubescens	B. tenuiscapa v pubesc.
B. 'Sanderiana Variegated'	B. glabra 'Harrissii'	Brachyscome dimorphocarpa	B. ciliaris
Bougainvillea 'Sanderiana'	B. glabra 'Sanderiana'	Brachyscome discolor	B. microcarpa
Bougainvillea 'Scarlet Glory'	B. x b. 'Scarlet Glory'	Brachyscome diversifolia v humilis	B. diversifolia
Bougainvillea 'Scarlett o' Hara'	B. 'San Diego Red'	B. diversifolia v maritima	B. diversifolia
Bougainvillea 'Singapore Pink'	B. glabra 'Doctor David Barry'	Brachyscome drummondii	B. ciliaris
		Brachyscome drummondii -Walp.	B. ciliaris
Bougainvillea 'Smartipants'	B. 'Torch Glow'	Brachyscome exilis v scabrida	B. exilis

Synonym	Current Name	Synonym	Current Name
Brachyscome glabra	B. multifida v dilatata	Brassica iberidifolia	B. juncea
Brachyscome glauca	B. aculeata	Brassica integrifolia	B. juncea
B. goniocarpa v eriogona	B. eriogona	Brassica japonica	B. juncea v crispifolia
Brachyscome heterodonta	B. dentata	Brassica lanceolata	B. juncea
Brachyscome heterophylla	B. angustifolia v heter.	Brassica napiformis	B. juncea
Brachyscome iberidifolia alba	B. iberidifolia	Brassica rugosa	B. juncea
Brachyscome iberidifolia v diffusa	B. iberidifolia	Brassica urbaniana	B. juncea
B. iberidifolia v divergens	B. iberidifolia	Brassica vesicaria	Eruca vesicaria
B. iberidifolia v glandulifera	B. iberidifolia	Brassica willdenowii	B. juncea
B. iberidifolia v huegeliana	B. iberidifolia	Brauneria purpurea	Echinacea purpurea
Brachyscome iberidifolia v major	B. iberidifolia	Bravoa geminiflora	Polianthes geminiflora
Brachyscome latisquamea	Pembertonia latisq.	Breea arvensis	Cirsium arvense
Brachyscome leucanthemifolia	B. ciliaris	Breea dioica -Less.	Cirsium arvense
Brachyscome linearifolia	B. angustifolia	Breea segetum	Cirsium setosum
B. linearifolia v heterophylla	B. angustifolia v heter.	Breea setosum	Cirsium setosum
B. linearifolia v linearifolia	B. angustifolia	Brevoortia	Dichelostemma
Brachyscome marginata	B. dentata	Brewsteria -F. Muell.	Cassia -L.
B. marginata v chrsoglossa	B. chrsoglossa	Breynia nivosa	B. disticha
B. marginata v chrysoglossa	B. chrysoglossa	Bridgesia spicata	Ercilla volubilis
B. marginata v marginata	B. dentata	Brittonastrum	Agastache
Brachyscome multicaulis	B. rigidula	Brittonastrum mexicanum	Agastache mexicana
Brachyscome neglecta	B. exilis	Briza capensis	B. maxima -L.
Brachyscome nivalis v alpina	B. tadgellii	Briza dalmatica	B. maxima -L.
Brachyscome oblongifolia	B. aculeata	Briza gracilescens	B. maxima -L.
Brachyscome pachyptera	B. lineariloba	Briza grandis	B. maxima -L.
Brachyscome parvula v lissocarpa	B. lissocarpa	Briza major	B. maxima -L.
Brachyscome perpusilla v tenella	B. perpusilla	Briza microclada	B. maxima -L.
Brachyscome scapiformis	B. aculeata	Briza monspessulana	B. maxima -L.
Brachyscome sieberi v gunnii	B. aculeata	Briza portenschlagii	B. maxima -L.
Brachyscome squalida	B. rigidula	Briza rubens	B. maxima -L.
Brachyscome stricta	B. aculeata	Briza rubra	B. maxima -L.
B. strongylospermoides	B. rigidula	Brodiaea 'Corrina'	Triteleia 'Corrina'
Brachyscome tenella	B. perpusilla	Brodiaea capitata	Dichelostemma
Brachyscome tenera	B. multifida v dilatata		capitatum
Brachysema acuminatum	B. celsianum	Brodiaea congesta	Dichelost. congestum
Brachysema lanceolatum	B. celsianum	Brodiaea douglasii	Triteleia grandiflora
Brachyspatha -Schott	Amorphophallus -	Brodiaea grandiflora	B. coronaria
	Blume	Brodiaea hyacinthina	Triteleia hyacinthina
Brachystephium leucanthemoides	Brachyscome	Brodiaea ida-maia	Dichelost. ida-maia
	diversifolia	Brodiaea ixioides	Triteleia ixioides
Brachytropis	Polygala	Brodiaea laxa	Triteleia laxa
Bracomotia officinarum	Elymus repens	Brodiaea lutea	Triteleia lixioides
Bracteantha	Xerochrysum	Brodiaea peduncularis	Triteleia peduncularis
Bracteantha acuminata	Xerochr. subundulatum	Brodiaea pulchella	Dichelost. capitatum
Bracteantha acuminata -De Candolle	B. subundulata	Brodiaea purdyi	B. minor
Brasenia peltata	B. schreberi	Brodiaea rosea	B. coronaria
Brassaia	Schefflera	Brodiaea uniflora	Ipheion uniflorum
Brassica alba	Sinapsis alba	Brodiaea volubilis	Dichelostemma volubile
Brassica argyi	B. juncea	Bromus burkartii	B. mango
Brassica besseriana	B. juncea	Bromus canadensis	B. ciliatus -L.
Brassica cernua	B. juncea	Bromus catharticus	B. unioloides
Brassica eruca	Eruca vesicaria	Bromus ciliaris	B. ciliatus -L.
Brassica erucoides	Eruca vesicaria	Bromus diandrus	B. rigidus
Brassica hirta	Sinapsis alba	Bromus dudleyi	B. ciliatus -L.
Brassica hispida	Eruca vesicaria	Bromus glabrescens	B. inermis

Synonym	Current Name	Synonym	Current Name
Bromus glomeratus	Dactylis glomerata -L.	Bryophyllum	Kalanchoe
Bromus hordaceus	B. thominii	Bryophyllum daigremontianum	Kalanc. daigremontiana
Bromus macrostachys	B. lanceolatus	Bryophyllum tubiflorum	Kalanchoe delagoensis
Bromus marginatus breviaristatus	B. breviaristatus	Bryophyllum uniflorum	Kalanchoe uniflora
Bromus tatewakii	B. inermis	Buda rubra	Spergularia rubra
Brossea procumbens	Gaultheria procumbens	Buddleia	Buddleja
Broussonetia kaempferi h.	B. kazinoki	Buddleja brevifolia	B. abbreviata
Broussonetia monoica	B. kazinoki	Buddleja curviflora h.	B. japonica -Hemsl.
Broussonetia papyrifera 'Dissecta'	B. papyrif. 'Laciniata'	Buddleja davidii 'Fascination'	B. davidii 'Fascinating'
Broussonetia secundiflora	Sophora secundiflora	Buddleja davidii 'Glasnevin Blue'	B. davidii 'Glasnevin'
Broussonetia sieboldii -Blume	B. kazinoki	B. davidii 'Nanho Petite Indigo'	B. davidii 'Nanho Blue'
Browallia elata	B. americana	B. davidii 'Nanho Petite Purple'	B. d. 'Nanho Purple'
Browallia jamesonii	Streptosolen jamesonii	Buddleja davidii 'Petite Indigo'	B. davidii 'Nanho Blue'
Browallia major h.	B. speciosa	Buddleja davidii 'Petite Plum'	B. d. 'Nanho Purple'
Brownea grandiceps	B. ariza	Buddleja davidii 'Pink Charming'	B. davidii 'Charming'
Brownea princeps	B. ariza	Buddleja davidii 'Pink Delight'	B. 'Pink Delight'
Bruckenthalia	Erica	Buddleja heliophila	B. delavayi
Bruckenthalia spiculifolia	Erica spiculifolia	Buddleja hemsleyana -Koehne	B. albiflora -Hemsl.
Brugmansia 'Variegata Sunset'	B. x candida	B. longifolia -Gagnep. not H.B.K.	B. pterocaulis
	'Variegata'	Buddleja nicodemia	B. madagascariensis
Brugmansia bicolor	B. sanguinea	Buddleja paniculata h.	B. crispa - Benth.
Brugmansia cornigera	B. arborea	Buddleja shimidzuana	B. davidii
Brugmansia meteloides	Datura inoxia	Buddleja sterniana	B. crispa
Brugmansia rosei	B. sanguinea ssp	Buddleja tibetica	B. crispa
	sanguinea v flava	Buddleja tibetica v farreri	B. farreri
Brugmansia sanguinea 'Rosea'	B. x insignis pink	Buddleja variabilis -Hemsl.	B. davidii -Franch.
Brugmansia suaveolens rosea	B. x insignis pink	Buddleja variabilis v nanhoensis	B. davidii v nanhoensis
B. suaveolens x versicolor	B. x insignis	Buddleja x madagasiatica -Pike	B. x lewisiana -Everett
Brugmansia versicolor misapplied	B. arborea	Buergeria stellata	Magnolia stellata
Brugmansia x candida 'Plena'	B. arborea 'Knightii'	Bugula reptans	Ajuga reptans -L.
Brunfelsia bonodora (unv)	B. australis (unv)	Bulbine caulescens	B. frutescens
Brunfelsia calycina	B. pauciflora	Bulbinella setosa	B. cauda-felis
Brunfelsia eximia	B. pauciflora	Bulbinopsis	Bulbine
Brunfelsia hopeana	B. uniflora	Bulbocastanum linnaei	Bunium bulbocastanum
Brunfelsia latifolia (unv)	B. australis (unv)	Bumalda trifolia	Staphylea bumalda
Brunfelsia pauciflora v calycina	B. pauciflora	Bunias cakile	Cakile maritima
Brunnera macrophylla 'Alba'	B. m. 'Betty Bowring'	Bunium carvi	Carum carvi
Brunnera macrophylla 'Variegata'	B. macrophylla	Bunium flexuosum	Conopodium majus
	'Dawson's White'	Buphthalmum angulosum copper	B. longifolium
Brunnera myosotidiflora	B. macrophylla	Buphthalmum flexile	B. salicifolium
Brunsvigia multiflora	B. orientalis	Buphthalmum grandiflorum	B. salicifolium
Brunsvigia rosea 'Minor'	Amaryllis belladonna	Buphthalmum helianthoides	Heliopsis helianthoides
Bryanthus aleuticus	Phyllodoce aleutica	Buphthalmum nutans	Bidens cernua
Bryanthus breweri -A.Gr.	Phyllodoce breweri	B. salicifolium 'Golden Beauty'	B. sal. 'Golden Wonder'
Bryanthus empetriformis	Phyll. empetriformis	Buphthalmum speciosum	Telekia speciosa
Bryanthus erectus -Lindl.	x Phyllothamus erectus	Bupleurum angulosum copper	B. longifolium
Bryanthus glanduliflora	Phyllodoce glanduliflo.	Bupleurum chinense	B. falcatum
Bryanthus musciformis	B. gmelinii -D.Don	Bupleurum chinense octoradiatum	B. octoradiatum
Bryanthus polifolius	Daboecia cantabrica	B. rot. 'Leprechaun Green Gold'	B. rotundifolium 'Green
Bryanthus taxifolius -A.Gr.	Phyllodoce caerulea		Gold'
Bryonia cretica ssp dioica	B. dioica	Bupleurum scorzoneriifolium	B. falcatum
Bryonia grandis	Coccinia grandis	Burchellia capensis	B. bubalina
Bryonia pedunculosa	Herpetospermum	Bursa	Capsella
	pedunculosum	Bursera aloexylon	B. glabrifolia
Bryonia tenuifolia	Abobra tenuifolia	Butea frondosa	B. monosperma

Synonym	Current Name	Synonym	Current Name
Butneria mohrii -Small	Calycanthus mohrii	Cajuputi ericifolia	Melaleuca ericifolia
Buxus 'Newport Blue'	B. sempervirens 'Newport Blue'	Cajuputi hypericifolia	Melaleuca hypericifolia
		Cajuputi leucadendron	Melaleuca leucandra
Buxus arborescens	B. sempervirens	Cajuputi pubescens	Melaleuca lanceolata
Buxus aurea 'Marginata'	B. semp. 'Marginata'	Cajuputi pulchella	Melaleuca pulchella
Buxus colchica	B. sempervirens	Cajuputi wilsonii	Melaleuca wilsonii
Buxus hyrcana	B. sempervirens	Cakile edentula	Cakile maritima
Buxus japonica	B. microphylla v japon.	Caladiopsis Engl.	Chlorospatha -Engl.
Buxus japonica 'Nana'	B. microphylla	Caladium esculentum	Colocasia esculenta
Buxus microphylla 'Asiatic Winter'	B. mic. 'Winter Gem'	Caladium x hortulanum	C. bicolor
Buxus microphylla 'Winter Gem'	B. sinica v insularis 'Winter Gem'	Calamagrostis argentea	Stipa calamagrostis
		Calamagrostis colorata	Phalaris arundinacea
Buxus microphylla v insularis	B. sinica v insularis	Calamagrostis longifolia	Calamovilfa longifolia
Buxus microphylla v koreana	B. sinica v insularis	Calamagrostis splendens misapplied	Stipa calamagrostis
Buxus microphylla v riparia	B. riparia	Calamintha acinos	Acinos arvensis
Buxus microphylla v sinica	B. sinica	Calamintha alpina	Acinos alpinus
Buxus sempervirens 'Argentea'	B. sempervirens 'Argenteovariegata'	Calamintha arvensis	Acinos arvensis
		Calamintha chinensis	Clinopodium chinense
B. semp. 'Aurea Maculata Pendula'	B. sempervirens 'Aurea Pendula' (V)	Calamintha clinopodium	Clinopodium vulgare
		Calamintha corsica	Acinos corsicus
B. sempervirens 'Aurea Maculata'	B. sempervirens 'Argenteovariegata'	Calamintha exigua	Acinos rotundifolius
		Calamintha glabella	C. arkansana
B. sempervirens 'Aurea Marginata'	B. s. 'Marginata'	Calamintha glabra	C. arkansana
Buxus sempervirens 'Aurea'	B. sempervirens 'Argenteovariegata'	Calamintha graveolens	Acinos rotundifolius
		Calamintha hederacea	Glechoma hederacea
B. sempervirens 'Aureomarginata'	B. s. 'Marginata'	Calamintha nepetoides	C. nepeta ssp nepeta
Buxus sempervirens 'Blue Spire'	B. s. 'Blue Cone'	Calamintha nuttallii	C. arkansana
Buxus sempervirens 'Elata'	B. s. 'Angustifolia'	Calamintha officinalis misapplied	C. ascendens
Buxus sempervirens 'Gold Tip'	B. s. 'Notata'	Calamintha sylvatica	C. menthifolia
Buxus sempervirens 'Greenpeace'	B. sempervirens 'Graham Blandy'	Calamintha umbrosa	Clinopodium umbrosum
B. sempervirens 'Handsworthii'	B. sempervirens 'Handsworthensis'	Calamintha vulgaris	Clinopodium vulgare
		Calandrinia caulescens	C. ciliata
Buxus sempervirens 'Horizontalis'	B. s. 'Prostrata'	Calandrinia megarhiza	Claytonia megarhiza
B. sempervirens 'Japonica Aurea'	B. sempervirens 'Latifolia Maculata'	Calandrinia megarhiza v nivalis	Claytonia meg. v nivalis
		Calandrinia menziesii	C. ciliata menziesii
B. sempervirens 'Kingsville Dwarf'	B. micr. 'Compacta'	Calandrinia sibirica	Claytonia sibirica
Buxus sempervirens 'Kingsville'	B. micr. 'Compacta'	Calanthe bicolor	C. discolor v flava
B. sempervirens 'Langley Pendula'	B. s. 'Langley Beauty'	Calanthe striata	C. sieboldii
Buxus sempervirens 'Latifolia'	B. s. 'Bullata'	Calathea albicans	C. micans
Buxus sempervirens 'Longifolia'	B. s. 'Angustifolia'	Calathea discolor	C. lutea
B. sempervirens 'Silver Variegated'	B. s.'Elegantisima'	Calathea insignis	C. lancifolia
Buxus sempervirens 'Thymifolia'	B. s. 'Rosmarinifolia'	Calathea kegeljanii	C. bella
Buxus sempervirens v riparia	B. riparia	Calathea oppenheimiana	Ctenanthe oppenheim.
Cacalia bulbifera	C. farfarifolia	Calathea orbiculata	C. truncata
Cacalia coccinea	Emilia coccinea	Calathea ornata	C. majestica
Cacalia odoratus	Senecio odoratus	Calceolaria acutifolia	C. polyrhiza
Cacalia sagittata	Emilia coccinea	Calceolaria plantaginea	C. biflora
Cacalia sonchifolia	Emilia sonchifolia	Calceolaria rugosa -Ruiz & Pavon	C. integrifolia -Murr.
Cachrys maritima	Crithmum maritimum	Calceolaria scabiosifolia	C. tripartita
Cactus microdasys	Opuntia microdasys	Calceolaria violacea -Cav.	Jovellana violacea
Caesalpinia sepiaria	C. decapetala	Calea leptophylla -Forst. f.	Cassinia leptophylla
Caesalpinia sepiaria v japonica	C. japonica	Calibanus caespitosus -Rose	C. hookeri
Caesalpinia violacea	Jovellana violacea	Calicitrapa jacea	Centaurea jacea -L.
Caesia parviflora vittata	C. vittata	Calicotome infesta	C. villosa

Synonym	Current Name	Synonym	Current Name
Calla aethiopica	Zantedeschia aethiop.	Callitriche virens	C. hermaphroditica
Calla sancta	Arum palaestinum	Callitris arenosa	C. columellaris
Calladium -R.Br.	Caladium -Vent.	Callitris cupressiformis	C. rhomboidea
Callerya reticulata	Millettia reticulata	Callitris glauca	C. columellaris
Calliandra brevipes	C. selloi	Callitris huegelii (unv)	C. glaucophylla
Calliandra inaequilatera	C. haematocephala	Callitris preissii ssp verrucosa	C. verrucosa
Calliandra inermis	Gleditsia triacanthos f inermis	Callitris tasmanica -Benth	C. rhomboidea
		Calluna alpina	C. vulgaris
Callianthemum rutifolium	C. coriandrifolium	Calluna atlantica	C. vulgaris
Callicarpa giraldiana -Schneid.	C. bodinieri v giraldii	Calluna beleziana	C. vulgaris
C. giraldiana v subcanescens	C. bodinieri -Levl.	Calluna brumalis	C. vulgaris
Callicarpa giraldii -Rehd.	C. bodinieri v giraldii	Calluna erica	C. vulgaris
Callicarpa koreana h.	C. dichotoma	Calluna obiensis	C. vulgaris
Callicarpa longifolia -Hemsl.not Lam.	C. japonica v angustata	Calluna oviformis	C. vulgaris
Callicarpa purpurea - Juss.	C. dichotoma	Calluna pyrenaica	C. vulgaris
Callicarpa vastifolia	Viburnum rhytidophyllum	Calluna sagittifolia	C. vulgaris
		Calluna vulgaris 'Alba Elongata'	C. v. 'Mair's Variety'
Callicore rosea	Amaryllis belladonna	Calluna vulgaris 'Alba Flore Pleno'	C. vulgaris 'Plena'
Calligonum canescens	Atriplex canescens	Calluna vulgaris 'Aureifolia'	C. vulgaris 'Hammondii Aureifolia'
Calligonum pallasia	C. aphyllum		
Calliopsis cardaminifolia	Coreopsis tinctoria	Calluna vulgaris 'Camla'	C. v. 'County Wicklow'
Calliopsis tinctoria	Coreopsis tinctoria	C.vulgaris 'Doctor Murray's White'	C. v. 'Mullardoch'
Calliprora ixioides	Triteleia ixioides	C.v. 'Elegantissima Walter Ingwersen'	C.v.'Walter Ingwersen'
Callirhoe lineariloba	C. involucrata	Calluna vulgaris 'Elongata'	C. v. 'Mair's Variety'
Callirhoe pedata	C. leiocarpa	Calluna vulgaris 'Foxii Lett's Form'	C. v. 'Velvet Dome'
Callisace dahurica	Angelica dahurica	Calluna vulgaris 'Hammondii Aurea'	C. vulgaris 'Hammondii Aureifolia'
Callistachys obtusifolia	Chorizema obtusifolium		
Callistemma chinense	Callistephus chinensis	Calluna vulgaris 'Hiemalis Southcote'	C. vulgaris 'Durfordii'
Callistemma hortense	Callistephus chinensis	Calluna vulgaris 'Hirsuta Compacta'	C. v. 'Sister Anne'
Callistemon 'Armidale'	C. pungens	Calluna vulgaris 'J.F.Letts'	C. v. 'John F.Letts'
Callistemon 'Gilesii'	C. pungens	Calluna vulgaris 'Marinka'	C. v. 'Red Carpet'
Callistemon 'Lana'	C. pungens	C. vulgaris 'Mousehole Compact'	C. vulgaris 'Mousehole'
Callistemon 'Severn River'	C. pungens	Calluna vulgaris 'Pepper and Salt'	C. vulgaris 'Hugh Nicholson'
Callistemon 'White Anzac'	C. citrinus 'White Anzac'		
		Calluna vulgaris 'Pink Beale'	C. vulgaris 'H.E.Beale'
Callistemon citrinus 'Albus'	C. cit. 'White Anzac'	Calluna vulgaris 'Rigida Prostrata'	C. vulgaris 'Alba Rigida'
Callistemon glaucus	C. speciosus	Calluna vulgaris 'Rowland Haagen'	C. v. 'Roland Haagen'
Callistemon juniperus	Melaleuca nodosa	Calluna vulgaris 'Serlei Grandiflora'	C. v. 'Serlei Rubra'
Callistemon laevis h.	C. rugulosus	Calluna vulgaris 'Snowball'	C. v. 'My Dream'
Callistemon lanceolatus -(Sm.) DC.	C. citrinus	Calluna vulgaris 'Spring Charm'	C. v. 'Spring Torch'
Callistemon nervosus	Melaleuca nervosa	Calluna vulgaris 'Sunningdale'	C. vulgaris 'Finale'
C. pallidus 'Australflora Candleglow'	C. pall. 'Candle Glow'	Calluna vulgaris 'White Bouquet'	C. vulgaris 'Alba Plena'
Callistemon paludosus	C. sieberi -DC.	Calluna vulgaris 'White Princess'	C. v. 'White Queen'
Callistemon sieberi misapplied	C. pityoides	Calluna vulgaris Red October	C. v. 'Rote Oktober'
Callistephus hortensis	C. chinensis	Calocedrus decurrens 'Nana'	C. dec. 'Depressa'
Callitriche angustifolia	C. hermaphroditica	Calocephalus brownii	Leucophyta brownii
Callitriche autumnalis	C. hermaphroditica	Calochortus caerulens	C. tolmiei
Callitriche bifida	C. hermaphroditica	Calochortus eurycarpus	C. nitidus
Callitriche confervoides	C. hermaphroditica	Calochortus lilacinus	C. uniflorus
Callitriche decussata	C. hermaphroditica	Calochortus luteus -non Dougl.	C. nuttallii
Callitriche foliosa	C. hermaphroditica	Calochortus maweanus	C. tolmiei
Callitriche glomerata	C. hermaphroditica	Calochortus nuttallii aureus	C. aureus
Callitriche sessilis	C. hermaphroditica	Calomeria africana	Helichrysum africanum
Callitriche stellaria	C. hermaphroditica	Calomeria epapposa	Helichr. epapposum
Callitriche verna	C. palustris	Calomeria infausta	Helichrysum infaustum

Synonym	Current Name
Calonyction	Ipomoea
Calonyction aculeatum	Ipomoea alba
Calonyction album	Ipomoea alba
Calostigma -Schott	Philodendron -Schott
Calothamnus suberosus	Melaleuca suberosa
Calothyrsus californica -Spach	Aesculus californica
Caltha alpestris	C. palustris
Caltha alpina	C. palustris
Caltha arctica	C. palustris
Caltha asarifolia	C. palustris
Caltha biflora	C. leptosepala
Caltha cornuta	C. palustris
Caltha fistulosa	C. palustris
Caltha flabelliifolia	C. palustris
Caltha funstonii	C. palustris
Caltha gracilis	C. sinogracilis
Caltha guerangerii	C. palustris
Caltha laeta	C. palustris v palustris
Caltha latifolia	C. palustris
Caltha longirostris	C. palustris
Caltha major -Mill.	C. palustris
Caltha minor	C. palustris v radicans
Caltha minor -Mill.	C. palustris
Caltha napalensis	C. palustris
Caltha pallidiflora	C. palustris
Caltha palustris 'Plena'	C. pal. v pal. 'Plena'
Caltha palustris minor	C. palustris v radicans
Caltha paniculata	C. palustris
Caltha polypetala h.	C. palustris v palustris
Caltha populago	C. palustris
Caltha pumila	C. palustris
Caltha pusilla	C. natans
Caltha radicans	C. palustris v radicans
Caltha ranunculoides	C. palustris
Caltha rostrata	C. palustris
Caltha rotundifolia	C. leptosepala
Caltha zetlandica	C. palustris
Calycanthus chinensis	Sinocalycanthus chin.
Calycanthus fertilis	C. floridus v glaucus
Calycanthus fertilis 'Purpureus'	C. floridus v glaucus 'Purpureus'
Calycanthus fertilis v laevigatus	C. floridus v glaucus
Calycanthus floridus v laevigatus	C. floridus v glaucus
Calycanthus glaucus -Willd.	C. floridus v glaucus
Calycanthus laevigatus -Willd.	C. floridus v glaucus
Calycanthus macrophyllus h.	C. occidentalis
Calycanthus praecox -L.	Chimonanthus praecox
Calycanthus sterilis -Walt.	C. floridus -L.
Calycothrix cuspidata	Calytrix breviseta ssp breviseta
Calydorea speciosa	C. xiphioides
Calypso borealis	C. bulbosa
Calyptridium umbellatum	Spraguea umbellata
Calyptrocoryne -Schott	Theriophonium -Blume
Calyptrostegia angustifolia	Pimelea angustifolia

Synonym	Current Name
Calyptrostegia nervosa	Pimelea angustifolia
Calysphyrum floridum	Weigela florida
Calystegia dahurica	C. pellita
Calystegia japonica 'Flore Pleno'	C. hederacea 'Flore Pleno'
Calythropsis aurea	Calytrix ecalycata
Camara	Lantana
Camassia esculenta -Lindl.	C. quamash
Camassia fraseri	C. scilloides
Camassia leichtlinii 'Alba' h.	C. leichtlinii ssp leicht.
Camassia leichtlinii 'Blauwe Donau'	C. leichtlinii ssp suksdorfii 'Blauwe Donau'
Camassia leichtlinii Blue Danube	C. leichtlinii ssp suksdorfii 'Blauwe Donau'
Camassia suksdorfii Blue Danube	C. leichtlinii ssp suksdorfii 'Blauwe Donau'
Camellia 'Auburn White'	C. japonica 'Mrs Bertha A. Harms'
Camellia 'Baby Face'	C. reticulata 'Tongzimian'
Camellia 'Barchi'	C. japonica 'Contessa Samailoff'
Camellia 'Bertha Harms Blush'	C. japonica 'Mrs Bertha A. Harms'
Camellia 'Chandler's Elegans'	C. japonica 'Elegans'
Camellia 'Contessa Lavinia Maggi'	C. jap. 'Lavinia Maggi'
Camellia 'Cornish Snow Michael'	C. 'Michael'
Camellia 'Cornish Snow Winton'	C. 'Winton'
Camellia 'Czar'	C. jap. 'The Czar'
Camellia 'Dawn'	C. x vernalis 'Ginryu'
Camellia 'Delia Williams'	C. x williamsii 'Citation'
Camellia 'Donckelaeri'	C. japonica 'Masayoshi'
Camellia 'Eclipsis'	C. jap. 'Press's Eclipse'
Camellia 'Faustina Lechi'	C. japonica 'Faustina'
Camellia 'Frau Minna Seidel'	C. japonica 'Otome'
Camellia 'Hiemalis Hiryu'	C. hiemalis 'Kanjiro'
Camellia 'Imbricata Rubra'	C. japonica 'Imbricata'
Camellia 'Jury's Charity'	C. x williamsii 'Charity'
Camellia 'Jury's Yellow'	C. x w. 'Jury's Yellow'
Camellia 'Lavender Queen'	C. sasanqua 'Lavender Queen'
C. 'Madame Victor de Bisschop'	C. japonica 'Le Leys'
Camellia 'Magnolia Queen'	C. j. 'Priscilla Brooks'
Camellia 'Pink Spangles'	C. j. 'Mathotiana Rosea'
Camellia 'Portuense'	C. japonica 'Japonica Variegata'
Camellia 'Robert Fortune'	C. reticulata 'Songzilin'
Camellia 'Salonica'	C. x williamsii 'Shimna'
Camellia 'Splendens'	C. japonica 'Coccinea'
Camellia 'Stella Polare'	C. jap. 'Etoile Polaire'
Camellia 'Tinsie'	C. japonica 'Bokuhan'
Camellia 'Toko'	C. sas. 'Azuma-beni'
Camellia 'Tomorrow Supreme'	C. japonica 'Tomorrow Variegated'
Camellia 'Tricolor Sieboldii'	C. japonica 'Tricolor'

Synonym	Current Name	Synonym	Current Name
Camellia 'Usu-otome'	C. japonica 'Otome'	Camellia japonica 'Mathotiana Rubra'	C. j. 'Julia Drayton'
Camellia 'Waterloo'	C. j. 'Etherington White'	Camellia japonica 'Mermaid'	C. j. 'Kingyo-tsubaki'
Camellia 'Yukihaki'	C. japonica 'Yukishiro'	C. japonica 'Monstruosa Rubra'	C. j. 'Gigantea Red'
Camellia axillaris -Roxb. ex Ker	Gordonia axillaris	Camellia japonica 'Mrs Sander'	C. japonica 'Gauntlettii'
Camellia bohea	C. sinensis	Camellia japonica 'Nagasaki'	C. japonica 'Mikenjaku'
Camellia caudata gracilis	C. gracilis	Camellia japonica 'Nigra'	C. j. 'Konronkoku'
Camellia chrysantha	C. nitidissima v nitidis.	Camellia japonica 'Paul's Apollo'	C. japonica 'Apollo'
Camellia drupifera	C. kissi	Camellia japonica 'Paul's Jupiter'	C. japonica 'Jupiter'
Camellia japonica 'Alba Grandiflora'	C. japonica 'Alba Plena'	Camellia japonica 'Peachblossom'	C. j. 'Fleur Dipater'
Camellia japonica 'Are-jishi'	C. j. 'Beni-arajishi'	Camellia japonica 'Pink Perfection'	C. japonica 'Otome'
Camellia japonica 'Augusto Pinto'	C. japonica 'Augusto Leal de Gouveia Pinto'	Camellia japonica 'Pope Pius IX'	C. japonica 'Prince Eugene Napoleon'
Camellia japonica 'Baron Gomer'	C. j. 'Comte de Gomer'	C. japonica 'Pride of Descanso'	C. japonica 'Yukibotan'
Camellia japonica 'Blackburnia'	C. j. 'Althaeiflora'	Camellia japonica 'Purity'	C. japonica 'Shiragiku'
Camellia japonica 'Bush Hill Beauty'	C. japonica 'Lady de Saumarez'	Camellia japonica 'Purple Emperor'	C. j. 'Julia Drayton'
		Camellia japonica 'Quercifolia'	C. j. 'Kingyo-tsubaki'
C. japonica 'Chandleri Elegans'	C. japonica 'Elegans'	Camellia japonica 'Rainbow'	C. japonica 'O-niji'
Camellia japonica 'Charming Betty'	C. j. 'Funny Face Betty'	Camellia japonica 'Shin-akebono'	C. japonica 'Akebono'
Camellia japonica 'Colonel Firey'	C. japonica 'C.M.Hovey'	Camellia japonica 'Sieboldii'	C. japonica 'Tricolor'
Camellia japonica 'Compton's Brow'	C. japonica 'Gauntlettii'	Camellia japonica 'Silver Moon'	C. japonica 'K. Sawada'
C. japonica 'Contessa Lavinia Maggi'	C. j. 'Lavinia Maggi'	Camellia japonica 'Tinsie'	C. japonica 'Bokuhan'
Camellia japonica 'Daikagura White'	C. japonica 'Shirodaikagura'	Camellia japonica 'Tricolor Red'	C. japonica 'Lady de Saumarez'
Camellia japonica 'Daitairin'	C. j. 'Dewatairin'	C. japonica 'Victor de Bisschop'	C. japonica 'Le Lys'
Camellia japonica 'Devoniensis'	C. japonica 'Devonia'	C. japonica 'Victor Emmanuel'	C. j. 'Blood of China'
Camellia japonica 'Donckelaeri'	C. japonica 'Masayoshi'	Camellia japonica 'Wisley White'	C. j. 'Hakurakuten'
C. japonica 'Duchesse de Rohan'	C. j. 'Preston Rose'	Camellia japonica 'Yoibijin'	C. japonica 'Suibijin'
Camellia japonica 'Effendee'	C. sas. 'Rosea Plena'	Camellia japonica Herme	C. j. 'Hikarugenji'
Camellia japonica 'Elegant Beauty'	C. x w. 'Elegant Beauty'	Camellia japonica ssp rusticana	C. rusticana
Camellia japonica 'Fimbriata Alba'	C. japonica 'Fimbriata'	Camellia maliiflora	C. maliflora
C. japonica 'Fimbriata Superba'	C. j. 'Fred Sander'	Camellia reticulata 'Flore Pleno'	C. reticulata 'Songzilin'
Camellia japonica 'Fishtail'	C. j. 'Kingyo-tsubaki'	Camellia reticulata 'Pagoda'	C. reticulata 'Songzilin'
C. japonica 'General Lamorciere'	C. japonica 'Marguerite Gouillon'	Camellia reticulata 'Semi Plena'	C. ret. 'Captain Rawes'
		Camellia saluenensis 'Apple Blossom'	C. 'Showa-wabisuke'
Camellia japonica 'Glen 40'	C. japonica 'Coquettii'	Camellia saluenensis x japonica	C. x williamsii
Camellia japonica 'Hassaku'	C. j. 'Hassaku-shibori'	Camellia sasanqua 'Bonanza'	C. hiemalis 'Bonanza'
Camellia japonica 'Hatsuzakura'	C. j. 'Dewatairin'	Camellia sasanqua 'Dazzler'	C. hiemalis 'Dazzler'
Camellia japonica 'Joy Sander'	C. j. 'Apple Blossom'	Camellia sasanqua 'Flamingo'	C. sas. 'Fukuzutsumi'
Camellia japonica 'Kellingtoniana'	C. j. 'Gigantea'	Camellia sasanqua 'Flore Pleno'	C. maliflora
Camellia japonica 'Kishu-tsukasa'	C. j. 'Admiral Nimitz'	C. sasanqua 'Sparkling Burgundy'	C. hiemalis 'Sparkling Burgundy'
Camellia japonica 'Kouron-jura'	C. j. 'Konronkoku'		
Camellia japonica 'Lady Clare'	C. japonica 'Akashigata'	Camellia thea -Link.	C. sinensis
Camellia japonica 'Lady Marion'	C. japonica 'Kumasaka'	Camellia theifera -Griff.	C. sinensis
C. japonica 'Lady Vansittart Red'	C. japonica 'Lady Vansittart Pink'	Camellia vernalis 'Dawn'	C. vernalis 'Ginryu'
		Camissonia brevipes	Oenothera brevipes
C. japonica 'Lady Vansittart Shell'	C. j. 'Yours Truly'	Cammarum hyemale	Eranthis hyemalis
Camellia japonica 'Laurel Leaf'	C. j. 'Lalla Rookh'	Campanula 'Elizabeth'	C. takesimana 'Elizabeth'
Camellia japonica 'Lotus'	C. japonica 'Gauntlettii'		
C.jap. 'Madame Victor de Bisschop'	C. japonica 'Madame de Bisschop'	Campanula 'Marion Fisher'	C. x haylodgensis 'Marion Fisher'
Camellia japonica 'Magellan'	C. j. 'Dona Herzilia de Frietas Magalhaes'	Campanula 'Warley White'	C. x h. 'Warley White'
		Campanula 'Warleyensis'	C. x h. 'Warley White'
Camellia japonica 'Magnoliiflora Alba'	C. j. 'Miyakodori'	Campanula abietana	C. patula spp abietana
Camellia japonica 'Magnoliiflora'	C. japonica 'Hagoromo'	Campanula acuminata	C. americana
C. japonica 'Mathotiana Purple King'	C. j. 'Julia Drayton'	Campanula acutangula	C. arvatica

Synonym	Current Name	Synonym	Current Name
Campanula alaskana	C. rotundifolia v alask.	Campanula latisepala	C. rotundifolia
Campanula alliarifolia 'Ivory Bells'	C. alliarifolia	Campanula leutweinii	C. incurva
Campanula allionii	C. alpestris	Campanula linifolia	C. carnica
Campanula alpina ssp orbelica	C. orbelica	Campanula linifolia -not L.	C. rotundifolia
Campanula amabilis 'Planiflora'	C. persicifolia v planif.	Campanula loreyi	C. ramosissima
Campanula asteroides	C. americana	Campanula lunariifolia	C. rapunculoides
Campanula asturica	C. rotundifolia	Campanula macdougalii	C. rotundifolia
Campanula aucheri	C. saxifraga ssp auch.	Campanula medium 'Calycanthema'	C. medium v calycant.
Campanula bellardii	C. cochlearifolia	C. medium 'Cup and Saucer'	C. medium v calycant.
Campanula betulaefolia	C. betulifolia	Campanula microdonta	C. puctata
Campanula bocconei	C. rotundifolia	Campanula minor	C. rotundifolia
Campanula capoduroi	C. rotundifolia	Campanula minuta	C. rotundifolia
Campanula carpatica 'Turbinata'	C. carpatica v turbina.	Campanula morifolia	C. rapunculoides
Campanula carpatica Blue Clips	C. carp. 'Blaue Clips'	Campanula muralis	C. portenschlagiana
Campanula carpatica White Clips	C.c.f alba 'WeisseClips'	Campanula neglecta	C. rapunculoides
Campanula cephallenica	C. garganica ssp cep.	Campanula nitida	C. persicifolia v
C. cochleariifolia 'Warleyensis'	C. x haylodgensis		planiflora
	'Warley White'	Campanula nitida v planiflora	C. persicifolia v planif.
Campanula contracta	C. rapunculoides	Campanula nutans	C. rapunculoides
Campanula cordifolia	C. carpatica	Campanula olympica h.	C. rotundifolia
Campanula cordifolia -K.Koch	C. rapunculoides		'Olympica'
Campanula crenata	C. rapunculoides	Campanula ossetica	Symphyandra ossetica
Campanula crystallocalyx	C. persicifolia	Campanula pallida ssp tibetica	C. cashmeriana
Campanula dasyantha	C. chamissonis	Campanula parviflora -Lam.	C. sibirica
Campanula denticulata	C. betulifolia	Campanula pennina	C. rotundifolia
Campanula dubia	C. rotundifolia	Campanula persicifolia 'Alba Plena'	C. per. 'Alba Coronata'
Campanula elatines fenestrellata	C. fenestrellata	C. persicifolia 'Caerulea Coronata'	C. pers. 'Coronata'
Campanula elatines v garganica	C. garganica	Campanula persicifolia 'Flore Pleno'	C. pers. double blue
Campanula eriocarpa	C. latifolia 'Eriocarpa'	C. persicifolia 'George Chiswell'	C. per. 'Chettle Charm'
Campanula filiformis	C. rotundifolia	Campanula persicifolia 'Hetty'	C. persicifolia
Campanula finitima	C. betulifolia		'Hampstead White'
Campanula garganica 'Aurea'	C. g. 'Dickson's Gold'	C. pers. 'White Cup and Saucer'	C. persicifolia cup and
Campanula gieseckiana -not vest.	C. rotundifolia		saucer white
Campanula glauca	Platycodon	C. persicifolia 'Wortham Belle'	C. persicifolia
	grandiflorus		'Bennett's Blue'
Campanula glomerata 'Nana Alba'	C. gl. v alba 'Alba Nana'	C.a persicifolia ssp sessiliflora	C. latiloba
C. glomerata Crown of Snow	C. glomerata v alba	Campanula persicifolia v nitida	C. persicifolia v planif.
	'Schneekrone'	Campanula petiolata	C. rotundifolia
Campanula grandiflora	Platycodon grandiflor.	Campanula pilosa	C. chamissonis
Campanula grandis	C. latiloba	Campanula pilosa v dasyantha	C. chamissonis
Campanula groenlandica	C. rotundifolia	Campanula planiflora	C. pers. v planiflora
Campanula herzegovinensis	C. hercegovina	Campanula polymorpha	C. rotundifolia
Campanula heterodoxa	C. rotundifolia	C. poscharskyana 'Glandore'	C. 'Glandore'
Campanula heterophylla	C. rotundifolia	Campanula pratensis	C. rotundifolia
Campanula hondoensis	C. puctata	Campanula prenanthoides	Asyneuma prenanth.
Campanula hostii	C. rotundifolia	Campanula punctata v takesimana	C. takesimana
Campanula illinoiensis	C. americana	Campanula pusilla	C. cochleariifolia
Campanula infundibuliformis	C. rapunculoides	Campanula racemosa	C. rotundifolia
Campanula intercedens	C. rotundifolia	Campanula rapunculiformis	C. rapunculoides
C. isophylla 'Mayi' misapplied	C. 'Balchiniana'	Campanula recurva	C. incurva
Campanula isophylla 'Variegata'	C. 'Balchiniana'	Campanula remotiflora	Adenorpha remotiflora
Campanula istriaca	C. garganica	Campanula rhomboidalis -Gorter	C. rapunculoides
Campanula jenkinsae	C. rotundifolia	Campanula rhomboidea -not Murray	C. rapunculoides
Campanula lactiflora alba	C. lactiflora white	Campanula rigida	C. rapunculoides
Campanula langsdorffiana	C. rotundifolia	C. rotundifolia 'Caerulea Plena'	C. rot. 'Flore Pleno'

Synonym	Current Name	Synonym	Current Name
Campanula ruthenica	C. rapunculoides	Canna 'King Midas'	C. 'Richard Wallace'
Campanula sacajaweana	C. rotundifolia	Canna 'Liberte'	C. 'Wyoming'
Campanula scheuchzeri	C. rotundifolia	Canna 'Malawiensis Variegata'	C. 'Striata'
Campanula tatrae	C. rotundifolia	Canna 'Orchid'	C. 'City of Portland'
Campanula trachelioides	C. rapunculoides	Canna 'Pretoria'	C. 'Striata'
Campanula trachelium -not L.	C. puctata	Canna 'Salmon Pink'	C. 'Pfitzer's Salmon Pink'
Campanula triphylla	Adenorpha triphylla		
Campanula tubulosa	C. buseri	Canna 'Striata' misapplied	C. 'Stuttgart'
Campanula turbinata	C. carpatica v turbin.	Canna 'Yellow Humbert' misapplied	C. 'Richard Wallace'
Campanula ucranica	C. rapunculoides	Canna achiras	C. edulis
Campanula urticifolia	C. trachelium -L.	Canna Assault	C. 'Assaut'
Campanula valdensis	C. rotundifolia	Canna edulis	C. indica
Campanula variifolia	C. rotundifolia	Canna esculenta	C. edulis
Campanula velutina	C. lanata	Canna Firebird	C. 'Oiseau de Feu'
Campanula vidalii	Azorina vidalii	Canna iridiflora misapplied	C. x ehemannii
Campanula wanneri	Symphyandra wanneri	Canna King Humbert orange-red	C. 'Roi Humbert'
Campanula wiedmannii	C. rotundifolia	Canna malawiensis 'Variegata'	C. 'Striata'
Campanula x haylodgensis	C. x haylod. 'Plena'	Cannabis chinensis	C. sativa
Campanula x innesii	C. 'John Innes'	Cannabis foetens	C. sativa
Campanula x Symphyandra	Campanula	Cannabis generalis	C. sativa
Campanula x wockei	C. x wockei 'Puck'	Cannabis gigantea	C. sativa
Campanulastrum americanum	Campanula americana	Cannabis indica	C. sativa
Campanumoea	Codonopsis	Cannabis macrosperma	C. sativa
Campe barbarea	Barbarea vulgaris	Cannabis ruderalis	C. sativa
Campe verna	Barbarea verna	Cantua dependens -Pers.	C. buxifolia -Juss.
Campe vulgaria	Barbarea vulgaris	Capnorchis spectabilis	Dicentra spectabilis
Campelia zanonia	Tradescantia zanonia	Capparis rupestris	C. spinosa
Camphoromyrtus behrii	Babingtonia behrii	Capraria lanceolata -L.f.	Freylinia lanceolata
Camphoromyrtus crenulata	Babingtonia crenulata	Caprifolium	Lonicera
Camphoromyrtus pluriflora	Babingtonia pluriflora	Caprifolium occidentale	Lonicera ciliosa
Campsis adrepens -Lour.	Campsis grandiflora	Capsella agrestis	C. bursa-pastoris
Campsis atrosanguinea	Bignonia capreolata 'Atrosanguinea'	Capsella alpestris	C. bursa-pastoris
		Capsella apetala	C. bursa-pastoris
Campsis chinensis -(Lam). Voss	Campsis grandiflora	Capsella bursa	C. bursa-pastoris
Campsis fortunei -Seem.	Paulownia fortunei	Capsella hyrcana	C. bursa-pastoris
Campsis radicans 'Yellow Trumpet'	Campsis rad. f flava	Capsella integrifolia	C. bursa-pastoris
Camptosorus rhizophyllus	Asplenium rhizophyllum	Capsella pastoris	C. bursa-pastoris
Campylandra	Tupistra	Capsella polymorpha	C. bursa-pastoris
Campylopus cerastoides-Spach	Hypericum cerast.	Capsella praecox	C. bursa-pastoris
Canangium odoratum	Cananga odorata	Capsella rubella	C. bursa-pastoris
Canarina campanula	C. canariensis	Capsella ruderalis	C. bursa-pastoris
Canavalia maritima	C. rosea	Capsella sabulosa	C. bursa-pastoris
Candarum -Reich. ex Schott&Endl.	Amorphophallus - Blume	Capsella stenocarpa	C. bursa-pastoris
		Capsella triangularis	C. bursa-pastoris
Candollea	Hibbertia	Capsella virgata	C. bursa-pastoris
Candollea cuneiformis	Hibbertia cuneiformis	Capsicum annuum v acuminatum	C. annuum
Candollea desmophylla	Hibbertia desmophylla	Capsicum annuum v minimum	C. glabriusculum
Candollea fasciculata	Hibbertia depressa	Capsicum microcarpum	C. baccatum
Candollea helianthemoides	Hibbertia helianthem.	Capsicum minimum	C. frutescens
Candollea kochioides	Hibbertia depressa	Capsicum sinense	C. chinense
Candollea teretifolia	Hibbertia hibbertoides	Caragana arborescens v crasse-aculeata -(Bois) R.J.Moore	
Canella alba	C. winterana		C. boissii -Schneid.
Canna 'Confettii'	C. 'Colibri'	C. arborescens v cuneifolia	C. x sophorifolia
Canna 'Durban' orange-flowered	C. 'Tropicanna' (Phaison)	Caragana argentea -Lam.	Halimodendron halodendron

Synonym	Current Name	Synonym	Current Name
Caragana caragana	C. arborescens	Carduus serratuloides	Cirsium serratuloides
Caragana chamlagu -Lam.	C. sinica	Carduus tuberosus	Cirsium tuberosum
Caragana crassicaulis	C. nubigena	Carduus vulgaris	Cirsium vulgare
Caragana cuneifolia -Dipp.	C. x sophorifolia	Carelia houstoniana	Ageratum
Caragana frutescens -DC.	C. frutex - (L). K.Koch		houstonianum
Caragana fruticosa	C. arborescens	Carex 'Evergold'	C. oshimensis
C. gerardiana v glabrescens	C. franchetiana		'Evergold'
C. microphylla v crasse-aculeata	C. boissii -Schneid.	Carex 'Hime-kan-suge'	C. conica
C. pygmaea v grandiflora -Dipp.	C. grandiflora	Carex 'Kan-suge'	C. morrowii
Caragana redowskii -DC.	C. fruticosa	Carex acuta v nigra	C. nigra
Caragana sibirica	C. arborescens	Carex ambusta	C. saxatilis
Caralluma albocastanea	Orbeopsis albocast.	Carex caespitosa	C. nigra
Caralluma dummeri	Pachycymbium dumm.	Carex canadensis	C. lupulina
Caralluma lutea	Orbeopsis lutea	Carex comans 'Small Red'	C. comans 'Taranaki'
Caralluma pillansii	Quaqua pillansii	Carex compacta	C. saxatilis
Carbenia benedicta	Cnicus benedictus	Carex conica 'Hime-kan-suge'	C. conica 'Snowline'
Cardamine asarifolia misapplied	Pachyphragma	Carex cristata -not Clairville	C. cristatella
	macrophyllum	Carex elata 'Bowles' Golden'	C. elata 'Aurea'
Cardamine dasyloba	C. leucantha	Carex forsteri	C. pseudocyperus
Cardamine diphylla	Dentaria diphylla	Carex fortunei	C. morrowii
Cardamine geifolia	C. fauriei	Carex fortunei 'Variegata'	C. m. 'Variegata'
Cardamine laciniata	C. cconcatenata	Carex fraseri	Cymophyllus
Cardamine latifolia -Vahl	C. raphanifolia		fraserianus
Cardamine maxima	Dentaria maxima	Carex fraserianus	Cym. fraserianus
Cardamine micrantha	C. hirsuta	Carex fusca ssp goodenowii	C. nigra
Cardamine multicaulis	C. hirsuta	Carex glauca -Scopoli	C. flacca ssp flacca
Cardamine nasturtiifolia	C. schinziana	Carex goodenowii	C. nigra
Cardamine parviflora	C. hirsuta	Carex granularis v haleana	C. granularis
Cardamine purpurea	C. douglasii	Carex hachijoensis 'Evergold'	C. oshimensis
Cardamine rhomboidea	C. bulbosa		'Evergold'
Cardamine sylvatica	C. flexuosa	Carex haleana	C. granularis
Cardamine tetrandra	C. hirsuta	Carex laevirostris	C. utriculata
Cardamine umbellata	C. oligosperma	Carex longibracteata	C. myosurus
Cardamine umbrosa -not L.	C. hirsuta	Carex longirostris	C. sprengelii
Carduus acanthoides	Cirsium palustre	Carex microsperma	C. vulinoidea
Carduus acaulos	Cirsium acaulon	Carex miliaris	C. saxatilis
Carduus arvensis	Cirsium arvense	Carex morrowii 'Evergold'	C. oshim. 'Evergold'
Carduus benedictus	Cnicus benedictus	Carex morrowii h.	C. hachijoensis
Carduus bulbosus	Cirsium tuberosum	Carex morrowii h.	C. oshimensis
Carduus chailletii	Cirsium palustre	Carex multiflora	C. vulinoidea
Carduus coccinatum	Cirsium drummondii	Carex nigra 'Variegata'	C. nigra 'On-line'
Carduus discolor	Cirsium discolor	Carex ornithopoda 'Aurea'	C. ornith. 'Variegata'
Carduus eriophorus	Cirsium eriophorum	Carex paludosa	C. acutiformis
Carduus lacinatus	Cirsium palustre	Carex physocarpa	C. saxatilis
Carduus lanatus	Cirsium arvense	Carex pulla	C. saxatilis
Carduus lanceolatus	Cirsium vulgare	Carex pulla v laxa	C. saxatilis
Carduus linearis	Cirsium lineare	Carex rectior	C. granularis
Carduus macrocephalus	Jurinea dolomiaea	Carex rhomalea	C. saxatilis
Carduus marianus	Silybum marianum	Carex rhynchophysa	C. utriculata
Carduus muticus	Cirsium muticum	Carex riparia 'Bowles' Golden'	C. elata 'Aurea'
Carduus nemoralis	Cirsium vulgare	Carex rostrata utriculata	C. utriculata
Carduus oblanceolatus	Cirsium oblanceolatus	Carex scabrior	C. vulinoidea
Carduus palustris	Cirsium palustre	Carex secta v tenuiculmis	C. tenuiculmis
Carduus pitcheri	Cirsium pitcheri	Carex setacea	C. vulinoidea
Carduus pumilus	Cirsium drummondii	Carex shriveri	C. granularis

Synonym	Current Name	Synonym	Current Name
Carex stricta -Goodenough	C. elata -All.	Carya alba -Nutt.	C. ovata -(Mill.) K.Koch
Carex stricta 'Aurea'	C. elata 'Aurea'	Carya amara -Nutt.	C. cordiformis
Carex stricta 'Bowles' Golden'	C. elata 'Aurea'	Carya arkansas	C. texana
Carex tentaculata	C. lurida	Carya bickleyi	C. texana
Carissa grandiflora	C. macrocarpa	Carya buckleyi v arkansana	C. texana
Carissa spectabilis	Acokanthera oblongifolia	Carya leiodermis	C. glabra
		Carya magnifloridana	C. glabra
Carlina acaulis v caulescens	C. acaulis ssp simplex	Carya megacarpa	C. glabra
Carlomohria carolina	Halesia carolina	Carya microcarpa -Nutt. in part	C. ovalis
Carmichaelia australis -some	C. arborea	Carya olivaeformis -Nutt.	C. illinoinensis
C. australis v egmontiana	C. egmontiana	Carya ovata australis	C. carolinae-
Carmichaelia australis v grandiflora	C. grandiflora		septentrionalis
Carmichaelia ensyii v orbiculata	C. orbiculata -Colenso	Carya pecan -(Marsh.) Engl. & Graebn. not (Walt.) Nutt.	
Carota sativa	Daucus carota		C. illinoinensis
Carota sylvestris	Daucus carota	Carya porcina -Nutt.	C. glabra -(Mill.) Sweet
Carpesium hieracioides	C. glossophyllum	Carya sulcata -Nutt.	C. laciniosa
Carpesium thunbergianum	C. abrotanoides	Carya texana v arkansana	C. texana
Carpinus americana -Michx.	C. caroliniana -Walt.	Carya villosa	C. texana
Carpinus betulus 'Pyramidalis'	C. betulus 'Fastigiata'	Caryophyllus	Syzigium
Carpinus caucasica	C. betulus	Caryopteris mastacanthus -Schau	C. incana
Carpinus duinensis -Scop.	C. orientalis -Mill.	Caryopteris sinensis	C. incana
Carpinus fargesii	C. viminea	Caryopteris tangutica -Maxim.	C. incana -(Houtt.) Miq.
Carpinus fargesii -Franch.	C. laxiflora v macrostachya -Oliver	Cassandra	Chamaedaphne
		Cassebeera atropurpurea	Pellaea atropurpurea
Carpinus laxiflora v microstachya	C. viminea	Cassia acclinis	Senna acclinis
Carpinus ostrya -L. in part	Ostrya carpinifolia	Cassia aciphylla	Senna aciphylla
Carpinus ostrya -L. in part	Ostrya virginiana	Cassia alata	Senna alata
Carpinus tschonoskii v henryana	C. henryana	Cassia angustifolia	Senna alexandrina
Carpinus virginiana -Mill.	Ostrya virginiana	Cassia arboresens	Senna surattensis ssp
Carpinus yedoensis -Maxim.	C. tschonoskii -Maxim.		sulfurea
Carpobrotus chilensis	C. aequilateralus	Cassia artemisoides	Senna artemisoides
Carpobrotus crystallinum	Mesembryanthemum crystallinum	Cassia artemisoides ssp circinnata	Senna circinnata
		Cassia artemisoides ssp glaucifolia	Senna glaucifolia
Carpodontos lucida	Eucryphia lucida	C.artemisoides ssp hamersleyensis	Senna hamersleyensis
Carpodontos lucida -Labill.	Eucryphia lucida	Cassia artemisoides ssp symonii	Senna symonii
Carpogymnia dryopteris	Gymnocarpium dryop.	Cassia artemisoides v eremophila	Senna artemisoides
Carum anisum	Pimpinella anisum		ssp petiolaris
Carum aromaticum	C. carvi	Cassia artemisoides v phyllodinea	Senna artemisoides
Carum bulbocastanum	Bunium persicum		ssp petiolaris
Carum copticum	Trachyspermum ammi	Cassia australis	Senna barronfieldii
Carum decussatum	C. carvi	Cassia australis v glaucescens	Senna costata
Carum ferulaefolium	Bunium ferulaceum	Cassia australis v revoluta	Senna aciphylla
Carum gairdneri	Perideridia gairdneri	Cassia barclayana	Senna barclayana
Carum gracile	C. carvi	Cassia barclayana v barclayana	Senna barclayana
Carum graveolens	Apium graveolens	Cassia barclayana v pubescens	Senna clavigera
Carum officinale	C. carvi	Cassia barronfieldii	Senna barronfieldii
Carum origanum	Perideridia oregana	Cassia brewsteri v sylvestris	C. queenslandica
Carum petroselinum	Petroselinum crispum	Cassia caniculata	Senna artemisoides
Carum podagraria	Aegopodium podagr.		ssp zygophylla
Carum rosellum	C. carvi	Cassia cardiosperma	Senna cardiosperma
Carum segetum	Petroselinum segetum	C. cardiosperma ssp cuthbertsonii	Senna cuthbertsonii
Carum sisarum	Sium sisarum	Cassia cardiosperma ssp flexuosa	Senna flexuosa
Carum velenovskyi	C. carvi	Cassia cardiosperma ssp manicula	Senna manicula
Carvi careum	Carum carvi	Cassia cardiosperma ssp pilocarina	Senna pilocarina
Carya alba -K.Koch not Nutt	C. tomentosa	Cassia cardiosperma ssp stowardii	Senna stowardii

Synonym	Current Name	Synonym	Current Name
Cassia chamaecrista	Chamaecrista fasciculata	Cassia nemophila v zygophylla	S. art. ssp zygophylla
		Cassia neurophylla	Senna goniodes
Cassia charlesiana	Senna charlesiana	Cassia nigricans	Chamaecrista
Cassia circinata	Senna circinata		nigricans
Cassia cladophylla	Senna cladophylla	Cassia nomame	Chamaecrista nomame
Cassia coluteoides	Senna pendula	Cassia notabilis	Senna notabilis
Cassia concinna	Chamaecrista concinna	Cassia obtusa	Senna septemtrionalis
Cassia coronilloides	Senna coronilloides	Cassia obtusa	Senna x floribunda
Cassia corymbosa	Senna corymbosa	Cassia obtusifolia	Senna obtusifolia
Cassia corymbosa -Lam.	Senna corymbosa	Cassia occidentalis	Senna occidentalis
Cassia corymbosa v plurijuga	Senna x floribunda	Cassia occidentalis v schinifolia	Senna barclayana
Cassia costata	Senna costata	Cassia odorata	Senna barronfieldii
Cassia curvistyla	Senna curvistyla	Cassia oligoclada v goniodes	Senna goniodes
Cassia cuthbertsonii	Senna cuthbertsonii	Cassia oligoclada v gracilis	Senna oligoclada
Cassia deplanchei	Senna gaudichaudii	Cassia oligoclada v oligoclada	Senna oligoclada
Cassia desolata v involucrata	Senna artemisioides ssp helmsii	Cassia oligoclada v subsinguliflora	Senna goniodes
		Cassia oligophylla v sericea	Senna sericea
Cassia didymobotrya	Senna didymobotrya	Cassia phyllodinea	Senna artemisoides ssp petiolaris
Cassia enneaphylla	Senna surattensis ssp sulfurea	Cassia planitiicola	Senna planitiicola
Cassia excelsa	C. fistula	Cassia platypoda	Senna artemisoides ssp petiolaris
Cassia fasciculata	Chamaecrista fascicul.		
Cassia fastigiata	Senna surattensis	Cassia pleurocarpa	Senna pluerocarpa
Cassia ferraria	Senna ferraria	Cassia pleurocarpa v angustifolia	Senna pleuroc. v ang.
Cassia fistuloides	C. fistula	Cassia pleurocarpa v longifolia	Senna pleuroc. v long.
Cassia floribunda	Senna x floribunda	Cassia pruinosa	S. glutinosa ssp pruin.
Cassia gaudichaudii	Senna gaudichaudii	Cassia retusa	Senna gaudichaudii
Cassia glauca	Senna surattensis ssp sulfurea	Cassia retusa v dietrichiae	Senna gaudichaudii
		Cassia retusa v retusa	Senna gaudichaudii
Cassia glauca v koenigii	Senna surattensis	Cassia retusa v typica	Senna gaudichaudii
Cassia glauca v suffruticosa	Senna surattensis	Cassia revoluta	Senna aciphylla
Cassia glutinosa	Senna glutinosa	Cassia rhombifolia	C. fistula
Cassia glutinosa ssp ferraria	Senna ferraria	Cassia robusta	Chamaecrista fasciculata
Cassia goniodes	Senna goniodes		
Cassia hamersleyensis	Senna hamersleyensis	Cassia rotundifolia	C. fistula
Cassia harneyi	Chamaecrista nigricans	Cassia schinifolia	Senna barclayana
		Cassia senna	Senna alexandrina
Cassia heptanthera	Senna heptanthera	Cassia siamea	Senna siamea
Cassia heteroloba	Senna artemisoides ssp petiolaris	Cassia sophera	Senna clavigera
		Cassia sophera v barclayana	Senna barclayana
Cassia hirsuta	Senna hirsuta	Cassia sophera v clavigera	Senna clavigera
Cassia horsfelddii	Senna gaudichaudii	Cassia sophera v pubescens	Senna clavigera
Cassia indecora v glabrata	Senna pendula v glab.	Cassia sophera v schinifolia	Senna barclayana
Cassia lancifolia	Senna barclayana	Cassia stowardii	Senna stowardii
Cassia leptoclada	Senna leptoclada	Cassia sturtii	Senna artemisoides ssp sturtii
Cassia longipes	Chamaecrista longipes		
Cassia magnifolia	Senna magnifolia	Cassia sturtii v coriacea	S. art. ssp coriacea
Cassia manicula	Senna manicula	Cassia sturtii v involucrata	S. art. ssp helmsii
Cassia marilandica	Senna marilandica	Cassia sturtii v tomentosa	S. art. ssp helmsii
Cassia marksiana	C. brewsteri v marks.	Cassia suffruticosa	Senna surattensis
Cassia medsgeri	Senna marilandica	Cassia sulfurea	S. surattensis ssp sulf.
Cassia mimosoides ssp nomame	Chamaecrista nomame	Cassia surattensis	Senna surattensis
Cassia nemophila	S. art. ssp coriacea	Cassia surattensis ssp suffruticosa	Senna surattensis
Cassia nemophila v coriacea	S. art. ssp coriacea	Cassia teretifolia	S. art. ssp artem.
Cassia nemophila v platypoda	S. art. ssp petiolaris	Cassia teretiuscula	Senna art. ssp artem.

Synonym	Current Name	Synonym	Current Name
Cassia timorensis	Senna timorensis	Casuarina dielsiana	Allocasuarina dielsiana
Cassia tomentella	C. brewsteri v tom.	Casuarina distyla	Allocasuarina distyla
Cassia tomentosa	C. multiglandulosa	Casuarina distyla v paludosa	Allocasuarina paludosa
Cassia tora	Senna tora	Casuarina distyla v prostrata	Allocasuarina paludosa
Cassia tora v obtusifolia	Senna obtusifolia	Casuarina distyla v rigida	Allocasuarina rigida
Cassia venusta	Senna vensuta	Casuarina dorrienii	Allocasuarina
Cassia x floribunda	Senna x floribunda		huegeliana
Cassia zygophylla	S. art. ssp zygophylla	Casuarina drummondiana	Allocasuarina drumm.
Cassine magellanica -Lam.	Maytenus magellanica	Casuarina echinata	Allocas. thuyoides
Cassinia fulvida	C. leptophylla ssp fulv.	C. equisetifolia v equisetifolia	C. equisetifolia ssp eq.
Cassinia fulvida -(Hook f.)	C. leptophylla ssp fulv.	Casuarina equisetifolia v incana	C. equisetifolia ssp inc.
Cassinia vauvilliersii	C. lep. ssp vauvilliersii	Casuarina equisetifolia v typica	C. equisetifolia ssp eq.
Cassiope 'Askival Freebird'	C. Freebird Group	Casuarina ericoides	Allocasuarina torulosa
Cassiope 'Askival Snow-wreath'	C. Snow-wreath Group	Casuarina excelsa	Allocas. verticillata
Cassiope oxycoccoides -A.Gr.	Pieris nana	Casuarina fibrosa	Allocasuarina fibrosa
Cassiope rigida h.	C. lycopodioides	Casuarina fraseriana	Allocasuarina fraser.
	'Rigida'	Casuarina glauca	C. obtusa
Castalia alba	Nymphaea alba	Casuarina grevilleoides	Allocasuarina grevill.
Castalia speciosa	Nymphaea alba	Casuarina gunnii	Allocas. verticillata
Castanea americana -Raf.	C. dentata	Casuarina helmsii	Allocasuarina helmsii
Castanea arkansana -Sarg.	C. ozarkensis -Ashe	Casuarina horrida	Allocas. corniculata
Castanea ashei	C. pumila v ashei	Casuarina huegeliana	Allocas. huegeliana
Castanea bungeana -Blume	C. mollissima -Blume	Casuarina humilis	Allocasuarina humilis
Castanea castanea	C. dentata	Casuarina humilis v humilis	Allocasuarina humilis
Castanea chrysophylla -Hook.	Chrysolepis chrysop.	Casuarina humilis v macrocarpa	Allocasuarina humilis
Castanea duclouxii -Dode	C. mollissima -Blume	Casuarina incana	C. equisetifolia ssp inc.
Castanea hupehensis -Dode	C. mollissima -Blume	Casuarina inophloia	Allocasuarina inophloia
Castanea japonica -Blume	C. crenata	Casuarina lehmanniana	Allocasuarina lehmann.
Castanea nana -Muhl.	C. alnifolia -Nutt.	Casuarina leidophloia	C. cristata
C. sativa 'Argenteovariegata'	C. sat. 'Albomarginata'	Casuarina leptoclada	Allocasuarina littoralis
Castanea sativa 'Aureomarginata'	C. sativa 'Variegata'	Casuarina leptotrema	Allocasuarina helmsii
Castanea sativa 'Macrocarpa'	C. s. 'Marron de Lyon'	Casuarina littoralis	Allocasuarina littoralis
Castanea sativa v americana	C. dentata	Casuarina luehmannii	Allocasuarina luehman.
Castanea sempervirens -Kellogg	Chrysolepis semperv.	Casuarina lugubris	Allocasuarina torulosa
Castanea vesca -Gaertn.	C. sativa -Mill.	Casuarina macrocarpa	Allocas. verticillata
Castanea vulgaris -Lam.	C. sativa -Mill.	Casuarina microstachya	Allocas. microstachya
Castanopsis chrysophylla -Hook.	Chrysolepis chrysop.	Casuarina microstrobilis	A. lehmanniana ssp leh.
Castanopsis henryi -Skan	Castanea henryi	Casuarina moesta	Allocasuarina littoralis
Castanopsis sempervirens	Chrysolepis semperv.	Casuarina monilifera	Allocas. monilifera
Castilleja acuminata	C. setentrionalis	Casuarina muelleriana	Allocas. muelleriana
Casuarina acuaria	Allocasuarina acuaria	Casuarina nana	Allocasuarina nana
Casuarina acutivalvis	Allocasuarina acutiv.	Casuarina paludosa	Allocasuarina paludosa
Casuarina baxteriana	Allocasuarina lehman	Casuarina paludosa v paludosa	Allocasuarina paludosa
	niana ssp lehmanniana	Casuarina paludosa v robusta	A. mackliniana ssp m.
Casuarina bicuspidata	Allocasuarina paludosa	Casuarina paradoxa	Allocasuarina parad.
Casuarina cambagei	C. cristata	Casuarina pinaster	Allocasuarina pinaster
Casuarina campestris	Allocasuarina camp.	Casuarina preissiana	Allocasuarina humilis
C. campestris ssp eriochlamys	Allocasuarina eriochl.	Casuarina prinsepiana	A. acutivalvis ssp prin.
Casuarina campestris ssp grossa	Allocasuarina eri	Casuarina pumila	Allocasuarina paludosa
	ochlamys ssp grossa	Casuarina pumila v hirtella	Allocasuarina paludosa
C. campestris ssp tessellata	Allocasuarina tessell.	Casuarina pusilla	Allocasuarina pusilla
Casuarina corniculata	Allocasuarina cornic.	Casuarina quadrivalvis	Allocas. verticillata
Casuarina cristata v pauper	C. pauper	Casuarina quadrivalvis v cristata	C. cristata
Casuarina decaisneana	Allocasuarina decaisn.	C. quadrivalvis v macrocarpa	Allocas. verticillata
Casuarina decussata	Allocasuarina decuss.	C. quadrivalvis v quadrivalvis	Allocas. verticillata

57

Synonym	Current Name	Synonym	Current Name
C. quadrivalvis v spectabilis	Allocas. verticillata	Caucalis daucoides	C. platycarpa
Casuarina ramosissima	Allocas. ramosissima	Caucalis daucus	Daucua carota
Casuarina rigida	Allocasuarina rigida	Caucalis gingidium	Daucua carota
Casuarina scleroclada	Allocas. scleroclada	Caucalis gummifera	Daucua carota
Casuarina selaginoides	Allocasuarina humilis	Caucalis hispanica	Daucua carota
Casuarina spinosissima	Allocas. spinosissima	Caucalis lappula	C. platycarpa
Casuarina stowardii	Allocas. acutivalvis	Caulinia flexilis	Najas flexilis
Casuarina stricta	Allocas. verticillata	Caulinia glabrata	Kennedia glabrata
Casuarina stricta v fraseriana	Allocas. fraseriana	Caulinia macrophylla	Kennedia macrophylla
Casuarina stricta v rigida	Allocasuarina rigida	Cautleya lutea	C. gracilis
Casuarina stricta v stricta	Allocas. verticillata	Cavendishia bracteata	C. acuminata
Casuarina suberosa	Allocasuarina littoralis	Cayratia thomsonii	Parthenocissus thoms.
Casuarina suberosa v baxteriana	Allocasuarina lehman niana ssp lehmanniana	Ceanothus 'Brilliant'	C. x veitchianus
		Ceanothus 'Comtesse de Paris'	C. x delileanus 'Comtesse de Paris'
Casuarina suberosa v muelleriana	Allocas. muelleriana	Ceanothus 'Diamond Heights'	C. griseus v horizontal is 'Diamond Heights'
Casuarina suberosa v suberosa	Allocasuarina littoralis		
Casuarina suberosa v typica	Allocasuarina littoralis	Ceanothus 'Edinensis'	C. 'Edinburgh'
Casuarina tenuissima	Allocasuarina torulosa	Ceanothus 'Point Millerton'	C. thyrsiflorus 'Millerton Point'
Casuarina tephrosperma	Allocasuarina humilis		
Casuarina tessellata	Allocas. tessellata	Ceanothus 'Snow Flurries'	C. thyrs. 'Snow Flurry'
Casuarina thuyoides	Allocas. thuyoides	Ceanothus 'Yankee Point'	C. griseus v horizontal is 'Yankee Point'
Casuarina torulosa	Allocasuarina torulosa		
Casuarina torulosa f gracilior	Allocas. fraseriana	Ceanothus 'Zanzibar'	C. 'Pershore Zanzibar'
Casuarina torulosa f torulosa	Allocasuarina torulosa	Ceanothus azureus -Desf.	C. coeruleus -Lag.
Casuarina trichodon	Allocas. trichodon	Ceanothus cuneatus v ramulosus	C. ramulosus
Casuarina verticillata	Allocas. verticillata	Ceanothus dentatus 'Russellianus'	C. x lobbianus 'Russellianus'
Catalpa bignonioides 'Aureomarginata'	C. bignon. 'Koehnei'		
		Ceanothus dentatus misapplied	C. x lobbianus
Catalpa bignonioides 'Purpurea'	C. x erubescens 'Purpurea'	Ceanothus dentatus v floribundus h.	C. x veitchianus
		Ceanothus dentatus v impressus	C. impressus
Catalpa duclouxii -Dode	C. fargesii f douclouxii	Ceanothus floribundus -Hook.	C. dentatus v floribun dus -(Hook.) Trel.
Catalpa henryi	C. ovata		
Catalpa kaempferi -Sieb.	C. ovata -G.Don	Ceanothus herbaceus	C. ovatus
Catalpa sutchuensis -Dode	C. fargesii f douclouxii	Ceanothus impressus 'Puget Blue'	C. 'Puget Blue'
Catalpa syringaefolia -Sims	C. bignonioides -Walt.	C. integerrimus v parvifolius	C. parvifolius
Catalpa teasii -Dode	C. x erubescens -Carr.	Ceanothus intermedius	C. americanus
Catalpa vestita -Diels	C. fargesii -Bureau	Ceanothus jepsonii v purpureus	C. purpureus -Jeps.
Catalpa x hybrida -Spaeth	C. x erubescens -Carr.	Ceanothus macrophyllus	C. americanus
Catananche propinqua	C. caerulea -L.	Ceanothus officinalis	C. americanus
Cataria vulgaris	Nepeta cataria	Ceanothus oreganus -Nutt.	C. sanguineus -Pursch
Catenaria caudata	Desmodium caudatum	Ceanothus prostratus v divergens	C. divergens -Parry
Cathartocarpus excelsus	Cassia fistula	Ceanothus prostratus v grandifolius	C. gloriosus
Cathartocarpus fistula	Cassia fistula	Ceanothus prostratus v profugus	C. pumilus -Greene
Cathartocarpus fistuloides	Cassia fistula	Ceanothus repens	C. thyrsiflorus v rep.
Cathartocarpus rhombifolius	Cassia fistula	Ceanothus rigidus	C. cuneatus v rigidus
Cathcartia villosa	Meconopsis villosa	Ceanothus rigidus v pallens -Sprag.	C. rigidus -Nutt.
Cattleya aurea	Cattleya dowiana	Ceanothus tardiflorus	C. americanus
Cattleya guatemalensis	Cattleya deckeri	Ceanothus thyrsiflorus v griseus	C. griseus
Cattleya labiata v dowiana	Cattleya dowiana	Ceanothus trinervius	C. americanus
Cattleya labiata v mossiae	Cattleya mossiae	Ceanothus virgatius	C. americanus
Cattleya Mother's Favourite	Cattleya 'Jose Marti'	Ceanothus x pallidus 'Albus Plenus'	C. x pallidus 'Plenus'
Caucalis abyssinica	Daucua carota	Ceanothus x regius 'Cynthia Postan'	C. 'Cynthia Postan'
Caucalis anthriscus	Torilis japonica	Cebatha carolina -(L.) Britton	Coccolus carolinus
Caucalis carnosa	Daucua carota	Cebatha orbiculata -O.Kuntze	Coccolus orbiculatus
Caucalis carota	Daucua carota		

Synonym	Current Name
Cedrela sinensis -Juss.	Toona sinensis
Cedronella cana	Agastache cana
Cedronella foeniculum	Agastache foeniculum
Cedronella japonica	Agastache rugosa
Cedronella mexicana	Agastache mexicana
Cedronella mississippiensis -Bosc.	C. laevigata
C. occidentalis v crassifolia .	C. occ. v cordata
Cedronella triphylla	C. canariensis
Cedrus deodara 'Prostrata'	C. deodora 'Pendula'
Cedrus deodara 'Pygmaea'	C. deodora 'Pygmy'
Cedrus deodara v robusta	C. deodara 'Robusta'
Cedrus libani 'Pendula Sargentii'	C. libani 'Sargentii'
Cedrus libani ssp atlantica	C. atlantica
Cedrus libani ssp atlantica f glauca	C. atl. Glauca Group
Cedrus libani v brevifolia -Hook. f.	C. brevifolia
Cedrus libanitica -Trew	C. libani -A.Richard
Celastrus alatus -Thunb.	Euonymus alatus
Celastrus articulatus -Thunb.	C. orbiculatus -Thunb.
Celastrus hypoglaucus -Hemsl.	C. hypoleucus
Celastrus japonica -(Thunb.) K.Koch	Orixa japonica -Thunb.
Celastrus latifolius -Hemsl.	C. angulatus
Celastrus paniculatus	C. dependens
Celastrus punctatus	C. orbiculatus v punct.
Celastrus spiciformis	C. vaniotii -(Levl) Rehd.
Celeria graveolens	Apium graveolens
Celmisia coriacea misapplied	C. semicordata
Celmisia coriacea Raoul	C. mackaui
Celmisia webbiana	C. walkeri
Celmisia webbii	C. walkeri
Celosia cristata	C. argentea v cristata
Celosia margaritacea -L.	C. argentea -L.
Celosia pyramidalis	C. argentea v cristata
Celosia swinhoei -Hemsl.	C. argentea -L.
Celsia	Verbascum
Celsia acaulis	Verbascum acaule
Celsioverbascum	Verbascum
Celtis aurantiaca	C. koraiensis
Celtis bungeana v jessoensis	C. jessoensis
Celtis davidiana -Carr.	C. bungeana -Blume
Celtis helleri	C. lindheimeri
Celtis japonica	C. sinensis
Celtis laevigata reticulata	C. reticulata
Celtis mississippiensis -Bosc.	C. laevigata -Willd.
Celtis muka -Sieb.	Aphananthe aspera
Celtis occidentalis v crassifolia	C. occ. v cordata
Celtis pumila -(Muhl.) Pursh	C. occidentalis v pumila
Celtis serotina	C. tetandra
Celtis trinervi	C. tetandra
Cenchrus longisetus	Pennisetum villosum
Cenekia rapunculoides	Campanula rapuncul.
Centaurea 'Pulchra Major'	Stemmacantha centauroides
Centaurea albertii	C. scabiosa -L.
Centaurea angustifolia -Mill.	C. montana -L.
Centaurea aterrima	C. nigra -L.

Synonym	Current Name
Centaurea badensis	C. scabiosa -L.
Centaurea borealis	C. scabiosa -L.
Centaurea calcarea	C. scabiosa -L.
Centaurea cana	C. triumfettii ssp cana
Centaurea candidissima -Lamarck	C. rutifolia
Centaurea candidissima h.	C. cineraria
Centaurea commutata	C. jacea
Centaurea consimilis -sensu	C. nigra -L.
Centaurea coriacea	C. scabiosa -L.
Centaurea cyaneum	C. cyanus
Centaurea cyanocephala	C. cyanus
Centaurea cynaroides	Leuzea centauroides
Centaurea decipiens	C. jacea
Centaurea fischeri	C. cheiranthifolia v purpurascens
Centaurea gymnocarpa	C. cineraria
Centaurea integrifolia	C. nigra -L.
Centaurea jungens	C. jacea
Centaurea lanata	C. cyanus
Centaurea mixta	C. raphanina
Centaurea monantha	Rhaponticum uniflorum
Centaurea montana 'Rosea'	C. montana 'Carnea'
Centaurea moschata	Amberboa moschata
Centaurea nervosa	C. uniflora ssp nervosa
Centaurea obscura	C. nigra -L.
Centaurea pulchra	C. cyanus
Centaurea pygmaea	C. depressa
Centaurea rhapontica	Leuzea rhapontica
Centaurea segetalis	C. cyanus
Centaurea stricta	C. triumfettii ssp stric.
Centaurea suaveolens	Amberboa moschata
Centaurea subjacea	C. jacea
Centaurea tatrae	C. scabiosa -L.
Centaurea thuillier	C. jacea
Centaurea umbrosa	C. cyanus
Centaurea variifolia	C. scabiosa -L.
Centaurea vertesensis	C. scabiosa -L.
Centaurium chloodes	C. confertum
Centaurium minus	C. erythraea
Centaurium portense	C. scilloides
Centaurium umbellatum	C. erythraea
Centipeda minuta	C. minima
Centipeda orbicularis	C. minima
Centradenia rosea	C. inaequilateralis
Cephalaria tatarica	C. gigantea
Cephalocereus euphorbioides	Neobuxbaumia euphor.
Cephalonoplos arvense	Cirsium arvense
Cephalotaxus drupacea	C. harringtonia v drup.
Cephalotaxus drupacea 'Prostrata'	C. harrin. 'Prostrata'
C. drupacea v pedunculata	C. harrin. v drupacea
Cephalotaxus drupacea v sinensis	C. harringtonia v sin.
Cephalotaxus fortunei 'Prostrata'	C. fortunei 'Prostrate Spreader'
Cephalotaxus pedunculata	C. harringtonia
Cephalotaxus sinensis	C. harringtonia v sin.

Synonym	Current Name	Synonym	Current Name
Cerastium aquaticum	Myosoton aquaticum	C. magnificum f pendulum	C. japonicum f pendul.
Cerastium atratum	C. alpinum	Cercinthodes virginicum	Mertensia virginica
Cerastium columnae	C. tomentosum -L.	Cercis japonica	C. chinensis
Cerastium elatum	C. tomentosum -L.	Cercis occidentalis	C. canadensis v occ.
Cerastium glomeratum	C. viscosum	Cercis siliquastrum 'Alba'	C. siliquastrum f albida
Cerastium lanatum	C. alpinum v lanatum	Cercocarpus alnifolius	C. montanus
Cerastium longifolium	C. tomentosum -L.	Cercocarpus betulifolius -Hook.	C. betuloides
Cerastium repens	C. biebersteinii	Cercocarpus breviflorus	C. montanus v
Cerastium squalidum	C. alpinum		paucidentatus
Cerastium triviale	C. holosteoides	C. parvifolius -Hook. & Arn. in part	C. montanus -Raf.
Cerastium villosum	C. alpinum v lanatum	Cercocarpus parvifolius v glaber	C. betuloides
Cerastium vulgatum hallaisanense	C. fontanum	Cercocarpus traskiae -Eastw.	C. betuloides v traski.
Cerasus acuminata	Prunus undulata	Cerefolium fabricius	Anthriscus sylvestris
Cerasus campanulata	Prunus campanulata	Cerefolium sylvestris	Anthriscus sylvestris
Cerasus cerasoides	Prunus cerasoides	Cereus emoryi	Bergerocactus emoryi
Cerasus clarofolia	Prunus pilosiuscula	Cereus flagelliformis	Aporocactus flagellif.
Cerasus communis -Poit. & Turpin	Prunus cerasus -L.	Cereus forbesii	C. validus
Cerasus demissa	Prunus virginiana dem.	Cereus gigantea	Carnegiea gigantea
Cerasus dielsiana	Prunus dielsiana	Cereus peruvianus h.	C. uruguayanus
Cerasus fruticosa	Prunus fruticosa	Cereus undatus	Hylocereus undatus
Cerasus glandulosa	Prunus glandulosa	Ceriman	Monstera deliciosa
Cerasus gondouinii -Poit. & Turpin	Prunus x gondouinii	Cerinthe alpina	C. glabra
Cerasus humilis	Prunus humilis	Ceropegia disticha ssp haygarthii	C. haygarthii
Cerasus incana	Prunus incana	Ceropegia lanceolata	C. longifolia
Cerasus incisa	Prunus incisa	Ceropegia purpureum	C. elegans
Cerasus japonica	Prunus japonica	Ceropegia sandersoniae	C. sandersonii
Cerasus laurocerasus	Prunus laurocerasus	Ceropegia woodii	C. linearis ssp woodii
Cerasus lyonii	Prunus lyonii	Cervispina cathartica	Rhamnus cathartica
Cerasus mahaleb	Prunus mahaleb	Cestrum purpureum	C. elegans
Cerasus maximowiczii	Prunus maximowiczii	Cestrum purpureum misapplied	Iochroma cyaneum
Cerasus napaulensis	Prunus napaulensis		'Trebah'
Cerasus nigra	Prunus avium	Cestrum violaceum misapplied	Iochroma c. 'Trebah'
Cerasus pensylvanica	Prunus pensylvanica	Ceterach	Asplenium
Cerasus prostrata	Prunus prostrata	Ceterach officinarum	Asplenium ceterach
Cerasus pseudocerasus	Prunus pseudocerasus	Chaenomeles lagenaria	C. speciosa
Cerasus serrula	Prunus serrula	C. lagenaria v cathayensis	C. cathayensis
Cerasus serrulata	Prunus serrulata	Chaenomeles lagenaria v wilsonii	C. cathayensis
Cerasus subhirtella	Prunus subhirtella	Chaenomeles maulei	C. japonica
Cerasus sylvestris	Prunus avium	Chaenomeles sinensis	Pseudocydonia sinens.
Cerasus sylvestris -Lund.	Prunus avium -L.	C. speciosa 'Apple Blossom'	C. sp. 'Moerloosei'
Cerasus tomentosa	Prunus tomentosa	Chaenomeles speciosa 'Choshan'	C. x superba 'Yaegaki'
Cerasus vulgaris -Mill.	Prunus cerasus -L.	Chaenomeles vedrariensis h.	C. x vilmoriniana
Ceratochloa carinatus	Bromus carinatus	Chaenorrhinum praetermissum	C. minus
Ceratoides lanata	Krascheninnikovia lan.	Chaenorrhinum viscidum	C. minus
Ceratophyllum apiculatum	C. demersum	Chaerophyllum alpinum	Anthriscus sylvestris
Ceratophyllum missionis	C. demersum	Chaerophyllum aristatum	Osmorhiza aristata
Ceratophyllum oxyacanthum	C. demersum	Chaerophyllum ghilanicum	Anthriscus sylvestris
Ceratophyllum tricorne	C. demersum	C. hirsutum 'Rubrifolium'	C. hirutum 'Roseum'
Ceratophyllum tricuspidatum	C. demersum	Chaerophyllum infestum	Anthriscus sylvestris
Ceratophyllum unicorne	C. demersum	Chaerophyllum nemerosum	Anthriscus sylvestris
Ceratostigma polhillii - Bulley	C. minus -Prain	Chaerophyllum sativum	Anthriscus cerefolium
Cerbera odallam (unv)	C. manghas	Chamaecereus silvestrii	Echinopsis
Cercidophyllum jap. 'Pendulum'	C. japon. f pendulum		chamaecereus
Cercidophyllum japonicum Red Fox	C. japonicum 'Rotfuchs'	Chamaecissos hederaceus	Glechoma hederacea
C. japonicum v magnificum -Nakai	C. magnificum -Nakai	Chamaecladon -Miq.	Homalomena -Schott

Synonym	Current Name	Synonym	Current Name
Chamaecyparis breviramea	C. obtusa	Chamaecyparis obtusa 'Graciosa'	C. obtusa 'Loenik'
Chamaecyparis decussata h.	Platycladus orientalis	C. obtusa 'Nana Bassett'	C. obtusa 'Bassett'
Chamaecyparis filifera	Cupressus pisifera	C. obtusa 'Nana Caespitosa'	C. obtusa 'Caespitosa'
	'Filifera'	C. obtusa 'Nana Flabelliformis'	C. o. 'Flabelliformis'
Chamaecyparis funebris	Cupressus funebris	C. obtusa 'Nana Intermedia'	C. obtusa 'Intermedia'
Chamaecyparis keteleri	C. obtusa	C. obtusa 'Nana Juniperoides'	C. o. 'Juniperoides'
C. lawsoniana 'Albospica Nana'	C. l. 'Nana Albospica'	C. obtusa 'Nana Kosteri'	C. obtusa 'Kosteri'
C. lawsoniana 'Allumii Aurea'	C. l. 'Alumigold'	C. obtusa 'Nana Minima'	C. obtusa 'Minima'
C. lawsoniana 'Argentea'	C. l'Argenteovariegata'	C. obtusa 'Nana Repens'	C. obtusa 'Repens'
C. lawsoniana 'Backhouse Silver'	C. lawsoniana	Chamaecyparis obtusa 'Nana Rigida'	C. obtusa 'Rigid Dwarf'
	'Pygmaea Argentea'	C. obtusa 'Nana Spiralis'	C. obtusa 'Spiralis'
C. lawsoniana 'Blue Nantais'	C. l. 'Bleu Nantais'	C. obtusa 'Nana Variegata'	C. obtusa 'Mariesii'
C. lawsoniana 'Columnaris Aurea'	C. l. 'Golden Spire'	Chamaecyparis obtusa 'Sanderi'	Thuja orientalis
C. lawsoniana 'Dwarf Blue'	C. l. 'Pick's Dwarf Blue'		'Sanderi'
C. lawsoniana 'Ellwood's Variegata'	C. l. 'Ellwood's White'	Chamaecyparis obtusa 'Torulosa'	C. o. 'Corralliformis'
C. lawsoniana 'Erecta Witzeliana'	C. l. 'Witzeliana'	Chamaecyparis pendula	C. obtusa
C. lawsoniana 'Fletcheri Aurea'	C.l'Yellow Transparent'	C. pisifera 'Aurea Nana' misapplied	C. p. 'Strathmore'
C. lawsoniana 'Fletcheri Somerset'	C. l. 'Somerset'	C. pisifera 'Cyanoviridis'	C. pisifera 'Boulevard'
C. lawsoniana 'Fletcheri Variegata'	C. lawsoniana	C. pisifera 'Dwarf Blue'	C. pisifera 'Squarrosa
	'Fletcher's White'		Intermedia'
C. lawsoniana 'Glauca Kooy'	C. lawsoniana 'Kooy'	C. pisifera 'Filifera Aurea Nana'	C. p. 'Golden Mop'
C. lawsoniana 'Glauca Spek'	C. lawsoniana 'Spek'	C. pisifera 'Filifera Nana Aurea'	C. p. 'Golden Mop'
C. lawsoniana 'Globosa Filiformis'	C. lawsoniana	C. pisifera 'Filifera Sungold'	C. pisifera 'Sungold'
	'Filiformis Compacta'	Chamaecyparis pisifera 'Gold Dust'	C. p. 'Plumosa Aurea'
Chamaecyparis lawsoniana 'Globus'	C. lawsoniana	C. pisifera 'Nana Aurea'	C. p. 'Strathmore'
	'Barabits' Globe'	C. pisifera 'Plumosa Densa'	C. pisifera 'Plumosa
C. lawsoniana 'Green Spire'	C. l. 'Green Pillar'		Compressa'
C. lawsoniana 'Hogger's Blue Gown'	C. l. 'Blue Gown'	C. pisifera 'Plumosa Purple Dome'	C. p. 'Purple Dome'
C. l. 'Jackman's Green Hedger'	C. l. 'Green Hedger'	Chamaecyparis pisifera 'Pygmaea'	C. pisifera 'Plumosa
C. lawsoniana 'Jackman's Variety'	C. l. 'Green Pillar'		Pygmaea'
C. lawsoniana 'Lane' h.	C. l. 'Lanei Aurea'	Chamaecyparis pisifera 'Rogersii'	C.p. 'Plumosa Rogersii'
C. lawsoniana 'Masonii'	C. l. 'Erecta Filiformis'	C. p. 'Squarrosa Argentea Pygmaea'	C. pisifera 'Squarrosa
C. lawsoniana 'Milford Blue Jacket'	C. l. 'Blue Jacket'		Intermedia'
C. lawsoniana 'Minima Argentea'	C. l. 'Nana Argentea'	C. pisifera 'Squarrosa Minima'	C. pisifera 'Squarrosa
C. lawsoniana 'Minima Densa'	C. lawsoniana 'Minima'		Intermedia'
C. lawsoniana 'Nana Lutea'	C. l. 'Lutea Nana'	C. pisifera 'Squarrosa Snow'	C. pisifera 'Snow'
C. lawsoniana 'Nyewoods'	C. lawsoniana	C. pisifera 'Squarrosa Veitchii'	C. pisifera 'Squarrosa'
	'Chilworth Silver'	Chamaecyparis sphaeroides -Spach	C. thyoides
Chamaecyparis lawsoniana 'Nymph'	C. l. 'Ellwood's Nymph'	Chamaecyparis thyoides 'Kewensis'	C. thyoides 'Glauca'
C. lawsoniana 'Rogersii'	C. l. 'Nana Rogersii'	C. thyoides 'Leptoclada Nana'	C. thyoides
C. lawsoniana 'Smithii Aurea'	C. l. 'Lutea Smithii'		'Andelyensis Nana'
Chamaecyparis lawsoniana 'Smithii'	C. l. 'Lutea Smithii'	C. thyoides 'Leptoclada'	C. t. 'Andelyensis'
Chamaecyparis lawsoniana 'Smithii'	C. l. 'Lutea Smithii'	Chamaecyparis thyoides 'Red Star'	C. thyoides 'Rubicon'
C. l. 'Triomphe de Boskoop'	C.l.'Triomf vanBoskoop'	Chamaecytisus austriacus	Cytisus austriacus
C. lawsoniana 'Van Pelt's Blue'	C. l. 'Pelt's Blue'	Chamaecytisus hirsutus v demissus	C. demissus
C. lawsoniana 'Yellow Queen'	C. l. 'Golden Queen'	Chamaecytisus purpureus	C. purpureus -Scop.
C. lawsoniana 'Yellow Success'	C. l. 'Golden Queen'	C. purpureus 'Incarnatus'	C. p. 'Atropurpureus'
C. lawsoniana Pot of Gold	C. l. 'Golden Pot'	Chamaedaphne angustifolia	C. calyculata
Chamaecyparis leylandii	x Cupressocyparis ley.	Chamaedaphne crispa	C. calyculata
C. nootkatensis 'Argentovariegata'	C. noot. 'Variegata'	Chamaedaphne latifolia	Kalmia latifolia
Chamaecyparis nootkatensis 'Aurea'	C. nootkatensis 'Lutea'	Chamaedorea erumpens	C. seifrizii
C. obtusa 'Aureovariegata'	C. obtusa 'Opaal'	Chamaedorea metallica misapplied	C. microspadix
C. obtusa 'Chima-anihiba'	C. o. 'Pygmaea Densa'	Chamaedrys officinalis	Teucrium chamaedrys
C. obtusa 'Crippsii Aurea'	C. obtusa 'Crippsii'	Chamaefilix platyneuros	Asplenium platyneuron
Chamaecyparis obtusa 'Densa'	C. obtusa 'Nana Densa'	Chamaefilix ruta-muraria	Asplenium ruta-mur.

Synonym	Current Name	Synonym	Current Name
Chamaelaucium	Chamelaucium	Chelidonium haematodes	C. majus
Chamaelirium carolinianum	C. luteum	Chelidonium japonicum	Hylomecon japonica
Chamaemelum arvense	Anthemis arvensis -L.	Chelidonium ruderale	C. majus
Chamaemelum leucanthemum	Leucanthemum vulgare	Chelidonium umbelliferum	C. majus
Chamaemelum ptarmica	Achillea ptarmica	Chelidonium vulgare	C. majus
Chamaemelum segetum	Glebionis segetum	Chelone alba -Moench	C. glabra -L.
Chamaenerion	Chamerion	Chelone barbata	Penstemon barbatus
Chamaenerion angustifolium	Epilobium angustifolium	Chelone capitata	C. glabra -L.
		Chelone chlorantha	C. glabra -L.
Chamaenerion latifolium	Epilobium latifolium	Chelone digitalis	Penstemon digitalis
Chamaepericlymenum	Cornus	Chelone elatior	C. glabra -L.
Chamaepericlymenum canadense	Cornus canadensis	Chelone lanceolata	C. glabra -L.
Chamaepericlymenum suecicum	Cornus suecica	Chelone linifolia	C. glabra -L.
Chamaerops excelsa -Thunberg	Rhapis excelsa	Chelone maculata	C. glabra -L.
Chamaerops excelsa misapplied	Trachycarpus fortunei	Chelone montana	C. glabra -L.
Chamaerops fortunei	Trachycarpus fortunei	Chelone obliqua v alba	C. glabra
Chamaerops humilis v cerifera	C. humilis v argentea	Chelone tomentosa	C. glabra -L.
Chamaespartium	Genista	Chenopodium acuminatum virgatum	C. virgatum
Chamaespartium sagittale	Genista sagittalis -L.	Chenopodium album leptophyllum	C. leptophyllum
C. sagittale ssp delphinense	Genista delphinensis	Chenopodium amaranti-color	C. giganteum
Chamaesphacos ilicifolius misapplied	Siphocranion macranthium	Chenopodium anthelminticum	C. ambrosioides anth.
		Chenopodium berlandieri bushianum	C. bushianum
Chamaesyce hirta	Euphorbia hirta	Chenopodium berlandieri nuttalliae	C. nuttalliae
Chamaesyce serpyllifolia	Euphorbia serpyllifolia	Chenopodium blitum	C. foliosum
Chamelaucium brownii	Verticordia brownii	C. capitatum parvicapitatum	C. overi
Chamelaucium plumosum	Verticordia plumosa	Chenopodium cornutum	C. gaveolens
Chamelaucium verticordinum	V. verticordina	C. desiccatum leptophylloides	C. pratericola
Chamomilla recutita	Matricaria recutita	Chenopodium foetidum	C. schraderianum
Chartolepis glastifolia	Centaurea glastifolia	Chenopodium fremontii incanum	C. incanum
Chasea virgata	Panicum virgatum	Chenopodium gigantospermum	C. simplex
Cheilanthes arborescens	Hypolepis dicksonioides	C. hybridum gigantospermum	C. simplex
		Chenopodium leptophyllum -not Nutt.	C. pratericola
Cheilanthes caudata v caudata	C. caudata	Chenopodium littorale	Atriplex littoralis
Cheilanthes cavernicola	C. pumilio	Chenopodium nigrum	Suaeda nigra
Cheilanthes clelandii	C. sieberi ssp sieberi	Chenopodium olidum	C. vulvaria
Cheilanthes dicksonioides	Hypolepis dickson.	Chenopodium reticulatum	C. album
Cheilanthes dunlopii	C. pumilio	Chenopodium salsum	Suaeda salsa
Cheilanthes fragrans	C. pteridioides	Chenopodium scoparia	Bassia scoparia
Cheilanthes hirsuta	C. nudiuscula	Chenopodium serotinum -not L.	C. ficifolium
Cheilanthes pinnatifida	C. caudata	Chenopodium subspicatum	Atriplex dioica
Cheilanthes pseudovillea	C. sieberi ssp pseudov.	Chenopodium viride	C. suecicum
Cheilanthes siliquosa	Aspidotis densa	Chersydium -Schott	Dracontium -L.
Cheilanthes tenuifolia v tenuissima	C. nitida	Chesneya nubigena	Caragana nubigena
Cheilanthes tenuissima	C. nitida	Chiapasia nelsonii	Disocactus nelsonii
Cheilanthes vellea	C. brownii	Chiastophyllum oppositifolium 'Frosted Jade'	
Cheiranthus	Erysimum		C. opp. 'Jim's Pride'
Cheiranthus annus	Matthiola incana	Chiastophyllum simplicifolium	C. oppositifolium
Cheiranthus fenestralis	Matthiola incana	Chiliotrichum amelloides -DC.	C. diffusum
Cheiranthus graecus	Matthiola incana	Chiliotrichum amelloideum -Cass.	C. diffusum
Cheiranthus hortensis	Matthiola incana	Chiliotrichum rosmarinifolium	C. diffusum
Cheiranthus incanus	Matthiola incana	Chimonanthus fragrans -Lindl.	C. praecox -(L.) Link
Cheiridopsis candidissima	C. denticulata	Chimonanthus praecox 'Concolor'	C. praecox v luteus
Cheiridopsis purpurata	C. purpurea	Chimonanthus praecox 'Luteus'	C. praecox v luteus
Cheirostemon platanoides (unv)	Chiranthodendron pentadactylon	Chimonobambusa falcata	Drepanostachyum falcatum

Synonym	Current Name	Synonym	Current Name
Chimonobambusa hookeriana	Himalayacalamus falconeri 'Damarapa'	Chorizema superbum	C. cordatum
		Chorizema triangulare	C. ilicifolium
Chiogenes	Gaultheria	Chorizema varium	C. varium
Chiogenes hispidula	Gaultheria hispidula	Chorozema	Chorizema
Chiogenes serpyllifolia -Salis.	Gaultheria hispidula	Choryzema	Chorizema
Chionanthus virginicus v pubescens	C. virg. v maritimus	Chosenia arbutifolia	Salix arbutifolia
Chionocloa conspicua 'Rubra'	C. rubra	Chosenia arbutifolia	Salix arbutifolia -Pall.
Chionodoxa cretica	C. nana	Chosenia bracteosa -(Turcz). Nakai	Salix arbutifolia -Pall.
Chionodoxa forbesii Siehei Group	C. siehei	Christella dentata v caespitosa	C. dentata
Chionodoxa gigantea	C. luciliae Gigantea Gr.	Chronanthus biflorus	Cytisus fontanesii
Chionodoxa luciliae misapplied	C. forbesii	Chrozophora verbascifolia	C. obliqua
Chionodoxa Siehei group	C. siehei	Chrysalidocarpus	Dypsis
Chionodoxa tmolusi	C. forbesii 'Tmoli'	Chrysalidocarpus lutescens	Dypsis lutescens
Chionographis lutea	C. japonica	Chrysanthemopsis	Rhodanthemum
Chiranthodendron californicum	Fremontodendron cali.	Chrysanthemum 'Apricot Enbee Wedding'	
Chlonanthes montana	Chelone glabra		C. 'Bronze Enbee Wedding'
Chlonanthes tomentosa	Chelone glabra		
Chlora perfoliata	Blackstonia perfoliata	Chrysanthemum 'Bronze Mei-kyo'	C. 'Bronze Elegance'
Chloranthus brachystachys	Sarcandra glabra	Chrysanthemum 'Bronze Pamela'	C. 'Pamela'
Chloranthus mandschuricus	C. japonicus	Chrysanthemum 'Cottage Pink'	C. 'Emperor of China'
Chloris distichophylla	Eustachys distichophyl.	Chrysanthemum 'Golden Margaret'	C. 'Gold Margaret'
Chlorogalum leichtlinii	Camassia leichtlinii	Chrysanthemum 'Jessie Cooper'	C. 'Mrs Jessie Cooper'
Chlorophytum capense h.	C. comosum	Chrysanthemum 'Orange Margaret'	C. 'Fleet Margaret'
Chlorophytum laxum 'Variegatum'	C. laxum 'Bichetii'	Chrysanthemum 'Peach Margaret'	C. 'Salmon Margaret'
Choisya ternata 'Brica'	C. ternata 'Sundance'	C. 'Primrose Courtier'	C. 'Yellow Courtier'
Choisya ternata 'Moonsleeper'	C. ternata 'Sundance'	C. 'Primrose Margaret'	C. 'Buff Margaret'
Chondrilla prenanthoides	C. chondrilloides	Chrysanthemum 'Red Glory'	C. 'Red Woolman's Glory'
Chondrosum gracile	Bouteloua gracilis		
Chorisia insignis	Ceiba insignis (unv)	Chrysanthemum 'Tom Parr'	C. 'Doctor Tom Parr'
Chorisia speciosa	Ceiba speciosa (unv)	Chrysanthemum alpinum	Leucanthemopsis alp.
Chorispora elegans sabulosa	C. sabulosa	Chrysanthemum anethifolium -not (Willd.) Steud.	
Chorizema angustifolium	C. glycinifolium		Argyranthemum foeniculaceum
Chorizema capillipes	C. glycinifolium		
C. cordatum v spinosissimum	C. cordatum	Chrysanthemum arcticum -Linnaeus	Arctanthemum arct.
Chorizema coriaceum	Gastrolobium coriac.	Chrysanthemum argenteum	Tanacetum argenteum
Chorizema costatum	C. dicksonii	Chrysanthemum balsamita	Tanacetum balsamita
Chorizema costatum v brevifolium	C. dicksonii	Chrysanthemum boreale	Dendranthema lavandulifolium
Chorizema costatum v costatum	C. dicksonii		
Chorizema costatum v lanceolatum	C. dicksonii	Chrysanthemum catananche	Rhodanthemum cat.
Chorizema costatum v lineare	C. dicksonii	Chrysanthemum cinerariifolium	Tanacetum cinerariif.
Chorizema denticulatum	C. ilicifolium	Chrysanthemum clusii	Tanacetum corymbo sum ssp clusii
Chorizema ericifolium	C. racemosum		
Chorizema flavum	C. cordatum	Chrysanthemum coccineum	Tanacetum coccineum
Chorizema genistifolia	Daviesia umbellata	Chrysanthemum corymbosum	Tanacetum corymbos.
Chorizema gomphocarpum	C. parviflorum	Chrysanthemum densum	Tanacetum d.ssp amani
Chorizema henchmannii	C. aciculare	Chrysanthemum foeniculaceum	Argyranthemum foen.
Chorizema heterophyllum	Gastrolobium heteroph.	Chrysanthemum foeniculaceum h.	Argyranthemum foen. misapplied
Chorizema lineare	G. ebracteolatum		
Chorizema magnifolium	G. racemosum	Chrysanthemum frutescens	Argyranthemum frut.
Chorizema ovatum	C. rhombeum	Chrysanthemum gayanum	Rhodanthemum gay.
Chorizema parvifolium	C. nervosum	Chrysanthemum haradjanii	Tanacetum haradjanii
Chorizema platylobioides	Mirbelia platylobioidea	Chrysanthemum hosmariense	Rhodanthemum hosm.
Chorizema pubescens	C. carinatum	Chrysanthemum indicum	Dendranthema indicum
Chorizema sericeum	Gastrolobium sericeum	Chrysanthemum indicum boreale	Dendranthema lavandulifolium
Chorizema spectabile	C. diversifolium		

Synonym	Current Name	Synonym	Current Name
Chrysanthemum ircutianum	Leucanthemum vulgare	Cicer lens	Lens culinaris
Chrysanthemum lacustre	Leucanthemum vulgare	Cicer soongaricum	C. microphyllum
Chrysanthemum leucanthemum	Leucanthemum vulgare	Cichorium byzantinum	C. intybus
Chrysanthemum macrophyllum	Tanacetum macrophyll.	Cichorium caeruleum	C. intybus
Chrysanthemum majus	Tanacetum balsamita	Cichorium casnia	C. intybus
Chrysanthemum maresii	Rhodanthemum hosmariense	Cichorium cicorea	C. intybus
		Cichorium commune	C. intybus
Chrysanthemum mawii	Rhodanthemum gayanum	Cichorium cosnia	C. intybus
		Cichorium divaricatum	C. intybus
Chrysanthemum maximum -Ramond	Leucanthemum maxim.	Cichorium glabratum	C. intybus
C. maximum misapplied	L. x superbum	Cichorium hirsutum	C. intybus
Chrysanthemum naktongense	Chrysanthemum zawadskii v latilobum	Cichorium officinale	C. intybus
		Cichorium perenne	C. intybus
Chrysanthemum nipponicum	Nipponanthemum nipp.	Cichorium rigidum	C. intybus
Chrysanthemum nubigenum	Dendranthema nubig.	Cichorium sativum	C. intybus
Chrysanthemum pacificum	Ajania pacifica	Cichorium sylvestre	C. intybus
Chrysanthemum parthenium	Tanacetum parthenium	Cicuta angustifolia	C. virosa -L.
Chrysanthemum pectinata	Leucanthemopsis pect.	Cicuta bolandri	C. maculata
Chrysanthemum praeteritium	Tanacetum praeterit.	Cicuta curtissii	C. maculata
Chrysanthemum ptarmiciflorum	Tanacetum ptarmicifl.	Cicuta mackenziana	C. virosa -L.
Chrysanthemum radicans	Leucanthemopsis pectinata	Cicuta maculata	Conium maculatum
		Cicuta major	Conium maculatum
Chrysanthemum roseum	Tanacetum coccineum	Cicuta mexicana	Conium maculatum
Chrysanthemum rubellum	C. zawadskii	Cicuta nipponica	C. virosa -L.
Chrysanthemum segetum	Glebionis segetum	Cicuta occidentalis	C. maculata
Chrysanthemum serotinum	Leucanthemella serot.	Cicuta officinalis	Conium maculatum
Chrysanthemum sibiricum	Arctanthemum arcticum	Cicuta orientalis	C. virosa -L.
		Cicuta victorinii	C. maculata
Chrysanthemum sinense	C. morifolium	Cicuta virosa -not L.	C. maculata
Chrysanthemum tanacetum	Tanacetum balsamita	Cicuta virosa v maculata	C. maculata
Chrysanthemum tricolor	C. carinatum	Cicuta vulgaris	Conium maculatum
Chrysanthemum uliginosum	Leucanthemella serotina	Cicutaria aquatica	Cicuta virosa -L.
		Cicutaria bulbifera	Cicuta bulbifera
Chrysanthemum vulgare	Tanacetum vulgare	Cicutaria vulgaris	Anthriscus sylvestris
Chrysanthemum welwitschii	Glebionis segetum	Cimicifuga acerina	Actaea japonica
Chrysanthemum x koreanum	Dendranthema grandiflorum	Cimicifuga americana	Actaea podocarpa
		Cimicifuga cordifolia -Pursh	Actaea americana
Chrysanthemum x superbum	Leucanthemum x sup.	Cimicifuga foetida	Actaea cimicifuga
Chrysobactron hookeri	Bulbinella hookeri	Cimicifuga japonica acerina	Actaea japonica
Chrysocoma graveolens -Nutt.	Chrysothamnus grav.	Cimicifuga palmata	Trautvetteria caroliniensis
Chrysocyanthus amurensis	Adonis amurensis		
Chrysolarix amabilis	Pseudolarix amabilis	Cimicifuga racemosa 'Purpurea'	Actaea simplex Atropurpurea Group
Chrysolepis chrysophylla 'Obtusata'	C. c. 'Obovata'		
Chrysolepis vacciniifolia	Quercus vacciniifolia	Cimicifuga racemosa v cordifolia	Actaea rubifolia
Chrysoplenium americanum	C. oppositifolium	Cimicifuga ramosa	A. s. 'Pritchard's Giant'
Chrysopsis	Heterotheca	Cimicifuga rubifolia	Actaea cordifolia
Chrysorhoe nitens	Verticordia nitens	Cimicifuga rubra alba	Actaea r. f neglecta
Chrysorhoe serrata	Verticordia serrata	Cimicifuga simplec 'Atropurpurea'	A. s. Atropurpurea Gr.
Chrysothamnus nauseosus graveolens		Cimicifuga simplex	Actaea simplex
	C. graveolens	C. simplex 'Bernard Mitchell'	A. s. Atropurpurea Gr. 'Bernard Mitchell'
Chusquea andina -Phil.	C. culeou -E.Desv.		
Chusquea breviglumis h.	C. culeou 'Tenuis'	Cimicifuga simplex 'Brunette'	A. s. Atropurpurea Group 'Brunette'
Chusquea culeou 'Breviglumis'	C. culeou 'Tenuis'		
Cibotium assamicum	C. barometz	C. simplex 'Hillside Black Beauty'	A. s. Atropurpurea Gr. 'Hillside Black Beauty'
Cicer jacquemontii	C. microphyllum		

64

Synonym	Current Name	Synonym	Current Name
Cimicifuga simplex 'James Compton'	A. s. Atropurpurea Gr. 'James Compton'	Cissus voinieriana	Tetrastigma voinier.
Cimicifuga simplex ramosa	A. s. 'Pritchard's Giant'	Cistus 'Anne Palmer'	C. x fernandesiae 'Anne Palmer'
Cimicifuga simplex v simplex	A. s. 'Pritchard's Giant'	Cistus 'Barnsley Pink'	C. 'Grayswood Pink'
Cimicifuga spicata v rubra	Actaea rubra	Cistus 'Blanche'	C. ladanifer 'Blanche'
Cineraria cruentus h.	Pericallis x hybrida	Cistus 'Chelsea Pink'	C. 'Grayswood Pink'
Cineraria farfara	Tussilago farfara	Cistus 'Merrist Wood Cream'	x Halimiocistus
Cineraria florists'	Pericallis x hybrida		wintonensis 'Merrist
Cineraria maritima	Senecio cineraria		Wood Cream'
Cineraria x hybrida	Pericallis x hybrida	Cistus 'Paladin'	C. ladanifer 'Paladin'
Cinnamomum aromaticum	C. cassia	Cistus 'Peggy Sammons'	C. x argenteus 'Peggy
Cinnamomum verum	C. zeylanicum		Sammons'
Cirrhopetalum guttulatum	Bulbophyllum guttulat.	Cistus 'Roseus'	C. x pulverulentus
Cirrhopetalum medusae	Bulbophyllum medusae	Cistus 'Silver Pink' misapplied	C. 'Grayswood Pink'
Cirsium abyssinicum	C. vulgare	Cistus 'Snowflake'	C. 'Snow Fire'
Cirsium albicans	C. arvense	Cistus 'Sunset'	C. x pulverul. 'Sunset'
Cirsium argentum	C. arvense	Cistus 'Tania Compton'	C. x creticus ssp
Cirsium balearicum	C. vulgare		creticus f albus 'Tania
Cirsium bigelovii	C. mutticum		Compton'
Cirsium boreale	C. kamtschaticum	Cistus 'Thrive'	C.x obtusifolius 'Thrive'
Cirsium chailletii	C. palustre	Cistus albanicus	C. sintenisii
Cirsium crinitum	C. vulgare	Cistus algarvensis -Sims	Halimium ocymoides
Cirsium diacantha	Ptilostemon diacantha	Cistus alpestris -Jacq.	Helianthemum
Cirsium drummondii	C. foliosum		oelandicum ssp alp.
Cirsium helenioides	C. heterophyllum	Cistus alyssoides -Lam.	Halimium alyssoides
Cirsium incanum	C. arvense	Cistus apenninus -L.	Helianthemum apenn.
Cirsium involucratum	C. verutum	Cistus atriplicifolius -Lam.	Halimium atriplicifolium
Cirsium japonicum ussuriense	C. maackii	Cistus bourgeanus -Coss.	C. libanotis -L.
Cirsium lanatum	C. arvense	Cistus candidissimus -Dun.	C. symphytifolius ssp
Cirsium lanceolatum	C. vulgare		leucophyllus
Cirsium laushanense	C. chinense	Cistus canus -L.	Helianthemum canum
Cirsium linkii	C. vulgare	Cistus coeris	C. x hybridus
Cirsium microcephalum	C. vulgare	Cistus complicatus -Lam.	C. parviflorus -Lam.
Cirsium nemorale	C. vulgare	Cistus crispus 'Prostratus'	C. crispus -Linnaeus
Cirsium nipponicum amplexifolium	C. amplexifolium	Cistus crispus 'Sunset'	C. x pulverulentus
Cirsium oblanceolatum	C. flodmanii		'Sunset'
Cirsium segetum	C. setosum	Cistus crispus misapplied	C. x pulverulentus
Cirsium setosum	C. arvense	Cistus croceus -Desf.	Helianthemum croceum
Cirsium strigosum	C. vulgare	Cistus formosus -Curt.	Halimium lasianthum
Cirsium tanakae	C. oligophyllum		ssp formosum
Cirsium undulatum	C. flodmanii	Cistus glaucus -Cav. not Pourr.	Helianthemum croceum
Cirsium weyrichii	C. kamtschaticum	Cistus grandiflorus -Scop.	Helianthemum nummul
Cissus bainesii	Cyphostemma bainesii		arium ssp grandifl.
Cissus brevipedunculata -Maxim.	Ampelopsis glandulosa v brevipedunculata	Cistus halimifolius -L.	Halimium halimifolium
		Cistus hirsutus -Lam 1786	C. inflatus
Cissus capensis	Rhoicissus capensis	Cistus hirsutus v psilosepalus	C. inflatus
Cissus davidiana -Carr.	Ampelopsis humulifolia	Cistus incanus	C. creticus ssp inc.
Cissus hederacea	Parthenocissus quinquefolia	Cistus incanus ssp creticus	C. creticus ssp cretic.
		Cistus incanus ssp incanus	C. creticus ssp inc.
Cissus juttae	Cyphostemma juttae	Cistus ingwerseniana	x Halimiocistus
Cissus orientalis -Lam.	Ampelopsis orientalis		'Ingwersenii'
Cissus thomsonii	Cayratia thomsonii	Cistus italicus -L.	Helianthemum
Cissus veitchii -Carr.	Parthenocissus tricuspidata		oelandicum ssp italic.
		Cistus ladanifer misapplied	C. x cyprius
Cissus vitifolia -Boiss.	Ampelopsis vitifolia	Cistus ladanifer Palhinhae Group	C. ladanifer v sulcatus

Synonym	Current Name	Synonym	Current Name
Cistus ladaniferus	C. ladanifer	Citrullus vulgaris	C. lanatus
Cistus ladaniferus f latifolius	C. ladanifer v sulcatus	Citrus aurantium v bergamia	C. bergamia
Cistus lasianthus -Lam.	Halimium lasianthum	Citrus aurantium v sinensis	C. sinensis
Cistus lunulatus -All.	Helianthemum lunulat.	Citrus bigarradia	C. aurantium
Cistus nummularius -L.	Helianthemum nummul.	Citrus Calamondin	x Citrofortunella mic.
Cistus ochreatus -Chr.Smith	C. symphytifolius ssp leucophyllus	Citrus deliciosa	C. x nobilis
		Citrus japonica	Fortunella japonica
Cistus ochreatus -not Chr.Smith	C. obsekiifolius	Citrus Kumquat	Fortunella margarita
Cistus ocymoides -Lam.	Halimium ocymoides	Citrus limon 'Quatre Saisons'	C. l. 'Garey's Eureka'
Cistus oelandicus -L.	Helianthemum oelandic.	Citrus limon x sinensis	C. x meyeri
Cistus palhinae	C. ladanifer v sulcatus	Citrus limonum	C. limon
Cistus parviflorus misapplied	C. 'Grayswood Pink'	Citrus madurensis	Fortunella japonica
Cistus polifolius -Huds.	Helianthemum apenninum -(L.) Mill.	Citrus medica 'Cidro Digitado'	C. medica v digitata
		Citrus medica v sarcodactylis	C. medica v digitata
Cistus polymorphus -Willk.	C. populifolius ssp major	Citrus microcarpa Philippine Lime	x Citrofortunella mic.
		Citrus mitis	x Citrofortunella mic.
Cistus populifolius v lasiocalyx	C. pop. ssp major	Citrus reticulata 'Suntina'	C. reticulata 'Nova'
Cistus psilosepalus	C. inflatus	Citrus reticulata Satsuma Group	C. unshiu
Cistus revolii h.	x Halimiocistus sahucii	Citrus reticulata x paradisi	C. x tangelo
Cistus roseus -Jacq.	Helianthemum apenninum v roseum	Citrus sinensis 'Jaffa'	C. sinensis 'Shamouti'
		Citrus trifoliata -L.	Poncirus trifoliata
C. rosmarinifolius -Pourr. in part	C. clusii -Dun.	Citrus vulgaris	C. aurantium
Cistus sahucii -Coste & Soulie	x Halimiocistus sahucii	Citrus x limonia	C. limon
Cistus salvifolius x monspeliensis	C. x florentinus	Cladium jamaicense	C. mariscus
Cistus scabrosus -Ait.	Halimium alyssoides	Cladorhiza maculata	Corallorhiza maculata
Cistus symphytifolius v leucophyllus	C. symp. ssp leucoph.	Cladothamnus	Elliottia
Cistus tomentosus -Scop. not Sm.	Helianthemum nummularium ssp tomentosum	Cladrastis amurensis	Maackia amurensis
		Cladrastis amurensis v buergeri	Maackia amurensis
Cistus umbellatus -L.	Halimium umbellatum	Cladrastis faurei -Levl.	Maackia fauriei
Cistus vaginatus - Ait.	C. symphitifolius -Lam.	Cladrastis kentukea 'Rosea'	C. k. 'Perkin's Pink'
Cistus villosus -L.	C. creticus ssp cretic.	Cladrastis lutea -(Michx.) K.Koch	C. kentukea
Cistus wintonensis	x Halimiocistus winton.	Cladrastis tinctoria -Raf.	C. kentukea
Cistus x corbariensis	C. x hybridus	Clarkia elegans	C. unguiculata
Cistus x dansereaui 'Albiflorus'	C. x d. 'Portmeirion'	Clarkia grandiflora	C. amoena
Cistus x delilei -Burnat	C. x pulverulentus	Claytonia alsinoides	C. sibirica
Cistus x florentinus misapplied	x Halimiocistus 'Ingwersenii'	Claytonia australasica	Neopaxia australasica
		Claytonia parvifolia	Naiocrene parvifolia
Cistus x laxus 'Snow Queen'	C. x laxus 'Snow White'	Claytonia spathulifolia	C. caroliniana
Cistus x longifolius	C. x nigricans	Claytonia virginica v spathulifolia	C. caroliniana
Cistus x loretii -Rouy & Foue	C. x stenophyllus	Cleistocactus jujuyensis	C. hyalacanthus
Cistus x loretii misapplied	C. x dansereaui	Cleistocactus wendlandiorum	C. brookei
Cistus x lusitanicus -Maund	C. x dansereaui	Clematis 'Andre Devillers'	C. 'Directeur Andre Devillers'
Cistus x obtusifolius misapplied	C. x nigricans		
C. x pulverulentus 'Warley Rose'	C. x crispatus 'Warley Rose'	Clematis 'Betina'	C. 'Red Beetroot Beauty'
Cistus x purpureus 'Betty Taudevin'	C. x purpureus	Clematis 'Bicolor'	C. florida v sieboldiana
Cistus x recognitus -Rouy & Fouc.	C. x glaucus -Pourr.	Clematis 'Blue Boy'	C.diversifolia 'Blue Boy'
C.x verguinii v albiflorus misapplied	C. x dansereaui 'Portmeirion'	Clematis 'Blue Boy' (L/P)	C. 'Elsa Spath'
		Clematis 'Blue Rain'	C. 'Sinee Dozhd'
Citharexylon cyanocarpum	R. spinosus	Clematis 'Campanile'	C. x bonstedtii 'Campanile'
Citharexylum quadrangulare	C. spinosum		
Citharexylum subserratum	C. spinosum	Clematis 'Capitaine Thuilleaux'	C. 'Souvenir du Capitaine Thuilleaux'
Citrofortunella mitis	x Citrofortunella microcarpa		
		Clematis 'Cardinal Wyszynski'	C.'Kardynal Wyszynski'
Citronella mucronata	C. gongonha	Clematis 'Citra'	C. 'Claudius'

Synonym	Current Name
Clematis 'Dorothy Walton'	C. 'Bagatelle'
Clematis 'Etoile Nacree'	C. 'Sakurahime'
Clematis 'Eximia'	C. 'Ballerina in Blue'
Clematis 'Floralia'	C. 'Floral Feast'
Clematis 'Grandiflora Sanguinea'	C. 'Sodertalje'
C. 'Jackmannii Superba' misapplied	C. 'Gipsy Queen'
Clematis 'Madame le Coultre'	C. 'Marie Boisselot'
Clematis 'Morning Cloud'	C. 'Yukikomachi'
Clematis 'Mother Theresa'	C. 'Matka Teresa'
Clematis 'Mrs Oud'	C. 'Mevrouv Oud'
Clematis 'Mrs Robert Brydon'	C. x jouiniana 'Mrs Robert Brydon'
Clematis 'North Star'	C. 'Pohjanael'
Clematis 'Pamela Jackman'	C. alpina 'Pamela Jackman'
Clematis 'Pink Champagne'	C. 'Kakio'
Clematis 'Primrose Star'	C. 'Star'
Clematis 'Pruinina'	C. 'Plum Beauty'
Clematis 'Purpurea Plena Elegans'	C. viticella 'Purpurea Plena Elegans'
Clematis 'Ramona'	C. 'Hybrida Sieboldii'
Clematis 'Red Cooler'	C. 'Crimson King'
Clematis 'Signe'	C. 'Kasmu'
Clematis 'Snowdrift'	C. armandii 'Snowdrift'
Clematis 'The Princess of Wales' (L)	C. 'Princess of Wales'
Clematis 'The Princess of Wales' (T)	C. 'Princess Diana' (T)
Clematis 'Tinkerbell'	C. 'Shiva'
Clematis 'Wada's Primrose'	C. patens 'Manshuu Ki'
Clematis 'Xerxes' misapplied	C. 'Elsa Spath'
Clematis 'Yellow Queen' -Holland	C. patens 'Manshuu ki'
Clematis 'Yellow Queen' Lundell	C. 'Moonlight'
Clematis alpina 'Albiflora'	C. sibirica
Clematis alpina 'Blue Giant'	C. alp. 'Frances Rivis'
Clematis alpina 'Columbine White'	C. a. 'White Columbine'
Clematis alpina 'Jan Lindmark'	C. 'Jan Lindmark'
Clematis alpina 'Tage Lundell'	C. 'Tage Lundell'
Clematis alpina ssp sibirica	C. sibirica
Clematis alpina v alba -Davis	C. sibirica
Clematis anshunensis	C. clarkeana
Clematis aphylla -Colenso	C. afoliata -Buchan.
Clematis armandii 'Meyeniana'	C. armandii 'Little White Charm'
Clematis balearica -Pers.	C. cirrhosa -L.
Clematis balearica -Rich.	C. cirrhosa v balearica
Clematis barbellata 'Pruinina'	C. 'Pruinina'
Clematis Black Madonna	C. 'Czarna Madonna'
Clematis Blue Angel	C. 'Blekitny Aniol'
Clematis buchananiana -not DC.	C. rehderiana -Craib
Clematis calycina -Ait.	C. cirrhosa
Clematis chinensis misapplied	C. terniflora
Clematis chrysantha	C. tangutica
Clematis chrysantha v paucidentata	C. hilariae
Clematis chrysocoma misapplied	C. spooneri
Clematis chrysocoma misapplied	C. x vedrariensis
Clematis coccinea -Engelm.	C. texensis -Buckl.

Synonym	Current Name
Clematis coerulea -Lindl.	C. patens
Clematis colensoi -Hook 1864	C. hookeriana
Clematis crispa 'Rosea'	C. crispa 'Cylindrica'
Clematis cunninghamii	C. parviflora
Clematis davidiana -Velot.	C. heracleifolia v dav.
Clematis dioscoreifolia	C. terniflora
Clematis dioscoreifolia v robusta	C. terniflora
Clematis douglasii	C. hirsutissima
Clematis fargesii -Franch.	C. potaninii
Clematis fargesii v souliei	C. potaninii v potaninii
Clematis finetiana h.	C. paniculata
C. flammula 'Rubra Marginata'	C. x triternata 'Rubromarginata'
Clematis flammula v robusta -Carr.	C. terniflora
Clematis florida 'Alba Plena'	C. florida 'Flore Pleno'
Clematis florida 'Bicolor'	C. florida v sieboldiana
Clematis florida 'Plena'	C. florida 'Flore Pleno'
Clematis florida 'Sieboldii'	C. florida v sieboldiana
Clematis florida v bicolor	C. florida v sieboldiana
Clematis forrestii -W.W.Sm	C. napaulensis -DC.
Clematis fusca h.	C. japonica
Clematis fusca koreana	C. koreana
Clematis fusca v kamtschatica	C. fusca v fusca
Clematis glauca -Turc.	C. intricata
Clematis grata h.	C. x jouiniana
Clematis graveolens -Lindl.	C. orientalis -L.
Clematis hendersonii -Hend.	C. x diversifolia 'Hendersonii'
Clematis hendersonii -Koch	C. x diversifolia 'Hendersonii'
Clematis hendersonii -Standley	C. x diversifolia 'Hendersonii'
Clematis heracleifolia 'Alan Bloom'	C.tabulosa 'Alan Bloom'
Clematis heracleifolia v davidiana	C. tabulosa
Clematis heracleifolia v stans	C. stans -Sieb. & Zucc.
Clematis hexapetala -Forster	C. forsteri
Clematis hexapetala misapplied	C. recta ssp recta v lasiosepala
Clematis hexasepala	C. forsteri
Clematis hirsutissima	C. douglasii
Clematis ianthina	C. fusca v violacea
Clematis indivisa	C. paniculata
Clematis integrifolia 'Hendersonii'	C. x div. 'Hendersonii'
Clematis integrifolia 'Olgae'	C. x diversifolia 'Olgae'
Clematis integrifolia white	C. integ. v albiflora
Clematis ispahanica	C. orientalis -Linnaeus
Clematis japonica v obvallata	C. obvallata
Clematis John Paul II	C. 'Jan Pawel II'
Clematis koreana 'Brunette'	C. 'Brunette'
Clematis kousabotan -Decne.	C. stans -Sieb. & Zucc.
Clematis leiocarpa -Oliver	C. uncinata -Benth.
Clematis liaotungensis	C. mandschurica
Clematis macropetala 'Alborosea'	C. 'Blushing Ballerina'
Clematis macropetala 'Blue Bird'	C. 'Blue Bird'
Clematis macropetala 'Blue Lagoon'	C. macrop. 'Lagoon' - Jackman 1959

Synonym	Current Name	Synonym	Current Name
Clematis macropetala 'Floralia'	C. 'Florali Feast'	C. 'The Princess of Wales'	C. 'Princess Diana'
Clematis macropetala 'Harry Smith'	C. macropetala 'Chili'	Clematis thunbergii -Steudel	C. hirsuta
Clematis macropetala 'Jan Lindmark'	C. 'Jan Lindmark'	Clematis thunbergii h.	C. terniflora
C. macrop. 'Lagoon' -Jackman 1956	C. m. 'Maidwell Hall'	Clematis trifoliata -Thunb.	Akebia trifoliata
C. macropetala 'Magnus Johnson'	C. m. 'M. Johnson'	Clematis tubulosa -Turcz.	C. heracleifolia -DC.
C. macropetala 'Margot Koster'	C. m. 'M. Koster'	Clematis veitcheriana -Craib.	C. rehderiana
Clematis macropetala 'Markhamii'	C. 'Markham's Pink'	Clematis vernayi	C. tibetana ssp vernayi
Clematis macropetala 'White Moth'	C. alpina ssp sibirica 'White Moth'	Clematis verrierensis h.	C. x vedrariensis
		Clematis verticillaris -DC.	C. occidentalis
Clematis macropetala 'White Swan'	C. 'White Swan'	Clematis violacea -A. DC. f.	C. x triternata -DC.
Clematis Masquerade	C. 'Maskarad'	Clematis virginiana -Hooker	C. ligusticifolia
Clematis maximowicziana	C. terniflora	Clematis virginiana misapplied	C. vitalba
Clematis meyeniana v pavoliniana	C. finetiana	Clematis viticella 'Abundance'	C. 'Abundance'
Clematis minor	C. chinensis	Clematis viticella 'Alba Luxurians'	C. 'Alba Luxurians'
Clematis montana 'Grandiflora'	C. m. f grandiflora	Clematis viticella 'Betty Corning'	C. 'Betty Corning'
Clematis montana 'Rubens Superba'	C. montana 'Superba'	Clematis viticella 'Etoile Violette'	C. 'Etoile Violette'
Clematis montana 'Spooneri'	C. spooneri	Clematis viticella 'Mary Rose'	C. viticella 'Flore Pleno'
Clematis montana alba	C. montana	Clematis viticella 'Minuet'	C. 'Minuet'
Clematis montana v sericea	C. spooneri	Clematis viticella 'Polish Spirit'	C. 'Polish Spirit'
Clematis nepalensis	C. barbellata	Clematis viticella 'Venosa Violacea'	C. 'Venosa Violacea'
Clematis nutans h.	C. rehderiana -Craib	Clematis Vivienne	C. 'Beth Currie'
Clematis nutans v thyrsoidea	C. rehderiana -Craib	Clematis x fargesioides	C. 'Paul Farges'
Clematis obvallata	C. japonica v obvallata	Clematis x vedrariensis 'Rosea'	C. 'Spooneri Rosea'
Clematis Opaline	C. 'Asagasumi'	Clematis x violacea	C. x triternata
Clematis orientalis 'Bill MacKenzie'	C. 'Bill MacKenzie'	Clematopsis	Clematis
Clematis orientalis 'Orange Peel'	C. tibetana ssp vernayi 'Orange Peel'	Clementsia	Rhodiola
		Cleome pungens h.	C. hassleriana
Clematis orientalis 'Sherriffii'	C. tibetana ssp vernayi LS&E 13342	Cleome spinosa h.	C. hassleriana
		Clerodendrum chinense 'Pleniflorum'	C. chinense v chinense
Clematis orientalis h	C. tibetana ssp vernayi	Clerodendrum fallax	C. speciosissimum
Clematis orientalis misapplied	C. tibetana ssp vernayi	Clerodendrum fargesii -Dode	C. trichotomum v farg.
Clematis orientalis v tangutica	C. tangutica	Clerodendrum foetidum -Bunge	C. bungei -Steud.
Clematis orientalis v tenuiloba	C. columbiana v ten.	C. fragrans v pleniflorum	C. chinense v chinense
Clematis paniculata -Gmel.	C. indivisa	Clerodendrum philippinum	C. chinense v chinense
Clematis paniculata -Thunb.	C. terniflora	Clethra canescens h.	C. barbinervis
Clematis parviflora -DC.	C. campaniflora	Clethra kawadana -Yanagita	C. barbinervis
Clematis parviloba	C. pierotii	Clethra paniculata	C. alnifolia 'Paniculata'
Clematis pavoliniana Pamp.	C. finetiana	Clethra scandens -Franch.	Clematoclethra scand.
Clematis potaninii v souliei	C. potaninii v potaninii	Clethra tomentosa -Lam.	C. alnifolia v pubescens
Clematis recta 'Serious Black'	C. recta 'Lime Close'	Clethra wilsonii	C. fargesii
Clematis recta v mandschurica	C. mandschurica	Clethropsis nitida -Spach	Alnus nitida
Clematis sibirica	C. alpina ssp sibirica	Cleyera fortunei	C. japonica 'Fortunei'
Clematis simsii -Small	C. pitcheri	Cleyera fortunei 'Variegata'	C. japonica 'Fortunei'
Clematis simsii -Sweet	C. crispa	Cleyera japonica v kaempferiana	C. japonica v japonica
Clematis spooneri 'Rosea'	C. x vedrariensis 'Rosea'	Cleyera ochnacea -DC.	C. japonica -Thunb.
		Cleyera ochnacea v kaempferiana	C. japonica v japonica
Clematis Summer Snow	C. 'Paul Farges'	Cleyera ochnacea v wallichiana -DC.	C. japonica v wallich.
Clematis tangutica 'Aureolin'	C. 'Aureolin'	Clianthus 'Red Admiral'	C. puniceus
Clematis tangutica 'Bill MacKenzie'	C. 'Bill MacKenzie'	Clianthus 'Red Cardinal'	C. puniceus
Clematis tenuiloba	C. columbiana v tenuil.	Clianthus 'White Heron'	C. puniceus 'Albus'
Clematis terniflora v mandschurica	C. mandschurica	Clianthus dampieri	C. formosus
Clematis terniflora v robusta	C. ternifl. v terniflora	Clianthus maximus -Col.	C. puniceus v maximus
C. texensis 'Duchess of Albany'	C. 'Duchess of Albany'	Clianthus puniceus 'Flamingo'	C. puniceus 'Roseus'
C. texensis 'Etoile Rose'	C. 'Etoile Rose'	Clianthus puniceus v magnificus -h.	C. puniceus v maximus
Clematis texensis 'Gravetye Beauty'	C. 'Gravetye Beauty'	Cliftonia ligustrina -(Willd.) Spreng.	C. monophylla

Synonym	Current Name
Clinopodium acinos	Acinos arvensis
Clinopodium arkansanum	Calamintha arkansana
Clinopodium ascendens	Calamintha ascendens
Clinopodium calamintha	Calamintha nepeta
Clinopodium glabellum	Calamintha arkansana
Clinopodium glabrum	Calamintha arkansana
Clinopodium grandiflorum	Calamintha grandiflora
Clintonia alpina	C. udensis
Clintonia ciliata	C. umbellata
Clompanus acerifolia	Brachychiton acerif.
Clompanus australis	Brachychiton australis
Clompanus bidwillii	Brachychiton bidwillii
Clusia rosea	C. major
Clypeola maritima -L.	Lobularia maritima
Cneorum tricoccum -L.	C. tricoccon
Cnicus candicans -Wall.	Cirsium arvense
Cnicus centauroides	Leuzea centauroides
Cnicus dipsacolepis	Cirsium dipsacolepis
Cnicus discolor	Cirsium discolor
Cnicus eriophorus	Cirsium eriophorum
Cnicus lacteus	Cirsium palustre
Cnicus lanceolatus	Cirsium vulgare
Cnicus nipponicus	Cirsium nipponicum
Cnicus oleraceus	Cirsium oleraceum
Cnicus palustris	Cirsium palustre
Cnicus pitcheri	Cirsium pitcheri
Cnicus purpuratus	Cirsium purpuratum
Cnicus segetum	Cirsium setosum
Cnicus serratuloides	Cirsium serratuloides
Cnicus spicatus	Cirsium spicatum
Cnicus strigosus	Cirsium vulgare
Cnicus tuberosus	Cirsium tuberosum
Cnicus undulatus	Cirsium flodmanii
Cnicus uniflorus	Rhaponticum uniflorum
Cnicus verutus	Cirsium verutum
Cnidium canadense	Conioselinum chinense
Cnidium chinense	Conioselinum chinense
Coccinia cordifolia	C. grandis
Coccinia indica	C. grandis
Cocculus thunbergii	C. orbiculatus
Cocculus trilobus -(Thunb). DC.	C. orbiculatus
Cochlearia armoracia	Armoracia rusticana
Cochlearia coronopus	C. squamatus
Cochlearia globosa	Rorippa globosa
Cochlearia groenlandica	C. vulgaris groenland.
Cochlearia lancifolia	Armoracia rusticana
Cocos capitata	Butia capitata
Cocos chilensis -Mol.	Jubaea chilensis
Cocos plumosa	Syagrus romanzoffiana
Cocos weddelliana	Lytocaryum weddell.
Codonopsis convolvulacea 'Alba'	C. grey-wilsonii 'Himal Snow'
C. convolvulacea Forrest's form	C. forrestii -Diels
C. convolvulacea misapplied	C. grey-wilsonii
Codonopsis forrestii misapplied	C. grey-wilsonii

Synonym	Current Name
Codonopsis handeliana	C. tubulosa
Codonopsis nepalensis -Grey Wilson	C. grey-wilsonii
Codonopsis silvestris	C. pilosula
Codonopsis tangshen misapplied	C. rotundifolia v angustifolia
Codonopsis tibetica	C. convolvulacea
Codonopsis ussuriensis	C. lanceolata
Coeloglossom x Dactylorhiza	x Dactyloglossom
Coelogyne ochracea	C. nitida
Coelopleurum actaeiflorum	C. lucidum
Coelopleurum lucidum	Angelica lucida
Coenopleurum longipes	Angelica lucida
Coenopleurum maritimum	Angelica lucida
Coix agrestis	C. lacryma-jobi -L.
Coix arundinacea	C. lacryma-jobi -L.
Coix exaltata	C. lacryma-jobi -L.
Coix ovata	C. lacryma-jobi -L.
Coix poilanei	C. lacryma-jobi -L.
Coix stenocarpa	C. lacryma-jobi -L.
Coix tubulosa	C. lacryma-jobi -L.
Cola vera	C. nitida
Colchicum 'Conquest'	C. 'Glory of Heemstede'
Colchicum autumnale 'Major'	C. byzantium
Colchicum autumnale 'Pannonicum'	C. a. 'Nancy Lindsay'
Colchicum autumnale 'Plenum'	C. a. 'Pleniflorum'
C. autumnale 'Roseum Plenum'	C. a. 'Pleniflorum'
C. autumnale minor album plenum	C. a. 'Alboplenum'
Colchicum autumnale v major	C. byzantium
Colchicum autumnale v minor	C. autumnale
Colchicum bornmuelleri misapplied	C. speciosum v bornmuelleri h.
Colchicum bowlesianum	C. bivonae
Colchicum bulbocodium	Bulbocodium vernum
Colchicum byzantium 'Album'	C. byz. 'Innocence'
Colchicum crociflorum	C. kesselringii
Colchicum doerfleri	C. hungaricum
Colchicum illyricum	C. giganteum
Colchicum laetum h.	C. parnassicum
Colchicum latifolium	C. bivonae
Colchicum minor album plenum	C. a. 'Alboplenum'
Colchicum neapolitanum	C. longiflorum
Colchicum procurrens	C. boissieri
Colchicum sibthorpii	C. bivonae
Colchicum speciosum v illyricum	C. giganteum
Colchicum visianii	C. bivonae
Coleostephus myconis	Chrysanthemum multicaule
Coleus	Solenostemon
Coleus amboinicus	Plectranthus amboinic.
Coleus barbatus	Plectranthus barbatus
Coleus blumei	Solenostemon scutellarioides
Coleus blumei v verschaffeltii	S. scutellarioides
Coleus forskohlii	Plectranthus barbatus
Coleus thyrsoideus	Plectranthus thyrsoid.

Synonym	Current Name	Synonym	Current Name
Colletia armata	C. hystrix	Conchium aciculare -Sm. ex Vent.	Hakea sericea
Colletia armata 'Rosea'	C. hystrix 'Rosea'	Conchium compressum	Hakea sericea
Colletia bictoniensis -Lind.	C. paradoxa	Conchium cornutum	Hakea gibbosa
Colletia crenata -Clos	Discaria crenata	Conchium sphaeroideum	Hakea gibbosa
Colletia cruciata	C. paradoxa	Conchium teretifolium	Hakea epiglottis
Colletia discolor -Hook.	Discaria discolor	Condalia obovata	C. hookeri
Colletia infausta -N.E. Br.	C. spinosissima	Conioselinum benthami	C. chinense
Colletia serratifolia -Vent.	Discaria serratifolia	Conioselinum bipinnatum	C. chinense
Colletia spinosa -Lindl.	C. infausta -N.E.Br.	Conioselinum canadense	C. chinense
Colletia spinosa h.	C. paradoxa	Conioselinum gmelinii	C. pacificum
Colletia spinosa v armata	C. hystrix	Conioselinum kamtschaticum	C. chinense
Colletia valdiviana -Phil.	C. hystrix	Conioselinum pacificum	C. chinense
Collinia elegans	Chamaedorea elegans	Conioselinum pumilum	C. chinense
Collinsia bicolor -Benth	C. heterophylla	Conioselinum univittatum	C. vaginatum
Collomia cavanillesii	C. biflora	Conium arracacia	Arracacia xanthorrhiza
Collomia debilis v larsenii	C. larsenii		
Colmeiroa carpodetoidesth	Corokia carpodetoides	Conium chaerophylloides	Conium maculatum
Colobogynium -Schott	Schismatoglottis	Conium cicuta	Conium maculatum
Colocasia 'Jet Black Wonder'	C. esculenta 'Black Magic'	Conium croaticum	Conium maculatum
		Conium divaricatum	Conium maculatum
Colocasia 'Midnight Magic'	C. esc. 'Black Magic'	Conium leiocarpum	Conium maculatum
Colocasia affinis 'Illustris'	C. esculenta 'Illustris'	Conium maculosum	Conium maculatum
Colocasia antiquorum	C. esculenta	Conium tenuifolium	Conium maculatum
Colocasia antiquorum 'Illustris'	C. esculenta 'Illustris'	Conophallus -Schott	Amorphophallus -Blume
Colocasia antiquorum esculenta	C. esculenta		
Colocynthis vulgaris	Citrullus colocynthis	Conophytum longum	Ophthalmophyllum long.
Colquhounia coccinea v mollis	C. coccinea v vestita		
Columnea 'Stavanger Variegated'	C. 'Broget Stavanger'	Conopodium denudatum	C. majus
Columnea hirta 'Variegata'	C. 'Light Prince'	Conoxylon florida	Cornus florida -L.
Columnea ovata -Cav.	Asterantbera ovata	Conringia thaliana	Arabidopsis thaliana
Colura potentilloides	C. geoides	Consolea falcata	Opuntia falcata
Colutea cruenta -Ait.	C. orientalis -Mill.	Consolida ambigua	C. ajacis
Colutea halepica -Lam.	C. istria -Mill.	Consolida gayana	C. ajacis
Colutea longialata -Koehne	C. ciliata -Boiss.	Convallaria biflora	Polygonatum biflorum
Colutea persica misapplied	C. buhsei	Convallaria commutata	Polygonatum biflorum
Colutea pocockii -Ait.	C. istria -Mill.	Convallaria japonica	Ophiopogon jaburan
Coluteocarpus reticulatus	C. vesicarius	C. majalis 'Gerard Debureaux'	C. m. 'Green Tapestry'
Colymbada badensis	Centaurea scabiosa	Convallaria majalis keiskei	C. keiskei
Colymbada calcarea	Centaurea scabiosa	Convallaria racemosa	Smilacina racemosa
Colymbada scabiosa	Centaurea scabiosa	Convallaria stellata	Smilacina stellata
Comandra umbellata pallida	C. pallida	Convallaria verticillata	Polygonatum verticill.
Comarostaphylis	Arctostaphylos	Convolvuloides purpurea	Ipomoea purpurea
Comarostaphylis diversifolia	Arcostaphylos diversif.	Convolvulus ambigens	C. arvensis
Comarum	Potentilla	Convolvulus auriculatus	C. arvensis
Comarum palustre	Potentilla palustris	Convolvulus cherleri	C. arvensis
Commelina angustifolia	C. erecta angustifolia	Convolvulus corsicus	C. arvensis
Commelina coelestis	C. tuberosa Coelestis Group	Convolvulus elegantissimus	C. althaeoides ssp tenuissimus
Commelina hirtella	C. erecta	Convolvulus fischerianus	C. arvensis
Commelina virginica h.	C. erecta	Convolvulus incanus -not Vahl	C. arvensis
Commiphora molmol	C. myrrha	Convolvulus jalapa	Ipomoea purga
Comptonia asplenifolia -(L.) Ait.	C. peregrina v asplen.	Convolvulus longipedicellatus	C. arvensis
Comptonia peregrina v tomentosa	C. peregrina	Convolvulus mauritanicus	C. sabatius
Conanthera simsii	C. campanulata	Convolvulus minor	C. tricolor
Conchium	Hakea	Convolvulus mutabilis	Ipomoea purpurea

Synonym	Current Name	Synonym	Current Name
Convolvulus nitidus	C. boissieri	Coreopsis Sun Child	C. 'Sonnenkind'
Convolvulus panduratus	Ipomoea pandurata	C. verticillata 'Golden Shower'	C. vert. 'Grandiflora'
Convolvulus prostratus -not Forssk	C. arvensis	Coriandrum cicuta	Cicuta virosa -L.
Convolvulus purpureus	Ipomoea purpurea	Coriandrum diversifolium	Cicuta sativum -L.
Convolvulus sagittifolius	C. arvensis	Coriandrum globosum	Cicuta sativum -L.
Convolvulus sepium	Calystegia sepium	Coriandrum majus	Cicuta sativum -L.
Convolvulus soldanella	Calystegia soldanella	Coriandrum melphitense	Cicuta sativum -L.
Conyza squarrosa	Inula conyza	Coriaria riscifolia microphylla	C. microphylla
Conyzella canadensis	Conyza canadensis	Coriaria thymifolia	C. microphylla
Cooperanthes	Zephyranthes	Coridothymus capitatus	Thymus capitatus
Cooperia	Zephyranthes	Cornidia integerrima -Hook. & Arn.	Hydrangea serratifolia
Copaifera nitida	C. lansdorfii	Cornidia serratifolia -Hook. & Arn.	Hydrangea serratifolia
Copaifera sellowii	C. lansdorfii	Cornus 'Kelsey's Dwarf'	C. sericea 'Kelseyi'
Copiapoa barquitensis	C. hypogaea	Cornus alba -many authors not L.	C. stolonifera -Michx.
Copiapoa haseltoniana	C. cinerea v gigantea	Cornus alba 'Argenteovariegata'	C. alba 'Variegata'
Coprosma acerosa	C. brunnea	Cornus alba 'Atrosanguinea'	C. alba 'Sibirica'
Coprosma acerosa f brunnea	C. brunnea	Cornus alba 'Hessei' misapplied	C. sanguinea
Coprosma australis	C. grandifolia		'Compressa'
Coprosma baueri -Endl.	C. prisca -W .R. B. Oliv.		
Coprosma baueri misapplied	C. repens	Cornus alba 'Westonbirt'	C. alba 'Sibirica'
Coprosma baueriana	C. prisca	Cornus alternifolia 'Variegata'	C. alt. 'Argentea'
Coprosma billardierei	C. quadrifida	Cornus angustifolia	C. linifolia
Coprosma perpusilla	C. pumila	Cornus asperifolia h.	C. drummondii
Coprosma petriei atropurpurea	C. atropurpurea	Cornus baileyi -Coult. & Evans	C. stolonifera 'Baileyi'
Coprosma quadrifida	C. billardieri	Cornus brachypoda -C.A.Mey.	C. macrophylla -Wall.
Coprosma repens	C. pumila	Cornus brachypoda h.	C. controversa
Coprosma robusta 'Williamsii'	C. robusta 'Williamsii	Cornus candidissima -Marsh.	C. racemosa -Lam.
	Variegata'	Cornus chilensis -Mol.	Aristotelia chilensis
Coprosma villosa	C. pilosa	Cornus circinata -L'Herit	C. rugosa -Lam.
Coptidium lapponicum	Ranunculus lapponicus	Cornus coerulea	C. amomum
Coptis anemonaefolia	C. japonica	C. controversa 'Variegata' Fran's	C. con. 'Fran's Type'
Coptis groenlandica	C. trifolia	Cornus florida 'Tricolor'	C. florida 'Welchii'
Coptis japonica major	C. brachypetala	Cornus foemina	C. stricta
Coptis orientalis	C. japonica	Cornus hessei misapplied	C. sang. 'Compressa'
Coptis teetoides	C. teeta	Cornus japonicum	Viburnum japonicum
Corbularia bulbocodium	Narcissus bulbocodium	Cornus mas 'Elegantissima'	C. mas
Corchorus hirtus	Zelkova serrata		'Aureoelegantissima'
Corchorus japonicus -Thunb.	Kerria japonica	Cornus mas 'Tricolor'	C. mas
Corchorus scandens -Thunb.	Rhodotypos scandens		'Aureoelegantissima'
Cordia thyrsiflora -Sieb. & Zucc.	Ehretia acuminata v	Cornus mascula -L.	C. mas -L.
	obovata	Cornus microcarpa -Nash	C. asperifolia -Michx.
Cordyline fruticosa 'Red Draceana'	C. fruticosa 'Firebrand'	Cornus nuttallii 'Ascona'	C. 'Ascona'
Cordyline terminalis	C. fruticosa	Cornus paniculata -L'Herit.	C. racemosa -Lam.
Coreopsis auriculata Cutting Gold	C. a. 'Schnittgold'	Cornus paucinervis	C. quinquenervis
Coreopsis Baby Sun	C. 'Sonnenkind'	C. pubescens -not Willd. ex Schultes	C. occidentalis -Cov.
Coreopsis cardaminifolia	C. tinctoria	Cornus purpusii -Koehne	C. obliqua -Raf.
Coreopsis crassifolia	C. lanceolata	Cornus sanguinea 'Compressa'	C. hessei
Coreopsis grandiflora Ruby Throat	C. g. 'Rotkehlchen'	Cornus sanguinea 'Winter Flame'	C. s.a 'Winter Beauty'
Coreopsis harveyana	C. grandiflora	Cornus sanguinea v australis	C. australis - C.A.Mey.
Coreopsis heterogyna	C. lanceolata	Cornus sericea -L.	C. stolonifera
Coreopsis heterolepis	C. grandiflora	Cornus sericea 'White Spot'	C. sericea 'White Gold'
Coreopsis maximiliani	Helianthus maximiliani	Cornus stolonifera 'Kelsey's Dwarf'	C. sericea 'Kelseyi'
Coreopsis quadricornis	Bidens cernua	Cornus stolonifera 'Nana'	C. sericea 'Kelseyi'
Coreopsis saxicola	C. grandiflora	Cornus stolonifera 'White Spot'	C. sericea 'White Gold'
Coreopsis stenophylla	C. tinctoria	Cornus stolonifera f baileyi	C. sericea 'Baileyi'
		Cornus stolonifera v baileyi	C. sericea 'Baileyi'

Synonym	Current Name	Synonym	Current Name
Cornus tatarica -Mill.	C. alba -L.	C. caucasica v alba misapplied	C. malkensis
Cornus wilsoniana h. not Wanger.	C. walteri -Wanger.	Corydalis chinensis	C. edulis
Cornus x rutgersiensis 'Ruth Ellen'	C. 'Ruth Ellen'	Corydalis decipiens	C. solida ssp incisa
Corokia x virgata 'Erecta'	C. x v. 'Cheesemanii'	Corydalis fabacea	C. intermedia
Coronaria flos-cuculi	Lychnis flos-cuculi	Corydalis flexuosa 'Blue Dragon'	C. fl. 'Purple Leaf'
Coronilla cappadocica	C. orientalis	Corydalis glauca	C. sempervirens
Coronilla comosa	Hippocrepis comosa	Corydalis halleri	C. solida
Coronilla emerus -L.	Hippocrepis emerus	Corydalis micropoda	C. edulis
Coronilla glauca -L.	C. valentina ssp glauca	Corydalis parnassica	C. blanda ssp parnass.
Coronilla stipularis -Lam.	C. valentina -L.	Corydalis pseudofumaria alba	C. ochroleuca
Coronopus procumbens	C. squamatus	Corydalis ramosa -Wall.	C. vaginans -Royle
Coronopus ruellii	C. squamatus	Corydalis scandens	Dicentra scandens
Correa 'Carmine Bells'	C. 'Dusky Bells'	Corydalis solida f transsylvanica	C. solida ssp solida
Correa 'Harrisii'	C. 'Mannii'	Corydalis solida ssp densiflora	C. solida ssp incisa
Correa 'Pink Bells'	C. 'Dusky Bells'	Corydalis thalictrifolia -Franchet	C. saxicola
Correa 'Rubra'	C. 'Dusky Bells'	Corydalis transsylvanica	C. solida ssp solida
Correa affinis	C. aemula	Corylopsis gotoana -Mak.	C. glabrescens v got.
Correa cardinalis	C. reflexa v speciosa	Corylopsis platypetala	C. sinensis v
Correa ferruginea	C. lawrenceana v law.		calvescens
Correa latrobeana	C. lawrenceana v lat.	Corylopsis platypetala v laevis	C. sin. v calvescens
Correa lawrenceana v ferruginea	C. lawrenceana v law.	Corylopsis veitchiana	C. sinensis v
Correa lawrenceana v glabra	C. lawrenceana v law.		calvescens f veitchiana
Correa leucoclada	C. glabra v leucocl.	Corylopsis willmottiae	C. sinensis v sinensis
Correa macrocalyx	C. lawrenceana v mac.	Corylus avellana 'Bollwylle'	C. maxima 'Halle'sche
Correa reflexa	C. eburnea		Riesennuss'
Correa reflexa v cardinalis	C. reflexa v speciosa	Corylus avellana 'Laciniata'	C. a. 'Heterophylla'
Correa reflexa v coriacea	C. backhouseana v cor.	C. avellana 'Merveille deBollwyller'	C. maxima 'Halle'sche
Correa reflexa v glabra	C. glabra		Riesennuss'
Correa reflexa v nummulariifolia	C. speciosa v nummul.	C. avellana 'Nottingham Prolific'	C. avellana 'Pearson's
Correa reflexa v reflexa	C. cordifolia		Prolific'
Correa rotundifolia	C. alba v pannosa	Corylus avellana 'Purpurea'	C. a. 'Fuscorubra'
Correa rubra v glabra	C. glabra	Corylus avellana 'Quercifolia'	C. a. 'Heterophylla'
Correa rubra v magacalyx	C. glabra v leucoclada	Corylus colurna v chinensis	C. chinensis -Franch.
Correa rubra v turnbulllii	C. glabra v turnbullii	Corylus colurna x avellana	C. x colurnoides
Correa schlechtandalii	C. glabra v turnbullii	Corylus Early Long Zeller	C. 'Lang Tidlig Zeller'
Correa speciosa	C. reflexa v speciosa	Corylus ferox v tibetica	C. tibetica -Batal.
Correa speciosa v cardinalis	C. reflexa v speciosa	Corylus intermedia	C. x colurnoides
Correa speciosa v glabra	C. glabra	Corylus lacera -Wall.	C. jacquemontii
Correa speciosa v leucoclada	C. glabra v leucoclada	Corylus mandschurica	C. sieboldiana v mand.
Correa turnbulllii	C. glabra v turnbullii	C. maxima 'White Spanish Filbert'	C. m. 'White Filbert'
Cortaderia argentea	C. selloana	C. maxima 'Witpit Lambertsnoot'	C. m. 'White Filbert'
Cortaderia conspicua	Chionochloa conspicua	Corylus maxima 'Atropurpurea'	C. maxima 'Purpurea'
Cortaderia conspicua fulvida	C. fulvida	C. maxima 'Fertile de Coutard'	C. m. 'White Filbert'
Cortaderia fulvida misapplied	C. richardii	C. maxima 'Fruhe van Frauendorf'	C. maxima 'Red Filbert'
Cortaderia richardii misapplied	C. fulvida	C. maxima 'Grote Lambertsnoot'	C. m. 'Kentish Cob'
Cortaderia selloana 'Gold Band'	C. s. 'Aureolineata'	Corylus maxima 'Lambert's Filbert'	C. m. 'Kentish Cob'
Cortaderia selloana 'Silver Stripe'	C. selloana 'Albolineata'	Corylus maxima 'Longue d'Espagne'	C. m. 'Kentish Cob'
Cortaderia Toe Toe	C. richardii	C. maxima 'Monsiuer de Bouweller'	C. maxima 'Halle'sche
Corydalis 'Blue Dragon'	C. fl. 'Purple Leaf'		Riesennuss'
Corydalis 'Blue Panda'	C. fl. 'Blue Panda'	Corylus maxima 'Purple Filbert'	C. maxima 'Purpurea'
Corydalis alexeenkoana ssp vittae	C. vittae	Corylus maxima 'Red Zellernut'	C. maxima 'Red Filbert'
Corydalis ambigua h.	C. fumariifolia	Corylus maxima 'Spanish White'	C. m. 'White Filbert'
Corydalis bulbosa -De Candolle	C. solida	Corylus maxima Halle Giant	C. maxima 'Halle'sche
Corydalis bulbosa misapplied	C. cava		Riesennuss'
Corydalis canadensis	Dicentra canadensis	Corylus maxima New Giant	C. m 'Neue Riesennuss'

Synonym	Current Name	Synonym	Current Name
Corylus rostrata -Ait.	C. cornuta -Marsh	Cotoneaster buxifolius f vellaeus	C. astrophorus
Corylus tubulosa -Willd.	C. maxima -Mill.	Cotoneaster conspicuus v decorus	C.conspicuus 'Decorus'
Corymbia	Eucalyptus	(regarded as typical of the form, and a synonym)	
Corynabutilon	Abutilon	Cotoneaster dammeri 'Eicholz'	C. radicans 'Eichholz'
Corynabutilon ochsenii	Abutilon ochsenii	Cotoneaster dammeri 'Oakwood'	C. radicans 'Eichholz'
Corynabutilon vitifolium	Abutilon vitifolium	C. dammeri 'Streibs Findling'	C. 'Streib's Finding'
Corynanthe yohimbe	Pausinystalia yohimbe	Cotoneaster dammeri v radicans	C. radicans
Corynophallus -Schott	Amorphophallus - Blume	C. dammeri v radicans misapplied	C. dammeri 'Major'
		Cotoneaster dielsianus v elegans	C. elegans
Corypha australis	Livistona australis	Cotoneaster distichus	C. nitidus
Coryphantha calochlora	C. nickelsiae	Cotoneaster distichus v tongolensis	C. splendens
Coryphantha conoidea	Neolloydia conoidea	Cotoneaster duthieanus 'Boer'	C. apiculatus
Coryphantha radians	C. cornifera	Cotoneaster fontanesii -Spach	C. racemiflorus
Coryphantha vivipara	Escobaria vivipara	Cotoneaster franchetii v sternianus	C. sternianus
Cosbaea coccinea	Kadsura coccinea	Cotoneaster frigidus 'Xanthocarpus'	C. f. 'Fructu Luteo'
Cosmos sulphureus 'Lemon Queen'	C. s. 'Butterkist'	Cotoneaster frigidus f fructu-luteo	C. f. 'Fructu Luteo'
Cosmos sulphureus 'Yellow Garden'	C. s. 'Butterkist'	C. glaucophyllus f serotinus	C. serotinus
Costus igneus	C. cuspidatus	C. glaucophyllus f serotinus (unv)	C. glaucophyllus
Cotinus americanus	C. obovatus	C. glaucophyllus v vestitus	C. vestitus
C. coggygria 'Atrourpurpureus'	C. coggygria Purpureus Group	C. hebephyllus v majusculus	C. majusculus
		Cotoneaster hjelmqvistii 'Robustus'	C. hjelmqvistii
Cotinus coggygria 'Flame'	C. 'Flame'	C. hjelmqvistii 'Rotundifolius'	C. hjelmqvistii
Cotinus coggygria 'Foliis Purpureis'	C. coggygria Rubrifolius Group	Cotoneaster horizontalis 'Robustus'	C. hjelmqvistii
		C. horizontalis 'Variegatus'	C. atropurpureus 'Variegatus'
Cotoneaster 'Gnom'	C. salicifolius 'Gnom'		
Cotoneaster 'Autumn Fire'	C. 'Herbstfeuer'	C. horizontalis v adpressus	C. adpressus -Bois
Cotoneaster 'Eastleigh'	C. prostratus 'Eastleigh'	C. horizontalis v perpusillus	C. perpusillus
		Cotoneaster horizontalis v wilsonii	C. ascendens
Cotoneaster 'Erlinda'	C. x suecicus 'Erlinda'	Cotoneaster humifusus	C. dammeri
Cotoneaster 'Herbstfeuer'	C. salicifolius 'Herbstfeuer'	Cotoneaster incanus	C. hebephyllus v inc.
		Cotoneaster insignis (some)	C. lindleyi -Steud.
Cotoneaster 'Highlight'	C. pluriflorus	C. melanocarpus v laxiflorus	C. laxiflorus-Lindl.
Cotoneaster 'Hybridus Pendulus'	C. sal. 'Pendulus'	Cotoneaster melanotrichus	C. cochleatus
Cotoneaster 'John Waterer'	C. x watereri 'John Waterer'	C. melanotrichus 'Donard Gem'	C. astrophorus
		C. microphyllus 'Teulon Porter'	C. astrophorus
Cotoneaster 'Pershore Coral'	C. frigidus 'Pershore Coral'	C. microphyllus f melanotrichus	C. cochleatus
		C. microphyllus misapplied	C. purpurascens
Cotoneaster 'Rothschilianus'	C. salicifolius 'Rothschildianus'	C. microphyllus v cochleatus	C. cochleatus
		C. m. v cochleatus misapplied	C. cashmiriensis
Cotoneaster 'Royal Beauty'	C. x suecicus 'Coral Beauty'	C. microphyllus v conspicuus	C.conspicuus 'Decorus'
		(regarded as typical of the form, and a synonym)	
Cotoneaster acutifolius -Lindl.	C. lucidus -Schlecht	C. microphyllus v glacialis -Hook	C. congestus -Baker
C. acutifolius v laetevirens	C. laetevirens	C. microphyllus v thymifolius	C. integrifolius
Cotoneaster acutifolius v villosulus	C. villosulus	C. m. v thymifolius misapplied	C. linearifolius
Cotoneaster adpressus 'Tom Thumb'	C. adp. 'Little Gem'	C. microphyllus v uva-ursi	C. rotundifolius -Wall.
Cotoneaster adpressus v praecox	C. nanshan -Vilm.	ex Lind. some disagree (C.prostratus -Baker)	
Cotoneaster affinis v bacillaris	C. bacillaris -Lindl.	Cotoneaster Mooncreeper	C. dammeri 'Mooncreeper'
Cotoneaster angustifolia -Franch.	Pyracantha angustifol.		
Cotoneaster applanatus -Duthie	C. dielsianus -Pritz	Cotoneaster multiflorus h.	C. purpurascens
Cotoneaster bullatus 'Firebird'	C. ignescens	Cotoneaster multiflorus v calocarpus	C. calocarpus
Cotoneaster bullatus f floribundus	C. bullatus	Cotoneaster nanshan 'Boer'	C. apiculatus
C. bullatus v macrophyllus	C. rehderi -Pojark	Cotoneaster nebrodensis	C. tomentosus -Lind.
Cotoneaster buxifolius -Bak.	C. marginatus	Cotoneaster nitidifolius	C. glomerulatus
Cotoneaster buxifolius 'Brno'	C. marginatus 'Brno'	Cotoneaster nummularius -Lind.	C. lindleyi -Steud.
Cotoneaster buxifolius blue-leaved	C. lidjiangensis	Cotoneaster parneyi	C. lacteus

Synonym	Current Name	Synonym	Current Name
Cotoneaster permutatus	C. pluriflorus	Cotyledon alternans	Adromischus
Cotoneaster praecox 'Boer'	C. apiculatus		maculatus
C. procumbens 'Streib's Findling'	C. 'Streib's Findling'	Cotyledon chrysantha	Rosularia chrysantha
Cotoneaster prostratus -Bak.	C. rotundifolius	Cotyledon cooperi	Adromischus cooperi
Cotoneaster prostratus v lanatus	C. marginatus	Cotyledon edulis	Dudleya edulis
Cotoneaster pyracantha -(L.) Spach	Pyracantha coccinea	Cotyledon gibbiflora v metallica	Echeveria gibbiflora v
Cotoneaster pyrenaicus	C. congestus -Baker		metallica
C. racemiflorus v nummularius	C. nummularius	Cotyledon lanceolata	Dudleya lanceolata
Cotoneaster racemiflorus v veitchii	C. veitchii	Cotyledon maculata	Adromischus maculat.
Cotoneaster racemiflorus v veitchii	C. veitchii	Cotyledon oblonga	C. orbiculata v oblonga
Cotoneaster reflexus -Carr.	C. multiflorus -Bunge	Cotyledon oppositifolia	Chiastophyllum
Cotoneaster rotundifolius h.	C. nitidus		oppositifolium
C. rotundifolius v verruculosus	C. verruculosus -Diels	Cotyledon paniculata	Tylecodon paniculatus
Cotoneaster salicifolius 'Avondrood'	C. salicifolius 'Repens'	Cotyledon pulverulenta	Dudleya pulverulenta
Cotoneaster salicifolius 'Gnome'	C. salicifolius 'Gnom'	Cotyledon reticulata	Tylecodon reticulatus
Cotoneaster salicifolius 'Pendulus'	C. salicifolius 'Hybridus	Cotyledon simplicifolia	Chiastophyllum
	Pendulus'		oppositifolium
Cotoneaster salicif. Autumn Fire	C. s. 'Herbstfeuer'	C. tomentosa v ladismithensis	C. ladismithensis
Cotoneaster salicif. Park Carpet	C. s. 'Parkteppich'	C. tomentosa v ladismithensis	Tylecodon paniculatus
Cotoneaster salicifolius v floccosus	C. floccosus	Cotyledon trigyna (unv)	Adromischus
Cotoneaster salicifolius v rugosus	C. rugosus -Pritz.		umbraticola
C. salicifolius v rugosus h.	C. hylmoei	Cotyledon umbilicus-veneris	Umbilicus rupestris
C. schlechtendalii 'Blazovice'	C. marginatus	Cotyledon wallichii	Tylecodon papillaris
	'Blazovice'		ssp wallichii
Cotoneaster schlechtendalii 'Brno'	C. marginatus 'Brno'	Cotyledon zeyheri	Adromischus cristatus
Cotoneaster serotinus misapplied	C. meiophyllus		v zeyheri
Cotoneaster simonsii 'Newryensis'	C. newryensis -Lem.	Coumarouna odorata	Dipteryx odorata
Cotoneaster simonsii v newryensis	C. newryensis -Lem.	Cowania mexicana v stansburiana	Purshia stanburyana
Cotoneaster splendens 'Sabrina'	C. splendens	Cowania purpurea -Zucc.	Purshia plicata -D.Don
Cotoneaster thymifolius -Lindl.	C. integrifolius	Cowania stansburiana -Torr.	Purshia stanburyana
Cotoneaster vulgaris -Lind.	C. integerrimus -Med.	Crambe aspera	C. tataria
Cotoneaster wardii misapplied	C. mairei	Crambe litwinowii	C. glauca
Cotoneaster wheeleri h.	C. marginatus	Crassula arborescens	C. atropurpurea v
C. x suecicus 'Skogsholmen'	C. x s. 'Skogholm'		arborescens
Cotoneaster x watereri 'Avonbank'	C. salicifolius	Crassula argentea	C. ovata
	'Avonbank'	Crassula corymbosula	C. capitella ssp
Cotoneaster x watereri 'Cornubia'	C. frigidus 'Cornubia'		thyrsiflora
Cotoneaster x watereri 'Pendulus'	C. 'Hybridus Pendulus'	Crassula deceptrix	C. deceptor
Cotula 'Platt's Black'	Leptinella squalida	Crassula lycopodioides	C. muscosa
	'Platt's Black'	Crassula maculata h.	Adromischus maculat.
Cotula atrata	Leptinella atrata	Crassula portulacea	C. ovata
Cotula atrata v dendyi	Leptinella dendyi	Crassula recurva	C. helmsii
Cotula goyenii	Leptinella goyenii	Crassula rosularis	C. orbicularis
Cotula minor	Leptinella minor	Crassula sedifolia	C. setulosa 'Milfordiae'
Cotula pectinata	Leptinella pectinata	Crassula sediformis	C. setulosa 'Milfordiae'
Cotula perpusilla	Leptinella pusilla	Crassula thyrsiflora	C. capitella ssp thyrsif.
Cotula potentillina	Leptinella potentillina	+ Crataegomespilus grandiflora	+ Crataegomespilus gr
Cotula potentilloides	Leptinella potentillina	Crataegus 'Praecox'	C. monogyna 'Biflora'
Cotula pyrethrifolia	Leptinella pyrethrifolia	Crataegus acutiloba -Sarg.	C. macrosperma v ac.
Cotula reptans	Leptinella scariosa	Crataegus arborescens -Ell.	C. viridis -L.
Cotula rotundata	Leptinella rotundata	Crataegus arbutifolia -Dryander	Photinia arbutifolia
Cotula scariosa	Leptinella scariosa	Crataegus aria -L.	Sorbus aria -L.
Cotula sericea	Leptinella albida	Crataegus aronia -Bosc	C. azarolus -L.
Cotula serrulata	Leptinella serrulata	Crataegus biflora	C. praecox
Cotula squalida	Leptinella squalida	Crataegus calpodendron	C. tomentosa -L.

Synonym	Current Name	Synonym	Current Name
Crataegus carrierei	C. x lavallei 'Carrierei'	Crataegus punctata 'Xanthocarpa'	C. punctata 'Aurea'
Crataegus celsiana -Dipp. not Bosc.	C. x dippeliana -Lange	Crataegus purpurea v altaica	C. altaica
Crataegus coccinea -L. in part	C. intricata Lange	Crataegus pyracantha -(L.) Med.	Pyracantha coccinea
Crataegus coccinea -L. in part	C. pedicillata -Sarg.	Crataegus rivularis -Nutt. C. douglasii -Lind.	
Crataegus coccinea v mollis	C. mollis	Crataegus rotundifolia -Lam.	C. ovalis -Med.
Crataegus coccinea v rotundifolia	C. chrysocarpa v phoenicia -Palmer	Crataegus rotundifolia -Moench	C. chrysocarpa v phoenicia -Palmer
Crataegus coccinoides v dilitata	C. dilatata -Sarg.	Crataegus sanguinea v villosa	C. maximowiczii
Crataegus cordata -Ait.	C. phaenopyrum	Crataegus schraderana -Ledeb.	C. schraderana
Crataegus crenulata -D.Don	Pyracantha crenulata	Crataegus serratifolia -Desf.	Photinia serratifolia
Crataegus crus-galli misapplied	C. persimilis 'Prunifolia'	Crataegus sinaica -Boiss.	C. azarolus v sinaica
		Crataegus spicata -Borkh.not Med.	Amelanchier spicata
Crataegus crus-galli v prunifolia	C.persimilis 'Prunifolia'	Crataegus stipulacea	C. pubescens f stip.
Crataegus fischeri -Schneid.	C. songorica -K.Koch	Crataegus stipulacea -Loud.	C. pubescens f stip.
Crataegus florentina -Zuccagni	Malus florentina	Crataegus tanacetifolia v leeana	C. x dippeliana -Lange
Crataegus glabra -Thunb.	Photinia glabra	Crataegus tournefortii -Griseb.	C. schraderana
Crataegus indica -L.	Rhamnus indica	Crataegus villosa -Thunb.	Photinia villosa
Crataegus korolkowii -Henry	C. wattiana	Crataegus viridis v nitida -Engel.	C. nitida -(engel.) Sarg.
Crataegus korolkowii -Schneid.	C. pinnatifida v major	Crawfurdia speciosa	Gentiana speciosa
Crataegus laciniata	C. orientalis	Crenularia	Aethionema
C. laevigata 'Coccinea Plena'	C. l. 'Paul's Scarlet'	Crepis erucifolia	C. bursifolia
Crataegus laevigata 'Flore Pleno'	C. laevigata 'Plena'	Crepis glauca	C. runcinata
Crataegus laevis -Thunb.	Photinia villosa v laevis	Crepis taraxacifolia	C. vesicaria
Crataegus leeana -(Loud.) Bean	C. x dippeliana -Lange	Crinitaria	Aster
Crataegus maroccana -Lindl.	C. azarolus v sinaica	Crinodendron dependens	Crinodendron patagua
Crataegus mexicana -DC.	C. pubescens f stipulacea	Crinum aquaticum	C. campanulatum
		Crinum caffrum	C. campanulatum
Crataegus microcarpa -Lindl.	C. spathulata -Michx.	Crinum capense	C. bulbispermum
Crataegus monogyna 'Fastigiata'	C. monogyna 'Stricta'	Crinum longifolium	C. bulbispermum
C. monogyna 'Inermis Compacta'	C. mon. 'Compacta'	Crinum x powellii 'Longifolium'	C. bulbispermum
Crataegus monogyna 'Praecox'	C. monogyna 'Biflora'	Crinum x powellii 'Roseum'	C. x powellii
Crataegus monogyna 'Tortuosa'	C. monogyna 'Flexuosa'	Crinum zeylanicum	C. latifolium v zeylan.
Crataegus monogyna f pendula	C. monogya 'Pendula'	Criogenes	Cypripedium
Crataegus monogyna f stricta	C. monogya 'Stricta'	Crocanthemum canadense	Helianthemum can.
Crataegus odoratissima -Lindl.	C. laciniata -Ucria	Crocosmia Old Hat	C. 'Walberton Red'
Crataegus orientalis -Bieb.	C. laciniata -Ucria	Crocosmia 'Citronella' h.	C. 'Golden Fleece'
Crataegus orientalis v sanguinea	C. schraderana	Crocosmia 'Darkleaf Apricot'	C. x crocosmiiflora 'Gerbe d'Or'
Crataegus oxyacantha	C. laevigata		
C. oxyacantha coccinea plena	C. laev. 'Paul's Scarlet'	Crocosmia 'Eldorado'	C. x croc. 'E.A.Bowles'
Crataegus oxyacantha f aurea	C. laevigata f aurea	Crocosmia 'Fire King' misapplied	C. x c. 'Jackanapes'
Crataegus oxyacantha paulii	C. laev. 'Paul's Scarlet'	Crocosmia 'George Davison' h.	C. x c.'Golden Glory'
Crataegus oxyacantha v biflora	C. monogya 'Biflora'	Crocosmia 'George Davison' h.	C. x c. 'Sulphurea'
Crataegus oxyacantha v oliveriana	C. oliveriana Crataegus	Crocosmia 'Golden Fleece' -Lemoine	C. x c. 'Gerbe d'Or'
oxyacantha v pendula	C. monogya 'Pendula'	Crocosmia 'Lady Wilson' h.	C. x c. 'Norwich Canary'
Crataegus oxyacantha v praecox	C. monogya 'Biflora'		
Crataegus oxyacantha v stricta	C. monogya 'Stricta'	Crocosmia 'Late Cornish'	C. x crocosmiiflora 'Queen Alexandra'
C. oxyacantha v xanthocarpa	C. laevigata f aurea		
Crataegus oxyacanthoides -Thuillier	C. laevigata -(Poir) DC. (C.oxyacantha L. Jacq.)	Crocosmia 'Mount Stewart'	C. x c. 'Jessie'
		Crocosmia 'Mr Bedford'	C. x c. 'Croesus'
Crataegus parvifolia -Ait.	C. uniflora -Muench.	Crocosmia 'Rowden Bronze'	C. x c. 'Gerbe d'Or'
Crataegus pedicillata	C. coccinea L.	Crocosmia 'Rowden Chrome'	C. x c. 'George Davison' -Davison
C. pedicillata v ellwangeriana	C. ellwangeriana		
Crataegus pentagyna v oliveriana	C. oliveriana Crataegus	Crocosmia 'Saturn'	C. 'Jupiter'
prunifolia -(Lam.) Pers.	C. persimilis 'Prunifolia'	Crocosmia aurea 'Lady MacKenzie'	C.xc. 'Emily MacKenzie'
		Crocosmia aurea 'Mrs Morrison'	C. x crocosmiiflora

Synonym	Current Name	Synonym	Current Name
	'Mrs Geoffrey Howard'	Crocus sieberi 'Bowles' White'	C. sieberi 'Albus'
Crocosmia aurea 'Princess'	C. x c. 'Red Knight'	Crocus speciosus f albus	C. speciosus 'Albus'
Crocosmia aurea 'Rheingold'	C. x c. 'Golden Glory'	Crocus susianus	C. angustifolius
C. a. 'Solfaterre Coleton Fishacre'	C. x c. 'Gerbe d'Or'	Crocus suterianus	C. olivieri ssp olivieri
Crocosmia aurea misapplied	C.x c. 'George Davison'	Crocus vernus 'Joan of Arc'	C. vernus 'Jeanne
Crocosmia aurea Newry seedling	C. x c. 'Prometheus'		d'Arc'
Crocosmia rosea	Tritonia disticha ssp	Crocus vernus 'Vanguard'	C. 'Vanguard'
	rubrolucens	C. vernus ssp vernus 'Grandiflorus'	C. vernus 'Purpureus
C.x crocosmiflora 'Lady MacKenzie'	C. x crocosmiiflora		Grandiflorus'
	'Emily MacKenzie'	Crocus x stellaris	C. x luteus 'Stellaris'
C. x crocosmiflora 'Mrs Morrison'	C. x crocosmiiflora	Crocus zonatus	C. kotschyanus ssp
	'Mrs Geoffrey Howard'		kotschyanus
C. x crocosmiflora 'Princess'	C. x crocosmiiflora	Crossandra undulifolia	C. infundibuliformis
	'Red Knight'	Crotalaria eriantha	C. sessiliflora
C. x crocosmiflora 'Rheingold'	C. x c. 'Golden Glory'	Croton congestum	Xylosma japonica
C. x c. 'Solfaterre Coleton Fishacre'	C. x c. 'Gerbe d'Or'	Croton japonicum -Thunb.	Mallotus japonicus
C. x crocosmiflora Newry seedling	C. x c. 'Prometheus'	Croton pictum	Codiaeum variegatum
Crocus 'Cloth of Gold'	C. angustifolius	Croton sebiferum	Sapium sebiferum
Crocus 'Dutch Yellow'	C. x luteus 'Golden	Crowea angustifolia v dentata	C. a. v platyphylla
	Yellow'	Crowea dentata	C. a. v platyphylla
Crocus 'Golden Mammoth'	C. x l. 'Golden Yellow'	Crowea latifolia	C. saligna
Crocus 'Large Yellow'	C. x l. 'Golden Yellow'	Crowea saligna v major	C. saligna
Crocus 'Mammoth Yellow'	C. x l. 'Golden Yellow'	Crowea saligna v stricta	C. saligna
Crocus 'Princess Beatrix'	C. chrysanthus	Crucianella stylosa	Phuopsis stylosa
	'Prinses Beatrix'	Crucifera alliaria	Alliaria petiolata
Crocus 'Purpureus'	C. vernus 'Purpureus	Crucifera armoracia	Armoracia rusticana
	Grandiflorus'	Crucifera aubrieta	Aubrieta deltoidea
Crocus 'Yellow Mammoth'	C. x l. 'Golden Yellow'	Crucifera barbarea	Barbarea vulgaris
Crocus albiflorus	C. vernus ssp albifl.	Crucifera capsella	Capsella bursa-
Crocus asturicus	C. serotinus ssp		pastoris
	salzmannii	Crucifera cardamine	Cardamine hirsuta
Crocus aureus	C. flavus ssp flavus	Crucifera isatis	Isatis tinctoria
Crocus biflorus v parkinsonii	C. biflorus ssp biflorus	Crucifera lepidium	Lepidium campestre
	'Parkinsonii'	Crucifera parviflora	Cardamine parviflora
Crocus biliottii	C. aerius	Crucifera raphanistrum	Raphanus raphan.
Crocus cancellatus v cilicicus	C. c. ssp cancellatus	Crucifera rubella	Capsella bursa-
Crocus candidus v subflavus	C. olivieri ssp olivieri		pastoris
Crocus cannulatus v chrysanthus	C. chrysanthus	Crucifera thaliana	Arabidopsis thaliana
C. cartwrightianus 'Albus' misap.	C. hadriaticus	Crucifera umbellata	Iberis umbellata
Crocus clusii	C. serotinus ssp clusii	Cryophytum crystallinum	Mesembryanthemum
Crocus cretensis	C. boryi		crystallinum
Crocus edulis	C. cancellatus	Cryphia	Prostanthera
Crocus flavus	C. flavus ssp flavus	Crypta minima	Elatine minima
Crocus goulimyi 'Albus'	C. goulimyi 'Mani White'	Crypta triandra	Elatine triandra
		Cryptandra rotundifolia	Pomaderris rotundif.
C. hadriaticus v chrysobelonicus	C. hadriaticus	Cryptanthopsis navioides	Orthophytum navioides
Crocus ionicus	C. boryi	Cryptanthus acaulis v ruber	C. acaulis 'Rubra'
Crocus iridiflorus	C. banaticus	Cryptanthus bromelioides v tricolor	C. b. 'Tricolor'
Crocus lazicus	C. scharojanii	Cryptocereus anthonyanus	Selenicereus anthony.
Crocus pulchellus 'Zephyr'	C. 'Zephyr'	Cryptocorine -A.Rich.	Cryptocoryne
Crocus salzmannii	C. serotinus ssp salz.	Cryptogramma crispa ssp acrostichoides	
Crocus sativus v cartwrightianus	C. cartwrightianus		Cryptogramma acrostic.
Crocus scepusiensis	C. vernus ssp vernus	Cryptomeria fortunei	C. japonica v sinensis
	v scepusiensis	C. japonica 'Albovariegata'	C. j. 'Nana Albospica'
Crocus sibiricus	C. sieberi	C. japonica 'Argenteovariegata'	C. j. 'Nana Albospica'

Synonym	Current Name	Synonym	Current Name
Cryptomeria japonica 'Enko-sugi'	C. j. 'Araucarioides'		'Pygmaea'
C. japonica 'Littleworth Dwarf'	C. j. 'Littleworth Gnom'	Cupressus hodginsii -Dunn	Fokienia hodginsii
C. japonica 'Lobbii Nana' h.	C. japonica 'Nana'	Cupressus japonica -L.f.	Cryptomeria japonica
Cryptomeria japonica 'Midare-sugi'	C. japonica 'Viridis'	Cupressus lambertiana -Gord.	C. macrocarpa -Gord.
C. japonica 'Monstrosa Nana'	C. j. 'Mankichi-sugi'	Cupressus lambertiana v fastigiata	C. mac. f fastigiata
Cryptomeria japonica 'Sekka-sugi'	C. japonica 'Cristata'	Cupressus lawsoniana -A.Murr.	Chamaecyparis
C. japonica 'Spiralis Elongata'	C. j. 'Spiraliter Falcata'		lawsoniana
Cryptomeria japonica 'Wogon'	C. japonica 'Aurea'	Cupressus leylandii -Dallim.&Jacks.	x Cupressocyparis
Cryptomeria japonica 'Yatsubusa'	C. japonica 'Tansu'		leylandii
Cryptomeria japonica 'Yore-sugi'	C. japonica 'Spiralis'	Cupressus lindleyi -Klotsch	C. lusitanica -Mill.
Cryptomeria sinensis	C. japonica v sinensis	Cupressus macrocarpa 'Globosa'	C. macrocarpa 'Globe'
Cryptostemma calendulaceum	Arctotheca calendula	C. macrocarpa 'Horizontalis Aurea'	C. m. 'Gold Spread'
Cryptotaenia canadensis japonica	C. japonica	Cupressus macrocarpa 'Lebretoni'	C. m. 'Variegata'
Cucubalus behen	Silene vulgaris	Cupressus macrocarpa 'Minimax'	C. m. 'Minima'
Cucumis colocynthis	Citrullus colocynthis	Cupressus macrocarpa 'Sulphurea'	C. m. 'Crippsii'
Cucurbita hispida	Benincasa hispida	Cupressus nootkatensis -D.Don	Chamaecyparis
Cudrania	Maclura		nootkatensis Cupressus
Cudrania tricuspidata	Maclura tricuspidata	obtusa	Chamaecyparis obtusa
Cuminum odorum	C. cyminum	Cupressus patula	Platycladus orientalis
Cunigunda perfoliata	Eupatorium perfoliatum	Cupressus pendula -Griff.	C. cashmeriana
Cunila fruticosa	Westringia fruticosa	Cupressus pisifera	Chamaecyparis pisif.
Cunila glabella	Calamintha arkansana	Cupressus pygmaea -(Lemm.) Sarg.	C. m.'Pygmaea'
Cunila mariana	C. origanoides	C. sempervirens 'Green Pencil'	C. s.'Green Spire'
Cunninghamia lanceolata 'Compacta'	C. lanceolata 'Bano'	C. sempervirens 'Pyrimidalis'	C. s. Stricta Group
Cunninghamia selaginoides	Athrotaxis selaginoides	C. sempervirens v sempervirens	C. s. Stricta Group
Cunninghamia sinensis -Rich.	C. lanceolata	Cupressus thuja	Platycladus orientalis
Cunninghamia unicaniculata	C. lanceolata	Cupressus thurifera -not H.B.K.	C. lusitanica v
Cupania sapida	Blighia sapida		benthamii -(Endl.) Carr.
Cuphea llavea	C. x purpurea	Cupressus thyoides -L.	Chamaecyparis thyoid.
Cuphea llavea 'Tiny Mice'	C. ll. 'Georgia Scarlet'	Cupressus torulosa v corneyana	C. corneyana
Cuphea llavea v miniata h.	C. x purpurea	Cupressus x leylandii	x Cupressocyparis
Cuphea miniata h.	C. x purpurea		leylandii
Cuphea platycentra	C. ignea	Curcuma domestica	C. longa
Cupressus arbor-vitae -Targ. Tozz.	Thuja occidentalis	Curmeria -Andre	Homalomena -Schott
Cupressus arizonica v bonita -h. some authors, not Lemm.		Currania dryopteris	Gymnocarpium dryop.
	C. arizonica v glabra	Curtonus	Crocosmia
Cupressus arizonica v bonita -Lemm.	C. arizonica v arizonica	Curtonus paniculatus	Crocosmia paniculata
Cupressus attenuata	Chamaecyparis	Cuscuaria -Schott	Scindapsus -Schott
	lawsoniana	Cuscuta curta	C. megalocarpa
Cupressus benthamii -Endl.	C. lusitanica v benth.	Cuscuta europea indica	C. europea
Cupressus disticha	Taxodium distihum	Cuscuta systyla	C. japonica
Cupressus filiformis h.	Platycladus orientalis	Cyananthus integer misapplied	C. microphyllus
Cupressus formosensis	Chamaecyparis form.	Cyananthus zhongdienensis	C. chungdienensis
Cupressus fragrans	Chamaecyparis	Cyanella capensis	C. hyacinthoides
	lawsoniana	Cyanella odoratissima	C. lutea
Cupressus funebris v glauca	C. cashmeriana -Carr	Cyanococcus hirsutus	Vaccinium hirsutum
Cupressus glabra	C. arizonica v glabra	Cyanococcus vacillans	Vaccinium vacillans
Cupressus glabra 'Arctic'	C. arizonica v arizonica	Cyanothamnus anethifolius	Boronia ramosa ssp
	'Arctic'		anethifolia
Cupressus glabra 'Compacta'	C. ariz. v g. 'Compacta'	Cyanothamnus tridactylites	Boronia anemonifolia
Cupressus glabra 'Nana'	C. ariz. v g. 'Compacta'	Cyanus angustifolius	Centaurea montana -L.
Cupressus glabra 'Pyramidalis'	C. arizonica	Cyanus arvensis -Moench	Centaurea cyanus
	'Pyramidalis'	Cyanus coriaceus	Centaurea scabiosa
Cupressus glauca -Lam.	C. lusitanica -Mill.	Cyanus dentato-folius -Gilib.	Centaurea cyanus
Cupressus goveniana v pygmaea	C. macrocarpa	Cyanus jacea	Centaurea jacea

Synonym	Current Name	Synonym	Current Name
Cyanus laciniatus	Centaurea scabiosa	Cydonia speciosa -Sweet	Chaenomeles speciosa
Cyanus niger	Centaurea nigra	Cydonia vulgaris -Pers.	C. oblonga -Mill.
Cyanus scabiosa	Centaurea scabiosa	Cyllenium -Schott	Biarum -Schott
Cyanus segetum -Hill.	Centaurea cyanus	Cymbalaria muralis 'Albiflora'	C. muralis 'Pallidor'
Cyanus vulgaris -Delarb.	Centaurea cyanus	Cymbidium grandiflorum	C. hookerianum
Cyathea boylei	C. cunninghamii	Cymbidium hyemale	Aplectrum hyemale
Cyathea filix-femina	Athyrium filix-femina	Cymbidium odontorhizon	Corallorhiza odontor.
Cyathodes acerosa -(Gaert.) R. Br.	C. juniperina Cyathodes	Cymbidium pendulum	C. aloifolium
colensoi	Leucopogon colensoi	Cymopterus glomeratus	C. acaulis
Cyathodes empetrifolia	Androstoma empetrif.	Cymopterus hendersonii	Pteryxia hendersonii
Cyathodes ericoides	Leucopogon ericoides	Cynachum erectum -L.	Cionura erecta
Cyathodes fasciculata	Leucopogon fascicul.	Cynara hystrix	C. baetica ssp
Cyathodes fraseri	Leucopogon fraseri		maroccana
Cyathodes juniperina	Leptecophylla juniper.	Cynara scolymus	C. cardunculus
Cyathodes parviflora	Leucopogon parvifl.		Scolymus Group
Cyathodes parvifolia	Leptecophylla juniperi	Cynodon phragmites	Phragmites australis
	na ssp parvifolia	Cynoglossom imeritinum	C. glochidiatum
Cycas kennedyana	C. papuana	Cynoglossom longiflorum	Lindelofia longiflora
Cycas thouarsii	C. rumphii	Cynoxylon	Cornus
Cyclachaena xanthifolia	Iva xanthifolia	Cypella plumbea	C. coelestis
Cyclamen alpinum	C. trochopteranthum	Cyperorchis elegans	Cymbidium elegans
Cyclamen coum 'Album'	C. coum f albissimum	Cyperus alternifolius 'Compactus'	C. involucratus 'Nanus'
Cyclamen coum v abchasicum	C. coum ssp	Cyperus alternifolius misapplied	C. involucratus
	caucasicum	Cyperus diffusus h.	C. albostriatus
Cyclamen creticum x repandum	C. x meiklei	Cyperus elegans h.	C. albostriatus
Cyclamen europaeum	C. purpurascens	Cyperus flabelliformis	C. involucratus
Cyclamen fatrense	C. purpurascens ssp p.	Cyperus haspan misapplied	C. papyrus 'Nanus'
	from Fatra, Slovakia	Cyperus isocladus h.	C. papyrus 'Nanus'
C. hederifolium v hederifolium f albiflorum 'Nettleton Silver'		Cyperus papyrus 'Mexico'	C. giganteus
C. hederifolium v hed. f albiflorum 'White Cloud'		Cyperus sumula h.	C. cyperoides
C. hed. v hederifolium f albiflorum 'White Bowles Apollo'		Cyperus vegetus	C. eragrostis
C. hederifolium v hederifolium f albiflorum		Cyphomandra crassicaulis	C. betacea
'Artemis' (Bowles Apollo Group)		Cypripedium bulbosum	Calypso bulbosa
Cyclamen ibericum	C. coum ssp	C. guttatum v yatabeanum	C. yatabeanum
	caucasicum	C. japonicum v formosanum	C. formosanum
Cyclamen ibericum album	C. c. ssp caucasicum	C. japonicum v japonicum	C. japonicum
Cyclamen latifolium	C. persicum	Cypripedium pubescens	C. parviflorum v pub.
Cyclamen neapolitanum	C. hederifolium	Cypripedium spectabile	C. reginae
Cyclamen orbiculatum	C. coum	Cyrtanthus lutescens	C. ochroleucus
Cyclamen peloponnesiacum	C. repandum ssp pelop	Cyrtanthus parviflorus	C. brachyscyphus
Cyclamen purpurascens v fatrense	C. purp. ssp purp.	Cyrtanthus purpureus	C. elatus
	from Fatra, Slovakia	Cyrtanthus speciosus	C. elatus
C. repandum 'Pelops' misapplied	C. repandum ssp	Cyrtochilum macranthum	Oncidium macranthum
	peloponnesiacum f pel.	Cyrtocladon -Griff	Homalomena -Schott
Cyclanthera explodens	C. brachystachya	Cyrtomium falcatum 'Mayi'	C. falcatum 'Cristatum'
Cyclobalanopsis acuta	Quercus acuta	Cyrtospadix -K.Koch	Caladium -Vent.
Cyclobalanopsis glauca	Quercus glauca	Cyrtostachys lakka	C. renda
Cyclobothra lutea	Calochortus barbatus	Cystopteris crenata	Diplazium sibiricum
Cydonia cathayensis -Hemsl.	Chaenomeles cathayen.	Cystopteris dryopteris	Gymnocarpium dryop.
Cydonia japonica -(Thunb.) Pers.	Chaenomeles speciosa	Cystopteris obtusata	Woodsia obtusa
Cydonia lagenaria -Loisel.	Chaenomeles speciosa	Cytherea bulbosa	Calypso bulbosa
Cydonia maulei -T.Moore	Chaenomeles speciosa	Cytisanthus horridus -(Vahl) Gams	Genista horrida
Cydonia oblonga 'Bereczcki'	C. oblonga 'Vranja'	Cytisanthus radiatus -(L.) Lang	Genista radiata
Cydonia oblonga 'Portugal'	C. oblonga 'Lusitanica'	Cytisus 'Andreanus'	C. scoparius f andr.
Cydonia sinensis	Pseudocydonia sinen.	Cytisus 'Porlock'	Genista 'Porlock'

Synonym	Current Name	Synonym	Current Name
Cytisus 'Warminster'	C. x praecox 'Warminster'		scotica cultivars
Cytisus adamii -Poiteau	+ Laburnocytisus 'Adamii'	Dacrydium bidwillii	Halocarpus bidwillii
		Dacrydium colensoi -Kirk	D. biforme
Cytisus albus -Hacq	Chamaecytisus albus	Dacrydium excelsum -D.Don	Dacrycarpus dacrydioides
Cytisus albus misapplied and Link	C. multiflorus		
Cytisus alpinus -Mill.	Laburnum alpinum	Dacrydium franklinii	Lagarostrobos frank.
Cytisus austriacus -L.	Chamaecytisus supinus	Dacrydium laxifolium	Lepidothamnus laxifol.
Cytisus canariensis -(L.) O.Kuntze	Genista canariensis -L.	Dacrydium plumosum -D.Don	Libocedrus plumosa
Cytisus candicans -(L.) DC.	Genista monspessulana	Dacrydium spicatum -D.Don	Prumnopitys taxifolia
Cytisus capitatus -Scop.	Chamaecytisus supinus	Dacrydium tetragonum	Microcachrys tetrag.
Cytisus demissus	Chamaecytisus hirsutus demissus	Dactylis ciliata	D. glomerata -L.
		Dactylis cynosuroides	Spartina pectinata
Cytisus everestianus -Carr.	Genista x spachiana	Dactylis glaucescens	D. glomerata -L.
Cytisus fragrans -Lam.	C. supranubius	Dactylis patens	Spartina patens
Cytisus glabrescens -Sart.	C. emeriflorus -Reichb.	Dactylorhiza comosa	D. majalis
Cytisus hirsutissimus -K. Koch	Chamaecytisus hirsut.	Dactylorhiza fuchsii x purpurella	D. x venusta
Cytisus hirsutus -L.	Chamaecytisus hirsut.	Dactylorhiza maculata ssp fuchsii	D. fuchsii
Cytisus hispanica	Genista hispanica	Dactylorhiza majalis ssp maderensis	D. foliosa
Cytisus holopetala	Genista radiata v nana	D. majalis ssp praetermissa	D. praetermissa
Cytisus kitaibelii -Vis. in part	C. procumbens	Dactylorhiza majalis x sambucina	D. 'Madonna'
Cytisus laburnum -L.	Laburnum anagyroides	Dactylorhiza mascula	Orchis mascula
Cytisus leucanthus -Waldst.	Chamaecytisus albus	Dahlia 'Black Cat'	D. 'Chat Noir'
Cytisus maderensis	Genista maderensis	Dahlia 'Dandy'	D. 'Harvest Dandy'
Cytisus monspessulanus -L.	Genista monspessulana	Dahlia 'Imp'	D. 'Harvest Imp'
Cytisus nigrescens	C. nigricans	Dahlia 'Inflammation'	D. 'Harvest Inflammation'
Cytisus nubigenus	C. supranubius		
Cytisus pilosus	Genista pilosa	Dahlia 'Paso Doble' misapplied	D. 'Freya's Paso Doble'
Cytisus proliferus v palmensis	C. palmensis	Dahlia 'Red Dwarf'	D. 'Harvest Red Dwarf'
Cytisus purpureus	Chamaecytisus purpureus	Dahlia 'Samantha'	D. 'Harvest Samantha'
		Dahlia 'Summer Night'	D.'Nuit d'Ete'
Cytisus racemosus h. and Nichols.	Genista x spachiana	Dahlia 'Tiny Tot'	D. 'Harvest Tiny Tot'
Cytisus radiatus -(L.) K.Koch	Genista radiata	Dahlia 'Unwins Dwarf'	D. Unwins Dwarf Group
Cytisus ramentaceus -Sieber	Petteria ramentacea	Dahlia excelsa	D. imperialis
Cytisus Red Favourite	C. 'Roter Favorit'	Dahlia Firebird	D. 'Vuurvogel'
Cytisus rhombifolius	Thermopsis rhombifol.	Dahlia Pride of Berlin	D. 'Stolze von Berlin'
Cytisus schipkaensis -Dieck.	Chamaecytisus albus	Daiswa	Paris
Cytisus scoparius v prostratus	C. scop. ssp maritimus	Dalibardia fragarioides	Waldsteinia fragarioid.
Cytisus sessilifolius	Cytisophyllum sessilif.	Dammara	Agathis
Cytisus supinus -L.	Chamaecytisus supinus	Danae Laurus -Med.	D. racemosa
Cytisus supinus v austriacus	Chamaecytisus supinus	Danthonia allenii	D. compressa
Cytisus sylvestris v pungens -Vis.	Genista sylvestris	Danthonia canadensis	D. intermedia
Cytisus tenera -Jacq.	Genista tenera	Danthonia cusickii	D. intermedia
Cytisus weldenii -Vis.	Petteria ramentacea	Danthonia faxonii	D. compressa
Cytisus wolgaricus -L.f.	Calophaca wolgarica	Danthonia glumosa	D. spicata
Cytisus x praecox 'Canary Bird'	C. x p.'Goldspeer'	Danthonia pinetorum	D. spicata
Cytisus x praecox 'Gold Spear'	C. x p. 'Goldspeer'	Danthonia spicata	D. compressa
Cytisus x spachianus -Webb	Genista x spachiana	Danthonia thermale	D. spicata
Cytisus x watereri -Wettst.	Laburnum x watereri	Daphne 'Bramdean'	D. x napolitana 'Bramdean'
Daboecia cantabrica 'Pink'	D. c. 'Donard Pink'		
D. cantabrica 'William Buchanan'	D. cantabrica ssp scotica 'William Buchanan'	Daphne 'Leila Haines' x arbuscula	D. x schlyteri
		Daphne 'Meon'	D. x napolitana 'Meon'
		Daphne altaica v lonilobata	D. longilobata
Daboecia daboecia	D. cantabrica	Daphne australis	D. sericea Collina Gr.
Daboecia polifolia v alba -D.Don	D. cantabrica f alba	Daphne buxifolia -Vahl	D. oleoides -Schreb.
Daboecia x scotica cultivars	D. cantabrica ssp	Daphne candida	D. alpina

Synonym	Current Name	Synonym	Current Name
Daphne cannabina -Wall. in part	D. bholua -Buch.-Ham.	Dasiphora davurica	P. fruticosa v davurica
Daphne cannabina -Wall. in part	D. papyracea	Dasiphora fruticosa -(L.) Rydb.	Potentilla fruticosa -L.
Daphne cneorum 'Grandiflora'	D.x napolitana 'Maxima'	Dasylirion caespitosum	Calibanus hookeri
Daphne collina	D. sericea Collina Gr.	Dasylirion gracile -Planchon	D. acrotrichum
Daphne collina v neapolitana	D. x napolitana	Dasylirion hartwegianum -J.Hook.	Calibanus hookeri
Daphne dauphinii -Loud.	D. x hybrida	Dasylirion hookeri -Lemaire	Calibanus hookeri
Daphne dauphinii h.	D. x hybrida	Dasylirion inerme -S.Watson	Nolina recurvata
Daphne florida.	D. mezereum -L.	Dasylirion longifolium -Zuccarini	Nolina longifolia
Daphne fortuni -Lindl.	D. genkwa	Dasylirion recurvatum	Nolina recurvata
Daphne gardneri -Wall.	Edgeworthia gardneri	Dasystephana andrewsii	Gentiana andrewsii
Daphne glandulosa -Bertol.	D. oleoides -Schreb.	Dasystephana saponaria	Gentiana andrewsii
Daphne indica h.	D. odora -Thunb.	Datura arborea	Brugmansia arborea
Daphne japonica -Thunb.	D. odora -Thunb.	Datura aurea	Brugmansia aurea
Daphne japonica 'Striata'	D. o. 'Aureomarginata'	Datura chlorantha	Brugmansia chlorantha
Daphne jasminea sensu -Griseb.	D. oleoides -Schreb.	Datura cornigera	Brugmansia arborea
Daphne kamtschatica v jezoensis	D. jezoensis	Datura inermis -Juss. ex Jacq.	D. stramonium v iner.
Daphne laureola purpurea h.	D. x houtteana -Lindl.	Datura meteloides	D. inoxia
Daphne mezereum 'Bowles' White'	D. m. 'Bowles' Variety'	Datura rosea	Brugmansia x insignis pink
Daphne mezereum 'Grandiflora'	D. m. v autumnalis		
Daphne mezereum v atropurpurea	D. x houtteana -Lindl.	Datura rosei	Brugmansia sanguinea
Daphne neapolitana -Lodd.	D. x napolitana	Datura sanguinea	Brugmansia sanguinea
Daphne odora 'Marginata'	D. o. 'Aureomarginata'	Datura suaveolens	Brugmansia suaveol.
Daphne odora v kiusiana	D. kiusiana -Miq.	Datura tatula -L.	D. stramonium v inermis
Daphne odora v leucantha	D. odora f alba		
Daphne oleoides v brachyloba	D. oleoides -Schreb.	Datura versicolor	Brugmansia versicolor
Daphne oleoides v buxifolia	D. oleoides -Schreb.	Datura versicolor 'Grand Marnier'	Brugmansia x candida 'Grand Marnier'
Daphne oleoides v glandulosa	D. oleoides -Schreb.		
Daphne oleoides v jasminea -Meissn.	D. oleoides -Schreb.	Datura wallichii	D. stramonium v inermis
Daphne oleoides v kosaninii	D. kosaninii -Stoyanov		
Daphne petraea 'Alba'	D. petraea 'Tremalzo'	Datura x candida	Brugmansia x candida
Daphne philippi -Gren. & Godr.	D. laureola v philippi	Daubentonia	Sesbania
Daphne rechingeri	D. mezereum -L.	Daucus abyssinica	D. carota
Daphne retusa	D. tangutica Retusa Gr.	Daucus aegypticus	D. carota
Daphne rupestris -Facc.	D. petraea	Daucus agrestis	D. carota
Daphne rupestris -Facchini	D. petraea -Leybold	Daucus azoricus	D. carota
Daphne verlotii -Gren. & Godr.	D. cneorum v verlotii	Daucus bactrianus	D. carota
Daphne wilsonii -Rehd.	D. tangutica -Maxim.	Daucus blanchei	D. carota
Daphne x burkwoodii 'Variegata' broad cream edge		Daucus bocconei	D. carota
	D. x b. 'Somerset Variegated'	Daucus caretanus	D. carota
Daphne x burkwoodii 'Variegata' broad gold edge		Daucus carnosus	D. carota
	D. x b. 'Somerset Gold Edge'	Daucus communis	D. carota
Daphne x burkwoodii 'Variegata' narrow gold edge		Daucus esculentus	D. carota
	D. x burkwoodii 'Carol Mackie'	Daucus exarmatus	D. carota
Daphnidostaphylos fendleriana	Arctostaphylos uva-ursi	Daucus fernandezii	D. carota
		Daucus gaditanus	D. carota
Daphniphyllum glaucescens h.	D. macropodon -Miq.	Daucus gingidium	D. carota
Daphniphyllum humile	D. himalaense ssp macropodum	Daucus gonzaloi	D. carota
		Daucus gummifer	D. carota
Daphniphyllum jezoense h. ex Bean	D. humile -Max.	Daucus halophilus	D. carota
Daphniphyllum macropodon v humile	D. humile -Max.	Daucus hispanicus	D. carota
Darwinia decumbens	Homoranthus decumb.	Daucus hispidus	D. carota
Darwinia fimbriata	D. squarrosa	Daucus lopadusanus	D. carota
Darwinia porteri	Homoranthus porteri	Daucus marcidus	D. carota
Darwinia taxifolia v biflora	D. biflora	Daucus maritimus	D. carota
Darwinia verticordina	Verticordia verticord.	Daucus matthioli	D. carota

Synonym	Current Name	Synonym	Current Name
Daucus mauritanicus	D. carota	Delphinium zalil	D. semibarbatum
Daucus maximus	D. carota	Dendranthema arcticum	Arctanthemum arct.
Daucus micranthus	D. carota	Dendranthema boreale	D. lavandulifolium
Daucus muricaulis	D. carota	Dendranthema cultivars	Chrysanthemum
Daucus neglectus	D. carota	Dendranthema nankingense	Chrysanthemum nan.
Daucus parviflorus	D. carota	Dendranthema pacificum	Ajania pacifica
Daucus polygamus	D. carota	Dendranthema weyrichii	Chrysanthemum wey.
Daucus rupestris	D. carota	Dendranthema zawadskii	Chrysanthemum zaw.
Daucus sativus	D. carota	Dendriopoterium	Sanguisorba
Daucus serratus	D. carota	Dendrium hugeri -Small	Leiophyllum buxifolium
Daucus siculus	D. carota		v hugeri
Daucus visnaga	Ammi visnaga	Dendrobenthamia	Cornus
Davallia bullata	D. mariesii	Dendrobium aggregatum	D. lindleyi
Davallia dubia v hirsuta	Lastreopsis silvestris	Dendrobium albertisii	D. antennatum
Davallia fejeenis	D. solida v fejeenis	Dendrobium hildebrandii	D. signatum
Davallia pyxidata	D. solida v pyxidata	Dendrobium phalaenopsis	D. biggibum v phalaen.
Davidia laeta -Dode in part	D. involucrata -Baill.	Dendrobium pierardii	D. aphyllum
Davidia laeta -Dode in part	D. involucrata v	Dendrobium suavissimum	D. chrysotoxum
	vilmoriniana	Dendromecon arborea -Greene	D. harfordii v
Decachaena baccata	Gaylussacia baccata		rhamnoides
Decamerium resinosum	Gaylussacia baccata	Dendromecon rhamnoides -Greene	D. harfordii v rhamn.
Decandolia effusa	Milium effusum	Dendromecon rigidum v harfordii	D. harfordii -Kell.
Decodon aquaticus	D. verticillatus	Denhamia -Schott	Culcasia -P. Beauv.
Delabechea	Brachychiton	Dennstaedtia punctilobula misapp.	Hypolepis millefolium
Delosperma 'Basutoland'	D. nubigenum	Dentaria bulbifera	Cardamine bulbifera
Delphinium 'Blue Butterfly'	D. grandiflorum 'Blue	Dentaria concatenata	Cardamine concatenat.
	Butterfly'	Dentaria dasyloba	Cardamine leucantha
Delphinium 'Lady Hambleden'	D. 'Patricia, Lady	Dentaria digitata	C. pentaphyllos
	Hambleden'	Dentaria diphylla	Cardamine diphylla
Delphinium 'Royal Flush'	D. 'Langdon's Royal	Dentaria douglasii	Cardamine douglasii
	Flush'	Dentaria enneaphylla	Cardamine enneaphyll.
Delphinium ajacis -L.	Consolida ajacis	Dentaria incisa	Cardamine diphylla
Delphinium ambiguum	Consolida ajacis	Dentaria laciniata	Cardamine concatenat.
D. ambiguum 'Pink Sensation'	D. x ruysii 'Pink	Dentaria leucantha	Cardamine leucantha
	Sensation'	Dentaria macrophyla dasyloba	Cardamine leucantha
Delphinium beesianum 'Andenken an August Koeneman'		Dentaria microphylla	Cardamine microphylla
	D. (Belladonna Group)	Dentaria pentaphylla	Cardamine pentaphyll.
	'Wendy'	Dentaria pinnata	Cardamine heptaphylla
D. beesianum 'Pink Sensation'	D. x ruysii 'Pink	Dentaria polyphylla	Cardamine kitaibelii
	Sensation'	Dentaria rhomboidea	Cardamine bulbosa
Delphinium 'Black Jack'	D. 'Black Arrow'	Deparia petersenii	Lunathyrium japonicum
Dephinium 'Black Sabbath'	D. 'Black Arrow'	Deringa canadensis	Cryptotaenia canaden.
Delphinium caucasicum	D. speciosum	Derwentia	Parahebe
D. cheilanthum brachycentron	D. brachycentron	Deschampsia caespitosa	Deschampsia cespitosa
Delphinium chinese	D. grandiflorum	D. cespitosa 'Fairy's Joke'	D. cespitosa v vivipara
Delphinium consolida	Consolida ajacis	Deschampsia cespitosa Bronze Veil	D. cespitosa
D. elatum 'Darkness Visible'	D. 'Black Arrow'		'Bronzeschleier'
Delphinium formosum h.	D. cheilanthum	Deschampsia cespitosa Gold Dust	D. c. 'Goldstaub'
Delphinium gayanum	Consolida ajacis	Deschampsia cespitosa Golden Dew	D. cespitosa 'Goldtau'
D. grandiflorum Blue Dwarf	D. gr. 'Blauer Zwerg'	D. cespitosa Golden Pendant	D. c. 'Goldgehange'
Delphinium napellus	Aconitum napellus	D. cespitosa Golden Shower	D. c. 'Goldgehange'
Delphinium nudicaule v luteum	D. luteum	Deschampsia cespitosa Golden Veil	D. c. 'Goldschleier'
Delphinium simplex	Consolida ajacis	Deschampsia flexuosa 'Aurea'	D. flexuosa 'Tatra Gold'
Delphinium stenosepalum	D. brachycentron	Desfontainia hookeri -Dun.	D. spinosa
Delphinium sulphureum h.	D. semibarbatum	Desfontainia spinosa f hookeri	D. spinosa

81

Synonym	Current Name	Synonym	Current Name
Desfontainia spinosa v chilensis	D. spinosa	Dianthus 'Cheryl'	D. 'Houndspool Cheryl'
Desmazeria	Catapodium rigidum	Dianthus 'Constance Finnis'	D. 'Fair Folly'
Desmesia -Raf.	Typhonium -Schott	Dianthus 'Diana'	D. Dona = 'Brecas'
Desmodium laburnifolium	D. caudatum	Dianthus 'Doris Ruby'	D. 'Houndspool Ruby'
Desmodium penduliflorum	Lespedeza thunbergii	Dianthus 'Double Irish'	D. 'Irish Pink'
Desmodium praestans	D. yunnanense	Dianthus 'Ember Rose'	D. 'Le Reve'
Desmodium thunbergii -DC.	Lespedeza thunbergii	Dianthus 'Emperor'	D. 'Bat's Double Red'
Desmodium tiliifolium	D. elegans	Dianthus 'Green Eyes'	D. 'Musgrave's Pink'
Deutzia 'Avalanche'	D. x maliflora 'Avalanche'	Dianthus 'Haytor'	D. 'Haytor White'
		Dianthus 'Heart Attack'	D. 'Tuxedo Black'
Deutzia 'Contraste'	D.x hybrida 'Contraste'	Dianthus 'Huntsman'	D. 'Allen's Huntsman'
Deutzia 'Pink Pompon'	D. 'Rosea Plena'	Dianthus 'Joan's Blood'	D. alpinus 'Joan's Blood'
Deutzia chunii	D. ningpoensis		
Deutzia corymbiflora -Lemoine	D. setchuenensis v corymbiflora	Dianthus 'La Bourbille'	D. 'La Bourboule'
		Dianthus 'Laced Prudence'	D. 'Prudence'
Deutzia corymbosa v hookerana	D. hookeriana	Dianthus 'Little Old Lady'	D. 'Chelsea Pink'
Deutzia crenata -Sieb. & Zucc.	D. scabra -Thunb.	Dianthus 'Madame Dubarry'	D. 'Dubarry'
Deutzia crenata 'Flore Pleno'	D. scabra 'Plena'	Dianthus 'Manningtree Pink'	D. 'Cedric's Oldest'
Deutzia crenata magnifica -Lemoine	D. x magnifica	Dianthus 'Maria'	D. 'Allen's Maria'
Deutzia crenata v taiwanensis	D. taiwanensis	Dianthus 'Mida'	D. 'Melody'
Deutzia discolor -Maxim.	D. maximowicziana	Dianthus 'Montrose Pink'	D. 'Cockenzie Pink'
Deutzia discolor elegantissima	D. x elegantissima	Dianthus 'Mrs Clark'	D. 'Nellie Clark'
Deutzia discolor v purpurascens	D. purpurascens	Dianthus 'Mrs N.Clark'	D. 'Nellie Clark'
Deutzia dumicola -W.W.Sm.	D. rehderana -Schneid.	Dianthus 'Musgrave's White'	D. 'Musgrave's Pink'
Deutzia gracilis 'Carminea'	D. x rosea 'Carminea'	Dianthus 'Oakington Rose'	D. 'Oakington'
Deutzia gracilis 'Nikko'	D. crenata v nakaiana 'Nikko'	Dianthus 'Old Blush'	D. 'Souvenir de la Malmaison'
Deutzia gracilis 'Rosea'	D. x rosea	Dianthus 'Patricia Bell'	D. turkestanicus 'Patricia Bell'
Deutzia gracilis 'Variegata'	D. gracilis 'Marmorata'		
Deutzia gracilis rosea -Lemoine	D. x rosea	Dianthus 'Pink Calypso'	D. 'Truly Yours'
Deutzia hookerana -Schneid.	D. hookeriana	Dianthus 'Princess Charming'	D. gratianopolitanus 'Princess Charming'
Deutzia hypoglauca -Rehd.	D. rubens -Rehd.		
Deutzia hypoleuca -Maxim.	D. maximowicziana	Dianthus 'Raby Castle'	D. 'Lord Chatham'
Deutzia parviflora h.	D. amurensis	Dianthus 'Reine de Henri'	D. 'Queen of Henri'
Deutzia parviflora v amurensis	D. amurensis	Dianthus 'Revell's Lady Wharncliffe'	D. 'Lady Wharncliffe'
Deutzia pubescens	D. crenata v pubesc.	Dianthus 'Ruby Doris'	D. 'Houndspool Ruby'
Deutzia sieboldiana -Maxim.	D. scabra	Dianthus 'Ruby'	D. 'Houndspool Ruby'
D. x hybrida 'Strawberry Fields'	D. 'Strawberry Fields'	Dianthus 'Russling Robin'	D. 'Fair Maid of Kent'
Deutzia x magnifica 'Rubra'	D. 'Strawberry Fields'	Dianthus 'Sir Cedric Morris'	D. 'Cedric's Oldest'
Deutzia x wellsii	D. scabra 'Candidissima'	Dianthus 'Square Eyes'	D. 'Old Square Eyes'
		Dianthus 'Tiny Rubies'	D. gratianopolitanus 'Tiny Rubies'
Diandriella -Engl.	Homalomena -Schott		
Dianella caerulea 'Variegata'	D. tasmanica 'Variegata'	Dianthus 'Tiverton'	D. 'Musgrave's Pink'
		Dianthus 'W.A.Musgrave'	D. 'Musgrave's Pink'
Dianella longifolia v porracea	D. porracea	Dianthus 'Washfield'	D. 'Musgrave's Pink'
Dianella revoluta v brevicaulis	D. brevicaulis	Dianthus 'White Sim'	D. 'White William Sim'
Dianthus 'A.J.Macself'	D. 'Dad's Favourite'	Dianthus alpester	D. furcatus
Dianthus 'Auvergne'	D. x arvernensis	Dianthus alpestris	D. furcatus
Dianthus 'Blush'	D. 'Souvenir de la Malmaison'	Dianthus androsaceus	D. pinifolius
		Dianthus atrorubens	D. carthusianorum Atrorubens Group
Dianthus 'Bourboule'	D. 'La Bourboule'		
Dianthus 'Brilliant'	D. deltoides 'Brilliant'	Dianthus caesius	D. gratianopolitanus
Dianthus 'Candy'	D. 'Sway Candy'	Dianthus caesius 'Compactus'	D. gratianopolitanus 'Compactus Eydangeri'
Dianthus 'Catherine's Choice'	D. 'Rhian's Choice'		
Dianthus 'Charles Musgrave'	D. 'Musgrave's Pink'	Dianthus ceretanicus	Herniaria glabra -L.

Synonym	Current Name	Synonym	Current Name
Dianthus Cheddar pink	D. gratianopolitanus	Dichopogon preissii	Arthropodium preissii
Dianthus cinnabarinus	D. biflorus	Dichopogon strictus	Arthropodium strictum
Dianthus deltoides Flashing Light	D. d. 'Leuchtfunk'	Dichosema racemosum	Chorizema racemosum
Dianthus Fringed pink	D. superbus	Dichotophyllum demersum	Ceratophyllum demers.
Dianthus haematocalyx 'Alpinus'	D. h. ssp pindicola	Dichromena	Rhynchospora
Dianthus hispanicus	D. pungens	Dichrophyllum marginatum	Euphorbia marginata
Dianthus inodorus	D. sylvestris	Dicksonia pilosiuscula	Dennstaedtia
Dianthus kitaibelii	D. petraeus ssp petraeus		punctilobula
		Diclytra spectabilis	Dicentra spectabilis
Dianthus musalae	D. microlepis v musalae	Dictamnus dasycarpus	D. albus
		Dictamnus fraxinella	D. albus v purpureus
Dianthus neglectus	D. pavonius	Dictamnus fraxinella albus	D. albus v purpureus
Dianthus noeanus	D. petraeus ssp noean.	Dictamnus fraxinella ruber	D. albus v purpureus
Dianthus pavonius roysii	D. 'Roysii'	Dictamnus purpureus	D. albus v purpureus
Dianthus pindicola	D. haematocalyx ssp pindicola	Didiscus coeruleus	Trachymene coerulea
		Didymochlaena lunulata	D. truncatula
Dianthus strictus v brachyanthus	D. integer ssp minutiflorus	Didymosperma caudatum	Arenga caudata
		Dieffenbachia 'Memoria'	D. seguine 'Memoria
Dianthus suendermannii	D. petraeus		Corsii'
Dianthus The Bloodie pink	D. 'Caesar's Mantle'	Dieffenbachia 'Pia'	D. seguine 'Pia'
Diapensia obovata	D. lapponica v obovata	Dieffenbachia 'Roehrsii'	D. s. 'Rudolph Roehrs'
Diapensia obtusifolia	D. lapponica v obovata	Dieffenbachia 'Rudolph Roehrs'	D. s. 'Rudolph Roehrs'
Diascia 'Apricot' h.	D. barberae 'Hopley's Apricot'	Dieffenbachia amoena h.	D. seguine 'Amoena'
		Dieffenbachia maculata	D. seguine
Diascia 'Blush'	D. integerrima 'Blush'	Dieffenbachia maculata	D. seguine 'Maculata'
Diascia 'Hector Harrison'	D. 'Salmon Supreme'	Dieffenbachia maculata 'Hi-colour'	D. s. 'Tropic Snow'
Diascia 'Jack Elliott'	D. vigilis 'Jack Elliott'	D. maculata 'Rudolph Roehrs'	D. s. 'Rudolph Roehrs'
Diascia 'Ruby Field'	D. barberae 'Ruby Field'	D. maculata 'Snow Queen'	D. s. 'Tropic Snow'
		D. maculata 'Tropic Topaz'	D. s. 'Tropic Snow'
Diascia cordata misapplied	D. barberae 'Fisher's Flora'	Dieffenbachia picta	D. seguine
		Dieffenbachia seguine 'Amoena'	D. 'Amoena'
Diascia cordifolia	D. b. 'Fisher's Flora'	Dieffenbachia x memoria-corsii	D. s. 'Memoria Corsii'
Diascia elegans misapplied	D. fetcaniensis	Dielytra	Dicentra
Diascia elegans misapplied	D. vigilis	Dierama 'Hermia'	D. dracomontanum
Diascia felthamii	D. fetcaniensis	Dierama ensifolium	D. pendulum
Diascia flanaganii -Hiern	D. stachyoides	Dierama pumilum -(Baker) N.E.Br.	D. pendulum v pumilum
Diascia flanaganii misapplied	D. vigilis	Dierama pumilum h.	D. dracomontanum
Diascia integerrima 'Alba'	D. integerrima 'Blush'	Diervilla acadiensis	D. lonicera -Mill.
Diascia integerrima 'Ivory Angel'	D. integerrima 'Blush'	Diervilla amabilis	Weigela florida
Diascia integrifolia	D. integerrima	Diervilla canadensis -Willd.	D. lonicera -Mill.
Diascia rigescens pale form	D. r. 'Anne Rennie'	Diervilla diervilla	D. lonicera -Mill.
Diascia x Linaria	Nemesia caerulea	Diervilla florida	Weigela florida
Diatrema purpurea	Ipomoea purpurea	Diervilla humilis -Pers.	D. lonicera -Mill.
Dicentra 'Boothman's Variety'	D. 'Stuart Boothman'	Diervilla longifolia	D. lonicera -Mill.
Dicentra eximia 'Alba'	D. eximia 'Snowdrift'	Diervilla lutea	D. lonicera -Mill.
Dicentra eximia 'Purity'	D. eximia 'Snowdrift'	Diervilla middendorffiana	Weigela middendorff.
Dicentra eximia 'Snowflake'	D. eximia 'Snowdrift'	Diervilla parviflora	D. lonicera -Mill.
Dicentra eximia h.	D. formosa	Diervilla pauciflora	Weigela florida
Dicentra oregona	D. formosa ssp oreg.	Diervilla rosea	Weigela florida
Dicentra thalictrifolia	D. scandens	Diervilla sessilifolia splendens -h.	D. x splendens
Dicera serrata -J.R. & G.Forst.	Aristotelia serrata	Diervilla tournefortii	D. lonicera -Mill.
Dichelostemma pulchellum	D. capitatum	Diervilla trifida	D. lonicera -Mill.
Dichondra repens misapplied	D. micrantha	Dietes huttonii	Moraea huttonii
Dichopogon capillipes	Arthropodium capllipes	Dietes vegeta h.	D. iridioides
Dichopogon fimbriatus	Arthropodium fimbriat.	Digitalis 'Flashing Spires'	D. lutea 'Flashing

Synonym	Current Name	Synonym	Current Name
	Spires'	Diplopappus ericoides -Lessing	Haplopappus ericoides
Digitalis ambigua	D. grandiflora	Diplosastera tinctoria	Coreopsis tinctoria
Digitalis apricot hybrids	D. purpurea 'Sutton's Apricot'	Diplycosia semi-infera -C.B.Clarke	Gaultheria semi-infera
		Dipsacus sylvestris	D. fullonum
Digitalis canariensis	Isoplexis canariensis	Dipteracanthus	Ruellia
Digitalis carnea	D. purpurea	Disa grandiflora	D. uniflora
Digitalis eriostachya	D. lutea	Discaria foliosa -Miers	D. crenata -(Clos) Reg.
Digitalis gyspergerae	D. purpurea	Discaria serratifolia h.	D. crenata
Digitalis heywoodii	D. purpurea ssp heyw.	Discocactus tricornis	D. placentiformis
Digitalis kishinskyi	D. parviflora	Disoon cordifolius	Myoporum cordifolium
Digitalis lamarckii h.	D. lanata	Disporum pullum	D. cantoniense
Digitalis libertiana	D. purpurea	Distegia involucrata	Lonicera involucrata
Digitalis micrantha	D. lutea ssp australis	Distegocarpus carpinus -Sieb.	Carpinus japonica
Digitalis orientalis	D. grandiflora	Distegocarpus cordatus	Carpinus cordata
Digitalis purpurascens	D. purpurea	Distegocarpus laxiflora	Carpinus laxiflora
Digitalis tomentosa	D. purpurea	Distictis 'Rivers'	D. 'Mrs. Rivers'
Digraphis arundinacea	Phalaris arundinacea	Diuranthera	Chlorophytum
Dillwynia glycinifolia	Chorizema glycinifolium	Dizygotheca elegantissima	Schefflera elegantiss.
Dimorphanthus elatus -Miq.	Aralia elata	Dochafa -Schott	Arisaema -Mart.
Dimorphanthus mandschuricus	Aralia elata	Docynia docynioides	D. rufifolia
Dimorphotheca annua	D. pluvialis	Docynia rufifolia -(H.Lev). Rehd	D. indica -(Wall).
Dimorphotheca aurantiaca h.	D. sinuata	Dodecatheon amethystinum	D. pulchellum
Dimorphotheca barberiae h.	Osteospermum jucundum	Dodecatheon cusickii	D. pulchellum ssp cus.
		Dodecatheon integrifolium	D. hendersonii
Dimorphotheca calandulacea	D. sinuata	Dodecatheon latifolium	D. hendersonii
Dimorphotheca ecklonis	Osteospermum ecklon.	Dodecatheon pauciflorum	D. meadia
Dimorphotheca jucunda	Osteospermum jucund.	Dodecatheon pauciflorum misapp.	D. pulchellum
Dioscorea opposita	D. batatas	Dodecatheon pulchellum radicatum	D. pulchellum
Diosma crenulata	Agathosma crenulata	Dodecatheon radicatum	D. pulchellum
Diosma pulchella	Agathosma pulchella	Dodecatheon tetrandrum	D. jeffreyi
Diosma uniflora -L.	Adenandra uniflora	Dodonaea acerosa	D. filifolia
Diosphaera asperuloides	Trachelium asperul.	Dodonaea adenophora v ovata	D. subglandulifera
Diosphaera dubia	Trachelium rumelianum	Dodonaea angustifolia	D. viscosa ssp angust.
Diotis ceratioides -(L.) Willd.	Eurotia ceratioides	Dodonaea bursariifolia v major	D. bursariifolia
Diotis lanata -Pursh.	Eurotia lanata	Dodonaea caleyana	D. boriniifolia
Dipidax	Onixotis	Dodonaea calycina	D. truncatiales
Diplacus	Mimulus	Dodonaea calycina v genuina	D. truncatiales
Diplacus glutinosus -(Wendl.) Nutt.	Mimulus aurantiacus	Dodonaea concinna	D. inaequifolia
Dipladenia	Mandevilla	Dodonaea cryptandroides	D. ericoides
Diplarrhena moraea W. Coast form	D. latifolia	Dodonaea cuneata	D. viscosa ssp cuneata
Diplazium acrostichoides	Deparia acrostichoides	Dodonaea deflexa	D. baueri
Diplazium japonicum	Deparia japonica	Dodonaea dioica	D. triquetra
Diplazium japonicum	Lunathyrium japonicum	Dodonaea ericifolia	D. filiformis
Diplazium littoralis	D. muralis	Dodonaea foliolosa	D. larreoides
Diplazium mandonis	D. muralis	Dodonaea hansenii	D. platyptera
Diplazium otophorum	Athyrium otophorum	Dodonaea heterophylla	D. triquetra
Diplazium otophorum	Athyrium otophorum	Dodonaea hirtella	D. boriniifolia
Diplazium platystylis	D. muralis	Dodonaea humifusa v hirtella	D. trifida
Diplazium polonica	D. muralis	Dodonaea kingii	D. viscosa ssp angustifolia
Diplazium scaposa	D. muralis		
Diplazium sommerfeldtii	Diplazium sibiricum	Dodonaea laurifolia	D. triquetra
Diplocyathus ciliata	Orbea ciliata	Dodonaea laurina	D. triquetra
Diplopappus chinensis	Callistephus chinensis	Dodonaea leptozyga	D. inaequifolia
Diplopappus chrysophyllus -Koehne	Cassina leptophylla ssp fulvida	Dodonaea lindleyana	D. triangularis
		Dodonaea longipes	D. triquetra

Synonym	Current Name	Synonym	Current Name
Dodonaea nematoidea	D. viscosa ssp burmanniana	Dortmannia inflata	Lobelia inflata
		Dortmannia kalmii	Lobelia kalmii
Dodonaea peduncularis v coriacea	D. coricaea	Dorycnium	Lotus
Dodonaea peduncularis v hirsuta	D. hirsuta	Dorycnium hirsutum -(L.) Ser.	Lotus hirsutus -L.
Dodonaea pinifolia v submutica	D. pinifolia	Dorycnium suffruticosum -Vill.	Lotus pentaphyllus ssp pentaphyllus
Dodonaea pterocaulis	D. ceratocarpa		
Dodonaea pubescens	D. peduncularis	Doryopteris elegans	Hemionitis elegans
Dodonaea repanda	D. viscosa ssp viscosa	Doryopteris pedata v palmata	D. palmata
Dodonaea salicifolia	D. viscosa ssp angustifolia	Douglasia idahoensis	Androsace idahoensis
		Douglasia laevigata	Androsace laevigata
Dodonaea salsolifolia	D. filiformis	Douglasia montana	Androsace montana
Dodonaea soraria	D. aptera	Douglasia nivalis	Androsace nivalis
Dodonaea submutica	D. pinifolia	Douglasia vitaliana	Vitaliana primuliflora
Dodonaea tenuifolia	D. subglandulifera	Doxantha capreolata -(L). Miers	Bignonia capreolata -L.
Dodonaea trigona	D. triangularis	Doxantha unguis-cati	Macfadyena unguis-c.
D. truncatiales v heterophylla	D. heteromorpha	Draba aizoon	D. lasiocarpa
Dodonaea umbellata	D. viscosa ssp angustifolia	Draba aureiformis	D. aurea
		Draba bertolonii -Boissier	D. loeseleurii
Dodonaea vestita v glabrescens	D. vestita	Draba bertolonii -Nyman	D. aspera
Dodonaea viscosa v laurina	D. polyandra	Draba bertolonii -Thell.	D. brachystemon
Dodonaea viscosa v megazyga	D. megazyga	Draba bryoides	D. rigida v bryoides
Doellingeria scabra	Aster scaber	Draba bryoides v imbricata	D. rigida v imbricata
Doellingeria umbellata	Aster umbellatus	Draba compacta	D. lasiocarpa Compacta Group
Dolichos lablab	Lablab purpureus		
Dolichos lignosus	Dipogon lignosus	Draba daurica	D. glabella
Dolichos niger	Lablab purpureus	Draba dicranoides	D. rigida
Dolichos pruriens	Mucuna pruriens	Draba eschscholtzii	D. alpina
Dolichos purpureus	Lablab purpureus	Draba imbricata	D. rigida v imbricata
Dolichothele baumii	Mammillaria baumii	Draba laurentiana	D. glabella
Dolichothele camptotricha	Mammillaria camptot.	Draba luteola	D. aurea
Dolomiaea macrocephala	Jurinea dolomiaea	Draba micropetala	D. alpina
Dombeya mastersii	D. burgessiae	Draba minganensis	D. aurea
Dombeya natalensis	D. tiliacea	Draba neomexicana	D. aurea
Dondia	Hacquetia	Draba olympica	D. bruniifolia
Doodia aspera v blechnoides	D. maxima	Draba pilosa	D. alpina
Doodia aspera v heterophylla	D. heterophylla	Draba pyrenaica	Petrocallis pyrenaica
Doodia caudata v caudata	D. caudata	Draba repens	D. sibirica
Doodia caudata v dimorpha	D. caudata	Draba rupestris	D. norvegica
Doodia caudata v laminosa	D. linearis	Draba scardica	D. lasiocarpa
Doodia caudata v lomarina	Blechnum ambiguum	Draba stylaris	D. incana Stylaris Gr.
Doodia media ssp australis	D. australis	Draba stylosa	D. aurea
Doodia media ssp media	D. media	Draba zahlbruckneriana	D. hoppeana
Doodia media v moorei	D. caudata	Dracaena australis -Forst. f.	Cordyline australis
Doodia squarrosa	D. caudata	Dracaena borealis	Clintonia borealis
Doronicum caucasicum	D. orientale	Dracaena cinta 'Tricolor'	D. marginata 'Tricolor'
Doronicum cordatum	D. columnae	Dracaena congesta	Cordyline stricta
Doronicum cordifolium	D. columnae	Dracaena deremensis	D. fragrans Deremensis Group
D. orientale 'Fruhlingspracht'	D. 'Fruhlingspracht'		
Doronicum plantagineum 'Excelsum'	D. x excelsum 'Harpur Crewe'	D. d. 'Souvenir de Schrijver'	D. fragrans Der. Gr. 'Warneckei'
D. plantagineum 'Harpur Crewe'	D.x ex. 'Harpur Crewe'	Dracaena deremensis 'Warneckei'	D. fragrans Der. Group 'Warneckei'
Doronicum Spring Beauty	D. 'Fruhlingspracht'		
Dorotheanthus littlewoodii	D. bellidiformis	Dracaena indivisa -Forst. f.	Cordyline indivisa
Dortmannia cardinalis	Lobelia cardinalis	Dracaena marginata 'Tricolor'	D. cincta 'Tricolor'
Dortmannia erinus	Lobelia erinus	Dracaena massangeana	D. fragrans

Synonym	Current Name	Synonym	Current Name
	'Massangeana'	Dryandra gilbertii	D. armata v armata
Dracaena stricta	Cordyline stricta	Dryandra multiserialis	D. obtusa
Dracaena umbellata	Clintonia unbellata	Dryandra mutica	D. foliolata
Dracamine pensylvanica	Cardamine pensylvan.	Dryandra nivea v adscendens	D. nivea
Dracamine purpurea	Cardamine douglasii	Dryandra nivea v venosa	D. nivea
Dracocephalum altaiense	D. imberbe	Dryandra patens	D. hewardiana
Dracocephalum canescens	Lallemantia canescens	Dryandra praemorsa v elongata	D. praemorsa v praem.
Dracocephalum govanianum	Nepeta govaniana	Dryandra pteridifolia v blechnifolia	D. blechnifolia
Dracocephalum mairei	D. renatii	Dryandra quinquedentata	D. sessilis v cygnorum
Dracocephalum moldavicum	D. moldavica	Dryas lanata	D. octopetala v
Dracocephalum prattii	Nepeta prattii		argentea
D. ruyschianum v speciosum	D. arguense	Dryas octopetala v vestita -Beck	D. octopetala v argent.
Dracocephalum sibiricum	Nepeta sibirica	Dryas tenella -Pursch	D. integrifolia
Dracocephalum speciosum	D. arguense	Dryasgeoides	Coluria geoides
Dracocephalum virginicum	Physostegia virginiana	Drymocodon rapunculoides	Campanula rapuncul.
Draconia campestris	Artemisia campestris	D. abbreviata -(DC.) Newm. misap.	D. oreades
Draconia dracunculus	Artemisia dracunculus	Dryopteris abbreviata -Newm.	D. affinis
Dracontium foetidum	Symplocarpus foetidus	Dryopteris aculeata	Polystichum aculeatum
Dracunculus muscivorus	Helicodiceros musciv.	D. affinis 'Crispa Congesta'	D. a. 'Crispa Gracilis'
Dregea corrugata	D. sinensis	D. affinis 'Cristata The King'	D. affinis 'Cristata'
Drejerella guttata	Justicia brandegeeana	Dryopteris affinis 'Tavelii'	D. affinis 'Stableri'
Drepanostachyum falconeri h.	Himalayacalamus falc.	Dryopteris aristata	D. dilatata
Drepanostachyum hookerianum	Himalayacalamus hook.	Dryopteris assimilis	D. expansa
Drepilia rhombifolia	Thermopsis rhombif.	Dryopteris atrata misapplied	D. cycadina
Drimys andina	D. winteri v andina	Dryopteris austriaca h.	D. dilatata
Drimys aromatica	D. lanceolata	Dryopteris austriaca misapplied	D. dilatata
Drimys axillaris	Pseudowintera axill.	Dryopteris austriaca v spinulosa	D. carthusiana
Drimys axillaris v colorata	Pseudowintera color.	Dryopteris baileyana	Lastreopsis microsora
Drimys chilensis -DC.	D. winteri v chilensis	Dryopteris borreri	D. affinis ssp borreri
Drimys colorata -Raoul	Pseudowintera color.	Dryopteris braunii	Polystichum braunii
Drimys piperita	Tasmannia glaucifolia	Dryopteris chrysocarpa	D. pseudofilix-mas
Drimys punctata -Lam.	D. winteri v winteri	Dryopteris claytoniana	D. clintoniana
Drimys purpurascens	Tasmannia purpuras.	Dryopteris cristata v clintoniana	D. clintoniana
Drimys winteri Latifolia Group	D. winteri v chilensis	Dryopteris decomposita v latiloba	Lastreopsis decomp.
Drimys winteri v punctata	D. winteri v winteri	Dryopteris decursive-pinnata	Phegopteris decursive-
Dropteris lonchitis	Polystichum lonchitis		pinnata
Drosera americana	D. intermedia	Dryopteris doniana	D. wallichiana
Drosera dichotoma	D. binata ssp dich.	Dryopteris erythrosora 'Prolifera'	D. e. v prolifera
Drosera foliosa	D. intermedia	D. filix-mas 'Crispa Congesta'	D. a. 'Crispa Gracilis'
Drosera intermedia x rotundifolia	D. x beleziana	Dryopteris filix-mas ssp oreades	D. oreades
Drosera media	D. intermedia	Dryopteris goldiana	D. goldieana
Dryandra arctotidis v tortifolia	D. tortifolia	Dryopteris goldieana ssp celsa	D. celsa
Dryandra ashbyi	D. fraseri v ashbyi	Dryopteris hexagonoptera	Phegopteris hexagonop.
Dryandra calophylla v acaulis	D. drummondii ssp	Dryopteris hikonensis	Dryopteris pacifica
	drummondii	Dryopteris hirtipes	D. cycadina
Dryandra carduacea	D. squarrosa ssp	Dryopteris kemulariae	D. x remota
	squarrosa	Dryopteris lanceolatocristata	D. carthusiana
Dryandra cryptocephala	D. seneciifolia	Dryopteris linnaeana	Gymnocarpium
Dryandra cuneata v brevifolia	D. cuneata		dryopteris
Dryandra cuneata v longifolia	D. cuneata	Dryopteris montana	Oreopteris
Dryandra cygnorum	D. sessilis v cygnorum		limbosperma
Dryandra dorrienii	D. falcata	Dryopteris munita	Polystichum munitum
Dryandra favosa	D. armata v armata	Dryopteris odontoloma	D. nigropaleacea
Dryandra floribunda v cordata	D. sessilis v cordata	Dryopteris odontoloma f brevifolia	D. stewartii
Dryandra floribunda v major	D. sessilis v cordata	Dryopteris oreopteris	Oreopteris limbosper.

Synonym	Current Name	Synonym	Current Name
Dryopteris palacea	D. wallichiana	Echinocactus chilensis	Neoporteria chilensis
Dryopteris parallelogramma	D. wallichiana	Echinocactus hartmannii	Discocactus hartmannii
Dryopteris parasiticum f keffordii	Christella subpubescens	Echinocactus ingens	E. platyacanthus
		Echinocactus myriostigma	Astrophytum myrios.
Dryopteris phegopteris	Phegopteris connectilis	Echinocactus ornatus	Astrophytum ornatum
Dryopteris poyseri	D. clintoniana	Echinocactus ritteri	Aztekium ritteri
Dryopteris pseudo-erythrosora	D. championii	Echinocactus scheeri	Sclerocactus scheeri
Dryopteris pseudo-filix-mas	D. pseudofilix-mas	Echinocactus uncinatus	Sclerocactus uncinat.
Dryopteris pseudomas	D. affinis	Echinocereus baileyi	E. reichenbachii v baileyi
Dryopteris remota	D. x remota		
Dryopteris setifera	Polystichum setiferum	Echinocereus procumbens	E. pentalophus
Dryopteris setifera ssp lobata	Polystichum aculeatum	Echinodorus ranunculoides	Baldellia ranunculoides
Dryopteris setosa -Kudo	D. crassirhizoma	Echinofossulocactus	Stenocactus
Dryopteris spinulosa	D. carthusiana	Echinofossulocactus lamellosus	Stenocactus crispatus
Dryopteris spinulosa ssp dilatata	D. dilatata	Echinofossulocactus pentacanthus	Stenocactus obvallatus
Dryopteris thelypteris	Thelypteris palustris	Echinofossulocactus violaciflorus	Stenocactus obvallatus
Dryopteris varia setosa	Polystichum discretum	Echinomastus macdowellii	Thelocactus macdow.
Dryopteris wurunuran	Lastreopsis wurun.	Echinopanax horridus	Oplopanax horridus
Duboisia campbellii	Eremophila saligna	Echinops albus	E. 'Nivalis'
Duchesnea chrysantha	D. indica	Echinops commutatus	E. exaltatus
Duchesnea indica 'Variegata'	D. indica 'Harlequin'	E. ritro 'Veitch's Blue' misapplied	E. ritro L.
Dugaldia hoopsii	Hymenoxis hoopesii	Echinops ritro h.	E. bannaticus
Dulcamara	Solanum	Echinops ritro tenuifolius	E. ritro ssp ruthenicus
Dunalia australis	Iochroma australe	Echinops ruthenicus h.	E. ritro ssp ruthenicus
Dunalia australis blue	Iochroma australe 'Bill Evans'	Echinopsis bridgesii	E. lageniformis
		Echinopsis multiplex	E. oxygona
Dunalia australis white	Iochroma australe 'Andean Snow'	Echinospartium horridum	Genista horrida
		Echinospartum	Genista
Duranta plumieri	D. erecta	Echioides longiflorum	Arnebia pulchra
Duranta repens	D. erecta	Echites grandiflora	Beaumontia grandiflora
Duvernoia	Justicia	Echites laxa -Ruiz & Pavon	Mandevilla laxa
Dyckia argentea	Hechtia argentea	Echium bourgaeanum	E. wildprettii
Dyckia remotiflora	D. rariflora	Echium carriezii	E. vulgare -L.
Dyckia sulphurea	D. brevifolia	Echium fastuosum	E. candicans
Dysosma pleiantha	Podophyllum pleianthum	Echium granatense	E. vulgare -L.
		Echium lacaitae	E. vulgare -L.
Dysphania botrys	Chenopodium botrys	Echium laetum	E. vulgare -L.
Dysphania graveolens	Chenopodium grav.	Echium lycopsis -not L.	E. plantagineum
Dysphania schraderiana	Chenopodium schrad.	Echium maritimum	E. plantagineum
Dyssodia tenuiloba	Thymophila tenuiloba	Echium murale	E. plantagineum
Eatonia purpurascens	Panicum virgatum	Echium petraeum -Tratt.	Moltkia petraea
Eccremocactus bradei	Weberocereus bradei	Echium pinnifolium	E. pininana
Eccremocarpus 'Ruber'	E. scaber f carmineus	Echium sennenii	E. plantagineum
Eccremocarpus ruber	E. scaber f carmineus	Echium violaceum	E. plantagineum
Echeveria cooperi	Adromischus cooperi	Eclipta alba	E. prostrata
Echeveria glauca -Bak.	E. secunda v glauca	Edgeworthia chrysantha f rubra h.	E. c. 'Red Dragon'
Echeveria obscura	E. agavoides	Edgeworthia papyrifera	E. chrysantha -Lindl.
Echeveria x fruticosa	Pachyveria glauca	Edraianthus caudatus	E. dalmaticus
Echeveria yuccoides	E. agavoides	Edraianthus croaticus	E. graminifolius
Echidnium -Schott	Dracontium -L.	Edraianthus graminifolius albus	E. gram. ssp niveus
Echidnopsis chrysantha	E. scutellata ssp planiflora	Edwardsia microphylla	Sophora microphylla
		Ehretia macrophylla h.	E. dicksonii
Echinacea purpurea 'Bright Star'	E. p. 'Leuchtstern'	Ehretia ovalifolia	E. acuminata v obovata
Echinocactus asterias	Astrophytum asterias	Ehretia thyrsiflora	E. acuminata v obovata
Echinocactus capricornis	Astrophytum capric.	Ehrhartia clandestina	Leersia oryzoides

Synonym	Current Name	Synonym	Current Name
Eichhornia speciosa	E. crassipes	Elliottia bracteata	Tripetaleia bracteata
Eichlerago	Prostanthera	Elliottia paniculata	Tripetaleia paniculata
Elaeagnus angustifolia Caspica Gr.	E. 'Quicksilver'	Elliottia pyroliflorus	Cladothamnus pyrol.
Elaeagnus angustifolia v orientalis	E. angustifolia	Elodea brandegeae	E. canadensis
Elaeagnus argentea -Moench	E. angustifolia -L.	Elodea crispa	Lagarosiphon major
Elaeagnus argentea -Pursh.	E. commutata -Rehd.	Elodea densa	Egeria densa
Elaeagnus crispa	E. umbellata	Elodea ioensis	E. canadensis
Elaeagnus edulis -Carr.	E. multiflora -Thunb.	Elodea latifolia	E. canadensis
Elaeagnus glabra 'Reflexa'	E. x reflexa	Elodea linearis	E. canadensis
Elaeagnus hortensis -Bieb.	E. angustifolia -L.	Elodea minor	E. nuttallii
Elaeagnus longipes -A.Gray	E. multiflora -Thunb.	Elodea occidentalis	E. nuttallii
Elaeagnus orientalis -L.	E. angustifolia v orient.	Elodea planchonii	E. canadensis
E. pungens 'Argenteovariegata'	E. pungens 'Variegata'	Elodea verticillata	E. nuttallii
Elaeagnus pungens 'Aurea'	E. pungens 'Dicksonii'	Elopium -Schott	Philodendron -Schott
Elaeagnus pungens 'Aureovariegata'	E. pungens 'Maculata'	Elsholtzia polystachya -Benth.	E. fruticosa
Elaeagnus pungens v reflexa	E. x reflexa	Elymus arenarius	Leymus arenarius
Elaeagnus rhamnoides	Hippophae rhamnoides	Elymus dumetorum	E. repens
Elaeagnus umbellata v parviflora	E. parvifolia	Elymus giganteus	Leymus racemosus
Elaeagnus x submacrophylla	E. x ebbingei h.	Elymus glaucus h.	E. hispidus
Elaeocarpus cyaneus -Ait. ex Sims	E. reticulatus	Elymus neogaeus	E. repens
Elaeocarpus peduncularis -Labill.	Aristotelia peduncul.	Elymus submuticus	E. curvatus
Elaeodendron fortunei -Turcz.	Euonymus fortunei	Elymus vaillantianus	E. repens
Elatine ambigua	E. triandra	Elytrygia repens	Elymus repens
Elatine chilensis	E. triandra	Elytrygia vaillantianum	Elymus repens
Elatine inaperta	E. triandra	Embothrium arenarium	Grevillea arenaria
Elatine orientalis	E. triandra	E. coccineum v lanceolatum	E. coccineum
Elatine senegalensis	E. triandra		Lanceolatum Group
Elatine triandra -not Schkuhr	E. americana	Embothrium crithmifolium	Lomatia silaifolia
Elatostema daveauanum	E. repens v repens	Embothrium ferrugineum -Cav.	Lomatia ferruginea
Eleocharis capitata	E. elliptica	Embothrium gilliesii -Meissn.	E. coccineum
Eleocharis compressa v borealis	E. elliptica	Embothrium herbaceum	Lomatia silaifolia
Eleocharis fernaldii	E. quinqueflora	Embothrium hirsutum -Lam.	Lomatia hirsuta
Eleocharis glaucus	E. erythropoda	Embothrium ilicifolium	Lomatia ilicifolia
Eleocharis halophila	E. uniglumis	Embothrium lanceolatum	E. coccineum
Eleocharis intersita	E. palustris		Lanceolatum Group
Eleocharis kamtschaticus	E. kamtschatica	Embothrium longifolium h.	E. coccineum
Eleocharis komarovii	E. kamtschatica		Longifolium Group
Eleocharis macounii	E. intermedia	Embothrium myricoideum -Gaertn.	Lomatia myricoides
Eleocharis mitrata	E. kamtschatica	Embothrium obliquum -Ruiz & Pavon	Lomatia hirsuta
Eleocharis pauciflora	E. quinqueflora	Embothrium salicifolium	Hakea salicifolia
Eleocharis perlonga	E. macrostachya	Embothrium salignum	Hakea salicifolia
Eleocharis quinqueflora	E. quinqueflora	Embothrium silaifolium -Sm.	Lomatia silaifolia
Eleocharis reclinata	E. intermedia	Embothrium tinctorium -Labill.	Lomatia tinctoria
Eleocharis sachalinensis	E. kamtschatica	Embothrium valdivianum -Gandoger	E. coccineum
Eleocharis savatieri	E. kamtschatica	Emilia flammea	E. coccinea
Eleocharis septentrionalis	E. uniglumis	Emilia javanica h.	E. coccinea
Eleocharis smallii	E. palustris	Emilia sagittata	E. coccinea
Eleocharis submersa	E. acicularis	Empetrum album -L.	Corema album
Eleocharis triflora -Kom.	E. kamtschatica	Empetrum conradii -Torr.	Corema conradii
Eleocharis vierhapperi	E. quinqueflora	E. nigrum f hermaphroditum	E. hermaphroditum
Eleocharis xyridiformis	E. macrostachya	Empetrum nigrum scoticum	E. hermaphroditum
Eleutherococcus pictus	Kalopanax septemlobus	Empetrum pinnatum -Lam.	M. pinnatus
Eleutherococcus septemlobus	Kalopanax septemlobus	Empetrum purpureum -Raf.	E. nigrum f purpureum
Eleutherococ. spinosus japonicus	E. japonicus	Empetrum rubrum ssp eamesii	E. eamesii
Elisena longipetala	Hymenocallis longipet.	Empleurosma virgata	Dodonaea pinifolia

Synonym	Current Name	Synonym	Current Name
Enallagma latifolia (unv)	Amphitecna latifolia	Epilobium steckerianum	E. hornemannii
Enantiosparton radiatum	Genista radiata	Epilobium villosum	Z. c. ssp mexicana
Encephalartos macdonnellii	Macrozamia macdonn.	Epilobium wilsonii h.	Z. chlorifolium
Endallax arundinacea	Phallaris arundinacea	Epilobium wyomingense	E. palustre
Endera -Regel	Taccarum -Brongn.	Epimedium colchicum	E. pinnatum ssp colch.
Endivia hortensis	Cichorium intybus	Epimedium cremeum	E. grandiflorum ssp
Endymion	Hyacinthoides		koreanum
Endymion hispanicus	Hyacinthoides hispanic.	Epimedium grandiflorum 'Violaceum'	E. gr. f violaceum
Endymion non-scriptus	Hyacinth. non-scripta	Epimedium hexandrum	Vancouveria hexandra
Enkianthus himalaicus	E. deflexus	Epimedium koreanum	E. gr. ssp koreanum
Enkianthus himalaicus v chinensis	E. chinensis -Franch.	Epimedium macranthum	E. grandiflorum
Enkianthus japonicus -Hook.f.	E. perulatus	Epimedium musschianum	E. x youngianum
Enkianthus matsudae -Komatsu	E. campanulatus v mat.	Epimedium pinnatum ssp elegans	E. p. ssp colchicum
Enkianthus palibinii -(Bean) Craib.	E. campanulatus v pal.	Epimedium sinense	E. sagittatum
Enkianthus pallidiflorus -Craib.	E. campanulatus f	Epimedium x omeiense 'Emei Shan'	E. x omeiense 'Akame'
	albiflorus -(Mak.) Mak.	Epimedium x youngianum 'Lilacinum'	E. x y. 'Roseum'
E. quinqueflorus v serrulatus -Wils.	E. serrulatus	Epipactis latifolia	E. helleborine
Enkianthus rubicundus	E. campanulatus v pal.	Epipactis pubescens	Goodyera pubescens
Enkianthus sinohimalaicus -Craib.	E. chinensis -Franch.	Epipactis willdenovii	Goodyera pubescens
Ensete ventricosum 'Rubrum'	E. ventricosum	Epiphyllanthus obovatus	Schlumbergera
	'Maurelii'		opuntioides
Ensolenanthe -Schott	Alocasia	Epiphyllum 'Gloria'	Epicactus 'Gloria'
Eopepon vitifolius	Trichosanthes kirilowii	Epiphyllum 'Jennifer Ann'	Epicactus 'Jennifer Ann'
Epacris apiculata	Rupicola apiculata	Epiphyllum 'M.A.Jeans'	Epicactus 'M.A.Jeans'
Epacris bawbawiensis	E. paludosa	Epiphyllum ackermannii	Nopalxochia ackerm.
Epacris heteronema v glacilais	E. glacialis	Epiphyllum macdougallii	Nopalxochia macdoug.
Epacris impressa v grandiflora	E. impressa	Epiphyllum strictum	Nopalxochia hookeri
Epacris microphylla v gunnii	E. gunnii	Epipremnopsis -Engl.	Amydrium -Schott
Epacris pumila	Pentachondra pumila	Epipremnum pictum 'Argyraeus'	Scindapsus pictus
Epacris secunda	Dracophyllum secund.		'Argyraeus'
Epacris tomentosa	E. impressa	Equisetum aphyllum	E. fluviatale
Ephedra andina -C.A.Mey.	E. americana v andina	Equisetum arenarium	E. palustre
Ephedra nebrodensis -Tineo	E. major -Host	Equisetum boreale	E. arvense
Epidendrum radicans	E. ibaguense	Equisetum calderi	E. arvense
Epigaea rubicunda	E. repens	Equisetum campestre	E. arvense
Epilobium angustifolium	Chamerion angustifol.	Equisetum capillare	E. sylvaticum
E. angustifolium f leucanthum	Chamerion	Equisetum heleocharis	E. fluviatale
	angustifolium 'Album'	Equisetum hyemale v robustum	E. hyemale v affine
Epilobium antipodum	E. crassjum	Equisetum lacustre	E. fluviatale
Epilobium californicum	Zauschneria californica	Equisetum limosum	E. fluviatale
	ssp angustifolia	Equisetum maximum	E. fluviatale
Epilobium californicum h.	Zauschneria californica	Equisetum mekongense	E. arvense
Epilobium canum	Z. c. ssp cana	Equisetum nemerosum	E. arvense
E. chlorifolium v kaikourense	Zauschneria chlorifol.	Equisetum nodosum	E. palustre
Epilobium densum	E. strictum	Equisetum opbraculense	E. sylvaticum
Epilobium dodonaei	Chamerion dodonaei	Equisetum ramosum	E. sylvaticum
Epilobium fleischeri	Chamerion fleischeri	Equisetum reptans	E. scirpoides
Epilobium garrettii	Z. c. ssp garrettii	Equisetum riparium	E. arvense
Epilobium hectorii	E. nummularifolium	Equisetum saxicola	E. arvense
Epilobium microphyllum	Z. californica ssp cana	Equisetum semifoliosum	E. fluviatale
Epilobium nesophilum	E. leptophyllum	Equisetum setaceum	E. scirpoides
Epilobium oliganthum	E. palustre	Equisetum tenellum -Fr.	E. palustre
Epilobium pylaieanum	E. palustre	Equisetum tuberosum	E. palustre
Epilobium rosmarinifolium	Chamerion dodonaei	Equisetum uliginosum	E. fluviatale
Epilobium septentrionale	Zauschneria septentr.	Equisetum umbrosum	E. sylvaticum

Synonym	Current Name	Synonym	Current Name
Eragrostis 'Silver Needles'	Agrostis canina 'Silver Needles'	Eremophila strehlowii	E. macdonnelii
		Eremophila turtonii	E. forrestii
Eragrostis abyssinica	E. tef	Eremophila woolsiana	E. lehmanniana
Eranthemum atropurpureum	Pseuderanthemum atr.	Eremurus altaicus	E. spectabilis
Eranthemum nervosum	E. pulchellum	Eremurus angustifolius	E. olgae
Eranthis cilicicus	E. hyemalis Cilicica Gr.	Eremurus aurantiacus	E. stenophyllus ssp au.
Eranthis keiskei	E. pinnatifida	Eremurus bungei	E. stenophyllus ssp stenophyllus
Eranthis x tubergenii	E. hyemalis Tubergenii Group	Eremurus caucasicus	E. spectabilis
Ercilla spicata -(Bert.) Moq.	E. volubilis -A.Juss.	Eremurus elwesii	E. aitchisonii
Erdisia	Corryocactus	Eremurus elwesii grandis h.	E. robustus
Erdisia erecta	Corryocactus erectus	Eremurus himalaicus elwesii	E. aitchisonii
Erdisia squarrosa	Corryocactus squarr.	Eremurus robustus elwesii	E. aitchisonii
Erechites apargiifolia	Senecio hipidulus	Eremurus stenophyllus v bungei	E. stenophyllus ssp st.
Erechites arguta	Senecio evansianus	Eremurus tauricus	E. spectabilis
Erechites arguta v aspera	Senecio glomeratus	Eremurus x isabellinus Fire Torch	E. x i. 'Feuerfackel'
Erechites arguta v bathurstiana	Senecio bathurstianus	Eremurus x isabellinus Snow Lance	E. x i. 'Schneelanze'
Erechites arguta v dissecta	Senecio bathurstianus	Erianthus	Saccharum
Erechites arguta v microcephala	Senecio laticostatus	Erica 'Heaven Scent'	E. x griffithsii 'Heaven Scent'
Erechites arguta v obovata	Senecio glomeratus		
Erechites atkinsoniae	Senecio bipinnatisectus	Erica arborea 'Arbora Gold'	E. a. 'Albert's Gold'
Erechites bathurstiana	Senecio bathurstianus	Erica arborea 'Arnold's Gold'	E. a. 'Albert's Gold'
Erechites candicans	Senecio georgianus	Erica arborea 'Pink Joy'	E. x veitchii 'Pink Joy'
Erechites erecta	S. quadridentatus	Erica bracteata	E. carnea
Erechites glabrescens	Senecio glabrescens	Erica campanulata -not Andr.	E. pageana -L.
Erechites glandulosa	S. campylocarpus	Erica carnea 'Amy Doncaster'	E. c. 'Treasure Trove'
Erechites glomerata	Senecio glomeratus	Erica carnea 'Mr. Reeves'	E. x darleyensis 'Darley Dale'
Erechites glomerata v glomerata	Senecio glomeratus	Erica carnea 'Myreton Ruby'	E. c. 'Myretoun Ruby'
Erechites glomerata v polycephala	Senecio glomeratus	Erica carnea 'Pink Beauty'	E. carnea 'Pink Pearl'
Erechites glomerata v subincisa	Senecio glomeratus	Erica carnea 'Sherwoodii'	E. carnea 'Sherwood Creeping'
Erechites glossantha	Senecio glossanthus		
Erechites gunnii	Senecio gunnii	Erica carnea 'Urville'	E. carnea 'Vivellii'
Erechites hispidula	Senecio hipidulus	Erica carnea 'Whisky'	E. carnea 'Bell's Extra Special'
Erechites lacerata	Senecio laceratus		
Erechites minima	Senecio minimus	Erica carnea 'White Glow'	E. x darleyensis 'White Glow'
Erechites muelleri	Senecio hipidulus		
Erechites picridioides	Senecio picridioides	Erica carnea 'White Perfection'	E. x darleyensis 'White Perfection'
Erechites prenanthoides	Senecio minimus		
E. prenanthoides v picridioides	Senecio picridioides	Erica cinerea 'Fulgida'	E. cinerea 'Coccinea'
Erechites pumila	Senecio minimus	Erica cinerea 'Graham Thomas'	E. cinerea 'C.G.Best'
E. quadridentata v glandulosa	S. campylocarpus	Erica cinerea 'Pink Lace'	E. cinerea 'Pink Ice'
Erechites quadridentata v gunnii	Senecio gunnii	Erica codonodes -Lindl.	E. lusitanica -Rudolph
Erechites sonchoides	Senecio biserratus	Erica corsica -DC.	E. terminalis -Salisb.
Erechites tenuiflora	Senecio tenuiflorus	Erica crawfurdii	E. mackayana
Eremophila bicolor	E. racemosa	Erica daboecia -L.	Daboecia cantabrica
Eremophila brownii	E. glabra	Erica decipiens	E. vagans
Eremophila brownii	E. grahamii	Erica erigena 'Compacta'	E. erigena 'Nana'
Eremophila calyina	E. duttonii	Erica erigena 'Irish Lemon'	E. x stuartii 'Irish Lemon'
Eremophila cunninghamii	E. oppositifolia		
Eremophila exotrachys	E. platythamnos	Erica herbacea	E. carnea
Eremophila gibbosifolia	E. gibbifolia	Erica herbacea -L.	E. carnea -L.
Eremophila kochii	E. resinosa	Erica hibernica	E. erigena -R.Ross
Eremophila leucophylla	E. forrestii	Erica hybrida 'Irish Lemon'	E. x stuartii 'Irish Lemon'
Eremophila mertrallii	E. caerulea		
Eremophila ramosissima	E. glutinosa		

Synonym	Current Name	Synonym	Current Name
Erica mackaiana flore pleno	E. mackayana 'Plena'	Erigeron Pink Triumph	E. 'Rosa Triumph'
Erica mackaiana-Bab.	E. mackayana -Bab.	Erigeron pyrenaicus -Rouy	Aster pyrenaeus
Erica mackaii -Hook.	E. mackayana -Bab.	Erigeron pyrenaicus h.	E. alpinus
Erica mackayana 'Crawfordii'	E. mackayana 'Plena'	Erigeron Red Sea	E. 'Rotes Meer'
Erica manipuliflora 'Waterfall'	E. man. 'Cascade'	E. rotundifolius 'Caerulescens'	Bellis rotundifolia
E. man. x vagans 'Valerie Griffiths'	E. x griffithsii 'Valerie Griffiths'		'Caerulescens'
		Erigeron salsuginosus	E. peregrinus
Erica mediterranea h.	E. erigena -R.Ross	Erigeron salsuginosus misapplied	Aster sibiricus
Erica mediterranea v hibernica	E. erigena -R.Ross	Erigeron Snow White	E. 'Schneewittchen'
Erica melanthera -Lodd. not L.	E. canaliculata	Erigeron trifidus	E. compositus v
Erica saxatilis	E. carnea		discoideus
Erica scoparia ssp scoparia 'Nana'	E. scoparia ssp scoparia 'Minima'	Erinacea pungens -Boiss.	E. anthyllis -Link
		Eriobotrya prionophylla -Franch.	Photinia prionophylla
E. scoparia ssp scoparia 'Pumila'	E. s. ssp s. 'Minima'	Eriocactus	Parodia
Erica stricta -Willd.	E. terminalis -Salisb.	Eriocactus apricus	Parodia concinna
Erica terminalis stricta	E. terminalis	Eriocapitella	Anemone
Erica tetralix 'Dr. Ronald Gray'	E. mackayana 'Doctor Ronald Gray'	Eriocereus jusbertii	Harrisia jusbertii
		Eriocereus martianus	Aporocactus mart.
Erica tetralix 'Lawsoniana'	E. mackayana 'Lawsoniana'	Eriocereus pomanensis	Harrisia bonplandii
		Eriogonum cespitosum ssp douglasii	E. douglasii
Erica tetralix 'Mollis'	E. tetralix 'Alba Mollis'	Eriogonum torreyanum	E. umbellatum v torr.
Erica tetralix 'Morning Glow'	E. x watsonii 'F.White'	Eriogynia hendersonii -Canby	Petrophytum henders.
Erica tetralix 'Plena'	E. mackayana 'Plena'	Eriogynia pectinata -(Pursh) Hook.	Luetkea pectinata
Erica tetralix 'Ruby's Velvet'	E. t. 'Ruby's Variety'	Eriolepis lanceolata	Cirsium vulgare
Erica vaga	E. vagans	Eriolobus florentina	Malus kansuensis
Erica vagans 'Alba Nana'	E. vagans 'Nana'	Eriolobus kansuensis	Malus kansuensis
Erica vulgaris -L.	Calluna vulgaris	Eriolobus trilobatus -(Labill.) Roem.	Malus trilobata
Erica x darleyensis 'Alba'	E. x d. 'Silberschmelze'	Eriolobus tschonkii -(Maxim.) Rehd.	Malus tschonkii
E. x darleyensis 'Cherry Stevens'	E. x d. 'Furzey'	Eriophyllum caespitosum	E. lanatum
Erica x darleyensis 'Darleyensis'	E. x d. 'Darley Dale'	Eriophyllum lutescens	E. lanatum v monoense
E. x d. 'Dunwood Splendour'	E. x darleyensis 'Arthur Johnson'	Eriostemon ambiens	Leioenema ambiens
		Eriostemon amblycarpus	Rhadinothamnus rudis ssp amblycarpus
Erica x darleyensis 'J.H.Brummage'	E. x darleyensis 'Jack H.Brummage'	Eriostemon amplifolius	Philotheca myoporoides
E. x d. 'Mediterranea Superba'	E. x d. 'Superba'	Eriostemon anceps	Rhadinothamnus anc.
Erica x darleyensis 'Pink Perfection'	E. x d. 'Darley Dale'	Eriostemon angustfolius	Philotheca angustifolia
Erica x darleyensis Molten Silver	E. x d. 'Silberschmelze'	E. angustfolius ssp angustifolius	Philotheca angustifolia
Erica x praegeri	E. x stuartii	E. angustfolius ssp montanus	Philotheca angustifolia ssp montana
Erica x stuartii 'Charles Stuart'	E. x stuartii 'Stuartii'	Eriostemon apiculatus	Philotheca apiculata
Erica x veitchii 'Albert's Gold'	E. arborea 'Albert's Gold'	Eriostemon apricis	Philotheca fitzgeraldii
		E. australasius ssp australasius	E. australasius
Erica x williamsiana	E. williamsii	Eriostemon australasius ssp banksii	E. banksii
Ericoides vulgaris -not Salis.	Calluna vulgaris	Eriostemon beckleri	Leioenema elatius ssp beckleri
Erigeron 'Profusion'	E. karvinskianus		
Erigeron Azure Fairy	E. 'Azurfee'	Eriostemon bilobum	Rhadinothamnus rudis ssp rudis
Erigeron Black Sea	E. 'Schwarzes Meer'		
Erigeron candensis	Conyza candensis	Eriostemon brachyphyllus	Leioenema microphyllum
Erigeron Darkest of All	E. 'Dunkelste Aller'		
Erigeron flabelliformis	E. compositus v discoideus	Eriostemon brevifolius	Philotheca brevifolia
		Eriostemon brucei	Philotheca brucei
Erigeron mesa-grande h.	E. macranthus	Eriostemon brucei ssp brevifolius	Philotheca brucei ssp brevifolia
Erigeron mucronatus	E. karvinskianus		
Erigeron multifidus	E. compositus	Eriostemon brucei ssp brucei	Philotheca brucei
Erigeron perennis	Bellis perennis		
Erigeron Pink Jewel	E. 'Rosa Juwel'		

Synonym	Current Name	Synonym	Current Name
Eriostemon brucei ssp cinereus	Philotheca brucei ssp cinerea	Eriostemon myoporoides	Philotheca myoporoides
Eriostemon buxifolius	Philotheca buxifolia	E. myoporoides ssp acutus	Philotheca myoporoid. ssp acuta
Eriostemon buxifolius ssp obovatus	Philotheca buxifolia ssp obovata	E. myoporoides ssp conduplicatus	Philotheca myoporoid. ssp conduplicata
Eriostemon buxifolius v ellipticus	Philotheca buxifolia ssp buxifolia	E. myoporoides ssp epilosus	Philotheca myoporoid. ssp epilosa
Eriostemon calycinus	Philotheca nodiflora ssp calycina	E. myoporoides ssp leichhardtii	Philotheca myoporoid. ssp leichhardtii
Eriostemon capitatus	Microcybe pauciflora ssp pauciflora	E. myoporoides ssp myoporoides	Philotheca myoporoid. ssp myoporoides
E. capitatus ssp baccharoides	Microcybe multiflora ssp baccharoides	E. myoporoides ssp queenslandicus	Philotheca myoporoid. ssp queenslandica
Eriostemon carruthersii	Leioenema carruthers.	Eriostemon neriifolius	Philotheca myoporoid. ssp myoporoides
Eriostemon coccineus	Philotheca coccinea		
Eriostemon coxii	Leioenema coxii	Eriostemon nodiflorus	Philotheca nodiflora
Eriostemon crowei	Crowea exalata	E. nodiflorus ssp lasiocalyx	Philotheca nodiflora ssp lasiocalyx
Eriostemon cuspidatus	Philotheca myopor. ssp myoporoides		
Eriostemon cymbiformis	Philotheca cymbiformis	E. nodiflorus ssp nodiflorus	Philotheca nodiflora
Eriostemon daviesii	Phebalium daviesii	E. nodiflorus v subglabriflorus	Philotheca nodiflora ssp nodiflora
Eriostemon deserti	Philotheca deserti		
Eriostemon difformis	Philotheca difformis	Eriostemon nudus	Leioenema nudum
E. difformis ssp smithianus	Philotheca d.ssp smith.	Eriostemon nutans	Philotheca nutans
Eriostemon difformis v difformis	Philotheca difformis	Eriostemon obcordatus	Philotheca verrucosa
Eriostemon difformis v teretifolius	Philotheca brevifolia	Eriostemon obovalis	Philotheca obovalis
Eriostemon dolabratus	Philotheca verrucosa	Eriostemon oldfieldii	Leioenema oldfieldii
Eriostemon ebracteatus	Philotheca spicata	Eriostemon ovatifolius	Nematolepis ovatifolia
Eriostemon effusus	Philotheca spicata	Eriostemon pachyphyllus	Philotheca pachyphylla
Eriostemon elatior	Leioenema elatius	Eriostemon paradoxus	Boronia ledifolia
Eriostemon ericifolius	Philotheca ericifolia	Eriostemon paradoxus	Boronia ledifolia
Eriostemon fabianoides	Boronia fabanoides	Eriostemon parvifolius	Philotheca difformis ssp smithiana
Eriostemon fabianoides	Boronia fabanoides		
Eriostemon falcatus	Philotheca falcata	Eriostemon phylicifolius	Leioenema phylicifolium
Eriostemon fitzgeraldii	Philotheca fitzgeraldii		
Eriostemon gardneri	Philotheca gardneri	Eriostemon phylicoides	Leioenema diosmeum
Eriostemon gibbosus	Philotheca fitzgeraldii	Eriostemon pinoides	Philotheca pinoides
Eriostemon glaber	Philotheca glabra	Eriostemon pleurandroides	Asterolasia phebalioides
Eriostemon glasshousiensis	P. myoporoides ssp leichhardtii	Eriostemon pungens	Philotheca pungens
Eriostemon gracilis	Philotheca salsolifolia ssp salsolifolia	Eriostemon racemosus	Philotheca spicata
		Eriostemon ralstonii	Leioenema ralstonii
Eriostemon halmaturorus	Philotheca linearis	Eriostemon rhombeus	Philotheca difformis ssp difformis
Eriostemon hillebrandii	Leioenema bilobum		
Eriostemon hillebrandii v longifolius	Leioenema bilobum	Eriostemon rhomboideus	Philotheca rhomboidea
Eriostemon hispidulus	Philotheca hispidula	Eriostemon rotundifolius	Leioenema rotundifol.
Eriostemon intermedius	P. deserti ssp deserti	Eriostemon salicifolius	E. australasius
Eriostemon lamprophyllus	Leioenema lamprophyl.	Eriostemon scaber	Philotheca scabra
Eriostemon lanceolatus	E. australasius	Eriostemon scabrum	Philotheca scabra
Eriostemon lanceolatus	E. australasius	Eriostemon sericeus	Philotheca sericea
Eriostemon lancifolius	Philotheca myoporoid. ssp myoporoides	Eriostemon serrulatus	Leioenema bilobum
		Eriostemon spicatus	Philotheca spicata
Eriostemon linearis	Philotheca linearis	Eriostemon sporadicus	Philotheca sporadica
Eriostemon microphyllus	Leioenema microphyl.	Eriostemon squameus	Nematolepis squamea
Eriostemon montanus	Leioenema montanum	Eriostemon stowardii	Philotheca tomentella

Synonym	Current Name	Synonym	Current Name
Eriostemon thryptomenoides	Philotheca thryptom.	Eryngium creticum Delaroux	E. proteiflorum
Eriostemon tomentellus	Philotheca tomentella	Eryngium decaisneanum	E. pandanifolium
Eriostemon trachyphyllus	Philotheca trachyphylla	Eryngium decaisneanum -Delaroux	E. proteiflorum
E. trachyphyllus v leichhardtii	Philotheca myoporoid. ssp leichhardtii	Eryngium Miss Wilmott's Ghost	E. giganteum
		Eryngium paniculatum	E. erburneum
Eriostemon trayningensis	Philotheca basistyla	Eryngium planum Blue Dwarf	E. p. 'Blauer Zwerg'
E. tuberculosus v magaphyllus	Phlebalium megaphyll.	Eryngium schwackeanum	E. horridum
Eriostemon umbellatus	Leioenema dentatum	Erysimum 'Devon Gold'	E. 'Plant World Gold'
Eriostemon verrucosus	Philotheca verrucosa	Erysimum 'Dorothy Elmhirst'	E. 'Mrs L.K.Elmhirst'
Eriostemon virgatus	Philotheca virgata	Erysimum 'E.A.Bowles'	E. 'Bowles' Mauve'
Eriostemon wonganensis	Philotheca wonganensis	Erysimum 'Harpur Crewe'	E. cheiri 'Harpur Crewe'
Eritrichium rupestre	E. canum	Erysimum 'Sissinghurst Variegated'	E. linifolium 'Variegatum'
Eritrichium sericeum	E. canum		
Eritrichium strictum	E. canum	Erysimum afghanicum h.	E. hieraciifolium
Erodium 'County Park'	E. foetidum 'County Park'	Erysimum alpinum h.	E. hieraciifolium
		Erysimum arenicola v torulosum	E. torulosum
Erodium 'Fran's Choice'	E. 'Fran's Delight'	Erysimum arkansanum	E. helveticum
Erodium 'Merstham Pink'	E. foetidum 'County Park'	Erysimum asperum	E. capitatum
		Erysimum barbarea	Barbarea vulgaris
Erodium absinthoides v amanum	E. amanum	Erysimum concinnum	E. suffrutescens
Erodium balearicum	E. x variabile 'Album'	Erysimum eseptatum	E. hieraciifolium
Erodium chamaedryoides	E. reichardii	Erysimum lanceolatum	E. hieraciifolium
Erodium chamaedryoides 'Roseum'	E. x variabile 'Roseum'	Erysimum marschallianum	E. hieraciifolium
Erodium daucoides misapplied	E. castellanum	Erysimum officinale	Sisymbrium officinale
Erodium foetidum 'Pallidum'	E. 'Pallidum'	Erysimum orientale	Conringia orientalis
Erodium guttatum misapplied	E. 'Katherine Joy'	Erysimum perfoliatum	Conringia orientalis
Erodium heteradenum	E. petraeum	Erysimum pinnatum	Descurainia pinnata
Erodium hymenodes -L'Her.	E. trifolium	Erysimum pumilum -De Candolle	E. helveticum
Erodium macradenum	E. glandulosum	Erysimum rupestre	E. pulchellum
Erodium manescavii	E. manescaui	Erysimum sintenisianum	E. alpestre
Erodium petraeum ssp crispum	E. cheilanthifolium	Erysimum strictum	E. hieraciifolium
Erodium petraeum ssp crispum	E. foetidum	Erysimum thalianum	Arabidopsis thalianum
Erodium petraeum ssp glandulosum	E. glandulosum	Erysimum violaceum	Cardamine violacea
Erodium reichardii cultivars	E. x variabile	E. x kewensis 'Harpur Crewe'	E. cheiri 'Harpur Crewe'
Erodium romanum	E. acaule		
Erodium salzmannii	E. cicutarium ssp cicutarium	Erythea	Brahea
		Erythraea	Centaurium
Erodium supracanum	E. rupestre	Erythraea centaurium	Centaurium erythraea
Erodium trichomanifolium misapp.	E. cheilanthifolium	Erythrina indica	E. variegata
Erodium x hybridum misapplied	E. 'Sara Francesca'	Erythrina princeps	E. humeana
Erpetion	Viola	Erythrina tomentosa	E. abyssinica
Erpetion hederaceum	Viola hederacea	Erythrochaete palmatifida	Ligularia japonica
Erpetion reniforme	Viola hederacea	Erythronium 'White Beauty'	E. californicum 'White Beauty'
Eruca muralis	Diplotaxis muralis		
Ervatamia coronaria	Tabernaemontana divaricata	Erythronium cliftonii h.	E. multiscapoideum Cliftonii Group
Ervum lens	Lens culinaris	E. grandiflorum ssp chrysandrum	E. grandiflorum
Eryngium alpinum 'Slieve Donard'	E. x zabelii 'Donard Variety'	Erythronium hartwegii	E. multiscapoideum
		Erythronium purdyi	E. multiscapoideum
Eryngium antihystericum	E. foetidum	E. revolutum 'White Beauty'	E. calif. 'White Beauty'
Eryngium balansae	E. erburneum	Erythrospermum hypoleucum	Celastrus hypoleucus -
Eryngium biebersteinianum	E. caeruleum	Escallonia 'Crimson Spire'	E. rubra 'Crimson Spire'
Eryngium bromeliifolium misapplied	E. agavifolium		
Eryngium caucasicum	E. caeruleum	Escallonia 'Hopley's Gold'	E. laevis 'Gold Brian'

Synonym	Current Name	Synonym	Current Name
Escallonia 'Ingramii'	E. rubra 'Ingramii'	Eucalyptus angusta	E. rigidula
Escallonia bellidifolia -Phil.	E. leucantha -Remy	Eucalyptus angustifolia	E. leptopoda
Escallonia duplicato-serrata -Remy	E. rubra	Eucalyptus angustifolia -Desf.	E. viminalis -Labill.
Escallonia floribunda h.	E. bifida -Link & Otto	E. angustissima ssp quaerenda	E. quaerenda
E. floribunda v montevidensis	E. bifida -Link & Otto	E. angustissoma ssp quaerenda	E. quaerenda
Escallonia fonckii -Phil.	E. alpina -DC.	Eucalyptus apocynifolia	Angophora costata
Escallonia fonkii	E. alpina -DC.	E. apodophylla ssp provecta	E. apodophylla
Escallonia glaberrima -Phil.	E. alpina -DC.	E. approximans ssp codonocarpa	E. microcodon
Escallonia glandulosa -Lodd.not Sm.	E. illinita -Presl	Eucalyptus archeri	E. gunnii -Hook. f.
Escallonia glutinosa -Phil.	E. rubra v glutinosa	Eucalyptus argentea	E. melliodora
Escallonia grahamiana -Hook. & Arn.	E. illinita -Presl	Eucalyptus aurantiaca	E. miniata
Escallonia macrantha -Hook. & Arn.	E. rubra v macrantha	Eucalyptus australiana	E. radiata
Escallonia microphylla h.	E. rubra	Eucalyptus australiana v nitida	E. nitida
Escallonia montana	E. rubra v uniflora	Eucalyptus barklyensis	E. microtheca
Escallonia montevidensis	E. bifida -Link & Otto	Eucalyptus baxteri v pedicellata	E. baxteri
Escallonia organensis -Gardn.	E. laevis -(Vell.) Sleum.	Eucalyptus behriana v purpurascens	E. albopurpurea
Escallonia philippiana -(A.Engl).Mast.	E. virgata	Eucalyptus bennettiae	E. x bennettiae
Escallonia pterocladon -Hook.	E. rosea -Griseb.	Eucalyptus benthamii v benthamii	E. benthamii
Escallonia punctata -DC.	E. rubra Escallonia	Eucalyptus benthamii v dorrigoensis	E. diorrigoensis
rubra 'Pygmaea'	E. rubra 'Woodside'	Eucalyptus beyeriana	E. beyeri
Escallonia rubra v pubescens	E. x mollis -Phil.	Eucalyptus bicolor v parviflora	E. brownii
Escallonia rubra v punctata	E. rubra	Eucalyptus bicolor v xanthophylla	E. normantonensis
Escallonia sanguinea h.	E. rubra	Eucalyptus bicostata	E. globulus ssp bicost.
Escallonia viscosa	E. illinita	Eucalyptus biturbinata	E. punctata
Esculus hipocastanea -(L.) Raf.	Aesculus hippocast.	Eucalyptus blackelyi v irrorata	E. blackelyi
Esmeralda sanderiana	Euanthe sanderiana	Eucalyptus blackelyi v parvifructa	E. blackelyi
Euacer	Acer	Eucalyptus blackwelliana	E. greeniana
Eubotryoides grayana	Leucothoe grayana	Eucalyptus botryoides v platycarpa	E. botryoides
Eubotrys racemosa -(L.) Nutt.	Leucothoe racemosa	Eucalyptus bowmannii	E. fibrosa ssp fibrosa
Eubotrys recurva -(Buckl.) Britt.	Leucothoe recurva	Eucalyptus brachycalyx v chindoo	E. brachycalyx
Eucalyptus acaciiformis v linearis	E. nicholii	Eucalyptus brachycalyx v protrusa	E. brachycalyx
Eucalyptus acervula	E. eugenioides	E. bridgesiana ssp malacoxylon	E. malacoxylon
Eucalyptus acervula -Miq. not Sieber	E. ovata -Labill.	E. bridgesiana v amblycorys	E. bridgesiana
Eucalyptus acmenoides v carnea	E. carnea	Eucalyptus brunnea	E. deanei
Eucalyptus acmenoides v rubra	E. carnea	Eucalyptus bynoeana	E. hamersleyana
Eucalyptus acmenoides v tenuipes	E. tenuipes	Eucalyptus byrnesii	E. greeniana
Eucalyptus acuminata -Hook.	E. camaldulensis v camaldulensis	Eucalyptus caeruescens	E. melliodora
		Eucalyptus calcicultrix	E. porosa
Eucalyptus aenea	E. viridis	Eucalyptus calcicultrix v calcicultrix	E. porosa
Eucalyptus agnata	E. occidentalis	Eucalyptus calcicultrix v porosa	E. porosa
Eucalyptus alaticaulis	E. cypellocarpa	Eucalyptus calophylla v maideniana	E. calophylla
Eucalyptus albens v elongata	E. albens	Eucalyptus calophylla v parviflora	E. calophylla
Eucalyptus alpina	E. serranensis	E. calycogona v celastroides	E. celastroides ssp celastroides
Eucalyptus alpina -Lindl.	E. serraensis		
Eucalyptus altior	E. oreades	Eucalyptus calycogona v gracilis	E. gracilis
Eucalyptus amagdalyina v regnans	E. regnans	Eucalyptus calycogona v staffordii	E. calycogona ss spaff.
Eucalyptus ambigua	E. stricta	E. camalduensis v acuminata	E. camaldulensis v camalduensis
Eucalyptus amplifolia v sessiliflora	E. amplifolia ssp sessil.		
Eucalyptus amygdalina v angustifolia	E. pulchella	E. camalduensis v brevirostris	E. camaldulensis v cam.
Eucalyptus amygdalina v latifolia	E. dives	Eucalyptus camaldulensis v pendula	E. camaldulensis v obtusa
Eucalyptus amygdalina v nitida	E. nitida		
Eucalyptus anceps	E. rugosa	E. camaldulensis v subcinerea	E. camaldulensis v obt.
Eucalyptus ancophila	E. paniculata	Eucalyptus cambagei	E. goniocalyx ssp goniocalyx
Eucalyptus andreeana	E. elata		
Eucalyptus angulosa v ceratocorys	E. ceratocorys	Eucalyptus cambagei v pallens	E. nortonii

Synonym	Current Name	Synonym	Current Name
Eucalyptus campanulata	E. andrewsii ssp camp.	Eucalyptus desertorum	E. deserticola ssp
Eucalyptus camphora ssp relicta	E. camphora ssp camp.		deserticola
Eucalyptus capitanea	E. ceratocorys	Eucalyptus desertorum	E. uncinata
Eucalyptus capitellata v latifolia	E. baxteri	Eucalyptus dextropinea	E. muelleriana
Eucalyptus centralis	E. terminalis	Eucalyptus disclusa	E. interstans
Eucalyptus chlorolampra	E. haematoxylon	Eucalyptus dissita	E. moorei ssp moorei
Eucalyptus cinerea v cinerea	E. cinerea ssp cinerea	Eucalyptus divaricata	E. gunnii ssp divaricata
Eucalyptus cinerea v multiflora	E. cephalocarpa	Eucalyptus divaricata	E. gunnii ssp divaricata
Eucalyptus cinerea v nova-anglica	E. nova-anglica	Eucalyptus diversifolia	E. macarthurii
Eucalyptus clavigera v dallachiana	E. cypellocarpa	E. diversifolia ssp megacarpa	E. diversifolia ssp
Eucalyptus clavigera v diffusa	E. pauciseta		diversifolia
Eucalyptus coccifera v parviflora	E. coccifera	Eucalyptus dolichocarpa	E. clarksoniana
Eucalyptus codonocarpa	E. approximans ssp co.	Eucalyptus dongarraensis	A. obtusiflora
Eucalyptus coerulea	E. caleyi ssp caleyi	Eucalyptus dorrienii	E. falcata
Eucalyptus comitae-vallis	E. brachycorys	Eucalyptus drepanophylla	E. crebra
Eucalyptus concolor	E. decipiens ssp	E. drepanophylla v leptophleba	E. leptophleba
	decipiens	Eucalyptus dumosa v conglobata	E. conglobata ssp cong.
Eucalyptus conglobata	E. conglobata ssp cong.	Eucalyptus dumosa v puncticulata	E. uncinata
Eucalyptus conglobata ssp fraseri	E. fraseri ssp fraseri	Eucalyptus dumosa v scyphocalyx	E. scyphocalyx
Eucalyptus conoidea	E. erythronema v	Eucalyptus durackiana	E. greeniana
	erythronema	E. ebbanoensis ssp glauciramula	E. e. ssp ebbanoensis
Eucalyptus contracta	E. acmenoides	Eucalyptus effusa ssp effusa	E. effusa
Eucalyptus coolabah ssp arida	E. coolabah	Eucalyptus effusa ssp exsul	E. effusa
Eucalyptus coolabah ssp excerata	E. coolabah	Eucalyptus elachyphylla	E. rosacea
Eucalyptus coolabah v rhodoclada	E. victrix	Eucalyptus elaeophora	E. goniocalyx ssp gon.
Eucalyptus cordata	E. pulverulenta	Eucalyptus epruinata	E. distans
Eucalyptus cordata -Lodd. not labill.	E. pulverulenta -Sims	Eucalyptus eremophila v grandiflora	E. aspratilis
Eucalyptus cordieri v brachypoma	E. goniocalyx ssp	Eucalyptus erythrocalyx	E. pyriformis
	goniocalyx	Eucalyptus euryphylla	Angophora euryphylla
Eucalyptus cordieri v nortonii	E. nortonii	Eucalyptus exserta v parvula	E. exserta
Eucalyptus coriacea -Schauer	E. pauciflora -Sieber	Eucalyptus exul	Angophora exul
Eucalyptus coriacea v alpina	E. pauciflora ssp	Eucalyptus fabrorum	E. obliqua
	niphophila	Eucalyptus falcata v ecostata	E. falcata
Eucalyptus corymbosa	E. gummifera	Eucalyptus falcifolia	E. obliqua
Eucalyptus corynocalyx	E. cladocalyx	Eucalyptus fergusonii ssp fergusonii	E. paniculata
Eucalyptus cosmophylla f leprosula	E. cosmophylla	Eucalyptus ferriticola ssp sitiens	E. ferriticola
Eucalyptus cosmophylla v rostrigera	E. cosmophylla	Eucalyptus fitzgeraldii	E. oligantha
Eucalyptus costata	E. incrassata	Eucalyptus floribunda	E. marginata ssp
Eucalyptus crassifolia	Angophora crassifolia		marginata
Eucalyptus crebra v citrata	E. staigeriana	Eucalyptus florida	Angophora floribunda
Eucalyptus crebra v macrocarpa	E. crebra	Eucalyptus foecunda v loxophleba	E. loxophleba ssp lox.
Eucalyptus cullenii v trivalvis	E. crullenii	Eucalyptus forsythii	E. melliodora
Eucalyptus cuspidata	E. angulosa	Eucalyptus fraxinoides v triflora	E. triflora
Eucalyptus cyanoclada	E. microtheca	Eucalyptus gigantea	E. globulus ssp globul.
Eucalyptus cyathiformis	E. caliginosa	Eucalyptus gigantea -not Dehnhardt	E. delegatensis
Eucalyptus dampieri	E. greeniana	Eucalyptus glandulosa	E. amygdalina
Eucalyptus daphnoides	E. coccifera	Eucalyptus globoidea v subsphaerica	E. globoidea
Eucalyptus darwinensis	E. foelscheana	Eucalyptus globulus ssp globulus	E. globulus
Eucalyptus dealbata v chlorocada	E. chlorocada	Eucalyptus globulus v st-johnii	E. globulus ssp
Eucalyptus dealbata v populnea	E. infera		pseudoglobulus
Eucalyptus debeuzevillei	E. pauciflora ssp deb.	E. gomphocephala v rhodoxylon	E. gomphocephala
Eucalyptus decepta	E. siderophloia	Eucalyptus goniantha v clelandii	E. clelandii
Eucalyptus decipiens v angustifolia	E. decipiens ssp	Eucalyptus goniocalyx v acuminata	E. cypellocarpa
	adesmophloia	Eucalyptus goniocalyx v nitens	E. nitens
Eucalyptus deformis	E. globoidea	Eucalyptus goniocalyx v pallens	E. nortonii

Synonym	Current Name	Synonym	Current Name
Eucalyptus goniocalyx v parviflora	E. cypellocarpa	Eucalyptus lamprocarpa	E. dumosa
Eucalyptus gracilis v breviflora	E. gracilis	Eucalyptus langii	E. cladocalyx
Eucalyptus gracilis v erecta	E. gracilis	E. lansdowneana ssp albopurpurea	E. albopurpurea
Eucalyptus gracilis v thozetii	E. thozetiana	E. lansdowneana v leucantha	E. albopurpurea
Eucalyptus gracilis v viminea	E. gracilis	Eucalyptus laophila	E. apiculata
Eucalyptus gracilis v yilgamensis	E. yilgamensis	E. largiflorens v xanthophylla	E. normantonensis
Eucalyptus granularis	E. rubida	Eucalyptus lata	E. orbifolia
Eucalyptus griffithsii v angustiuscula	E. griffithsii	Eucalyptus latisucula	E. moorei ssp moorei
Eucalyptus grossifolia	E. angulosa	Eucalyptus leiocarpa	Angophora leiocarpa
Eucalyptus gummifera v intermedia	E. intermedia	Eucalyptus leiophloia	E. foelscheana
Eucalyptus gunnii v glauca	E. glaucescens	Eucalyptus leiophloia v leiophloia	E. foelscheana
Eucalyptus gunnii v glauca	E. glaucescens	Eucalyptus leiophloia v lepidophoia	E. foelscheana
Eucalyptus gunnii v maculosa	E. mannifera ssp mannifera	Eucalyptus leptocalyx ssp leptocalyx	E. leptocalyx
		Eucalyptus leptocalyx ssp petilipes	E. leptocalyx
Eucalyptus gunnii v montana	E. gunnii -Hook.f.	Eucalyptus leptophylla v densa	E. leptophlylla
Eucalyptus gunnii v rubida	E. rubida	E. leptophylla v leptorryncha	E. foecunda
Eucalyptus gymnoteles	E. coolabah	E. leucoxylon ssp bellarinensis	E. leucoxylon ssp pru.
Eucalyptus haemastoma v capitata	E. racemosa	Eucalyptus leucoxylon ssp connata	E. leucoxylon ssp pru.
Eucalyptus haemastoma v inophloia	E. andrewsii ssp andrewsii	Eucalyptus leucoxylon ssp pauperita	E. leucoxylon ssp pru.
		Eucalyptus leucoxylon ssp petiolaris	E. petiolaris
Eucalyptus haemastoma v micratha	E. racemosa	Eucalyptus leucoxylon v angulata	E. leucoxylon ssp leuc.
E. haemastoma v sclerophylla	E. racemosa	E. leucoxylon v erythrostema	E. leucoxylon ssp leuc.
Eucalyptus helenae	E. microtheca	Eucalyptus leucoxylon v leucoxylon	E. leucoxylon ssp leuc.
Eucalyptus helmsii	E. platycoris	Eucalyptus leucoxylon v pallens	E. caleyi ssp caleyi
Eucalyptus hemiphloia v albens	E. albens	Eucalyptus leucoxylon v pallens	E. sideroxylon
Eucalyptus hemiphloia v albens	E. moluccana	Eucalyptus leucoxylon v pruinosa	E. leucoxylon ssp pru.
Eucalyptus hemiphloia v microcarpa	E. microcarpa	Eucalyptus leucoxylon v rugulosa	E. leucoxylon ssp leuc.
Eucalyptus hesperis	E. hamersleyana	Eucalyptus lindleyana	E. elata
Eucalyptus heterophylla	E. obliqua	Eucalyptus lindleyana v stenophylla	E. elata
Eucalyptus hillii v alleniana	E. oligantha	Eucalyptus linearis	E. pulchella
Eucalyptus hillii v hillii	E. oligantha	Eucalyptus longifolia	E. elata
Eucalyptus hirsuta	Angophora hispida	Eucalyptus longirostris	E. camaldulensis v camaldulensis
Eucalyptus hispida	Angophora hispida		
Eucalyptus incrassata v angulosa	E. angulosa	E. longirostris f brevirostris	E. c. v camaldulensis
Eucalyptus incrassata v conglobata	E. conglobata ssp cong.	E. longirostris f longirostris	E. c. v camaldulensis
Eucalyptus incrassata v costata	E. incrassata	Eucalyptus loxophleba v fruticosa	E. loxophleba ssp lox.
Eucalyptus incrassata v dumosa	E. dumosa	Eucalyptus loxophleba v fruticosa	E. loxophleba ssp supralaevis
Eucalyptus incrassata v gonianttha	E. goniantha ssp gon.		
Eucalyptus incrassata v protrusa	E. brachycalyx	Eucalyptus luehmanniana v altior	E. oreades
Eucalyptus incurva	E. gillenii	Eucalyptus macrocalyx	E. pyriformis
Eucalyptus infracorticata	E. gypsophila	Eucalyptus macrocera	E. cornuta
Eucalyptus inopina	Angophora inopina	E. macrorhyncha ssp cannonii	E. cannonii
Eucalyptus insignis	E. tereticornis	E. macrorhyncha v brachycorys	E. laevopinea
Eucalyptus insulana	E. exserta	Eucalyptus macrorhyncha v minor	E. macrocryhncha ssp macrorhyncha
Eucalyptus intertexta v diminuta	E. intertexta		
Eucalyptus intertexta v magna	E. orgadophila	E. macroryncha ssp cannonii	E. cannonii
Eucalyptus irritans	E. mediocris	Eucalyptus macta	E. resinifera ssp resinifera
Eucalyptus isingiana	E. pimpiniana		
Eucalyptus kakadu	E. foelscheana	Eucalyptus maculata v citriodora	E. citriodora
Eucalyptus kessellii ssp eugnosta	E. kessellii	Eucalyptus maculosa	E. mannifera ssp mannifera
Eucalyptus kessellii ssp kessellii	E. kessellii		
Eucalyptus kitsonii	E. kitsoniana	Eucalyptus mahoganii	E. marginata ssp marg.
Eucalyptus lactea	E. mannifera ssp praecox	Eucalyptus maidenii	E. globulus ssp maid.
		Eucalyptus mannifera ssp elliptica	E. elliptica
Eucalyptus laeviponea v minor	E. eugenioides	Eucalyptus mannifera ssp maculosa	E. mannifera ssp mann.

Synonym	Current Name	Synonym	Current Name
Eucalyptus mannifera v elliptica	E. mannifera elliptica	Eucalyptus odorata v calcicultrix	E. porosa
Eucalyptus marginata v staeri	E. staeri	Eucalyptus odorata v woolsiana	E. pilligaensis
Eucalyptus mcquoidii	E. macquoidii	Eucalyptus oldfieldii v drummondii	E. drummondii
Eucalyptus meeboldii	E. concinna	Eucalyptus oleosa v angustiflora	A. oleosa
Eucalyptus melana	Angophora melanoxylon	Eucalyptus oleosa v borealis	E. horistes
		Eucalyptus oleosa v flocktoniae	E. flocktoniae ssp flocktoniae
Eucalyptus melissiodora	E. citriodora		
E. melliodora v brachycarpa	E. melliodora	Eucalyptus oleosa v glauca	E. transcontinentalis
Eucalyptus melliodora v elliptocarpa	E. melliodora	Eucalyptus oleosa v kochii	E. kochii ssp kochii
Eucalyptus mensalis	E. cameronii	Eucalyptus oleosa v longicornis	E. longicornis
Eucalyptus micrantha	E. racemosa	Eucalyptus oleosa v obtusa	E. oleosa ssp repleta
Eucalyptus micrantha v signata	E. racemosa	Eucalyptus oleosa v peeneri	E. peeneri
Eucalyptus microcodon	E. approximans ssp codonocarpa	Eucalyptus olivacea	E. macandra
		Eucalyptus opaca	E. terminalis
Eucalyptus microphylla	E. cunninghamii	Eucalyptus oresbia	E. cypellocarpa
Eucalyptus microphylla	E. moorei ssp moorei	Eucalyptus ovalifolia	E. polyanthemos
E. microtheca v cymbaliformis	E. microtheca	Eucalyptus ovalifolia v lanceolata	E. polyanthemos
Eucalyptus minnitrichii	E. orbifolia	Eucalyptus ovata ssp aquatica	E. camphora ssp camp.
Eucalyptus mitchellii	E. mitchelliana	Eucalyptus ovata v aquatica	E. aquatica
Eucalyptus mitrata	E. coronata	Eucalyptus ovata v aquatica -Blake.	E. aquatica
Eucalyptus molyneuxii	E. willsii ssp falciformis	Eucalyptus ovata v camphora	E. camphora ssp camp.
		Eucalyptus ovata v grandiflora	E. ovata
Eucalyptus montivaga	E. andrewsii ssp and.	E. pachycalyx ssp waajensis	E. pachycalyx
Eucalyptus moorei v latiiuscula	E. moorei ssp moorei	Eucalyptus pachyphylla v sessilis	E. serranensis
Eucalyptus morrisonii	E. kruseana	Eucalyptus pachyphylla v sessilis	E. sessilis
Eucalyptus muelleri	E. dumosa	Eucalyptus pallens	E. obliqua
Eucalyptus muelleri -T.B.Moore only	E. johnstonii -Maiden	Eucalyptus pallida	E. eudesmioides
Eucalyptus multiflora	E. robusta	Eucalyptus pallidifolia	E. brevifolia
Eucalyptus myriadena ssp parviflora	E. myriadena	Eucalyptus paludosa	E. ovata
Eucalyptus nervosa	A. obliqua	Eucalyptus paniculata ssp matutina	E. paniculata
Eucalyptus nigra	E. eugenioides	E. parramatensis v sphaerocalyx	E. parramattensis
Eucalyptus niphophila	E. pauciflora ssp niph.	Eucalyptus parvifolia	E. parvula
Eucalyptus nubila	E. fibrosa ssp nubila	Eucalyptus pastoralis	E. bigalerita
Eucalyptus nudicaulis	E. gillenii	Eucalyptus patentiflora	E. melliodora
Eucalyptus numerosa	E. elata	E. pauciflora ssp parvifructa	E. pauciflora ssp pauciflora
Eucalyptus obcordata	E. platypus		
Eucalyptus obliqua v alpina	E. delegatensis ssp delegatensis	Eucalyptus pauciflora v alpina	E. pauciflora ssp niphophila
Eucalyptus obliqua v degressa	E. obliqua	Eucalyptus pauciflora v nana	E. gregsoniana
Eucalyptus obliqua v megacarpa	E. obliqua	Eucalyptus perplexa	E. jensenii
Eucalyptus oblonga	E. globoidea	E. persistens ssp persistens	E. persistens
Eucalyptus oblonga	E. globoidea	E. persistens ssp tardecidens	E. tardecidens
Eucalyptus oblonga v rugulosa	E. globoidea	Eucalyptus phaeotricha	E. tindaliae
Eucalyptus obstans	E. burgessiana	Eucalyptus phellandra	E. radiata
Eucalyptus obstans	E. burgessiana	Eucalyptus phlebophylla	E. pauciflora -Sieber
E. obtusiflora ssp cowcowensis	E. obtusiflora	Eucalyptus pilularis v acmenoides	E. acmenoides
E. obtusiflora ssp dongarraensis	E. obtusiflora	Eucalyptus pilularis v pyriformis	E. pyrocarpa
E. obtusiflora v dendromorpha	E. dendromorpha	Eucalyptus placita	E. paniculata
Eucalyptus occidentalis v astringens	E. astringens	Eucalyptus platyphylla v tintinnans	E. tintinnans
Eucalyptus occidentalis v eremophila	E. eremophila	Eucalyptus platypodos	E. botryoides
Eucalyptus occidentalis v grandiflora	E. eremophila	Eucalyptus platypus v heterophylla	E. utilis
Eucalyptus occidentalis v macrandra	E. macandra	Eucalyptus platypus v nutans	E. nutans
Eucalyptus occidentalis v stenantha	E. aspratilis	Eucalyptus platypus v nutans	E. nutans
Eucalyptus ochrophylla	E. concinna	Eucalyptus pleurocorys	E. brachycalyx
Eucalyptus odorata	E. cajuputea	Eucalyptus populifolia	E. tereticornis

97

Synonym	Current Name	Synonym	Current Name
Eucalyptus populifolia ssp bimbii	E. populnea	Eucalyptus salicifolia	E. amygdalina
Eucalyptus portuensis	E. acmenoides	Eucalyptus salicifolia -Cav.	E. amygdalina
Eucalyptus praecox	E. mannifera ssp prae.	Eucalyptus saligna ssp botryoides	E. botryoides
Eucalyptus procera	E. obliqua	Eucalyptus saligna v parviflora	E. deanei
Eucalyptus prominula	E. capitellata	Eucalyptus saligna v protusa	E. saligna
Eucalyptus propinqua v major	E. major	Eucalyptus santalifolia	E. gunnii ssp
Eucalyptus pruinosa	E. pyriformis		diversifolia
Eucalyptus pryoriana	E. viminalis ssp pryor.	Eucalyptus santalifolia v baxteri	E. baxteri
Eucalyptus pseudoglobulus	E. globulus ssp	Eucalyptus saxicola	E. bridgesiana
	pseudoglobulus	Eucalyptus scias ssp callimastha	E. scias
Eucalyptus pulverulenta v lanceolata	E. cinerea ssp cinerea	Eucalyptus sclerophylla	E. racemosa
E. pulverulenta v lanceolata -Howitt	E. cinerea -Benth.	Eucalyptus scyphoidea	E. macrocryhncha ssp
Eucalyptus pulvigera	E. pulverulenta		macrorhyncha
Eucalyptus punctata v didyma	E. punctata	Eucalyptus scyphoidea	E. macrorhyncha ssp
Eucalyptus punctata v grandifolia	E. caniculata		macrorhyncha
Eucalyptus punctata v longirostrata	E. longirostrata	Eucalyptus seeana v constricta	E. bancroftii
E. purpurascens v petiolaris	E. gummifera	Eucalyptus serpeniticola	E. moorei ssp serpenit.
Eucalyptus pyriformis ssp yougiana	E. youngiana	Eucalyptus serpentinicola	E. moorei ssp serpenit.
Eucalyptus pyriformis v elongata	E. pyriformis	Eucalyptus shiressii	E. punctata
Eucalyptus pyriformis v kingsmillii	E. kingsmillii ssp	E. siderophloia f decorticans	E. decorticans
	kingsmillii	Eucalyptus siderophloia v glauca	E. fibrosa ssp nubila
Eucalyptus racemosa v macrocarpa	E. crebra	Eucalyptus siderophloia v rostrata	E. fibrosa ssp fibrosa
Eucalyptus racemosa v signata	E. racemosa	Eucalyptus sideroxylon ssp tricarpa	E. tricarpa
Eucalyptus radiata v australiana	E. radiata	Eucalyptus sideroxylon v pallens	E. caleyi ssp caleyi
Eucalyptus radiata v subexserta	E. radiata	Eucalyptus sieberiana	E. sieberi
Eucalyptus radiata v subplatyphylla	E. radiata	Eucalyptus signata	E. racemosa
Eucalyptus ralla	E. tenella	Eucalyptus silvestris -Rule	E. microcarpa
Eucalyptus robertsonii	E. radiata ssp roberts.	Eucalyptus simmondsii	E. nitida
E. raveretiana v jerichoensis	E. coolabah	E. spathulata ssp grandiflora	E. suggrandis
Eucalyptus redunca	E. wandoo	Eucalyptus spectatrix	E. stricta
Eucalyptus redunca v angustifolia	E. xanthonema	Eucalyptus spenceriana	E. tectifica
Eucalyptus redunca v elata	E. wandoo	Eucalyptus splachnicarpon	E. calophylla
Eucalyptus redunca v melanophloia	E. arachnaea	Eucalyptus spodophylla	E. pruinosa
Eucalyptus redunca v oxymitra	E. flavida	Eucalyptus stannariensis	E. cloeziana
Eucalyptus redunca v subangusta	E. subangusta	Eucalyptus stannicola	E. youmanii
Eucalyptus regnans f fastigiata	E. regnans	Eucalyptus stellulata v angustifolia	E. moorei ssp moorei
Eucalyptus resinifera v grandiflora	E. resinifera	Eucalyptus stoatei	E. forrestiana ssp
Eucalyptus resinifera v hemilampra	E. resinifera		stoatei
Eucalyptus resinifera v pellita	E. pellita	E. stuartiana -F.v. Muell. (1866)	E. bridgesiana
Eucalyptus resinifera v spectabilis	E. pellita	E. stuartiana -F.v.Muell.ex Miq.1859	E. ovata -Labill.
Eucalyptus risdonii v elata	E. delegatensis ssp	Eucalyptus stuartiana v amblycorys	E. bridgesiana
	tasmaniensis	Eucalyptus stuartiana v cordata	E. cinerea ssp cinerea
Eucalyptus robusta	E. botryoides	Eucalyptus stuartiana v gross	E. malacoxylon
Eucalyptus rossii	E. racemosa ssp rossii	Eucalyptus stuartiana v longifolia	E. ovata
Eucalyptus rostrata	E. camaldulensis v c.	Eucalyptus subcaerulea	E. agglomerata
Eucalyptus rostrata v acuminata	E. camaldulensis v c.	Eucalyptus subcrenulata	E. johnstonii -Maiden
Eucalyptus rostrata v borealis	E. camaldulensis v c.	Eucalyptus submultinervis	E. pauciflora -Sieber
Eucalyptus rostrata v brevirostris	E. camaldulensis v c.	Eucalyptus subtilior	E. youmanii
Eucalyptus rubida ssp canobolensis	E. canobolensis	Eucalyptus subulata	E. tereticornis
Eucalyptus rubida ssp rubida	E. granularis	Eucalyptus tamala	E. oraria
Eucalyptus rubida ssp septemflora	E. rubida	Eucalyptus tasmanica	E. delegatensis ssp
Eucalyptus rupicola	E. cunninghamii		tasmaniensis
Eucalyptus rydalensis	E. aggregata	Eucalyptus tasmanica	E. tenuiramis
Eucalyptus sabulosa	E. aromaphloia ssp	Eucalyptus tereticornis v bancroftii	E. bancroftii
	sabulosa	E. tereticornis v brachycorys	E. punctata

Synonym	Current Name	Synonym	Current Name
Eucalyptus tereticornis v brevifolia	E. prava	Eugenia aromatica	Syzygium aromaticum
Eucalyptus tereticornis v dealbata	E. dealbata	Eugenia australis h.	Syzygium paniculatum
Eucalyptus tereticornis v glaucina	E. glaucina	Eugenia caryophyllata	Syzygium aromaticum
Eucalyptus tereticornis v linearis	E. seeana	Eugenia chekan -DC.	Luma chequen
Eucalyptus tereticornis v pruiniflora	E. tereticornis	Eugenia chequen -Mol.	Luma chequen
Eucalyptus tereticornis v squamosa	E. squamosa	Eugenia malaccensis	Syzygium malaccense
Eucalyptus tereticrornis rostrata	E. camaldulensis v c.	Eugenia obcordata -Raoul	Lophomyrtus obcord.
Eucalyptus tessellaris v dallachiana	E. cypellocarpa	Eugenia paniculata	Syzygium paniculatum
Eucalyptus triantha v carnea	E. carnea	Eugenia smithii	Acmena smithii
Eucalyptus triplex	E. cinerea ssp triplex	Eugenia ugni -(Mol.) Hook.f.	Ugni molinae -Turcz.
Eucalyptus trivalva	E. trivalvis	Eulalia japonica	Miscanthus sinensis
Eucalyptus tropica	E. leptophlylla	Eunomia	Aethionema
Eucalyptus turbinata	E. oleosa	Eunomia oppositifolia	Aethionema oppositifol.
Eucalyptus umbellata	E. tereticornis	Euodia daniellii -(Benn.) Hemsl.	Tetradium daniellii
Eucalyptus umbellata v dealbata	E. dealbata	Euodia hupehensis -Dode	Tetradium daniellii
Eucalyptus umbellata v glaucina	E. glaucina		Hupehense Group
Eucalyptus umbellata v pruiniflora	E. tereticornis	Euodia ramiflora -A.Gr.	Orixa japonica -Thunb.
Eucalyptus umbra ssp carnea	E. carnea	Euodia velutina	Tetradium daniellii
Eucalyptus uncinata v latifolia	E. uncinata	Euodiopanax innovans	Eleutherococcus innov.
Eucalyptus uncinata v rostrata	E. transcontinentalis	Euonymoides scandens	Celastrus scandens -L.
Eucalyptus urceolaris	E. piperita ssp urceol.	Euonymus 'Microphyllus Aureus'	E. japonicus 'Micro
Eucalyptus uvida	E. acmenoides		phyllus Pulchellus'
Eucalyptus variegata -F. Muell.	E. citriodora	Euonymus 'Microphyllus Variegatus'	E. japonicus 'Microph
Eucalyptus verrucosa	E. verrucata		yllus Albovariegatus'
Eucalyptus viminalis v baeuerlenii	E. baeuerlenii	Euonymus alatus 'Ciliodentatus'	E. alatus 'Compactus'
Eucalyptus viminalis v dealbata	E. dealbata	Euonymus alatus 'Select'	E. alatus 'Fire Ball'
Eucalyptus viminalis v huberiana	E. v. ssp cygnetensis	Euonymus alatus Chicago Fire	E. a. 'Timber Creek'
Eucalyptus viminalis v microcarpa	E. rubida	Euonymus angustifolius	E. europaeus
Eucalyptus viminalis v pedicellaris	E. simithii	Euonymus bulgaricus	E. europaeus
Eucalyptus viminalis v raccemosa	E. v. ssp pryoriana	Euonymus europaeus 'Fructu-albo'	E. europaeus f albus
Eucalyptus virgata v altior	E. oreades	E. europaeus v hamiltonianus	E. hamiltonianus v
Eucalyptus virgata v fraxinoides	E. fraxinoides		lanceifolius
Eucalyptus virgata v triflora	E. triflora	Euonymus europaeus v latifolius	E. latifolius -(L.) Mill.
Eucalyptus viridis v ovata	E. viridis	Euonymus europaeus v maackii	E. hamiltonianus v ma.
Eucalyptus wiburdii	E. eugenioides	E. europaeus v macrophyllus	E. e. v intermedius
Eucalyptus wilkinsoniana	E. eugenioides	Euonymus farreri	E. nanus
E. wilkinsoniana v crassifructa	E. eugenioides	Euonymus fimbriatus h. not Wall.	E. pendulus -Wall.
Eucalyptus wimmerensis	E. viridis ssp wimm.	Euonymus floribundus	E. europaeus
Eucalyptus woodsiana	Angophora woodsiana	Euonymus fortunei 'Gold Spot'	E. fortunei 'Sunspot'
Eucalyptus woollsii	E. longifolia	Euonymus fortunei 'Gold Tip'	E. f. 'Golden Prince'
Eucalyptus woolsiana	E. microcarpa	Euonymus fortunei 'Gracilis'	E. fortunei 'Variegatus'
Eucalyptus yangoura	E. globoidea	Euonymus fortunei 'Silver Gem'	E. fortunei 'Variegatus'
Eucapnos spectabilis	Dicentra spectabilis	E. fortunei 'Versicolor Albus'	E. f. 'Silver Pillar'
Eucharidium	Clarkia	Euonymus hamiltonianus ssp hians	E. h. ssp sieboldianus
Eucharis grandiflora h.	E. amazonica	Euonymus hamiltonianus v australis	E. hamiltonianus -Wall.
Eucodonia 'Cornell Gem'	x Achicodonia 'Cornell Gem'	E. hamiltonianus v semipersistens	E. bungeanus v semip.
		Euonymus hamiltonianus v yedoensis	E. hamiltonianus ssp
Eucomis punctata	E. comosa		sieboldianus
Eucomis undulata	E. autumnalis	Euonymus hians -Koehne	E. h. ssp sieboldianus
Eucryphia 'Penwith' misapplied	E. cordifolia x E. lucida	Euonymus hibarimisake	E. japonicus
Eucryphia billardieri -Spach	E. lucida -(Labill.) Baill.		'Hibarimisake'
Eucryphia lucida v milliganii -Hook. f.	E. milliganii -Hook. f.	Euonymus japonicus 'Aureopictus'	E. japonicus 'Aureus'
Eucryphia pinnatifolia -Gay	E. glutinosa	E. japonicus 'Aureovariegatus'	E. japonicus 'Ovatus
E. x nymansensis 'Penwith' misap.	E. cordifolia x E. lucida		Aureus'
Eugenia apiculata -DC.	Luma apiculata	E. japonicus 'Duc d'Anjou' misapplied	E. japonicus

Synonym	Current Name	Synonym	Current Name
	'Viridivariegatus'	Eupatorium stoechadasum	E. fortunei
Euonymus japonicus 'Golden Pillar'	E. fortunei 'Golden Pillar'	Eupatorium truncatum	E. perfoliatum -L.
		Eupatorium urticifolium	E. rugosum
Euonymus japonicus 'Luna'	E. japonicus 'Aureus'	Eupatorium weinmannianum	E. ligustrinum
E. japonicus 'Macrophyllus Albus'	E. japonicus 'Latifolius Albomarginatus'	Euphorbia 'Golden Foam'	E. stricta
		Euphorbia amygdaloides 'Rubra'	E. amyg. 'Purpurea'
Euonymus japonicus 'Marieke'	E. japonicus 'Ovatus Aureus'	E. amyg. v robbiae x characias	E. x martini
		Euphorbia biglandulosa	E. rigida
E. japonicus 'Microphyllus Aureus'	E. j. 'Microphyllus Pulchellus'	E. characias ssp wulfenii 'Lambrook Gold' seed-raised	
			E. characias ssp wulfenii Margery Fish Group
E. j. 'Microphyllus Variegatus'	E. j. 'Microphyllus Albovariegatus'	E. characias ssp wulfenii 'Purpurea'	E. characias ssp wulf. 'Purple and Gold'
Euonymus japonicus 'Myrtifolius'	E. j. 'Microphyllus'	E. characias ssp wulfenii Kew form	E. characias ssp wulf. 'John Tomlinson'
E. j. 'Pulchellus Aureovariegatus'	E. j. 'Microphyllus Aureovariegatus'	Euphorbia cyparissias 'Betten'	E. x gayeri 'Betten'
Euonymus japonicus v acutus -Rehd.	E. fortunei radicans	E. cyparissias 'Clarice Howard'	E. cyp. 'Fens Ruby'
Euonymus lanceifolius -Loes.	E. hamiltonianus v lanc.	Euphorbia cyparissias 'Purpurea'	E. cyp. 'Fens Ruby'
Euonymus latifolius v planipes	E. planipes	Euphorbia epithymoides	E. polychroma
Euonymus latifolius v sachalinensis	E. sachalinensis	Euphorbia heterophylla h.	E. cyathophora
Euonymus lucidus -D.Don	E. pendulus -Wall.	Euphorbia longifolia -D Don	E. donii
Euonymus maackii -Rupr.	E. hamiltonianus v m.	Euphorbia longifolia -Lamarck	E. mellifera
Euonymus micranthus	E. bungeanus	Euphorbia longifolia misapplied	E. cornigera
Euonymus multiflorus	E. europaeus	Euphorbia macrostegia	E. erubescens
Euonymus nanus v koopmannii	E. nanus v turkestanicus	Euphorbia pilosa 'Major'	E. polychroma 'Major'
		Euphorbia pilulifera	E. hirta
Euonymus nikoensis -Nakai	E. hamiltonianus ssp sieboldianus -(Bl.) Hara	Euphorbia polychroma 'Purpurea'	E. polychroma 'Candy'
		Euphorbia polychroma 'Variegata'	E. polychroma 'Lacy'
Euonymus patens -Rehd.	E. kiautschovicus	Euphorbia reflexa	E. seguieriana ssp niciciana
Euonymus pulchellus h.	E. japonicus 'Micro phyllus Pulchellus'	Euphorbia robbiae	E. amygdaloides v robbiae
Euonymus radicans -Sieb.	E. fortunei v radicans		
Euonymus radicans v acutus	E. fortunei radicans	Euphorbia serrulata	E. stricta
Euonymus rosmarinifolius	E. nanus	Euphorbia sibthorpii -Boiss.	E. characias ssp wulfenii
Euonymus sachalinensis h.	E. planipes -Koehne		
Euonymus sargentianus	E. myrianthus -Hemsl.	Euphorbia splendens	E. milii
Euonymus scandens	Celastrus scandens -L.	Euphorbia uralensis	E. x pseudovirgata
Euonymus semiexsertus -Koehne	E. hamiltonianus ssp sieboldianus -(Bl.) Hara	Euphorbia variegata	E. marginata
		Euphorbia veneta -Willd.	E. characias ssp wulfenii
Euonymus sieboldianus -Bl.	E. hamiltonianus ssp sieboldianus -(Bl.) Hara	Euphorbia wallichii -Kohli	E. cornigera
		Euphorbia wallichii -Kohli	E. cornigera
Euonymus striatus	E. alatus	Euphorbia wallichii misapplied	E. donii
Euonymus subtriflorus -Blume	E. alatus v apterus	Euphorbia wulfenii -Hoppe ex Koch	E. characias ssp wulf.
Euonymus thunbergianus	E. alatus	Euphorbia x waldsteinii	E. virgata
Euonymus turkestanicus	E. nanus v turkestan.	Euphrasia verna	Odonites verna
Euonymus ussuriensis -Maxim.	E. macropterus -Rupr.	Euptelea davidiana -Baill.	E. pleiosperma
Euonymus vulgaris -Mill.	E. europaeus	Euptelea davidii	E. pleiosperma
Euonymus yedoensis -Koehne	E. hamiltonianus ssp sieboldianus -(Bl.) Hara	Euptelea delavayi -Van Tiegh.	E. pleiosperma
		Euptelea franchetii -Van Tiegh.	E. pleiosperma
Eupatorium ageratoides	E. rugosum	Eurya fortunei	Cleyera japonica 'Fortunei'
Eupatorium connatum	E. perfoliatum -L.		
Eupatorium ianthinum	E. sordidum	E. japonica 'Variegata' misapplied	Cleyera j. 'Fortunei'
Eupatorium japonicum v fortunei	E. fortunei	Eurya latifolia 'Variegata'	Cleyera j. 'Fortunei'
Eupatorium maculatum	E. purpureum ssp mac.	Eurya ochnacea -(DC.) Szysz.	Cleyera japonica
Eupatorium micranthum -Lessing	E. ligustrinum -DC.	Eurya pusilla -Sieb.	E. japonica -Thunb.
Eupatorium rugosum album	E. album		

Synonym	Current Name	Synonym	Current Name
Eurybia erubescens -DC.	Olearia erubescens	Fagus moorei -F.v.Muell.	Nothofagus moorei
Eurybia floribunda -Hook. f.	Olearia floribunda	Fagus pumila -L.	Castanea sativa
Eurybia forsteri -Hook. f.	Olearia paniculata	Fagus pumilio -Poepp. & Endl.	Nothofagus pumilio
Eurybia furfuracea	Olearia furfuracea	Fagus sieboldii -A. DC.	F. crenata -Blume
Eurybia gunniana -DC.	Olearia phlogopappa	Fagus sinensis -Oliver	F. longipetiolata
Eurybia hookeri -Sond.	Olearia hookeri	Fagus solandri -Hook. f.	Nothofagus solandri
Eurybia hygrophila	Olearia hygrophila	Fagus sylvatica 'Albovariegata'	F. s. 'Albomarginata'
Eurybia nummulariifolia -Hook. f.	Olearia nummulariifolia	Fagus sylvatica 'Argenteovariegata'	F. s. 'Albomarginata'
Eurybia obcordata -Hook. f.	Olearia obcordata	Fagus sylvatica 'Aureovariegata'	F. s. 'Luteovariegata'
Eurybia pannosa	Olearia pannosa	Fagus sylvatica 'Comptoniifolia'	F. s. v heterophylla
Eurybia persoonioides -DC.	Olearia persoonioides		'Comptoniifolia'
Eurybia solandri -Hook. f.	Olearia solandri	F. sylvatica 'Fastigiata' misapplied	F. sylvatica 'Dawyck'
Eurybia subrepanda -DC.	O. phlogopappa v subr.	Fagus sylvatica 'Red Obelisk'	F. s. 'Rohan Obelisk'
Eurybia traversii -F.v.Muell.	Olearia solandri	Fagus sylvatica 'Roseomarginata'	F.s.'Purpurea Tricolor'
Eurybia virgata -Hook. f.	Olearia virgata	Fagus sylvatica 'Tricolor' misap.	F.s.'Purpurea Tricolor'
Euryops evansii h. not Schlechter	E. acraeus	Fagus sylvatica Heterophylla Group	F. sylvatica v heterop.
Euryops sericeus	Ursinia sericeus	Fagus sylvatica Purple-leaved Group	F. sylvatica
Euscaphis staphyleoides	Euscaphis japonica		Atropurpurea Group
Eustoma russellianum	E. grandiflorum	F. sylvatica quercoides -not Pers.	F. sylvatica f laciniata
Eutereia -Raf.	Dracontium -L.	Fagus sylvatica v (f) pendula	F. sylvatica 'Pendula'
Eutrema wasabi	Wasabia japonica	F. s. v purpurea (f atropurpureus)	F. sylvatica
Evodia	Euodia		Atropurpurea Group
Evolvulus glomeratus h.	E. pilosus	F. sylvatica v asiatica -A.DC. in part	F. crenata -Blume
Evolvulus pilosus 'Blue Daze'	E. glomeratus 'Blue Daze'	F. sylvatica v asiatica -A.DC. in part	F. orientalis -Lipsky
		Fagus sylvatica v chinensis -Franch.	F. englerana -Seemen
Evonymus	Euonymus	Fagus sylvatica v laciniata	F. sylvatica f laciniata
Exochorda albertii -Reg.	E. korolkowii -Lav.	Fagus sylvatica v longipes -Oliver	F. longipetiolata
Exochorda albertii macrantha	E. x macrantha	F. s. v macrophylla -not Hohenacker	F. sylvatica f latifolia
Exochorda grandiflora -(Hook). Lindl.	E. racemosa	F. s. v macrophylla -Hohenacker	F. orientalis -Lipsky
Exochorda racemosa v wilsonii	E. giraldii v wilsonii	Fagus sylvatica v sieboldii	F. crenata -Blume
Exolepta calyculata	Chamaedaphne calycul.	Fagus-castanea dentata -Marsh.	Castanea dentata
Fabiana violacea h.	F. imbricata f violacea	Fallopia aubertii	F. baldschuanica
Fagara horrida -Thunb.	Gleditsia japonica -Miq.	F. japonica v compacta 'Fuji Snow'	F. j. v c. 'Milk Boy'
Fagopyrum cymosum	F. dibotrys	F. japonica v compacta 'Variegata'	F. j. v c. 'Milk Boy'
Fagopyrum dentatum	F. tataricum	Farfugium japonicum 'Albovariegatum'	
Fagopyrum emarginatum	F. esculentum		F. j. 'Argenteum'
Fagopyrum rotundatum	F. tataricum	Farfugium tussilagineum	F. japonicum
Fagopyrum sagittatum	F. esculentum	Fargesia grossa	Borinda grossa
Fagopyrum sarracenicum	F. esculentum	Fargesia spathacea misapplied	F. murieliae
Fagus americana -Sweet	F. grandifolia -Ehrh.	Farsetia clypeata	Fibigia clypeata
Fagus antarctica -Forst.f.	Nothofagus antarctica	Fascicularia andina	F. bicolor
Fagus antarctica v bicrenata	Nothofagus pumilio	Fascicularia kirchhoffiana	F. bicolor ssp
Fagus castanea -L.	Castanea pumila		canaliculata
Fagus cunninghamii -Hook.	Nothofagus cunningh.	F. pitcairniifolia misapplied	F. bicolor
Fagus dombeyi -Mirbel	Nothofagus dombeyi	Fatsia papyrifera	Tetrapanax papyrifer
Fagus ferruginea -Ait.	F. grandifolia -Ehrh.	Faucibarda acinos	Acinos arvensis
Fagus ferruginea v caroliniana	F. grandifolia v carol.	Fauria	Nephrophyllidium
Fagus fusca -Hook. f.	Nothofagus fusca	Feijoa	Acca
Fagus glutinosa -Poepp. & Endl.	Eucryphia glutinosa	Felicia amethystina	F. 'Snowman'
Fagus gunnii -Hook. f.	Nothofagus gunnii	Felicia capensis	F. amelloides
Fagus hohenackeriana -Palib.	F. orientalis -Lipsky	Felicia capensis 'Variegata'	F. amell. variegata
Fagus laciniata -F.W.Schmidt	F. sylvatica f laciniata	Felicia coelestis	F. amelloides
Fagus laciniata f heterophylla	F. sylvatica f laciniata	Felicia natalensis	F. rosulata
Fagus laciniata f quercifolia	F. sylvatica f laciniata	Felicia pappei	F. amoena
Fagus menziesii -Hook. f.	Nothofagus menziesii	Felipponia -Hick.	Mangonia -Schott

Synonym	Current Name	Synonym	Current Name
Felipponiella -Hick.	Mangonia -Schott		'Australis'
Fendlera wrightii -(A.Gr.) Heller	F. rupicola v wrightii	Ficus carica 'Noir de Provence'	F. carica 'Reculver'
Fenestraria rhopalophylla	F. aurantiaca f rhop.	Ficus carica 'White Genoa'	F. c. 'White Marseilles'
Ferocactus acanthodes h.	F. cylandraceus	Ficus diversifolia	F. deltoidea v diversif.
Ferocactus bicolor	Thelocactus bicolor	Ficus foveolata -Wallich	F. sarmentosa
Ferocactus crassihamatus	Sclerocactus uncina	Ficus indica	F. benghalensis
	tus v crassihamatus	Ficus nipponica h.	F. sagittata
Ferocactus setispinus	Thelocactus setispinus	Ficus pyrifolia -Burm. f.	Pyrus pyrifolia
Ferraria undulata	F. crispa	Ficus radicans	F. sagittata
Ferula 'Giant Bronze'	Foeniculum vulgare	Ficus radicans 'Variegata'	F. sagittata 'Variegata'
	'Giant Bronze'	Ficus repens h.	F. pumila -L.
Ferula chiliantha	F. communis ssp	Ficus retusa h.	F. microcarpa
	glauca	Ficus stipulata -Thunb.	F. pumila
Ferula communis 'Gigantea'	F. communis	Ficus stipulata 'Minima'	F. pumila 'Minima'
Ferula galbaniflua	F. gummosa	Ficus triangularis	F. natalensis ssp lepr.
Ferula marathophylla	Anethum graveolens	Filaginella uliginosa	Gnaphalium uliginosum
Festuca arenaria	F. rubra	Filago leontopodium	Leontopodium alpinum
Festuca batavica	F. filiformis	Filago stellata	Leontopodium alpinum
Festuca calodes	F. filiformis	Filipendula 'Queen of the Prairies'	F. rubra
Festuca capillata	F. filiformis	Filipendula alnifolia 'Variegata'	F. ulmaria 'Variegata'
Festuca carthusiana	F. filiformis	Filipendula digitata 'Nana'	F. multijuga
Festuca castaneicola	F. filiformis	Filipendula hexapetala	F. vulgaris
Festuca confinis	F. eskia	Filipendula hexapetala 'Flore Pleno'	F. vulgaris 'Multiplex'
Festuca crinum-ursi	F. eskia	Filipendula lobata	F. rubra
Festuca ericetorum	F. filiformis	Filipendula palmata 'Digitata Nana'	F. multijuga
Festuca finitima	F. filiformis	Filipendula palmata 'Elegantissima'	F. purpurea 'Elegans'
Festuca glauca 'Pallens'	F. longifolia	Filipendula palmata 'Nana'	F. multijuga
Festuca glauca 'Seven Seas'	F. valesiaca 'Silbersee'	Filipendula palmata purpurea	F. purpurea
Festuca glauca Blue Fox	F. glauca 'Blaufuchs'	Filipendula purpurea f alba	F. purpurea f albiflora
Festuca glauca Blue Glow	F. glauca 'Blauglut'	Filipendula rubra 'Magnifica'	F. rubra 'Venusta'
Festuca glauca Sea Blue	F. glauca 'Meerblau'	F. rubra 'Venusta Magnifica'	F. rubra 'Venusta'
Festuca glauca Sea Urchin	F. glauca 'Seeigel'	Filipendula vulgaris 'Flore Pleno'	F. vulgaris 'Multiplex'
Festuca glaucescens	F. rubra	Filipendula vulgaris 'Plena'	F. vulgaris 'Multiplex'
Festuca glomerata	Dactylis glomerata	Filix cristata	Dryopteris cristata
Festuca graniticola	F. filiformis	Filix mas marginalis	Dryopteris marginale
Festuca heteromalla	F. rubra	Filix pumila	Gymnocarpium
Festuca immodica	F. filiformis		dryopteris
Festuca inermis	Bromus inermis	Filix spinulosa	Dryopt. carthusiana
Festuca melancholica	F. filiformis	Filix thelypteris	Thelypteris palustris
Festuca multiflora	F. rubra	Filix-mas filix-mas -Farwell	Dryopteris filix-mas
Festuca myriostachys	F. filiformis	Filix-mas spinulosa	Dryop. carthusiana
Festuca nigrescens	F. rubra	Firmiana platanifolia -(L.f.) Marsigli	F. simplex
Festuca paludosa	F. filiformis	Fitroya patagonica	F. cupressoides
Festuca patuliflora	F. filiformis	Fittonia argyroneura	F. albivensis
Festuca querceticola	F. filiformis		Argyroneura Group
Festuca scoparia	F. gautieri	Fittonia verschaffeltii	F. albivensis
Festuca symei	F. filiformis		Verschaffeltii Group
Festuca tenuifolia	F. filiformis	Fitzroya patagonica -Lindl.	F. cupressoides
Festuca valesiaca 'Silver Sea'	F. valesiaca 'Silbersee'	Flacourtia japonica	Xylosma japonica
Festuca viridis	F. rubra v viridis	Flagellarisaema thunbergii	Arisaema thunbergii
Ficaria grandiflora	Ranunculus ficaria	Fockea capensis	F. crispa
Ficaria ranunculoides	Ranunculus ficaria	Foeniculum azoricum	F. vulgare
Ficaria verna	Ranunculus ficaria	Foeniculum capillaceum	F. vulgare
Ficaria verna 'Flore Pleno'	R. ficaria 'Flore Pleno'	Foeniculum carvi	Carum carvi
Ficus australis misapplied	F. rubiginosa	Foeniculum dulce	F. vulgare

Synonym	Current Name	Synonym	Current Name
Foeniculum foeniculum	F. vulgare	Fraxinus americana ssp texensis	F. texensis
Foeniculum officinale	F. vulgare	F.a.v albicans -(Buckl.)Lingelsh. part	F. texensis
Foeniculum panmorium	F. vulgare	Fraxinus americana v texensis	F. texensis
Foeniculum piperitum -Sweet 1826	F. vulgare	Fraxinus angustifolia 'Flame'	F. ang. 'Raywood'
Foeniculum vulgare 'Bronze'	F. vulgare 'Purpureum'	Fraxinus angustifolia ssp syriaca	F. syriaca
Fontanesia phillyraeoides	F. phyllyreoides	Fraxinus angustifolia v monophylla	F. ang. 'Monophylla'
Fontanesia phillyreoides v sinensis	F. fortunei -Carr.	Fraxinus bracteata -Hemsl.	F. griffithii -C.B.Clarke
Forasaccus ciliatus	Bromus ciliatus	Fraxinus bungeana -Hance not DC.	F. chinensis ssp
Forestiera neomexicana	F. pubescens		rhyncophylla
Forsythia 'Goldcluster'	F. 'Melee d'Or'	Fraxinus coriacea -S.Wats.	F. velutina -Torr.
Forsythia fortunei	F. suspensa v fortunei	Fraxinus densiflora -Linglesh.	F. paxiana -Lingelsh.
Forsythia fortunei -Lindl.	F. suspensa v forunei	F. excelsior 'Diversifolia Pendula'	F. excelsior
Forsythia Gold Curl	F. 'Boucle d'Or'		'Heterophylla Pendula'
Forsythia Gold Tide	F. 'Maree d'Or'	Fraxinus excelsior 'Monophylla'	F. ex. f diversifolia
Forsythia koreana -(Rehd.) Nakai	F. viridissima v kore.	Fraxinus excelsior v diversifolia	F. ex. f diversifolia
Forsythia saxatilis -(Nakai) Nakai	F. ovata v saxatilis	Fraxinus excelsior v heterophylla	F. ex. f diversifolia
Forsythia suspensa 'Variegata'	F. s. 'Taff's Arnold'	Fraxinus excelsior v monophylla	F. ex. f diversifolia
Fortunaea chinensis -Lindl.	Platycarya strobilacea	Fraxinus excelsior v simplicifolia	F. ex. f diversifolia
Fothergilla alnifolia -L.f.	F. gardenii -Murr.	Fraxinus heterophylla -Vahl	F. ex. f diversifolia
Fothergilla alnifolia v major -Sims	F. major -Lodd.	F. holotricha sensu -not Koehne	F. pallisiae -Wilmott
Fothergilla carolina -Britton	F. gardenii -Murr.	Fraxinus juglandifolia -Lam.	F. americana -L.
Fothergilla involucrata -Falconer	Parrotiopsis	Fraxinus lanceolata -Borkh.	F. pennsylvanica v
	jacquemontiana		subintegerrima
Fothergilla monticola -Ashe	F. major Monticola Gr.	F.longicuspis sensu Lingelsh. in part	F. sieboldiana -Blume
Fragaria 'Bowles' Double'	F. vesca 'Multiplex'	Fraxinus longicuspis v sieboldiana	F. sieboldiana -Blume
Fragaria 'Variegata'	F. x ananassa	Fraxinus macropetala -Eastw.	F. cuspidata -Torr.
	'Variegata'	Fraxinus mariesii	F. sieboldiana
Fragaria alpina	F. vesca	Fraxinus michauxii -Britt.	F. pennsylvanica
	'Semperflorens'	Fraxinus monophylla -Desf.	F. excelsior f
Fragaria alpina 'Alba'	F. vesca		diversifolia
	'Semperflorens Alba'	Fraxinus moorcroftiana -Brandis	F. xanthoxyloides
Fragaria alpina 'Fraise des Bois'	F. vesca	Fraxinus oregona -Nutt.	F. latifolia -Benth.
F. chiloensis 'Variegata' misapplied	F. x anan. 'Variegata'	Fraxinus oxycarpa	F. angustifolia ssp ox.
Fragaria indica	Duchesnea indica	Fraxinus oxycarpa 'Raywood'	F. ang. 'Raywood'
Fragaria vesca 'Flore Pleno'	F. vesca 'Multiplex'	Fraxinus oxycarpa v angustifolia	F. angustifolia -Vahl
F. vesca 'Plymouth Strawberry'	F. vesca 'Muricata'	Fraxinus oxycarpa v oligophylla	F. syriaca -Boiss.
F. vesca 'Variegata' misapplied	F. x anan. 'Variegata'	Fraxinus oxyphylla -Bieb.	F. angustifolia -Vahl
Frailea asterioides	F. castanea	Fraxinus oxyphylla v oligophylla	F. syriaca -Boiss.
Frailea pulcherrima	F. pygmaea	F. parvifolia -Willd. in part not Lam.	F. obliqua -Tausch
Francoa 'Purple Spike'	F. sonchifolia	F. pennsylvanica ssp oregona	F. latifolia -Benth.
	Rogerson's form	Fraxinus pennsylvanica ssp velutina	F. velutina -Torr.
Francoa glabrata	F. ramosa	Fraxinus pennsylvanica v lanceolata	F. p. v subintegerrima
Francoa ramosa alba	F. ramosa	Fraxinus pennsylvanica ssp oregona	F. pennsylvanica
Frangula alnus -Mill.	Rhamnus frangula -L.	F. platypoda -sensu Dall. not Oliver	F. spaethiana -Lingelsh.
Frangula californica	Rhamnus californica	Fraxinus potamophila -Herder	F. sogdiana -Bunge
Frangula frangula -H. Karst.	Rhamnus frangula -L.	Fraxinus potamophila -Herder	F. tomentosa -Michx. f.
Frangula pentapetala	Rhamnus frangula -L.	Fraxinus profunda -(Bush) Bush	F. tomentosa -Michx. f.
Frangula vulgaris	Rhamnus frangula -L.	Fraxinus pubescens -Lam.	F. pennsylvanica
Frankenia reuteri	F. thymifolia	Fraxinus rhyncophylla -Hance	F. chinensis ssp rhync.
Fraxinus 'Veltheimii'	F. angustifolia	F. rotundifolia -sensu Rehd + others	F. parvifolia -Lam.
	'Monophylla'	Fraxinus rotundifolia h. in part	F. obliqua -Tausch
Fraxinus acuminata -Lam.	F. americana -L.	Fraxinus sambucifolia -Lam.	F. nigra -Marsh.
Fraxinus alba -Marsh.	F. americana -L.	Fraxinus serratifolia h. not Michx.	F. spaethiana -Lingelsh.
Fraxinus albicans -Buckl. in part	F. texensis	Fraxinus sieboldiana -some not Bl.	F. spaethiana -Lingelsh.
Fraxinus americana ssp oregona	F. latifolia -Benth.	Fraxinus sogdiana -Dipp.	F. syriaca -Boiss.

Synonym	Current Name	Synonym	Current Name
Fraxinus spaethiana 'Veltheimii'	F. ang. 'Monophylla'	Fritillaria discolor	F. sewerzowii
F.stenocarpa -sensu Rehd. not Koidz	F. spaethiana -Lingelsh.	Fritillaria eastwoodiae	F. phaeanthera
Fraxinus suaveolens -W.W.Sm.	F. paxiana -Lingelsh.	Fritillaria eggeri	F. persica
Fraxinus syriaca	F. angustifolia ssp syr.	Fritillaria erzurumica	F. alburyana
Fraxinus tamariscifolia -Vahl	F. angustifolia -Vahl	Fritillaria esculenta	F. latifolia
Fraxinus turkestanica -Carr.	F. syriaca -Boiss.	Fritillaria exima	F. affinis
Fraxinus veltheimii -Dieck.	F. ang. 'Monophylla'	Fritillaria ferganensis	F. walujewii
Fraxinus velutina v coriacea	F. velutina -Torr.	Fritillaria fleischeri	F. fleischeriana
Fraxinus velutina v glabra -Rehd.	F. velutina -Torr.	Fritillaria fleischeri	F. pinardii
Fraxinus velutina v tourneyi -Rehd.	F. velutina -Torr.	Fritillaria floribunda	F. affinis
Fraxinus viridis	F. pennsylvanica	Fritillaria foliosa	F. crassifolia kurdica
Fraxinus willdenowiana	F. obliqua -Tausch	Fritillaria glaucoviridis	F. alfredae glaucov.
Freesia alba -Foster	F. lactea	Fritillaria gracilis	F. messanensis gracilis
Freesia alba -Watson	F. caryophyllacea	Fritillaria gracillima	F. atropurpurea
Freesia armstrongii	F. corymbosa	Fritillaria graeca ssp ionica	F. thessala
Freesia laxa	Anomatheca laxa	Fritillaria graminifolia	F. meleagris
Freesia refracta v alba	F. lactea	Fritillaria grayana	F. biflora
Fremontia	Fremontodendron	Fritillaria grossheimiana	F. crassifolia kurdica
Fremontia californica v mexicana	Fremontodendron mex.	Fritillaria guicciardii	F. graeca
Fremontia mexicana	Fremontodendron mex.	Fritillaria guilelmi-waldemarii	F. cirrhosa
Fremontia napense -Eastw.	Fremontodendron nap.	Fritillaria heterophylla	F. montana ruthenica
Frerea	Caralluma	Fritillaria hispanica	F. lusitanica
Frerea indica	Caralluma frerei	Fritillaria hutchinsonii	F. brandegeei
Freylinia cestroides -Colla	F. lanceolata	Fritillaria hutchinsonii	F. messanensis
Friesia peduncularis -(Labill.) DC.	Aristotelia peduncul.	Fritillaria illyrica	F. messanensis gracilis
Fritillaria adamantina	F. recurva	F. imperialis 'Crown upon Crown'	F. imperialis 'Prolifera'
Fritillaria aintabensis	F. imperialis	Fritillaria imperialis 'Lutea Maxima'	F. imp. 'Maxima Lutea'
Fritillaria algeriensis	F. messanensis	Fritillaria imperialis 'Maxima'	F. imp. 'Rubra Maxima'
Fritillaria alpina	F. pinardii	Fritillaria ineziana	F. biflora
Fritillaria altaica	F. thunbergii	Fritillaria inflexa	F. biflora
Fritillaria aquitanica	F. pyrenaica	Fritillaria intermis	F. acmopetala
Fritillaria arabica	F. persica	Fritillaria ionica	F. thessala
Fritillaria argolica	F. rhodokanakis	Fritillaria karadaghensis	F. crassifolia ssp kurdica
Fritillaria askabensis	F. raddeana		
Fritillaria askhabadensis	F. raddeana	Fritillaria lanceolata	F. affinis v tristulis
Fritillaria assyriaca h.	F. uva-vulpis	Fritillaria latifolia v nobilis	F. latifolia
Fritillaria aurea	F. latifolia	Fritillaria leucantha	F. thunbergii
Fritillaria biebersteiniana	F. latifolia	Fritillaria libanotica	F. persica
Fritillaria boissieri	F. lusitanica	Fritillaria longifolia	F. montana meleagroides
Fritillaria bonmaensis	F. delavayi		
Fritillaria bornmulleri	F. latifolia	Fritillaria lunellii	F. affinis
Fritillaria brevicaulis	F. armena	Fritillaria lurida	F. pyrenaica
Fritillaria burnetti	F. tubiformis	Fritillaria lutea Bieb.	F. collina
Fritillaria canasulata	F. assyriaca	Fritillaria lycia	F. acmopetala
Fritillaria carduchorum	F. minuta	Fritillaria macrandra	F. rhodokanakis
Fritillaria carica	F. bithynica carica	Fritillaria maria	F. lusitanica
Fritillaria caucasica	F. armena caucasica	Fritillaria mauritanica	F. messanensis
Fritillaria caussolesis	F. montana	Fritillaria meleagroides	F. montana meleagr.
Fritillaria citrina	F. bithynica	Fritillaria minor	F. montana ruthenica
Fritillaria coccinea	F. recurva	Fritillaria munbyi	F. messanensis
Fritillaria collina	F. latifolia collina	Fritillaria mutica	F. affinis
Fritillaria collincola	F. thunbergii	Fritillaria neglecta	F. messanensis ssp gracilis
Fritillaria contorta	F. meleagris contorta		
Fritillaria dasyphylla	F. bithynica	Fritillaria nigra h.	F. pyrenaica
Fritillaria delphinensis	F. tubiformis	Fritillaria nobilis	F. latifolia

104

Synonym	Current Name	Synonym	Current Name
Fritillaria ochridiana	F. graeca	Fuchsia 'Overbecks'	F. magellanica v molinae 'Sharpitor'
Fritillaria ojaiensis	F. affinis		
Fritillaria olympica	F. pontica	Fuchsia 'Pacific Grove' -Greene	F. 'Evelyn Steele Little'
Fritillaria ophioglosifolia	F. crassifolia	Fuchsia 'Princess Dollar'	F. 'Dollar Princess'
Fritillaria oranensis	F. messanensis	Fuchsia 'Prodigy'	F. 'Enfant Prodigue'
Fritillaria orientalis	F. tenella	Fuchsia 'Reflexa'	F. x bacillaris 'Reflexa'
Fritillaria orsiniana	F. montana	Fuchsia 'Reverend Elliott'	F. 'President Elliott'
Fritillaria parviflora	F. micrantha	Fuchsia 'Rufus The Red'	F. 'Rufus'
Fritillaria persica minor	F. persica	Fuchsia 'Schone Wilhelmine'	F. 'Die Schone Wilhelmine'
Fritillaria phaeanthera	F. affinis v gracilis		
Fritillaria pineticola	F. bithynica	Fuchsia 'Sharpitor'	F. magellanica v molinae 'Sharpitor'
Fritillaria pontica ionica	F. graeca thessala		
Fritillaria racemosa	F. montana	Fuchsia 'Thompsonii'	F. magellanica 'Thompsonii'
Fritillaria roderickii	F. grayana		
Fritillaria rubra major	F. imp. 'Rubra Maxima'	Fuchsia 'Tom West' misapplied	F. 'Mr. West'
Fritillaria schliemannii	F. bithynica	Fuchsia 'Traviata'	F. 'La Traviata'
Fritillaria sieheana	F. elwesii	Fuchsia 'Tricolor'	F. magellanica v gracilis 'Tricolor'
Fritillaria sphaciotica	F. messanensis		
Fritillaria stenophylla	F. lusitanica	Fuchsia 'Tricolorii'	F. m. v gr. 'Tricolor'
Fritillaria succulenta	F. biflora	Fuchsia 'Variegated Procumbens'	F. procumbens 'Wirral'
Fritillaria syriaca	F. pinardii	Fuchsia 'Versicolor'	F. mag. 'Versicolor'
Fritillaria tachengensis	F. yuminensis	Fuchsia 'Wendy' -Catt	F. 'Snowcap'
Fritillaria tenella	F. orientalis	Fuchsia 'White Ann'	F. 'Heidi Weiss'
Fritillaria thessalica	F. graeca thessala	Fuchsia 'White Pixie Wagtail'	F. 'Wagtails White Pixie'
Fritillaria tristis	F. obliqua		
Fritillaria tulipifera	F. armena	Fuchsia 'Whiteknights Goblin'	F. denticulata 'Whiteknights Goblin'
Fritillaria umbellata	F. pyrenaica		
Fritillaria unicolor	F. graeca	Fuchsia aprica -Lundell	F. microphylla ssp apr.
Fritillaria urmensis	F. graeca	Fuchsia aprica h.	F. x bacillaris
Fritillaria verticillata v thunbergii	F. thunbergii	Fuchsia arborea	F. arborescens
Fritillaria wanensis	F. crassifolia kurdica	Fuchsia boliviana -Britton	F. sanctae-rosae
Fritillaria zahnii	F. graeca	Fuchsia boliviana 'Alba'	F. boliviana v alba
Fuchsia 'Aubergine'	F. 'Gerharda's Aubergine'	Fuchsia boliviana f puberulenta	F. boliviana -Carriere
		Fuchsia boliviana v luxurians	F. boliviana v alba
Fuchsia 'Bornemann's Beste'	F. 'Georg Bornemann'	Fuchsia canescens misapplied	F. ampliata
Fuchsia 'Burning Bush'	F. 'Autumnale'	Fuchsia chonotica -F.Phil.	F. magellanica v chonotica
Fuchsia 'Cottinghamii'	F. x bacillaris 'Cottinghamii'		
		Fuchsia cinnabarina -McClintock	F. x bacillaris -Lindl.
Fuchsia 'Doctor'	F. 'The Doctor'	Fuchsia conica -Lindl.	F. magellanica v conica
Fuchsia 'Earl of Beaconsfield'	F. 'Laing's Hybrid'	Fuchsia cordifolia h.	F. splendens
Fuchsia 'Enstone'	F. magellanica v molinae 'Enstone'	Fuchsia corymbiflora alba	F. boliviana v alba
		Fuchsia corymbiflora misapplied	F. boliviana
Fuchsia 'Fascination'	F. 'Emile de Wildeman'	Fuchsia cylindracea misapplied	F. x bacillaris
Fuchsia 'Geertien'	F. 'Dutch Geertien'	Fuchsia decussata -not Ruiz & Pav.	F. mag. v gracilis
Fuchsia 'Heidi Weiss'	F. 'White Ann'	Fuchsia dependens	F. corymbiflora
Fuchsia 'Heinrich Henkel'	F. 'Andenken an Heinrich Henkel'	Fuchsia discolor -Lindl.	F. magellanica v discol.
		Fuchsia elegans -Salisb.	F. coccinea -Dryander
Fuchsia 'Hemsleyana'	F. microphylla ssp hemsleyana	Fuchsia Filigree	F. 'Filigraan'
		Fuchsia fulgens 'Gesneriana'	F. 'Gesneriana'
Fuchsia 'Herbe de Jacques'	F. 'Mr. West'	Fuchsia fulgens 'Rubra Grandiflora'	F. 'Rubra Grandiflora'
Fuchsia 'Koralle'	F. 'Coralle'	Fuchsia gracilis -Lindl.	F. mag. v gracilis
Fuchsia 'Leverhulme'	F. 'Leverkusen'	Fuchsia gracilis 'Variegata'	F. mag. v gracilis 'Variegata'
Fuchsia 'Logan Garden'	F. magellanica 'Logan Woods'		
		Fuchsia hidalgensis	F. microphylla ssp hid.
Fuchsia 'Oosje'	F. x bacillaris 'Oosje'	Fuchsia kirkii -Hook. f.	F. procumbens A.Cunn.

Synonym	Current Name	Synonym	Current Name
Fuchsia loxensis misapplied	F. 'Loxensis'	Galanthus cabardensis	G. transcaucasicus
Fuchsia loxensis misapplied	F. 'Speciosa'	Galanthus caucasicus	G. alpinus v alpinus
Fuchsia lycioides h.	F. 'Lycioides'	Galanthus caucasicus 'Comet'	G. elwesii 'Comet'
Fuchsia macrostema -Ruiz & Pavon	F. magellanica v macr.	Galanthus caucasicus h.	G. elwesii v
Fuchsia macrostema v conica	F. magellanica v conica		monostictus
Fuchsia macrostema v gracilis	F. mag. v gracilis	Galanthus caucasicus h. double	G. 'Lady Beatrix
Fuchsia magellanica 'Alba'	F. mag. v molinae		Stanley'
Fuchsia magellanica 'Globosa'	F. 'Globosa'	Galanthus caucasicus v hiemalis	G. elwesii v monostic
Fuchsia magellanica 'Riccartonii'	F. 'Riccartonii'		tus Hiemalis Group
Fuchsia michoacanensis misapplied	F. microphylla ssp	G. corcyrensis spring flowering	G. reginae-olgae ssp
	aprica		vernalis
Fuchsia minimiflora -Hemsley	F. mic. ssp minimiflora	G. corcyrensis winter flowering	G. r-o ssp r-olgae
Fuchsia minimiflora v hidalgensis	F. mic. ssp hidalgensis		Winter-flowering Gr.
Fuchsia montana -Cambess.	F. coccinea -Dryander	Galanthus elwesii v minor	G. gracilis
Fuchsia parviflora h.	F. x bacillaris	G. graecus -Orph. ex Boissier	G. elwesii
Fuchsia pendula -Salisb.	F. coccinea -Dryander	Galanthus graecus misapplied	G. gracilis
Fuchsia procumbens 'Argentea'	F. procumbens 'Wirral'	Galanthus ikariae Latifolius Group	G. platyphyllus
Fuchsia procumbens 'Variegata'	F. procumbens 'Wirral'	Galanthus ikariae ssp snogerupii	G. ikariae
Fuchsia pubescens -Cambess.	F. coccinea -Dryander	Galanthus kemulariae	G. transcaucasicus
Fuchsia reflexa h.	F. x bacillaris -Lindl.	Galanthus ketskovelii	G. transcaucasicus
Fuchsia regia v alpestris	F. alpestris	Galanthus lagodechianus	G. transcaucasicus
Fuchsia rosea -Ruiz & Pav.	F. lycioides -Andrews	Galanthus latifolius -Rupr.	G. platyphyllus
Fuchsia rosea h.	F. 'Globosa'	Galanthus lutescens	G. nivalis Sandersii Gr.
Fuchsia scandens	F. decussata	Galanthus nivalis 'Howick Yellow'	G. nivalis Sandersii Gr.
Fuchsia serratifolia -Hooker	F. austromontana	Galanthus nivalis 'Lutescens'	G. nivalis Sandersii Gr.
Fuchsia serratifolia -Ruiz & Pav.	F. denticulata	Galanthus nivalis v angustifolius	G. angustifolius
Fuchsia Sugarbush	F. 'Suikerbossie'	Galatella hauptii	Aster hauptii
Fuchsia sylvatica misapplied	F. nigricans	Galax aphylla	G. urceolata
Fuchsia tetradactyla misapplied	F. x bacillaris	Gale palustris -(Lam.) Chev.	Myrica gale -L.
Fuchsia vulcanica -Andre	F. ampliata	Galega 'Her Majesty'	G. 'His Majesty'
Fumaria cucullaria	Dicentra cucullaria	Galeobdolon	Lamium
Fumaria fungosa	Adlumia fungosa	Galeobdolon argentatum	Lamium galeobdolon
Fumaria incisa	Corydalis incisa		'Florentinum'
Fumaria lutea	Corydalis lutea	Galeobdolon luteum	Lamium galeobdolon
Fumaria pallida	Corydalis pallida	Galipea cusparia	G. officinalis
Fumaria spectabilis	Dicentra spectabilis	Galium aureum	G. firmum
Funkia	Hosta	Galium claytonii	Asperula tinctoria
Furcraea foetida 'Variegata'	F. foetida v mediopicta	Galium cruciata	Cruciata laevipes
F. foetida v mediopicta 'Variegata'	F. foetida v mediopicta	Galium littellili	G. kamtschaticum
Furcraea gigantea -Ventenat	F. foetida -(L.) Haworth	Galium perpusillum	Asperula perpusilla
Furcraea gigantea 'Mediopicta'	F. foetida v mediopicta	Galium rubioides	G. boreale -L.
Furcraea madagascariensis	F. foetida -(L.) Haworth	Galium septentrionale	G. boreale -L.
Gagea arvensis	G. villosa	Galium triandrum	Asperula tinctoria
Gaillardia aristata h.	G. x grandiflora	Galliaria albida	Amaranthus albus
Gaillardia Burgundy	G. 'Burgunder'	Galphimia nitida	G. glauca
Gaillardia Goblin	G. 'Kobold'	Galvezia spicata -Bert.	Ercilla volubilis
Gaillardia Golden Goblin	G. 'Goldkobold'	Gamblea innovans	Eleutherococcus innov.
Gaillardia Torchlight	G. 'Fackelschein'	Gamochlamys -Bak.	Spathantheum -Schott
Gaillardia Yellow Goblin	G. 'Goldkobold'	Gamogyne -N.E.Br.	Piptospatha -N.E.Br.
Galanthus 'Arnott's Seedling'	G. 'S.Arnott'	Gamolepis	Steirodiscus
Galanthus 'Sam Arnott'	G. 'S.Arnott'	Gardenia augusta	G. jasminoides
Galanthus 'Sandersii'	G. nivalis Sandersii Gr.	Gardenia augusta 'Hadley'	G. jasm. 'Belmont'
Galanthus 'Scharlockii'	G. n. Scharlockii Group	G. augusta 'Prostrata Variegata'	G. jasminoides
Galanthus 'The O'Mahoney'	G. 'Straffan'		'Radicans Variegata'
Galanthus byzantinus	G. plicatus ssp byzant.	Gardenia capensis	Rothmannia capensis

Synonym	Current Name	Synonym	Current Name
Gardenia florida h.	G. jasminoides	Genetyllis squarrosa	Darwinia squarrosa
Gardenia globosa	Rothmannia globosa	Genista 'Emerald Spreader'	G. pilosa 'Yellow
Gardenia grandiflora	G. jasminoides		Spreader'
Gardenia rothmannia	Rothmannia capensis	Genista ardoinoi	Cytisus ardoinoi
Garrya fadyenii h.	G. laurifolia ssp	Genista candicans -L.	G. monspessulana
	macrophylla	Genista cinerea h. not DC.	G. tenera
Gasteria liliputana	G. bicolor v liliputana	Genista dalmatica -Bartl.	G. sylvestris -Scop.
Gasteria pulchra	G. obliqua	Genista decumbens	Cytisus decumbens
Gasteria verrucosa	G. carinata v verruc.	Genista delphinensis	G. sagittalis ssp delph.
Gaultheria antipoda v depressa	G. depressa -Hook.f.	Genista diffusa -Willd.	Cytisus diffusus
Gaultheria antipoda v microphylla	G. macrostigma -Col.	Genista elatior -Koch	G. tinctoria v ovata
Gaultheria depressa v microphylla	G. macrostigma -Col.	Genista florida v atlantica -E.K.Balls	G. florida -L.
Gaultheria forrestii h.	Pieris formosa v forr.	Genista florida v maroccana -Ball	G. florida -L.
Gaultheria furens	G. insana	Genista fragrans	G. canariensis
Gaultheria laxiflora -Diels	G. yunnanensis	Genista genuensis -Pers.	G. januensis -Viv.
Gaultheria merrilliana h.	G. itoana -Hayata	Genista glabrescens -(Sart.) Briq.	Cytisus emeriflorus
G. mucronata Mother of Pearl	G. muc. 'Parelmoer'	Genista grandiflora -(Brot.) Spach	Cytisus grandiflorus
Gaultheria mucronata Signal	G. mucronata 'Signaal'	Genista hispanica ssp occidentalis	G. hispanica -L.
Gaultheria mucronata Snow White	G. muc. 'Sneeuwwitje'	Genista holopetala	G. radiata v nana
Gaultheria myrsinites -Hook.	G. humifusa	Genista humifusa	G. pulchella
Gaultheria nana -Colenso	G. parvula	Genista humilis	G. tinctoria
Gaultheria nummularioides 'Minuta'	G. n. v elliptica	G. lasiocarpa -Spach nom illegit.	G. tinctoria v humilior
Gaultheria ovalifolia -Wall.	G. fragrantissima	Genista lasiocarpa v perreymondii	G. tinctoria v humilior
Gaultheria perplexa -Cheesem.	G. macrostigma -Col.	Genista leptoclada -Spach	G. florida -L.
Gaultheria prostrata	G. myrsinoides	Genista mantica -Poll.	G. tinctoria v humilior
Gaultheria prostrata purpurea	G. myrsinoides	Genista monosperma -(L.) Lam.	Retama monosperma
Gaultheria pyrolifolia -C.B.Clarke	G. pyroloides	Genista ovata -Waldst. & Kit.	G. tinctoria v ovata
Gaultheria pyroloides v cuneata	G. cuneata	Genista ovata v humilior -Bertol.	G. tinctoria v humilior
Gaultheria repens	G. procumbens	Genista patula	G. tinctoria
Gaultheria rupestris v colensoi	G. colensoi -Hook.f	Genista perreymondii -Loisl.	G. tinctoria v humilior
Gaultheria rupestris v parvifolia	G. crassa -Allan	Genista pilosa 'Lemon Spreader'	G. p. 'Yellow Spreader'
G. rupestris v subcorymbosa	G. subcorymbosa -Col.	Genista polygalifolia -DC.	G. florida -L.
Gaultheria serpyllifolia	G. hispidula	Genista procumbens -Willd.	Cytisus procumbens
Gaultheria thibetica h.	G. thymifolia	Genista sagittalis minor	G. s. ssp delphinensis
Gaultheria veitchiana -Craib	G. hookeri -C.B.Clarke	Genista scariosa -Viv.	G. januensis -Viv.
Gaultheria willisiana -R.C.Davie	G. eriophylla	Genista spathulata -Spach	G. lydia -Boiss.
Gaura lindheimeri 'In The Pink'	G. lindheimeri	Genista sphacelata -Spach	G. fasselata -Decne.
	'Heather's Delight'	Genista striata	Cytisus striatus
Gaya lyallii -(Hook. f.) Baker	Hoheria lyallii - Hook. f.	Genista sylvestris v pungens	G. sylvestris -Scop.
Gaya lyallii v ribifolia -T.Kirk	Hoheria lyallii - Hook. f.	Genista tinctoria 'Plena'	G. t. 'Flore Pleno'
Gaylussacia baccata	Gaylussacia baccata	Genista tinctoria v elatior	G. tinctoria v ovata
Gaylussacia frondosa	Gaylussacia baccata	Genista tinctoria v lasiocarpa	G. tinctoria v humilior
Gaylussacia resinosa	Gaylussacia baccata	Genista triangularis -Willd.	G. januensis -Viv.
Gazania double yellow	G. 'Yellow Buttons'	Genista triquetra -not L'Herit.	G. januensis -Viv.
Gazania splendens	G. rigens	Genista villarsii	G. pulchella
Gazania uniflora	G. rigens v uniflora	Genista virgata -(Ait.) Link not Lam.	G. tenera
Geissorhiza rochensis	G. radians	G. virgata -Willd. not Lam.(Ait.) Link	G. tinctoria v ovata
Gelasine azurea	G. coerulea	Genista viscosa -Willd.	Adenocarpus viscosus
Gelidocalamus fangianus	Drepostachyum	Genistella sagittalis -(L.) Gams	Genista sagittalis -L.
	microphyllum	Gentiana 'Alpha'	G. x hexafarreri 'Alpha'
Gemmingia chinensis	Belamcanda chinensis	Gentiana 'Wellsii'	G. x macaulayi 'Wells'
Genetyllis fimbriata	Darwinia squarrosa		Variety'
Genetyllis macrostegia	Darwinia macrostegia	Gentiana acaulis 'Dinarica'	G. dinarica
Genetyllis meisneri	Darwinia oxylepis	Gentiana acaulis occidentalis	G. occidentalis
Genetyllis oxylepis	Darwinia oxylepis	Gentiana amarella	Gentianella amarella

107

Synonym	Current Name	Synonym	Current Name
Gentiana angulosa	G. verna ssp balcanica	Geranium 'Verguld Saffier'	G. 'Blue Sunrise'
Gentiana arethusae	G. hexaphylla	Geranium 'Victor Reiter'	G. pratense Victor Reiter Junior strain
Gentiana cashmeriana	Gentiana cachemirica		
Gentiana crinita	Gentianopsis crinita	Geranium aconitifolium -L'Herit.	G. rivulare
Gentiana excisa	G. acaulis	Geranium anemonifolium	G. palmatum
Gentiana fetissowii	G. macrophylla v fetis.	Geranium argenteum 'Purpureum'	G. x lindavicum 'Alanah'
Gentiana gracilipes 'Yuatensis'	G. macrophylla v fetis.	Geranium armenum	G. psilostemon
Gentiana hopei	G. trichotoma	Geranium atlanticum -Hooker	G. malviflorum
Gentiana kesselringii	G. walujewii	Geranium atlanticum h.	G. malviflorum
Gentiana kirishima rindo	G. scabra	Geranium bergianum h.	G. clarkei 'Kashmir Purple'
Gentiana kochiana	G. acaulis		
Gentiana kurroo v brevidens	G. dahurica	Geranium canariense	G. reuteri
Gentiana lagodechiana	G. septemfida v lagod.	Geranium candicans h.	G. lambertii
Gentiana macrophylla	G. burseri v villarsii	Geranium cicutarium	Erodium cicutarium
Gentiana mantica -Poll.	G. tinctoria v humilior	Geranium cinereum 'Apple Blossom'	G. x lindavicum 'Apple Blossom'
Gentiana menziesii	G. sceptrum		
Gentiana ochroleuca	G. villosa	Geranium cinereum 'Ballerina'	G. 'Ballerina' (Cinereum Group)
Gentiana phlogifolia	G. cruciata		
Gentiana przewalskii	G. nubigena	Geranium cinereum ssp nanum	G. nanum
Gentiana purdomii	G. gracilipes	Geranium clarkei 'Kashmir Blue'	G. 'Kashmir Blue'
Gentiana purgans -L.	Cytisus purgans	Geranium Crug strain	G. x antipodeum Crug strain
Gentiana saponaria -L.	G. andrewsii -Griseb.		
Gentiana scabra v saxatilis	G. scabra v buergeri	G. dalmaticum x macrorrhizum	G. x cantabrigiense
Gentiana sino-ornata 'Praecox'	G.xmacaulayi 'Praecox'	Geranium delavayi h.	G. sinense
Gentiana stylophora	Megacodon stylophor.	Geranium endressii 'Album'	G. 'Mary Mottram'
Gentiana verna ssp angulosa	G. verna ssp balcanica	G. endressii 'Prestbury White'	G. x oxonianum 'Prestbury Blush'
Gentiana verna ssp pontica	G. verna ssp balcanica		
Gentiana verna ssp tergestina	G. verna ssp balcanica	G. endressii 'Wargrave Pink'	G. x oxonianum 'Wargrave Pink'
Gentiana virgata -(Ait). Link	G. tenera		
Gentiana virgata -Willd.	G. tinctoria v virgata	Geranium eriostemon -Fischer	G. platyanthum
Gentiana wellsii	G. x macaulayi 'Wells' Variety'	Geranium grandiflorum	G. himalayense
		Geranium grandiflorum v alpinum	G. himalay. 'Gravetye'
Gentiana wutaiensis	G. macrophylla v fetissowii	Geranium grevilleanum	G. lambertii
		Geranium h.	Pelargonium
Gentiana x bernardii	G. x stevenagensis 'Bernardii'	G. himalayense 'Birch Double'	G. himalay. 'Plenum'
		Geranium himalayense alpinum	G. himalay. 'Gravetye'
Gentiana x hascombensis	G. septemfida v lagode chiana 'Hascombensis'	Geranium himalayense meeboldii	G. himalayense
		Geranium ibericum brachytrichon	G. gymnocaulon
Geogenanthus undatus	G. poepigii	Geranium ibericum misapplied	G. x magnificum
Geoprumnon succulentum	Astragalus crassicarpus	Geranium ibericum ssp jubatum	G. x magnificum
		Geranium ibericum v platypetalum	G. platypetalum
		G. ibericum v platypetalum h.	G. x magnificum
Geranium 'Baby Blue'	G. himalayense 'Baby Blue'	Geranium lancastrense	G. sanguineum v striatum
Geranium 'Buxton's Blue'	G. wallichianum 'Buxton's Variety'	Geranium laxum -Hanks	G. dissectum -L.
		Geranium libanoticum	G. libani
Geranium 'Claridge Druce'	G. x oxonianum 'Claridge Druce'	G. macrorrhizum 'Mount Olympus White'	G. macr. 'White-Ness'
Geranium 'Jean's Lilac'	G. x oxonianum 'Jean's Lilac'	G. macrorrhizum 'Mount Olympus'	G. macr. 'White-Ness'
Geranium 'Kate Folkard'	G. 'Kate'	Geranium macrorrhizum roseum	G. macrorrhizum
Geranium 'Little Devil'	G. 'Little David'	Geranium macrostylum 'Leonidas'	G. tuberosum 'Leonidas'
Geranium 'Mourning Widow'	G. phaeum v phaeum		
Geranium 'Southcombe Star'	G. x oxonianum f thurstonianum 'Southcombe Star'	Geranium meeboldii	G. himalayense
		Geranium microphyllum	G. potentilloides
		Geranium napuligerum misapplied	G. farreri

Synonym	Current Name	Synonym	Current Name
Geranium nodosum dark form	G. n. 'Swish Purple'	Geranium Wisley hybrid	G. 'Khan'
Geranium nodosum pale form	G. n. 'Svelte Lilac'	Geranium x lindavicum 'Purpureum'	G. x lindavicum 'Alanah'
Geranium phaeum 'Aureum'	G. p. 'Golden Spring'	G. x oxonianum 'Kurt's Variegated'	G. x oxon. 'Spring Fling'
Geranium phaeum black	G. phaeum v phaeum	G. x oxonianum 'Prestbury White'	G. x oxonianum
Geranium phaeum black-flowered	G. phaeum v phaeum		'Prestbury Blush'
Geranium platypetalum -Franchet	G. sinense	Geranium x oxonianum 'Stillingfleet'	G. x oxonianum
Geranium platypetalum misapplied	G. x magnificum		'Stillingfleet Keira'
Geranium pratense 'Bicolor'	G. pratense 'Striatum'	Geranium yunnanense misapplied	G. pogonanthum
Geranium pratense 'Flore Pleno'	G. pratense 'Plenum Violaceum'	Gerardia acuta	Agalinis acuta
		Gerardia purpurea	Agalinis purpurea
Geranium prate. 'Kashmir Purple'	G. clarkei 'Kashmir Purple'	Gerardia purpurea v paupercula	Agalinis paupercula
		Gerardia tenuifolia	Agalinis tenuifolia
Geranium prate. 'Kashmir White'	G. clarkei 'Kashmir White'	Gesneria cardinalis	Sinningia cardinalis
		Gesneria x cardosa	Sinningia x cardosa
G. pratense 'Plenum Purpureum'	G. pratense 'Plenum Violaceum'	Gesneria zebrina	Smithiantha zebrina
		Geum 'Feuerball'	G. 'Mrs J.Bradshaw'
Geranium pratense 'Rectum Album'	G. c. 'Kashmir White'	Geum 'Goldball'	G. 'Lady Stratheden'
Geranium pratense 'Roseum'	G. p. 'Rose Queen'	Geum 'Princess Juliana'	G. 'Prinses Juliana'
Geranium pratense 'Splish-Splash'	G. pratense 'Striatum'	Geum 'Werner Arends'	G. coccineum 'Werner Arends'
Geranium punctatum 'Variegatum'	G. phaeum 'Variegatum'		
Geranium punctatum h.	G. x monacense 'Muldoon'	Geum alpinum	G. montanum
		Geum borisii	G. 'Borisii'
Geranium pyrenaicum 'Bill Wallace'	G. pyr. 'Bill Wallis'	Geum camporum	G. canadense
Geranium rectum 'Album'	G. c. 'Kashmir White'	Geum chiloense 'Lady Stratheden'	G. 'Lady Stratheden'
Geranium renardii blue	G. r. 'Whiteknights'	Geum chiloense 'Mrs Bradshaw'	G. 'Mrs J.Bradshaw'
Geranium robertianum f bernettii	G. robertianum 'Album'	Geum ciliatum	G. triflorum
Geranium rubescens	G. yeoi	Geum coccineum h.	G. chiloense
Geranium sanguineum 'Fran's Star'	G. x oxonianum 'Fran's Star'	Geum magellanicum	G. parviflorum
		Geum perincisum	G. macrophyllum
G. sanguineum 'Hampshire Purple'	G. sanguineum 'New Hampshire Purple'	Geum quellyon	G. chiloense
		Geum reptans	Sieversia reptans
G. sanguineum 'Leed's Variety'	G. s. 'Rod Leeds'	Geum rivale 'Leonardii'	G.r. 'Leonard's Variety'
Geranium sanguineum 'Minutum'	G. sanguineum 'Droplet'	Geum strictum	G. aleppicum
Geranium sanguineum 'Nanum'	G. s. 'Little Bead'	Gilia aggregata	Ipomopsis aggregata
G. sanguineum 'Purple Flame'	G. s. 'New Hampshire Purple'	Gilia californica	Leptodactylon californ.
		Gilia stenothyrsa	Ipomopsis stenothyrsa
Geranium sanguineum 'Splendens'	G. sanguineum v striatum 'Splendens'	Gingidium montanum	Angelica sylvestris
		Ginseng quinquefolium	Panax quinquefolius
G. sanguineum v lancastrense	G. s. v striatum	Gladiolus 'Murieliae'	G. murieliae
G. sanguineum v prostratum	G. s. v striatum	Gladiolus blandus	G. carneus
Geranium sessiliflorum ssp novae-zelandiae 'Nigrescens'		Gladiolus blandus v carneus	G. carneus
G. sessiliflorum ssp novae-zelaniae 'Nigricans'		Gladiolus byzantinus	G. communis ssp byz.
Geranium sessiliflorum ssp novae-zelandiae red-leaved		Gladiolus callianthus 'Murieliae'	G. murieliae
G. sess. ssp novae-zelaniae 'Porter's Pass'		Gladiolus citrinus	G. trichonemifolius
Geranium stapfianum v roseum	G. orientalitibeticum	Gladiolus grandis	G. liliaceus
Geranium striatum	G. versicolor	Gladiolus hirsutus	G. caryophyllaceus
Geranium subcaulescens	G. cinereum v subc.	Gladiolus nanus h.	G. colvillei
Geranium thurstonianum	G. x oxonianum f thur.	Gladiolus natalensis	G. dalenii
Geranium tuberosum v charlesii	G. kotschyi v charlesii	Gladiolus nebulicola	G. natalensis
Geranium versicolor 'Kingston'	G. x oxonianum 'Kingston'	G. oppositiflorus ssp salmoneus	G. oppositiflorus
		Gladiolus primulinus	G. dalenii
Geranium versicolor 'White Lady'	G. v. 'Snow White'	Gladiolus psittacinus	G. dalenii
Geranium violareum	Pelargonium 'Splendide'	Gladiolus purpureoauratus	G. papilio Purpureoauratus Gr.
Geranium wilfordii misapplied	G. thunbergii	Gladiolus quartinianus	G. dalenii

Synonym	Current Name	Synonym	Current Name
Gladiolus segetum	G. italicus	Gnaphalium keriense	Anaphalis keriensis
Gladiolus x colvilei 'The Bride'	G. 'The Bride'	Gnaphalium leontopodium	Leontopodium alpinum
Glandularia bipinnatifida	Verbena bipinnatifida	Gnaphalium leucopsideum	Helichrysum leucops.
Glandularia canadensis	Verbena canadensis	Gnaphalium margaritaceum	Anaphalis margaritac.
Glandularia pulchella	Verbena tenera	Gnaphalium splendidum -Thunb.	Helichrysum splendid.
Glandulicactus crassihamatus	Sclerocactus uncina tus v crassihamatus	Gnaphalium subrigidum	Anaphalis subrigida
		Gnaphalium trinerve	Anaphalis trinervis
Glandulicactus uncinatus	Sclerocactus uncinat.	Godetia	Clarkia
Glaucidium palmatum 'Album'	G. p. v leucanthum	Godetia amoena	Clarkia amoena
Glaucium flavum aurantiacum	G. flavum f fulvum	Godetia biloba	Clarkia biloba
Glaucium flavum orange	G. flavum f fulvum	Godetia grandiflora	Clarkia amoena
Glaucium flavum red	G. corniculatum	Godetia viminea	Clarkia purpurea
Glaucium phoenicium	G. corniculatum	Godwinia -Seem.	Dracontium -L.
Glechonion hederaceum	Glechoma hederacea	Gonatanthus -Klot.	Remusatia -Schott
Gleditsia horrida -not Salisb.	G. japonica -Miq.	Goniurus -C.Presl.	Pothos -L.
Gleditsia horrida -Willd	G. sinensis -Lam.	Gonolobus condurango	Marsdenia condurango
Gleditsia inermis	G. triacanthos f inerm.	Goodenia radicans	Selliera radicans
G. triacanthos 'Inermis Aurea'	G. t. 'Sunburst'	Gordonia alatamaha -(Marsh.) Sarg.	Franklinia alatamaha
Gleditsia triacanthos 'Pendula'	G. triacanthos 'Bujotii'	Gordonia anomala -Spreng.	G. axillaris
Globularia aphyllanthes	G. punctata	Gordonia pubescens -L'Herit.	Franklinia alatamaha
Globularia bellidifolia	G. meridionalis	Gorteria rigens	Gazania rigens
Globularia cordifolia ssp bellidifolia	G. meridionalis	Gregorea	Douglasia
G. cordifolia ssp meridionalis	G. meridionalis	Grevillea 'Kentlyn'	G. 'Mason's Hybrid'
Globularia nana	G. repens	Grevillea 'Ned Kelly'	G. 'Mason's Hybrid'
Globularia pygmaea	G. meridionalis	Grevillea aculeolata	G. acuaria
Globularia willkommii	G. punctata	Grevillea aculeolata v longifolia	G. acuaria
Glochidion fortunei -Hance	G. sinicum	Grevillea adpressa	G. amplexans ssp adp.
Glomeraria alba	Amaranthus albus	Grevillea agrifolia v major	G. agrifolia ssp agrif.
Gloriosa carsonii	G. superba 'Carsonii'	Grevillea alpestris	G. alpina
Gloriosa lutea	G. superba 'Lutea'	Grevillea alpestris -Meissn.	G. alpina -Lindl.
Gloriosa minor	G. superba	G. alpestris v helianthemifolia	G. alpina
Gloriosa rothschildiana	G. superba 'Rothschildiana'	Grevillea alphonsiana	Hakea macrocarpa
		Grevillea alpina v aurea	G. alpina
Gloriosa simplex	G. superba	Grevillea alpina v dallachiana	G. alpina
Glossocomia ussuriensis	Codonopsis ussuriens.	Grevillea althoferi	G. althoferorum
Glossopteris scolopendrium	Asplenium scolopend.	Grevillea angulata v lancifolia	G. brevis
Gloxinia speciosa	Sinningia speciosa	Grevillea angustata	G. parellela
Glyceria aquatica	G. maxima	Grevillea angustiloba	G. ilicifolia v angustil.
Glyceria aquatica variegata	G. maxima v variegata	Grevillea apiciloba	G. hookeriana ssp apic.
Glyceria plicata	G. notata	Grevillea apiciloba v digitata	G. hookeriana ssp dig.
Glyceria spectabilis 'Variegata'	G. maxima v variegata	Grevillea approximata	G. ilicifolia ssp ilicifolia
Glycine apios	Apios americana	Grevillea aquifolium	G. infecunda
Glycine priceana	Apios priceana	Grevillea aquifolium	G. monticola
Glyciphylla hispidula	Gaultheria hispidula	Grevillea aquifolium v attenuata	G. aquifolium
Glycyrrhiza glandulifera	G. glabra	Grevillea aquifolium v truncata	G. aquifolium
Glycyrrhiza viscida	G. uralensis	Grevillea arenaria ssp canescens	G. montana
Glyptostrobus lineatus	G. pensilis	Grevillea arida	G. acuaria
Glyptostrobus sinensis	G. pensilis	Grevillea asparagoides	G. maxwellii
Gnaphalium 'Fairy Gold'	Helichrysum thians chanicum 'Goldkind'	Grevillea aspera v linearis	G. fasciculata
		Grevillea aspleniifolia v longifolia	G. longifolia
Gnaphalium americanum	Antennaria margaritacea	G. aspleniifolia v shepherdiana	G. aspleniifolia
		Grevillea aspleniifolia v typica	G. aspleniifolia
Gnaphalium boreale	Antenn. margaritacea	Grevillea australis v brevifolia	G. australis
Gnaphalium dioicum	Antennaria dioica	Grevillea australis v erecta	G. australis
Gnaphalium elatum	Helichrysum elatum	Grevillea australis v linearifolia	G. australis

Synonym	Current Name	Synonym	Current Name
Grevillea australis v montana	G. australis	Grevillea flabellifolia	G. hookeriana ssp
Grevillea australis v planifolia	G. australis		apiciloba
Grevillea australis v subulata	G. australis	Grevillea flexuosa v pauciloba	G. synapheae ssp
Grevillea australis v tenuifolia	G. australis		synapheae
Grevillea banksii 'Canberra Hybrid'	G. 'Canberra Gem'	Grevillea florida	G. uncinulata ssp flori.
Grevillea banksii v banksii	G. banksii	Grevillea forsteri h.	G. banksii
Grevillea banksii v forsteri	G. banksii	Grevillea gibbosa	G. glauca
Grevillea baueri v glabra	G. baueri	Grevillea glabella	G. rosmarinifolia ssp
Grevillea baueri v pubescens	G. lanigera		glabella
Grevillea behrii	G. ilicifolia ssp ilicifolia	Grevillea glabrata	G. manglesii ssp
Grevillea bipinnatifida v glabrata	G. bipinnatifida		manglesii
Grevillea bipinnatifida v vulgaris	G. bipinnatifida	Grevillea glabrata ssp dissectifolia	G. manglesii ssp diss.
Grevillea biternata	G. curviloba ssp	Grevillea glaucina	G. quercifolia
	incurva	Grevillea goodii ssp decora	G. decora
Grevillea biternata v leptostachya	G. biternata	Grevillea hakeoides ssp commutata	G. commutata
Grevillea blackallii	G. pityophylla	Grevillea hakeoides ssp stenophylla	G. stenophylla
Grevillea brachyantha	G. quercifolia	Grevillea helmsiana	G. plurijuga ssp
Grevillea brevicuspis	G. trifida		plurijuga
Grevillea brownii	G. depauperata	Grevillea heteroneura	G. parallela
Grevillea brownii	G. depaupterata	Grevillea heterophylla	G. refracta ssp
Grevillea callipteris	G. dryandri ssp dry.		refracta
Grevillea chrysodendrum	G. pteridifolia	Grevillea heterophylla v velutina	G. r. ssp refracta
Grevillea chrysophaea v canescens	G. chrysophaea	Grevillea hewardiana	G. coccinea
Grevillea cinerea v angustifolia	G. mucronulata	Grevillea ilicifolia v acortechinii	G. scortechinii
Grevillea cinerea v myrtacea	G. mucronulata	Grevillea ilicifolia v dilatata	G. dilatata
Grevillea cordata	G. shuttleworthiana	Grevillea integrifolia ssp biformis	G. biformis
	ssp shuttleworthiana	G. integrifolia ssp ceratocarpa	G. ceratocarpa
Grevillea cordigera	G. laurifolia	Grevillea jamesoniana	G. sarissa ssp sarissa
Grevillea ctenophylla	G. pectinata	Grevillea lactucifolia	G. quercifolia
Grevillea dallachiana	G. alpina	Grevillea lanigera 'Mt. Taboritha'	G. lanigera 'Compacta'
Grevillea diffusa ssp diffusa	G. capitellata	Grevillea lanigera 'Prostrate'	G. lanigera 'Compacta'
Grevillea diffusa ssp evansiana	G. evansiana	Grevillea latrobei	G. rosmarinifolia ssp
Grevillea dimorpha v angustifolia	G. dimorpha		rosmarinifolia
Grevillea dimorpha v lanceolata	G. dimorpha	Grevillea lavandulacea v latifolia	G. l. ssp lavandulacea
Grevillea dimorpha v latifolia	G. dimorpha	Grevillea lavandulacea v sericea	G. l. ssp lavandulacea
Grevillea dimorpha v linearis	G. dimorpha	Grevillea leucadendron	G. pyramidalis ssp leu.
Grevillea disjuncta ssp disjuncta	G. disjuncta	Grevillea lindleyana	G. wilsonii
Grevillea disjuncta ssp dolichopoda	G. dolichopoda	Grevillea linearis	G. linearifolia
Grevillea diversifolia v lobata	G. papillosa	Grevillea livea	G. stenobotrya
Grevillea diversifolia v rigida	G. curviloba ssp curvil.	Grevillea loboana	G. diversifolia ssp
G. drummondii ssp centristigma	G. centristigma		subtersericata
G. drummondii ssp pimeleoides	G. pimeleoides	Grevillea longiloba	G. pyramidalis ssp lon.
Grevillea dubia	G. speciosa	Grevillea longistyla	G. neglecta
Grevillea dumetorum	G. ilicifolia ssp lobata	Grevillea lycopodina	G. pilulifera
Grevillea ericifolia	G. lanigera	Grevillea macrostylis	G. tripartita ssp macr.
Grevillea ericifolia v muelleri	G. lanigera	Grevillea magnifica	G. petrophiloides ssp
Grevillea ericifolia v scabrella	G. lanigera		magnifica
G. eriostachya ssp eriostachya	G. eriostachya	G. manglesioides ssp papillosa	G. papillosa
Grevillea eriostachya ssp excelsior	G. excelsior	G. manglesioides v angustissima	G. diversifolia ssp
Grevillea fasciculata v divaricata	G. fasciculata		subtersericata
Grevillea fasciculata v dubia	G. fasciculata	Grevillea martinii	G. polybotrya
Grevillea fasciculata v linearis	G. fasciculata	Grevillea meisneriana	G. fasciculata
Grevillea fasciculata v stricta	G. fasciculata	Grevillea microcarpa	G. agrifolia ssp microc.
Grevillea ferruginea	G. arenaria ssp aren.	Grevillea mitchellii	G. pteridifolia
Grevillea filifolia	G. endlicheriana	Grevillea mucronulata v angustifolia	G. mucronulata

Synonym	Current Name	Synonym	Current Name
Grevillea neglecta	G. longistyla	Grevillea vestita v angustata	G. curviloba
Grevillea ninghanensis	G. deflexa	Grevillea victoriae v leptoneura	G. parvula
Grevillea nutans	G. rosmarinifolia ssp rosmarinifolia	Grevillea victorii	G. eriobotrya
		Grevillea viscidula	G. pyramidalis ssp
Grevillea obliqua	G. pyramidalis ssp leucadendron		leucadendron
		Grevillea williamsonii	G. aquifolium
Grevillea obtusiflora ssp granulifera	G. granulifera	Grevillea willsii ssp pachylostyla	G. pachylostyla
Grevillea occidentalis v lanceolata	G. occidentalis	Grewia oppositifolia - not DC.	G. optiva
Grevillea occidentalis v linearis	G. occidentalis	Grewia parviflora -Bge.	G. biloba -G.Don
Grevillea oleoides ssp dimorpha	G. dimorpha	Grindelia grandiflora -Hook.	G. squarrosa
Grevillea oxystigma	G. pilulifera	Grindelia perennis -A. Nelson	G. squarrosa
Grevillea oxystigma v acerosa	G. pilulifera	Grindelia robusta	G. camphorum
Grevillea oxystigma v heterophylla	G. pilulifera	Grindelia robusta v rigida	G. camphorum
Grevillea oxystigma v tenella	G. pilulifera	Grindelia serrulata -Rydb.	G. squarrosa
Grevillea pachypoda	G. mimosoides	Grindelia speciosa -Hook. & Arn.	G. chiloensis
Grevillea parviflora v acuaria	G. halmaturina	Griselinia lucida v macrophylla	G. lucida
Grevillea pedunculosa	G. nudiflora	Grossularia alpestris	Ribes alpinum
Grevillea pilosa ssp dissecta	G. dissecta	Guilandina dioica -L.	Gymnocladus dioica -L.
Grevillea pinaster v hirtella	G. hirtella	Guillauminia albiflora	Aloe albiflora
Grevillea pinnasecta	G. commutata ssp pinn.	Gunnera brasiliensis	G. manicata
Grevillea pinnatifida	G. baileyana	Gunnera chilensis	G. tinctoria
Grevillea platypoda	G. patentiloba ssp plat.	Gunnera scabra	G. tinctoria
Grevillea polybotrya	G. parallela	Guzmania 'Claret'	Neoregelia Claret Gr.
Grevillea pritzelii	G. h. sso hookeriana	Guzmania 'Surprise'	x Niduregelia 'Surprise'
Grevillea pteridifolia v mitchellii	G. pteridifolia		
Grevillea pteridifolia v typica	G. pteridifolia	Guzmania tricolor	G. monostachya
Grevillea punicea v crassifolia	G. speciosa	Gymnagathis teretifolia	Melaleuca teretifolia
Grevillea purdieana	G. nematophylla ssp n.	Gymnocalycium mihanovichii 'Hibotan'	
Grevillea rigens	G. dryandri ssp dry.		G. m. 'Red Head'
Grevillea rigidissima	G. huegelii	G. mihanovichii 'Red Cap'	G. m. 'Red Head'
Grevillea rogersii	G. lavandulacea ssp r.	Gymnocarpium phegopteris	Phegopteris connectilis
Grevillea rosea	G. l. ssp lavandulacea	Gymnocladus canadensis -Lam.	G. dioica -(L.) K.Koch
Grevillea rufa	G. pilosa	Gymnogramma	Gymnopteris
Grevillea sarmentosa	G. scortechinii ssp s.	Gymnogramma japonica	Coniogramme japonica
Grevillea segmentosa	G. leucopteris	Gymnogramma triangularis	Pityrogramma triang.
Grevillea sericostachya	G. pterosperma	Gymnomesium -Schott	Arum -L.
Grevillea shepherdii	G. aspleniifolia	Gymnothrix caudata	Pennisetum macrourum
Grevillea silaifolia	Lomatia silaifolia		
Grevillea simulans	G. pterosperma	Gynandropsis gynandra	Cleome gynandra
Grevillea speciosa ssp dimorpha	G. dimorpha	Gynandropsis pentaphylla	Cleome gynandra
Grevillea stenocarpa	G. biformis	Gynerium argenteum	Cortaderia selloana
Grevillea strangea	Strangea linearis	Gynura sarmentosa h.	G. aurantiaca 'Purple Passion'
Grevillea striata v lineata	G. striata		
Grevillea stuartii	G. australis	Gypsophila 'Rosy Veil'	G. 'Rosenschleier'
Grevillea sturtii	G. juncifolia ssp juncif.	Gypsophila aretioides 'Compacta'	G. a. 'Caucasica'
Grevillea sulphurea -A.Cunn.	G. juniperina f sulph.	Gypsophila ceballosii	G. elegans
Grevillea superba	G. plurijuga ssp sup.	Gypsophila dubia	G. repens 'Dubia'
Grevillea tenuifolia	G. australis	Gypsophila fratensis	G. repens 'Fratensis'
Grevillea thelemanniana ssp delta	G. delta	Gypsophila gracilescens	G. tenuifolia
Grevillea thelemanniana ssp fililoba	G. fililoba	Gypsophila paniculata Snowflake	G. p. 'Schneeflocke'
Grevillea thelemanniana ssp hirtella	G. hirtella	Gypsophila parviflora -Moench	G. paniculata
Grevillea tolminsis	G. x semperflorens	Gypsophila repens Pink Beauty	G. r. 'Rosa Schonheit'
Grevillea trineura	Hakea trineura	Gypsophila transylvanica	G. petraea
Grevillea umbellata sso acerosa	G. umbellata	Gypsophila Veil of Roses	G. 'Rosenschleier'
Grevillea variabilis	G. aquifolium	Gyrostachys	Spiranthes

Synonym	Current Name	Synonym	Current Name
Haageocereus acranthus	H. limensis	Hakea flexilis	H. nodosa
Haageocereus australis	H. decumbens	Hakea florida v latifolia	H. florida
Habenaria radiata	Pecteilis radiata	Hakea florigera	H. leucoptera
H.rhodopensis v ferdinandi-coburgii	H. ferdinandi-coburgii	Hakea glabella	H. prostrata
Habranthus andersonii	H. tubispathus	Hakea glabella ssp paucidentata	H. prostrata
Habranthus pratensis	Hippeastrum pratense	Hakea glabella ssp prostrata	H. prostrata
Habrothamnus elegans -Brongn.	Cestrum elegans	Hakea glabella v denticulata	H. denticulata
Hacquetia epipactis 'Variegata'	H. epipactis 'Thor'	Hakea glabra	H. teretifolia ssp teret.
Haemanthus carneus	Haemanthus albiflos	Hakea glabrifolia	H. microcarpa
Haemanthus kalbreyeri	Scadoxus multiflorus ssp multiflorus	Hakea glaucina	H. eriantha
		Hakea heterophylla	H. varia
Haemanthus katherinae	Scadoxus multiflorus ssp katherinae	Hakea ilicifolia v major	H. ilicifolia
		Hakea ilicifolia v minor	H. ilicifolia
Haemanthus magnificus	Scadoxus puniceus	Hakea incrassans	H. dactyloides
Haemanthus multiflorus	Scadoxus multiflorus	Hakea intricata	H. lissocarpha
Haemanthus natalensis	Scadoxus puniceus	Hakea ivoryi v glabrescens	H. divaricata
Haemanthus puniceus	Scadoxus puniceus	Hakea laciniosa	H. ceratophylla
Hakea acacioides	H. leucoptera ssp sericeps	Hakea lanigera	H. gibbosa
		Hakea lasiantha v angustifolia	H. lasianthoides
Hakea acicularis -Knight 1809	H. sericea	Hakea lativalvis	H. adnata
Hakea acicularis v lissosperma	H. lissosperma -R.Br.	Hakea leucadendron	H. incrassata
Hakea amplexicaulis v angustifolia	H. amplexicaulis	Hakea leucoptera ssp leucoptera	H. virgata
Hakea amplexicaulis v latifolia	H. amplexicaulis	Hakea ligustrina	H. oleifolia
Hakea amplifolia	H. florulenta	Hakea longicuspis	H. leucoptera ssp sericeps
Hakea arida	H. recurva ssp arida		
Hakea attenuata	H. varia	Hakea longiflora	H. erinacea v longiflora
Hakea auriculata v spathulata	H. spathulata	Hakea longifolia	H. lorea ssp borealis
Hakea betchei	H. eriantha	Hakea longispina	H. decurrens ssp physocarpa
Hakea bifrons	H. microcarpa		
Hakea bipinnatifida	H. lissocarpa	Hakea lorea v mollis	H. lorea ssp lorea
Hakea brachyrrhyncha	H. decurrens	Hakea lurida	H. rostrata
Hakea brookeana	H. obliqua ssp obliqua	Hakea microcarpa v bathurstiana	H. microcarpa
H. candolleana v campylorrhyncha	H. candolleana	Hakea microcarpa v tasmannica	H. microcarpa
Hakea canescens	H. cinerea	Hakea milliganii	H. epiglottis ssp millig.
Hakea carinata v trigonophylla	H. carinata	Hakea mimosoides	H. florulenta
Hakea ceratophylla v elongata	H. ceratophylla	Hakea mitchellii	H. muelleriana
Hakea ceratophylla v laciniata	H. ceratophylla	Hakea mixta	H. trifurcata
Hakea ceratophylla v subintegrifolia	H. ceratophylla	Hakea morrisoniana	H. macrocarpa
Hakea ceratophylla v tricuspis	H. ceratophylla	H. multilineata v grammatophylla	H. grammatophylla
Hakea coriacea	H. francisiana	Hakea nitida	H. pycnobotrys
Hakea costata v lanceolata	H. costata	Hakea pampliniana	H. rostrata
Hakea crassifolia	H. pandanicarpa ssp crassifolia	Hakea patula	H. microcarpa
		Hakea pectinata	H. drupacea
Hakea crassinervia	H. p. ssp crassifolia	Hakea pinifolia	H. gibbosa
Hakea cucullata v conchifolia	H. conchifolia	Hakea pubescens	H. gibbosa
Hakea cucullata v conchifolia	H. conchifolia	Hakea pugioniformis v sericea	H. teretifolia ssp teret.
Hakea cucullata v vulgaris	H. cucullata	Hakea pycnobotrys	H. nitida
Hakea cunninghamii	H. lorea ssp lorea	Hakea recondita	H. eriantha
Hakea cymbocarpa	H. eriantha	Hakea repanda	H. ferruginea
Hakea digyna	H. chordophylla	Hakea roei	H. pandanicarpa
Hakea dolichostyla	H. lasiocarpha	Hakea rubricaulis	Stenocarpus salignus
Hakea erinacea v longiflora	H. longiflora	Hakea rubriflora	H. denticulata
Hakea eucalyptiformis	H. eriantha	Hakea saligna	H. salicifolia
Hakea eucalyptoides	H. laurina	Hakea salisburiifolia	H. baxteri
Hakea falcata v subuninervis	H. candolleana	Hakea semiplena	H. nodosa

Synonym	Current Name	Synonym	Current Name
Hakea sericea h.	H. lissosperma -R.Br.	Hamamelis japonica v obtusata	H. japonica v
Hakea sericea v lissosperma	H. lissosperma -R.Br.		lfavopurpurascens -
Hakea stenocarpoides	Strangea stenocarp.		(Mak.) Rehd.
Hakea stricta	H. leucoptera	Hamamelis japonica v rubra -Kache	H. japonica 'Arborea'
Hakea suaveolens	H. drupacea	Hamamelis japonica v rubra h.	H. japonica v
Hakea suberea	H. lorea ssp lorea		flavopurpurascens
Hakea sulcata v scoparia	H. scoparia	Hamamelis mollis 'Aurantiaca'	H. 'Brevipetala'
Hakea tamminensis	H. gibbosa	Hamamelis mollis 'Brevipetala'	H. 'Brevipetala'
Hakea tenuifolia -Dum.-Cours.	H. sericea	Hamamelis mollis 'Pallida'	H. x int. 'Pallida'
Hakea tenuifolia v decurrens	H. decurrens	Hamamelis mollis 'Select'	H. x int. 'Westerstede'
Hakea tricuris	H. trifurcata	Hamamelis mollis 'Sunburst'	H. x int. 'Sunburst'
Hakea triformis	H. amplexicaulis	Hamamelis obtusata -Mak.	H. japonica v
Hakea trifurcata v eriantha	H. trifurcata		flavopurpurascens
Hakea trifurcata v sericantha	H. trifurcata	H. obtusata f flavopurpurascens	H. j. v flavopurpurasc.
Hakea trinervis	H. ambigua	Hamamelis persica -DC.	Parrotia persica
Hakea ulicina v angustifolia	H. ulicina	Hamamelis x intermedia 'Adonis'	H. x int. 'Ruby Glow'
Hakea ulicina v latifolia	H. repullans	H. x intermedia 'Copper Beauty'	H. x int. 'Jelena'
Hakea ulicina v macrocarpa	H. repullans	Hamamelis x intermedia 'Magic Fire'	H. x int. 'Feuerzauber'
Hakea undulata v subintegerrima	H. undulata	Hamamelis zuccariniana	H. japonica
Hakea virgata	H. leucoptera ssp leuc.	Hamatocactus crassihamatus	Sclerocactus uncina
Hakea vittata v glabriflora	H. decurrens ssp		tus v crassihamatus
	physocarpa	Hamatocactus hamatacanthus	Ferocactus hamatacan.
Hakonechloa macra 'Variegata'	H. macra 'Alboaurea'	Hamatocactus setispinus	Thelocactus setispinus
Halesia carolina v glabrescens	H. carolina -L.	Hamatocactus uncinatus	Sclerocactus uncinat.
Halesia carolina v monticola -Rehd.	H. monticola	Hamiltonia oblonga -(Bge) Franch.	Leptodermis oblonga
Halesia carolina v stenocarpa	H. carolina -L.	Hamiltonia pilosa -Franch.	Leptodermis pilosa
Halesia corymbosa	Pterostyrax corymb.	Hansalia -Schott	Amorphophallus
Halesia hispida	Pterostyrax hispida	Hapale -Schott	Hapaline -Schott
Halesia parviflora -Lindl. not Michx.	H. carolina -L.	Haplopappus acaulis	Stenotus acaulis
Halesia stenocarpa -K. Koch	H. carolina -L.	Haplopappus brandegeei	Erigeron aureus
Halesia tetraptera -Ellis	H. carolina -L.	Haplopappus coronopifolius	H. glutinosus
Halesia tetraptera f dialypetala	H. carolina f dialypetal.	Haplopappus lyallii	Tonestus lyallii
Halianthemum halimifolium	Halimium halimifolium	Haplopappus pygmaeus	Tonestus pygmaeus
Halimium commutatum -Pau	H. calycinum	Hardenbergia macrophylla	Kennedia macrophylla
Halimium formosum	H. lasianthum ssp for.	Hardenbergia monophylla	H. violacea
Halimium halimifolium misapplied	H. x pauanum	Hardenbergia violacea 'Alba'	H. v. 'White Crystal'
Halimium halimifolium misapplied	H. x santae	Harmogia	Babingtonia
Halimium libanotis	H. calycinum	Harrimanella	Cassiope
Halimium multiflorum -Dun.	H. halimifolium ssp	Harrisia pomanensis	H. bonplandii
	multiflorum	Hartia sinensis -Dunn	Stewartia
Halimium rosmarinifolium	H. calycinum		pteropetiolata
Halimium wintonense	x Halimiocistus winton.	Haworthia margaritifera	H. pumila
Halimodendron argenteum	H. halodendron	Haworthia planifolia	H. cymbiformis
Hamamelis 'Fire Charm'	H. x int. 'Feuerzauber'	Haworthia setata	H. arachnoidea
Hamamelis 'Magic Fire'	H. x int. 'Feuerzauber'	H. venosa ssp tessellata	H. tessellata
Hamamelis arborea	H. japonica 'Arborea'	Haynaldia	Dasypyrum
Hamamelis chinensis -R.Br.	Loropetalum chinense	Hebe 'Aoira'	H. recurva 'Aoira'
Hamamelis incarnata -Mak.	H. japonica v	Hebe 'Azurens'	H. 'Maori Gem'
	flavopurpurascens	Hebe 'Bowles' Variety'	H. 'Bowles' Hybrid'
Hamamelis japollis -Lange	H. x intermedia -Rehd.	Hebe 'Brill Blue'	Veronica x guthrieana
Hamamelis japonica 'Carmine Red'	H. x intermedia	Hebe 'Carl Teschner'	H. 'Youngii'
	'Carmine Red'	Hebe 'Cookiana'	H. stricta macroura
Hamamelis japonica 'Hiltingbury'	H. x int. 'Hiltingbury'		'Cookiana'
Hamamelis japonica 'Rubra Superba'	H. x int. 'Ruby Glow'	Hebe 'Diamant'	H. speciosa 'La
Hamamelis japonica v arborea	H. japonica 'Arborea'		Seduisante'

114

Synonym	Current Name	Synonym	Current Name
Hebe 'Dorothy Peach'	H. 'Watson's Pink'	Hebe bidwillii -of most authors	Parahebe decora
Hebe 'E.B.Anderson'	H. 'Caledonia'	Hebe bishopiana 'Champagne'	H. bishopiana
Hebe 'Emerald Dome'	H. 'Emerald Gem'	Hebe brachysiphon 'White Gem'	H. 'White Gem'
Hebe 'Emerald Green'	H. 'Emerald Green'		(Brachysiphon hybrid)
Hebe 'Eversley Seedling'	H. 'Bowles' Hybrid'	Hebe buchananii 'Nana'	H. buchananii 'Minor'
Hebe 'Gauntlettii'	H. 'Eveline'	H/ buchananii 'Sir George Fenwick'	H. b. 'Fenwickii'
Hebe 'Godefroyana'	H. pinguifolia	Hebe buxifolia 'Champagne'	H. x bishopiana
	'Godefroyana'	Hebe buxifolia misapplied	H. odora
Hebe 'Green Globe'	H. 'Emerald Gem'	Hebe catarractae -(Forst. f.) Wall	Parahebe catarractae
Hebe 'Hagleyensis'	H. 'Hagley Park'	Hebe colensoi 'Glauca'	H. 'Leonard Cockayne'
Hebe 'James Stirling'	H. ochracea 'James	Hebe cookiana	H. stricta macroura
	Stirling'		'Cookiana'
		Hebe darwiniana	H. glaucophylla
Hebe 'Knightshayes'	H. 'Caledonia'	Hebe elliptica 'Variegata'	H. x franciscana
Hebe 'La Seduisante'	H. speciosa 'La		'Variegata'
	Seduisante'		
Hebe 'Lady Ardilaun'	H. 'Amy'	Hebe hookeriana	Parahebe hookeriana
Hebe 'Lavender Spray'	H. 'Hartii'	Hebe laevis	H. venustula
Hebe 'Macewanii'	H. 'Mcewanii'	Hebe lapidosa	H. rupicola
Hebe 'Margery Fish'	H. 'Primley Gem'	Hebe latifolia	H. x franciscana 'Blue
Hebe 'Mckean'	H. 'Emerald Gem'		Gem'
Hebe 'Mercury'	H. pimeleoides	Hebe linifolia -(Hook. f.) Allan	Parahebe linifolia
	'Mercury'	Hebe loganioides	H. 'Loganioides'
Hebe 'Milmont Emerald'	H. 'Emerald Gem'	Hebe lyallii (Hook.f.) Allan	Parahebe lyallii Hebe
Hebe 'Pink Payne'	H. 'Gauntlettii'	lycopodioides 'Aurea'	H. armstrongii
Hebe 'Pink Pearl'	H. 'Gloriosa'	Hebe mackenii	H. 'Emerald Green'
Hebe 'Porlock Purple'	Parahebe catarractae	Hebe magellanica -Gmel.	H. elliptica
	'Delight'	Hebe muscoidea h.	H. 'Edinensis'
Hebe 'Purple Emperor'	H. 'Neil's Choice'	Hebe parviflora h.	H. 'Bowles' Hybrid'
Hebe 'Purple Queen'	H. 'Amy'	Hebe parviflora v angustifolia	H. stenophylla
Hebe 'Purple Tips' misapplied	H. speciosa 'Variegata'	Hebe parviflora v arborea	H. parviflora
Hebe 'Red Ruth'	H. 'Gauntletii'	Hebe pauciflora h.	H. 'Christensenii'
Hebe 'Royal Purple'	H. 'Alicia Amherst'	Hebe perfoliata	Parahebe perfoliata
H. 'Spender's Seedling' misapplied	H. stenophylla	Hebe Purple Pixie	H. 'Mohawk'
Hebe 'Sussex Carpet'	H. albicans 'Sussex	Hebe salicifolia 'Snow Wreath'	H. 'Snow Wreath'
	Carpet'	Hebe salicornioides 'Aurea'	H. propinqua 'Aurea'
Hebe 'Tom Marshall'	H. canterburiensis	Hebe selaginoides 'Ruddigore'	H. speciosa 'La
Hebe 'Tricolor'	H. speciosa 'Variegata'		Seduisante'
Hebe 'Veitchii'	H. 'Alicia Amherst'	Hebe selaginoides h.	H. 'Loganioides'
Hebe 'Waikiki'	H. 'Mrs Winder'	Hebe speciosa 'Johny Day'	H. 'Johny Day'
Hebe 'Wardiensis'	H. pinguifolia	Hebe speciosa 'Purple Queen'	H. 'Amy'
	'Wardiensis'	Hebe speciosa 'Ruddigore'	H. s. 'La Seduisante'
Hebe 'Warleyensis'	H. 'Mrs. Winder'	Hebe subalpina h.	H. rakaiensis
Hebe 'Willcoxii'	H. buchananii 'Sir	Hebe traversii h.	H. brachysiphon
	George Fenwick'	Hebe vernicosa v canterburiensis	H. canterburiensis
Hebe albicans 'Pewter Dome'	H. 'Pewter Dome'	H. x andersonii 'Argenteovariegata'	H. x a. 'Variegata'
Hebe albicans 'Red Edge'	H. 'Red Edge'	Hebe x andersonii 'Aureovariegata'	H. x andersonii 'Aurea'
Hebe albicans 'Snow Drift'	H. 'Snow Cover'	H. x franciscana 'Purple Tips' mis.	H. speciosa 'Variegata'
Hebe albicans prostrate form	H. albicans 'Snow	Hebe x franciscana 'Variegata'	H. 'Silver Queen'
	Cover'	Hebe x kirkii.	H. 'Kirkii'
Hebe allanii	H. amplexicaulis f hirta	Hedeoma arkansana	Calamintha arkansana
H. anomala -(J.B.Armstrong) Ckn.	H. odora	Hedeoma glabra	Calamintha arkansana
Hebe anomala misapplied	H. 'Imposter'	Hedera algeriensis	H. canariensis h.
Hebe aoira h.	H. recurva 'Aoira'	Hedera amurensis -Hibb.	H. colchica
Hebe azurea	H. venustula	Hedera azorica typica	H. azorica 'Sao Miguel'
Hebe bidwillii -(Hook.) Allan	Parahebe x bidwillii	Hedera canariensis 'Algeriensis'	H. canariensis h.

Synonym	Current Name
Hedera canariensis 'Cantabrian'	H. maroccana 'Spanish Canary'
Hedera canariensis 'Variegata'	H.c.'Gloire de Marengo'
Hedera canariensis v azorica	H. azorica
Hedera caucasigena	H. helix f caucasigena
Hedera chinensis	H. nepalensis v sinensis
Hedera chinensis typica	H. n. v sinensis
Hedera chrysocarpa -Walsh	H. helix ssp poetarum
Hedera cinerea -(Hibb.) Bean	H. nepalensis -K.Koch
Hedera colchica 'Arborescens'	H. c. 'Dendroides'
Hedera colchica 'Dentata Aurea'	H.c.'Dentata Variegata'
Hedera colchica 'My Heart'	H. colchica
Hedera colchica 'Paddy's Pride'	H. c. 'Sulphur Heart'
Hedera colchica 'Variegata'	H.c.'Dentata Variegata'
Hedera cristata	H. h. 'Parsley Crested'
Hedera helix 'Abundance'	H. helix 'California'
Hedera helix 'Albany'	H. hibernica 'Albany'
Hedera helix 'Anne Borch'	H. hielix 'Anne Marie'
Hedera helix 'Annette'	H. helix 'California'
Hedera helix 'Aran' misapplied	H. helix 'Rutherford's Arran'
Hedera helix 'Arran'	H. hibernica 'Arran'
Hedera helix 'Aurea Densa'	H. helix 'Aureovariegata'
Hedera helix 'Bird's Foot'	H. helix 'Pedata'
Hedera helix 'Brigette'	H. helix 'California'
Hedera helix 'Caenwoodiana'	H. helix 'Pedata'
Hedera helix 'Calico'	H. h. 'Schafer Three'
Hedera helix 'Chicago Variegated'	H. helix 'Harald'
Hedera helix 'Christian'	H. h. 'Direktor Badke'
Hedera helix 'Clotted Cream'	H. helix 'Caecilia'
Hedera helix 'Cristata Melanie'	H. helix 'Melanie'
Hedera helix 'Cristata'	H. h. 'Parsley Crested'
Hedera helix 'Curley-Q'	H. helix 'Dragon Claw'
Hedera helix 'Curleylocks'	H. h. 'Manda's Crested'
Hedera helix 'Curly Locks'	H. h. 'Manda's Crested'
Hedera helix 'Cuspidata Major'	H. hibernica 'Cuspidata Major'
Hedera helix 'Cuspidata Minor'	H. hibernica 'Cuspidata Minor'
Hedera helix 'Cyprus'	H. cypria
Hedera helix 'Deltoidea'	H. hibernica 'Deltoidea'
Hedera helix 'Digitata'	H. hibernica 'Digitata'
Hedera helix 'Discolor'	H. helix 'Dealbata'
Hedera helix 'Discolor'	H.h.'Minor Marmorata'
Hedera helix 'Dunloe Gap'	H. hibernica 'Dunloe Gap'
Hedera helix 'Emerald Gem'	H. helix 'Angularis'
Hedera helix 'Emerald Jewel'	H. helix 'Pittsburgh'
Hedera helix 'Erin'	H. helix 'Pin Oak'
Hedera helix 'Ester'	H. helix 'Harald'
Hedera helix 'Feastii'	H.h. 'Koniger's Auslese'
Hedera helix 'Fringette'	H. h. 'Manda Fringette'
Hedera helix 'Gold Harald'	H. helix 'Goldchild'

Synonym	Current Name
Hedera helix 'Golden Ann'	H. helix 'Ceridwen'
Hedera helix 'Golden Ester'	H. helix 'Ceridwen'
Hedera helix 'Golden Kolibri'	H. helix 'Midas Touch'
Hedera helix 'Golden Shamrock'	H. helix 'Golden Envoy'
Hedera helix 'Goldfinger'	H. helix 'Goldstern'
Hedera helix 'Goldheart'	H. h. 'Oro di Bogliasco'
Hedera helix 'Gracilis'	H. hibernica 'Gracilis'
Hedera helix 'Green Feather'	H. helix 'Triton'
Hedera helix 'Green Finger'	H. helix 'Tres Coupe'
Hedera helix 'Green Spear'	H. helix 'Spear Point'
Hedera helix 'Hahn's Green Ripple'	H. helix 'Green Ripple'
Hedera helix 'Hahn's Self-Branching'	H. helix 'Pittsburgh'
Hedera helix 'Hamilton'	H. hibernica 'Hamilton'
Hedera helix 'Harry Wood'	H. helix 'Modern Times'
Hedera helix 'Helvig'	H. helix 'White Knight'
Hedera helix 'Hibernica'	H. hibernica
Hedera helix 'Hispanica'	H. maderensis ssp iberica
Hedera helix 'Hite's Miniature'	H. h. 'Merion Beauty'
Hedera helix 'Holly'	H. h. 'Parsley Crested'
Hedera helix 'Ideal'	H. helix 'California'
Hedera helix 'Imp'	H. helix 'Brokamp'
Hedera helix 'Ingelise'	H. helix 'Sagittifolia Variegata'
Hedera helix 'Ingrid'	H. helix 'Harald'
Hedera helix 'Itsy Bitsy'	H. helix 'Pin Oak'
Hedera helix 'Jerusalem'	H. h. 'Schafer Three'
Hedera helix 'Jubilaum Goldherz'	H. helix 'Goldheart'
Hedera helix 'Jubilee Goldheart'	H. helix 'Goldheart'
Hedera helix 'Liz'	H. helix 'Eva'
Hedera helix 'Lucy Kay'	H. helix 'Lady Kay'
Hedera helix 'Maculata'	H. helix 'Minor Marmorata'
H. helix 'Marginata Elegantissima'	H. helix 'Tricolor'
Hedera helix 'Marginata Minor'	H. helix 'Cavendishii'
Hedera helix 'Marginata Rubra'	H. helix 'Tricolor'
Hedera helix 'Marmorata Minor'	H.h.'Minor Marmorata'
Hedera helix 'Marmorata'	H. helix 'Luzii'
Hedera helix 'Meagheri'	H. helix 'Green Feather'
Hedera helix 'Mini Green'	H. helix 'Ivalace'
Hedera helix 'Minima' -Hibb.	H. helix 'Donerailensis'
Hedera helix 'Minima' -M. Young	H. helix 'Congesta'
Hedera helix 'Minima' misapplied	H. helix 'Spetchley'
Hedera helix 'Miss Maroc'	H. h. 'Manda Fringette'
Hedera helix 'Oro di Bogliasco'	H. helix 'Goldheart'
Hedera helix 'Pallida'	H. hibernica 'Hibernica Variegata'
Hedera helix 'Parsley Crested'	H. hibernica 'Cristata'
Hedera helix 'Poetica Arborea'	H. helix ssp poetarum
Hedera helix 'Poetica'	H. helix f poetarum
Hedera helix 'Purpurea'	H. helix 'Atropurpurea'
Hedera helix 'Ray's Supreme'	H. helix 'Pittsburgh'
Hedera helix 'Rottingdean'	H. hib. 'Rottingdean'
Hedera helix 'Sagittifolia' -Hibb.	H. hib. 'Sagittifolia'
Hedera helix 'Sagittifolia' misapplied	H.h. 'Konigers Auslese'

Synonym	Current Name	Synonym	Current Name
Hedera helix 'Salt and Pepper'	H.h.'Minor Marmorata'	Helenium montanum	H. autumnale
Hedera helix 'Scutifolia'	H. helix 'Glymii'	Helenium parviflorum	H. autumnale
Hedera helix 'Silver Queen'	H. helix 'Tricolor'	Helenium Red and Gold	H. 'Rotgold'
Hedera helix 'Suzanne'	H. nepalensis v	Heleocharis intermedia	Eleocharis intermedia
	nepalensis 'Suzanne'	Helianthemum 'Everton Ruby'	H. 'Ben Ledi'
Hedera helix 'Tortuosa'	H. helix 'Glymii'	Helianthemum 'Fireball'	H. 'Mrs C. W. Earle'
Hedera helix 'Woodsii'	H. helix 'Modern Times'	Helianthemum 'Mrs Clay'	H. 'Fire Dragon'
Hedera helix ssp canariensis	H. canariensis -Willd.	Helianthemum 'Red Orient'	H. 'Supreme'
Hedera helix ssp hibernica	H. hibernica	Helianthemum 'Snow Queen'	H. 'The Bride'
Hedera helix ssp poetarum -Nyman	H. helix f poetarum	Helianthemum 'Wisley Pink'	H.'Rhodanthe Carneum'
Hedera helix v canariensis	H. canariensis -Willd.	Helianthemum 'Yellow Queen'	H. 'Golden Queen'
Hedera helix v chrysocarpa -DC.	H. nepalensis -K.Koch	Helianthemum algarvense	Halimium ocymoides
Hedera helix v chrysocarpa -Ten.	H. helix f poetarum	Helianthemum alpestre -(Jacq). DC.	H. oelandicum ssp alp.
Hedera helix v cinerea -Hibb.	H. nepalensis -K.Koch	H. alpestre serpyllifolium	H. nummularium ssp
Hedera helix v colchica -K.Koch	H. colchica		glabrum
Hedera helix v poetica -West.	H. helix f poetarum	Helianthemum alyssoides	Halimium alyssoides
Hedera helix v raegneriana -Nichols.	H. colchica	H. apenninum v rhodanthum	H. apenninum v roseum
Hedera helix v rhombea -Miq.	H. rhombea	Helianthemum atriplicifolium	Halimium atriplicifolium
Hedera hibernica 'Anne Marie'	H. helix 'Anne Marie'	Helianthemum chamaecistus -Mill.	H. nummularium
Hedera himalaica -Tobler	H. nepalensis -K.Koch	Helianthemum clusii	x Halimiocistus
Hedera japonica -W.Paul not Jung.	H. rhombea		'Ingwersenii'
H. pastuchovii -Troodos, Cyprus	H. cypria	Helianthemum formosum	Halimium lasianthum
Hedera poetarum -Bertol.	H. helix f poetarum		ssp formosum
Hedera quinquefolia -L.	Parthenocissus	Helianthemum glaucum -Pers.	H. croceum
	quinquefolia	Helianthemum globularifolium	Tuberaria globulariif.
Hedera regneriana -Hibb.	H. colchica	Helianthemum grandiflorum	H. nummularium ssp
Hedera rhombea 'Japonica'	H. rhombea		grandiflorum
Hedera tobleri -Nakai	H. rhombea	H. grandiflorum v glabrum	H. nummularium ssp
Hedychium coronarium v flavescens	H. flavescens		glabrum
Hedyotis caerulea	Houstonia caerulea	Helianthemum guttatum	Tuberaria guttata
Hedysarum canadense	Desmodium canadense	Helianthemum italicum -(L.) Pers.	H. oelandicum ssp ital.
Hedysarum caudatum	Desmodium caudatum	Helianthemum italicum ssp alpestre	H. oelandicum ssp alp.
Hedysarum incanum -Thunb.	Indigofera decora	Helianthemum lasianthum	Halimium lasianthum
Hedysarum incarnatum -Willd.	Indigofera decora	H. lasianthum ssp formosum	Halimium lasianthum
Hedysarum nudiflorum	Desmodium nudiflorum		ssp formosum
Hedysarum rotundifolium	Desmodium rotundifol.	H. nummularium v scopoli	H. nummularium ssp
Hedysarum sericeum	Lespedeza cuneata		tomentosum
Hedysarum tiliifolium -D.Don	Desmodium elegans	Helianthemum ocymoides	Halimium ocymoides
Heeria	Heterocentron	Helianthemum ovatum	H. nummularium ssp
Heimerliodendron	Pisonia		obscurum
Heimerliodendron brunonianum	Pisonia umbellifera	Helianthemum penicillatum	H. oelandicum ssp
Heimia salicifolia v grandiflora -Lindl.	H. salicifolia		italicum
Heleniastrum autumnale	Helenium autumnale	Helianthemum polifolium -Mill.	H. apenninum
Heleniastrum parviflorum	Helenium autumnale	Helianthemum rhodanthum -Dun.	H. apenninum v roseum
Helenium 'Gold Fox'	H. 'Goldfuchs'	H. rhodanthum v carneum -Dun.	H. apenninum v roseum
Helenium 'Gold Intoxication'	H. 'Goldrausch'	Helianthemum Rose Queen	H. 'Rosakonigin'
Helenium 'Mahogany'	H. 'Goldlackzwerg'	Helianthemum scabrosum	Halimium alyssoides
Helenium altissimum	H. autumnale	Helianthemum serpyllifolium	H. nummularium ssp
Helenium caniculatum	H. autumnale		glabrum
Helenium commutatum	H. autumnale	Helianthemum tomentosum	H. nummularium
Helenium Copper Spray	H. 'Kupfersprudel'	Helianthemum tuberaria	Tuberaria lignosa
Helenium Dark Beauty	H. 'Dunkelpracht'	Helianthemum vineale -Pers.	H. canum
Helenium Golden Youth	H. 'Goldene Jugend'	Helianthemum vulgare -Gaertn.	H. nummularium
Helenium grandiflorum -Nutt.	H. autumnale	Helianthemum vulgare v glabrum	H. nummularium ssp gl.
Helenium latifolium	H. autumnale	Helianthus 'Limelight'	H. 'Lemon Queen'

117

Synonym	Current Name	Synonym	Current Name
Helianthus alienus	H. giganteus	Helichrysum backhousei v kingii	Ozothamnus rodwayi v kingii
Helianthus aridus	H. annuus		
Helianthus borealis	H. giganteus	H. backhousei v oreophilus	Ozothamnus rodwayi
Helianthus cucumerifolius	H. debilis ssp cucumer.	Helichrysum baxteri	Chrysocephalus baxt.
Helianthus dalyi	H. maximiliani	Helichrysum bicolor	Xerochrysum bicolor
Helianthus decapetalus Morning Sun	H. 'Morgensonne'	Helichrysum bidwillii	Xerochrysum bidwillii
Helianthus instabilis	H. grosseserratus	Helichrysum blackallii	Xerochrysum blackallii
Helianthus jaegeri	H. annuus	Helichrysum blandowskianum	Argentipallium bland.
Helianthus lenticularis	H. annuus	H. blandowskianum v blandowsk.	Argentipallium bland.
Helianthus macrocarpus	H. annuus	H. blandowskianum v dichroon	Argentipallium bland.
Helianthus maximillianii	H. maximiliani	Helichrysum boormanii v boormanii	H. boormanii
Helianthus orgyalis	H. salicifolius	Helichrysum boormanii v gillivrayi	H. boormanii
Helianthus quinquenervis	Helianthella quinquen.	Helichrysum boormanii v tryonii	H. boormanii
Helianthus rigidus misapplied	H. x laetiflorus	Helichrysum boormanii v typicum	H. boormanii
Helianthus scaberrimus	H. x laetiflorus	Helichrysum bracteatum	Xerochrysum bracteatum
Helianthus sparsifolius	H. atrorubens		
Helianthus subcanescens	H. tuberosus	Helichrysum bracteatum v viscosum	Xerochrysum viscos.
Helianthus subtuberosus	H. giganteus	Helichrysum brevidecurrens	Ozothamnus tesselatus
Helianthus validus	H. giganteus	Helichrysum buftonii	Oz. costatifructus
Helichrysum 'Coco'	Xerochrysum bracteatum 'Coco'	Helichrysum cassinianum	Schoenia cassiniana
		Helichrysum cassinioides	Oz. cassinioides
Helichrysum 'County Park Silver'	Ozothamnus 'County Park Silver'	Helichrysum cassiope	Ozothamnus cassiope
		Helichrysum catadromum	Ozothamnus decurrens
Helichrysum 'Dargan Hill Monarch'	Xerochrysum bracte. 'Dargan Hill Monarch'	Helichrysum chrysanthum	Xerochrysum bracteatum
Helichrysum 'Elmstead'	H. stoechas 'White Barn'	Helichrysum coralloides	Ozothamnus corall.
		Helichrysum costatifructum	Ozothamnus costatifr.
Helichrysum 'Mo's Gold'	H. argyrophyllum	Helichrysum cuneifolium	Ozothamnus cuneifolius
Helichrysum 'Skynet'	Xerochrysum bracteatum 'Skynet'	Helichrysum davenportii	Lawrencella davenpor.
		Helichrysum dealbatum	Argentipallium dealbat.
Helichrysum acuminatum	Xerochrysum subundulatum	Helichrysum dendroideum	Ozothamnus ferruguneus
H. acuminatum v angustifolium	Xerochrysum palustre	Helichrysum diosmifolium	Ozothamnus diosmifol.
H. adenophorum v adenophorum	Xerochrysum adenop.	Helichrysum diosmifolium h. in part not (Vent.) Sweet	Ozothamn. thyrsoideus
Helichrysum adnatum	Ozothamnus adnatus		
Helichrysum adnatum v adnatum	Ozothamnus alpinus	Helichrysum diotophyllum	Ozothamnus diotophyll.
Helichrysum albicans	Leucochysum albicans	Helichrysum dockerii	Acanthocladium dock.
Helichrysum albicans v lanuginosum	Leucochysum albicans	Helichrysum drummondii	Rhodanthe chloro cephala ssp rosea
Helichrysum alpinum	Leucochysum albicans ssp alpinum		
		Helichrysum elatum v elatum	H. elatum
Helichrysum alveolatum -not DC.	H. splendidum	Helichrysum elatum v fraseri	H. elatum
H. ambiguum ssp vinaceum	Leiocarpa semicalva ssp vinacea	Helichrysum elatum v glutinosum	H. elatum
		Helichrysum elatum v lanuginosum	H. elatum
Helichrysum angustifolium	H. italicum	Helichrysum eremaeum	Chrysocephalum erem.
H. angustifolium -Cretan form	H. italicum ssp microphyllum	Helichrysum ericeteum -W.M.Curtis	Ozothamnus ericifolius
		Helichrysum ericeteum h.	Ozothamnus purpurascens -DC.
Helichrysum antennarium	Ozothamnus antennaria		
Helichrysum anthemoides	Rhodanthe anthem.	Helichrysum ericifolium h.	O. purpurascens -DC.
Helichrysum apiculatum	Chrysocephalus apicu.	Helichrysum ericoides	Dolichothrix ericoides
Helichrysum argophyllum	Ozothamnus argophyll.	Helichrysum eriocephalum	O. eriocephalus
Helichrysum asperum	Ozothamnus purpurascens	Helichrysum ferrugineum	O. ferrugineus
		H. ferrugineum v ferrugineum	Ozothamnus ferrugin.
Helichrysum ayersii	Schoenia ayersi	Helichrysum ferrugineum v gravesii	Oz. argophyllus
Helichrysum backhousei	Ozothamnus rodwayi	Helichrysum filifolium	Schoenia filifolia
H. backhousei v backhousei	Ozothamnus rodwayi	Helichrysum gatesii	Leiocarpa gilesii

118

Synonym	Current Name	Synonym	Current Name
Helichrysum glomeratum	H. aggregatum	Helichrysum ramosum	Ozothamnus ramosus
Helichrysum gracile	Ozothamnus ramosus	Helichrysum rigidulum	Waitzia suaveolens
Helichrysum grandiceps	Leucogenes grandiceps	Helichrysum rogersianum	Oz. rogersianus
Helichrysum gravesii	Oz. argophyllus	Helichrysum roseum	Rhodanthe chloro
Helichrysum grayi	Rhodanthe chloro		cephala ssp rosea
	cephala ssp rosea	Helichrysum roseum v davenportii	Lawrencella davenpor.
Helichrysum hookeri	Ozothamnus hookeri	Helichrysum roseum v patens	Lawrencella davenpor.
Helichrysum humboldtianum	Rhodanthe humboldt.	Helichrysum roseum v typicum	Lawrencella davenpor.
Helichrysum humile	Edmondia pinifolia	Helichrysum rosmarinifolium h. not (Labill.) Steud. ex Benth.	
	(unv)		Oz. thyrsoideus -DC.
Helichrysum incanum	Leucochrysum albicans	H. rosm. v purpurascens h.	Oz. rosmarinifolius
Helichrysum italicum 'Nanum'	H. microphyllum	Helichrysum rupesre h.	H. italicum
H. italicum ssp microphyllum	H. microphyllum	Helichrysum scutellifolium	Oz. scutellifolius
Helichrysum lanatum	H. thianschanicum	Helichrysum selaginoides	Oz. selaginoides
Helichrysum ledifolium -(DC.) Benth	Ozothamnus ledifolius	Helichrysum selago -(Hook.f.) Kirk	Ozothamnus selago
H. ledifolium ssp ericifolium	Ozothamnus ericifolius	Helichrysum semicalvum	Leiocarpa semicalva
H. ledifolium ssp purpurascens	Oz. purpurascens -DC.	Helichrysum semifertile	Schoenia ramosissima
Helichrysum leontopodium	Leucogenes leontopod.	H. semifertile v xanthoglossum	Schoenia ramosissima
Helichrysum leptolepis	Leiocarpa leptolepis	Helichrysum serotinum	H. italicum ssp serot.
Helichrysum lindleyi	Lawrencella rosea	Helichrysum serypllifolium	Plecostachys serpyll.
Helichrysum lucidum	Xerochr. bracteatum	Helichrysum sessile	H. sessilioides
Helichrysum lycopodioides	Oz. lycopodioides	Helichrysum siculum	H. stoechas ssp
Helichrysum macivorii	Schoenia macimorii		barrelieri
Helichrysum manglesii	Rhodanthe manglesii	Helichrysum spiceri	Argentipallium spiceri
Helichrysum marginatum misapplied	H. milfordiae	Helichrysum stipitatum	Leucochrysum stipit.
H. microphyllum misapplied	Plecostachys	Helichrysum stirlingii	Ozothamnus stirlingii
	serpyllifolia	Helichrysum subulifolium	Schoenia filifolia
Helichrysum molle	Leucochrysum molle	Helichrysum Sulphur Light	H. 'Schwefellicht'
Helichrysum niveum	Argentipallium niveum	Helichrysum tesselatum	Ozothamnus tesselatus
Helichrysum obcordatum v majus	Ozothamnus obcorda	H. thianschanicum Golden Baby	H. th. 'Goldkind'
	tus ssp major	Helichrysum thysoideum	Ozothamnus thyrsoid.
Helichrysum oblongifolium	Ozothamnus cuneifolius	Helichrysum trilineatum h. not DC.	H. splendidum
Helichrysum obovatum	Ozothamnus obovatus	Helichrysum tuckeri	Ozothamnus tuckeri
Helichrysum obovatum v longifolium	Ozothamnus obovatus	Helichrysum tumidum	Ozothamnus selago v
Helichrysum obtusifolium	Argentipallium obtusif.		tumidus
H. obtusifolium v obtusifolium	Argentipallium obtusif.	Helichrysum turbinatum	Schoenia filifolia ssp
H. obtusifolium v squamiger	Argentip. tephrodes		filifolia
H. obtusifolium v tephrodes	Argentip. tephrodes	Helichrysum vagans	Ozothamnus vagans
Helichrysum occidentale	Ozo. occidentalis	Helichrysum virgineum	H. sibthorpii
Helichrysum oldfieldii	Rhodanthe citrina	Helichrysum whitei	Ozothamnus whitei
Helichrysum panaerioides	Leiocarpa panaetioides	Helichrysum woodii	H. arwae
Helichrysum papillosum	Xerochrysum papillos.	Helicia scottiana	Xylomelum scottianum
Helichrysum petiolare 'Aureum'	H. petiolare 'Limelight'	Heliconia 'Guyana Red'	H. 'Bucky'
Helichrysum petiolatum	H. petiolare	Heliconia humilis	H. bihai
Helichrysum pholidotum	Xerochrysum pholidot.	Heliconia humilis h.	H. stricta 'Dwarf
Helichrysum pleurandroides	Ozothamnus ericifolius		Jamaican'
Helichrysum podolepidium	Anemocarpa podolepid.	Helicophyllum -Schott	Eminium
Helichrysum populifolium misapplied	H. hypoleucum	Heliophila longifolia	H. coronopifolia
Helichrysum pseudoturbinatum	Schoenia filifolia	Heliopsis Golden Plume	H. helianthoides v
Helichrysum pumilum v pumilum	H. pumilum		scabra 'Goldgefieder'
Helichrysum pumilum v spathulatum	H. pumilum	Heliopsis helianthoides 'Limelight'	Helianthus 'Lemon
Helichrysum purpurascens	Oz. purpurascens -DC.		Queen'
Helichrysum purpurascens h. in part not (DC.) W.M.Curtis		H. helianthoides v scabra Ballerina	Helianthus hel. v
	Oz. rosmarinifolius		sc. 'Spitzentanzerin'
Helichrysum ramosissimum	Schoenia ramosissima	H. hel. v scabra Golden Plume	Helianthus hel. v

Synonym	Current Name	Synonym	Current Name
	scabra 'Goldgefieder'	Helxine tatarica	Fagopyrum tataricum
H. hel. v scabra Goldgreenheart	Helianthus hel. v	Hemerocallis 'Brass Buckles'	H. 'Puddin'
	scabra 'Goldgrunherz'	Hemerocallis 'Golden Orchid'	H. 'Dubloon'
H. hel. v scabra Summer Sum	H. helianthoides v	H. 'Kwanso Flore Pleno Variegata'	H. fulva 'Variegated
	scabra 'Sommersonne'		Kwanso'
Heliopsis scabra	Helianthus hel. v	Hemerocallis 'Kwanso Flore Pleno'	H. f. 'Green Kwanso'
	scabra	Hemerocallis aurantiaca littorea	H. littorea
Heliosperma alpestris	Silene alpestris	Hemerocallis crocea	H. fulva
Heliotropium 'Dwarf marine'	H. 'Mini Marine'	Hemerocallis disticha	H. fulva
Heliotropium anchusifolium	H. amplexicaule	Hemerocallis flava	H. lilioasphodelus
Heliotropium corymbosum	H. arborescens	Hemerocallis serotina	H. thunbergii
Heliotropium peruvianum	H. arborescens	Hemerocallis vespertina	H. thunbergii
Helipterum	Syncarpha	Hemestheum thelypteris	Thelypteris palustris
Helipterum 'Paper Cascade'	Rhodanthe anthem	Hemicarpurus -Nees	Pinellia -Ten.
	oides 'Paper Cascade'	Hemigenia clotteniana	Prostanthera clotten.
Helipterum albicans	Leucochrysum albicans	Hemigraphis colorata	H. alternata
Helipterum anthemoides	Rhodanthe anthem.	Hemionitis japonica	Coniogramme japonica
Helipterum humboldtianum	Pteropogon humboldt.	Hepatica acuta	H. acutiloba
Helipterum manglesii	Rhodanthe manglesii	Hepatica anemonoides -Vest	H. nobilis
Helipterum roseum	Rhodanthe chloro	Hepatica angulosa	H. transsilvanica
	cephala ssp rosea	Hepatica asiatica	H. nobilis
Helleborine latifolia	Epipactis helleborine	Hepatica nobilis acuta	H. acutiloba
Helleborus abschasicus	H. orientalis ssp abs.	Hepatica nobilis acutiloba	H. acutiloba
Helleborus altifolius	H. niger -L.	Hepatica nobilis double pink	H. nobilis 'Rubra Plena'
H. argutifolius mottle-leaved	H. a. 'Pacific Frost'	Hepatica plena -Mill.	H. nobilis
Helleborus atrorubens misapplied	H. orientalis ssp	Hepatica triloba	H. nobilis
	abchasicus Early	Hepatica triloba v acuta	H. acutiloba
	Purple Group -Lamarck	Hepatica triloba v acutiloba	H. acutiloba
Helleborus bocconei ssp bocconei	H. multifidus ssp bocc.	Heptacodium jasminoides	H. miconioides
Helleborus colchicus	H. orientalis ssp	Heptapleurum	Schefflera
	abchasicus -Lam.	Heracleum antasiaticum	H. stevenii
Helleborus corsicus	H. argutifolius	Heracleum circassicum	H. mantegazzianum
Helleborus grandiflorus -Salis.	H. niger -L.	Heracleum giganteum	H. mantegazzianum
Helleborus hyemalis	Eranthis hyemalis	Heracleum graveolens	Anethum graveolens
Helleborus involucratus	Eranthis hyemalis	Heracleum grossheimii	H. mantegazzianum
Helleborus lividus ssp corsicus	H. argutifolius	Hermannia candicans	H. incana
Helleborus macrathus	H. niger -L.	Hermannia erodioides	H. depressa
Helleborus monanthos	Eranthis hyemalis	Hermannia verticillata	H. pinnata
Helleborus niger major	H. n. ssp macranthus	Herniaria ceretana	H. glabra -L.
Helleborus orientalis olympicus	H. or. ssp orientalis	Herniaria corrigioloides	H. glabra -L.
Helleborus pumilus	Coptis trifolia	Herniaria germanica	H. glabra -L.
H. torquatus Party Dress Group	H. Party Dress group	Hertia	Othonna
	hybrids	Hesperaloe whipplei	Yucca whipplei
Helleborus trifolius	Coptis trifolia	Hesperaloe yuccaefolia -Engelm.	H. parviflora
Helleborus x baueri	H. x sternii	Hesperantha buhrii	H. cucullata 'Rubra'
Helleborus x nigristern	H. x ericsmithii	Hesperantha coccinea	Schizostylis coccinea
Helonias dioica	Chamaelirium luteum	Hesperantha inflexa	H. vaginata
Heloniopsis breviscapa	H. orientalis v brevisc.	Hesperantha lutea	H. falcata
Heloniopsis grandiflora	H. orientalis v brevisc.	Hesperantha mossii	H. baurii
Heloniopsis japonica	H. orientalis	Hesperis elata	H. matronalis -L.
H. orientalis v yakusimensis	H. orientalis v kawanoi	Hesperis glabra	Matthiola incana
Helosciadium graveolens	Apium graveolens	Hesperis heterophylla	H. matronalis -L.
Helwingia rusciflora -Willd.	H. japonica	Hesperis hortensis	H. matronalis -L.
Helxine fagopyrum	Fagopyrum esculentum	Hesperis incana	Matthiola incana
Helxine soleirolii	Soleirolia soleirolii	Hesperis lutea	Sisymbrium luteum

Synonym	Current Name	Synonym	Current Name
Hesperis matronalis alba	H. m. v albiflora		moschatus
Hesperis oblongipetala	H. matronalis -L.	Hibiscus eetveldeanus	H. acetosella
Hesperis obtusa	H. matronalis -L.	Hibiscus esculentus	Abelmoschus esculent.
Hesperis pontica	H. matronalis -L.	Hibiscus hakeifolia	Alyogyne hakeifolia
Hesperis rupestris	Matthiola incana	Hibiscus huegelii	Alyogyne huegelii
Hesperis umbrosa	H. matronalis -L.	Hibiscus manihot	Abelmoschus manihot
Hesperis violaria	Matthiola incana	Hibiscus rosa-sinensis 'Dainty Pink'	H. r-sinensis 'Fantasia'
Hesperoscordum hyacinthinum	Triteleia hyacinthina	Hibiscus rosa-sinensis 'Full Moon'	H. rosa-sinensis 'Mrs.
Hesperoyucca	Yucca		James E. Hendry'
Hesperoyucca whipplei	Yucca whipplei -Torr.	Hibiscus rosa-sinensis 'La France'	H. r-sinensis 'Fantasia'
Heteroarisaema -Nakai	Arisaema -Mart.	H. rosa-sinensis 'Pink La France'	H. r-sinensis 'Fantasia'
Heterolobium -A.Peter	Gonatopus Heteromeles	Hibiscus rosa-sinensis 'Swan Lake'	H. r-s 'Dainty White'
	Photinia	H. rosa-sinensis 'White La France'	H. r.-s. 'Dainty White'
Heteromeles arbutifolia	H. salicifolia	Hibiscus simplex -L.	Firmiana simplex
Heterostalis -(Schott) Schott	Typhonium -Schott	Hibiscus syriacus 'Elegantissimus'	H. s. 'Lady Stanley'
Heterotheca mariana	Chrysopsis mariana	H. syriacus 'Meehanii' misapplied	H. syriacus 'Purpureus
Heterotropa	Asarum		Variegatus'
Heuchera 'Dennis Davidson'	H. 'Huntsman'	Hibiscus syriacus 'Variegatus'	H. syriacus 'Purpureus
Heuchera 'Greenfinch'	H. cylindrica		Variegatus'
	'Greenfinch'	Hibiscus syriacus Blue Bird	H. s. 'Oiseau Bleu'
Heuchera 'Monet'	H. sanguinea 'Monet'	Hicoria aquatica	Carya aquatica
Heuchera 'Ruffles'	H. micrantha 'Ruffles'	Hicoria carolinae-septentrionalis	Carya carolinae-
Heuchera 'Silver Streak'	x Heucherella 'Silver		septentrionalis
	Streak'	Hicoria cordiformis	Carya cordiformis
Heuchera 'Snow Storm'	H. sanguinea 'Snow	Hicoria laciniosa	Carya laciniosa
	Storm'	Hicoria ovata	Carya ovata
Heuchera Coral Bells	H. sanguinea	Hicoria sulcata	Carya laciniosa
Heuchera Feuerregen	H. 'Pluie de Feu'	Hicorius arkansana	Carya texana
Heuchera Firefly	H. 'Leuchtkafer'	Hicorius cordiformis	Carya cordiformis
Heuchera glauca	H. americana	Hicorius glabra	Carya glabra
Heuchera micans	H. rubescens	Hieracium aurantiacum	Pilosella aurantiaca
Heuchera pringlei	H. rubescens	Hieracium bombycinum	H. mixtum
Heuchera Rain of Fire	H. 'Pluie de Feu'	Hieracium brunneocroceum	Pilosella aurantiaca
Hexacentris mysorensis	Thunbergia mysorens.		ssp carpathicola
Hexastylis	Asarum	Hieracium maculatum	H. spilophaeum
Heyderia decurrens -(Torr.) K.Koch	Calocedrus decurrens	Hieracium pilosella	Pilosella officinarum
Heyderia macrolepis - (Kurz) Li	Calocedrus macrolepis	Hieracium praecox	H. glaucum
Hibbertia camforosma	H. fasciculata	Hieracium variegatum	Hypochaeris variegata
Hibbertia fasciculata v adunca	H. prostrata	Hieracium welwitschii	H. lanatum
Hibbertia fasciculata v glabrata	H. prostrata	Hieracium x stoloniflorum	Pilosella stoloniflora
Hibbertia fasciculata v prostrata	H. prostrata	Hierochloe borealis	H. odorata
Hibbertia fasciculata v pubigera	H. prostrata	Hippeastrum ackermannii	H. x acramannii
Hibbertia fasciculata v spiceri	H. prostrata	Hippeastrum advenum	Rhodophiala advena
Hibbertia holtzei	H. tasmannica	Hippeastrum bifidum	Rhodophiala bifida
Hibbertia kochii	H. diamesogeneos	Hippeastrum morelianum	H. aulicum
Hibbertia lineata v parviflora	H. diamesogeneos	Hippeastrum pratense	Rhodophiala pratensis
Hibbertia rhadinopoda	H. diamesogeneos	Hippeastrum procerum	Worsleya raineri
Hibbertia teretifolia	H. hemignosta	Hippeastrum roseum	Rhodophiala rosea
Hibbertia teretifolia v bisulcata	H. rupicola	Hippeastrum rutilum	H. striatum
Hibbertia teretifolia v hamata	H. hamata	Hippobroma	Laurentia
Hibbertia tetrandra	H. cuneiformis	Hippocastanum aesculus -Cav.	Aesculus
Hibbertia volubilis	H. scandens		hippocastanum
Hibiscus 'Red Shield'	H. acetosella	Hippocastanum vulgare -Gaertn.	Aes. hippocastanum
	'Coppertone'	Hippochaete scirpoides	Equisetum scirpoides
Hibiscus abelmoschus	Abelmoschus	Hippocrepis emerus	Coronilla emerus

Synonym	Current Name	Synonym	Current Name
Hippophae angustifolia	H. rhamnoides	Hosta 'Golden Circles'	H. 'Frances Williams'
Hippophae littoralis	H. rhamnoides	Hosta 'Golden Nakaiana'	H. 'Birchwood Parky's Gold'
Hippophae sibirica	H. rhamnoides		
Hippophae stourdziana	H. rhamnoides	Hosta 'Golden'	H. 'Birchwood Parky's Gold'
Hipposelinum levisticum	Levisticum officinale		
Hippuris fluviatilis	H. vulgaris -L.	Hosta 'Golden' (nakaiana)	H. 'Birchwood Parky's Gold'
Hippuris melanocarpa	H. vulgaris -L.		
Hippuris polyphylla	H. vulgaris -L.	Hosta 'Holstein'	H. 'Halcyon' (Tardiana)
Hisingera japonica	Xylosma japonica	Hosta 'Japan Boy'	H. 'Montreal'
Hisingera racemosa	Xylosma japonica	Hosta 'Japan Girl'	H. 'Mount Royal'
Hoheria lanceolata h.	H. sexstylosa v ovata	Hosta 'Kabitan'	H. sieboldii v sieboldii f kabitan
Hoheria lyallii v glabrata	H. glabrata		
Hoheria microphylla	H. angustifolia	Hosta 'Kifukurin' (kikutii)	H. 'Kifukurin Hyuga'
Hoheria ovata -Simpson & Thompson	H. sexstylosa -Col.	Hosta 'Marginata Alba' misapplied	H. 'Albomarginata'
Hoheria populnea v angustifolia	H. angustifolia -Raoul	Hosta 'Marginata Alba' misapplied	H. crispula
Hoheria populnea v lanceolata	H. sexstylosa	Hosta 'Mediovariegata' (undulata)	H. undulata v undulata
Hoheria populnea v lanceolata	H. sexstylosa -Col.	Hosta 'Minor' (ventricosa)	H. minor
Holcus bicolor	Sorghum bicolor	Hosta 'Mount Kirishima' (sieboldii)	H. 'Kirishima'
Holcus halepense	Sorghum halepense	Hosta 'Nana' (ventricosa)	H. minor
Holcus mollis 'Variegatus'	H. m. 'Albovariegatus'	H. 'Obscura Marginata' (fortunei)	H. fortunei v aureo marginata
Holcus sorghum	Sorghum bicolor		
Holodiscus discolor v dumosus	H. dumosus	Hosta 'Opipara'	H. opipara
Homaid -Adans.	Biarum -Schott	Hosta 'Phyllis Campbell' (fortunei)	H. 'Sharmon' (fortunei)
Homaida -Adans.	Biarum -Schott	Hosta 'Picta' (fortunei)	H. fortunei v albopicta
Homalocenchrus oryzoides	Leersia oryzoides	Hosta 'Robusta' (fortunei)	H. sieboldiana v eleg.
Homalocephala texensis	Echinocactus texensis	Hosta 'Rohdeifolia'	H. rohdeifolia
Homalosorus pycnocarpos	Diplazium pycnocarpon	Hosta 'Sazanami' (crispula)	H. crispula
Homeria breyniana	H. collina	Hosta 'Silver Crown'	H. 'Albomarginata'
Homeria breyniana v aurantiaca	H. flaccida	Hosta 'Thomas Hogg'	H. undulata v albomarginata
Homeria collina v aurantiaca	H. flaccida		
Homoglossum	Gladiolus	Hosta 'Tokudama Aureonebulosa'	H. tokudama f aureone.
Homoioceltis aspera -(Thunb.) Blume	Aphananthe aspera	Hosta 'Tokudama Flavocircinalis'	H. tokudama f flavoc.
Hookera coronaria	Brodiaea coronaria	Hosta 'Tokudama'	H. tokudama
Hoorebekia chiloensis -Cornelissen	Grindelia chiloensis	Hosta 'Undulata Albomarginata'	H. undulata v albomar.
Hortensia opuloides -Lam.	H. macrophylla	Hosta 'Undulata Erromena'	H.undulata v erromena
Hosta 'Alba' (sieboldiana)	H. 'Elegans Alba' (sieb.)	Hosta 'Undulata Univittata'	H. undulata v univittata
H. 'Argentea Variegata' (undulata)	H. undulata v undulata	Hosta 'Undulata'	H. undulata v undulata
Hosta 'Aurea' (sieboldii)	H. sieboldii f subcrocea	Hosta 'Variegata' (gracillima)	H. 'Vera Verde'
Hosta 'Aureoalba' (fortunei)	H. 'Spinners'	Hosta 'Variegata' (tokudama)	H. tokudama f aureone.
Hosta 'Aureomaculata' (fortunei)	H. fortunei v albopicta	Hosta 'Variegata' (undulata)	H. undulata v undulata
Hosta 'Aureostriata' (tardiva)	H. 'Inaho'	Hosta 'Variegata' (ventricosa)	H. 'Aureomarginata' (v)
Hosta 'Blue Angel' misapplied	H. sieboldiana v elegans	Hosta 'Variegated' (fluctuans)	H. 'Sagae'
		Hosta 'Ventricosa Aureomaculata'	H. ventricosa v aureo.
Hosta 'Carrie Ann'	H. 'Carrie'	Hosta 'Ventricosa Variegata'	H. 'Aureomarginata' (v)
Hosta 'Cream Delight' (undulata)	H. undulata v undulata	Hosta 'Ventricosa'	H. ventricosa
Hosta 'Cream Edge'	H. 'Fisher Cream Edge' (fortunei)	Hosta 'Verte' (sieboldii)	H. sieboldii f spathulata
		H. 'Viridis Marginata' (Tardiana Gr.)	H. sieboldii v sieboldii f kabitan
Hosta 'Crispula'	H. crispula		
Hosta 'Decorata'	H. decorata	Hosta 'Wayside Perfection'	H. 'Royal Standard'
Hosta 'Eldorado'	H. 'Frances Williams' (sieboldiana)	Hosta 'Windsor Gold'	H. 'Nancy Lindsay' (for)
		Hosta 'Wogon Giboshi'	H. 'Wogon' (sieboldii)
Hosta 'Elegans'	H. sieboldiana v eleg.	Hosta 'Wogon Gold'	H. 'Wogon' (sieboldii)
Hosta 'Fortis'	H.undulata v erromena	Hosta 'Yellow Edge' (fortunei)	H. fortunei v aureom.
Hosta 'Gigantea' (sieboldiana)	H. elata	Hosta 'Yellow Edge' (sieboldiana)	H. 'Frances Williams'
Hosta 'Golden Age'	H. 'Gold Haze'	Hosta albomarginata	H. sieboldii 'Paxton's

Synonym	Current Name
	Original'
Hosta albomarginata alba	H. sieboldii v alba
Hosta angustifolia	H. longissima
Hosta aureafolia	H. 'Starker Yellow Leaf'
Hosta bella	H. fortunei v obscura
Hosta caerulea	H. 'Caerulea' (ventric)
Hosta caerulea minor albiflora	H. sieboldii v alba
Hosta caput-avis	H. kikutii v caput-avis
Hosta fortunei f aurea	H. fortunei v albopicta f aurea
Hosta fortunei v gigantea	H. montana
H. fortunei v hyacinthina variegated	H. 'Crowned Imperial'
Hosta glauca	H. sieboldiana v eleg.
Hosta helonioides f albopicta	H. rohdeifolia
Hosta japonica	H. lancifolia
Hosta japonica fortis	H.undulata v erromena
Hosta japonica longifolia	H. longissima
Hosta japonica undulata	H. undulata
Hosta lancifolia fortis	H.undulata v erromena
Hosta lancifolia longifolia	H. longissima
Hosta lancifolia tardiflora	H. tardiflora
Hosta lancifolia v fortis	H. lancifolia
Hosta longipes h.	H. rectifolia
Hosta minor f alba h.	H. sieboldii v alba
Hosta nigrescens elatior	H. 'Krossa Regal'
Hosta plantaginea stenantha	H. plantaginea
Hosta plantaginea v grandiflora	H. pl. v japonica
Hosta sieboldiana 'Elegans'	H. sieboldii v elegans
Hosta sieboldiana 'Frances Williams'	H. 'Frances Williams'
Hosta sieboldiana glauca	H. tokudama
Hosta sieboldiana v thunbergiana	H. sieboldii f spathulata
Hosta sparsa	H. tardiflora
Hosta tosana caput-avis	H. kikutii v caput-avis
Hosta venusta yakusimensis	H. kikutii v yakusimen.
Hoteia chinensis	Astilbe chinensis
Houstonia caerulea h.	H. michauxii
Houstonia serpyllifolia	H. michauxii
Houttuynia californica	Anemopsis californica
Houttuynia cordata 'Plena'	H. cordata 'Flore Pleno'
Houttuynia cordata 'Terry Clarke'	H. cordata 'Boo-Boo'
Houttuynia cordata 'Tricolor'	H. cordata 'Chameleon'
Hovea beckeri	H. purpurea
Hovea celsii	H. elliptica
Hovea celsii	H. elliptica
Hovea crispa	H. trisperma
Hovea grandiflora	H. trisperma
Hovea heterophylla f decipiens	H. heterophylla
Hovea ilicifolia	H. chorizemifolia
Hovea leiocarpa	H. longipes
Hovea longifolia v aspera	H. asperifolia
Hovea longifolia v lanceolata	H. purpurea
Hovea longifolia v longifolia	H. purpurea
Hovea longifolia v montana	H. montana
Hovea longifolia v pannosa	H. ramulosa

Synonym	Current Name
Hovea longifolia v planifolia	H. planifolia
Hovea manglesii	H. trisperma
Hovea mucronata	H. apiculata
Hovea pungens v major	H. pungens
Hovea pungens v ulicina	H. pungens
Hovea purpurea v montana	H. montana
Hovea racemulosa	H. longifolia
Hovea rosmarinifolia v villosa	H. pannosa
Hovea splendens	H. trisperma
Hovea stricta v major	H. stricta
Hovea stricta v stricta	H. stricta
Hovea trisperma v crispa	H. trisperma
Hovea trisperma v grandiflora	H. trisperma
Hovea ulicina	H. pungens
Hovea villosa	H. pannosa
Hovenia acerba -Lindl.	H. dulcis -Thunb.
Howeia	Howea
Hoya bella	H. lanceolata ssp bella
Hoya darwinii h.	H. australis
Hoya fuscomarginata	H. pottsii
Hoya nepalensis	H. polyneura
Huernia primulina	H. thuretii v primulina
Hugueninia alpina	H. tanacetifolia
Humata pyxidata	Davallia solida v pyxid.
Humbertina -Buch.	Arophyton -Jum.
Humea africanum	Helichrysum africanum
Humea elegans	Calomeria amaranthoides
Humea epapposa	Helichrysum epappos.
Humea infausta	Helichrysum infaustum
Humea involucratum	Erymophyllum ramosum
Humea kempei	Ozothamnus kempei
Humea lawrencella	Lawrencella rosea
Humea lawrencella v davenportii	Lawrencella davenpor.
Humulus scandens	H. japonicus
Huntleya burtii	H. meleagris
Hutchinsia	Pritzelago
Hutchinsia auerswaldii	Thlaspi alpina
Hutchinsia rotundifolia	Thlaspi cepaeifolium ssp rotundifolius
Hyacinthella dalmatica	H. pallens
Hyacinthoides hispanica Donau	H. hispanica 'Danube'
Hyacinthus amethystinus	Brimeura amethystina
Hyacinthus azureus	Muscari azureum
Hyacinthus candicans	Galtonia candicans
Hyacinthus comosus 'Plumosus'	Muscari c. 'Plumosum'
Hyacinthus fastigiatus	Brimeura fastigiata
Hyacinthus orientalis 'Salmonetta'	H. o. 'Oranje Boven'
Hyacinthus orientalis Snow White	H. o. 'Sneeuwwitje'
Hyacinthus romanus	Bellevalia romana
Hydnostachyon -Liebm.	Spathiphyllum -Schott
Hydragonum calyculatum	Chamaedaphne calycul.
Hydrangea 'Blue Tit'	H. macrophylla 'Blaumeise'

Synonym	Current Name	Synonym	Current Name
Hydrangea 'Sterilis'	H. arborescens ssp discolor 'Sterilis'	Hydrangea macrophylla 'Variegata'	H. m. 'Maculata'
		Hydrangea macrophylla 'Vibraye'	H. m. 'Generale Vicomtesse de Vibraye'
Hydrangea acuminata -Sieb. & Zucc.	H. serrata		
Hydrangea altissima -Wall.	H. anomala -D.Don	H. macrophylla 'Vicomte de Vibraye'	H. m. 'Generale Vicomtesse de Vibraye'
H. anomala v cordifolia dwarf form	H. anomala ssp petiolaris v cordifolia	H. macrophylla 'White Swan'	H. m. 'Le Cygne'
Hydrangea arborescens v discolor	H. arb. ssp discolor	H. macrophylla 'White Wave'	H. m. 'Mariesii Grandiflora'
Hydrangea aspera 'Rosthornii'	H. aspera ssp robusta		
Hydrangea aspera 'Silver Slipper'	H. microphylla 'Ayesha'	Hydrangea macrophylla Alpen Glow	H. m. 'Alpengluhen'
Hydrangea aspera ssp robusta	H. longipes -Franch.	H. macrophylla Blue Butterfly	H. m. 'Blauling'
Hydrangea aspera v macrophylla	H. aspera ssp strigosa	H. macrophylla Blue Prince	H. m. 'Blauer Prinz'
Hydrangea aspera v strigosior	H. aspera -D.Don	Hydrangea macrophylla Bluebird	H. m. 'Blauling'
Hydrangea aspera v velutina -Rehd.	H. aspera -D.Don	Hydrangea macrophylla Dragonfly	H. macrophylla Dragonfly = 'Holbella'
Hydrangea bretschneideri	H. heteromalla Bretschneideri Group	Hydrangea macrophylla f normalis	H. m. v normalis -Wils.
Hydrangea chinensis -Maxim.	H. scandens ssp chinensis	Hydrangea macrophylla Firelight	H. m. 'Leuchtfeuer'
		Hydrangea macrophylla Fireworks	H. macrophylla 'Hanabi'
Hydrangea cinerea -Small	H. arborescens ssp discolor	H. macrophylla Fireworks Blue	H. m. 'Jogasaki'
		H. macrophylla Fireworks Pink	H. m. 'Jogasaki'
Hydrangea cinerea 'Sterilis'	H. arborescens ssp discolor 'Sterilis'	H. macrophylla Fireworks White	H. macrophylla 'Hanabi'
		H. macrophylla Gentian Dome	H. m. 'Enziandom'
Hydrangea davidii -Franch.	H. scandens ssp chinensis	H. macrophylla Lady Katsuko	H. m. 'Frau Katsuko'
		Hydrangea macrophylla Morning Red	H. m. 'Morgenrot'
Hydrangea dumicola -W.W.Sm.	H. heteromalla -D.Don	Hydrangea macrophylla Nightingale	H. m. 'Nachtigall'
Hydrangea fulvescens -Rehd.	H. aspera -D.Don	Hydrangea macrophylla Pheasant	H. macrophylla 'Fasan'
Hydrangea hortensia -Sieb.	H. macrophylla	Hydrangea macrophylla Pigeon	H. macrophylla 'Taube'
Hydrangea hortensis -Sm.	H. macrophylla	Hydrangea macrophylla Pink Elf	H. macrophylla 'Pia'
Hydrangea hypoglauca -Rehd.	H. heteromalla -D.Don	H. macrophylla Queen Wilhelmina	H. macrophylla 'Koningin Wilhelmina'
Hydrangea integerrima	H. serratifolia		
H. japonica -Sieb. at least in part	H. serrata	Hydrangea macrophylla Redbreast	H. m. 'Rotkehlchen'
Hydrangea kawakamii -Hayata	H. aspera -D.Don	H. macrophylla Sister Therese	H. m. 'Soeur Therese'
Hydrangea khasiana	H. heteromalla -D.Don	Hydrangea macrophylla ssp serrata -(Thunb.) Mak. in part	H. serrata
Hydrangea longifolia -Hayata	H. involucrata -Sieb.		
Hydrangea macrophylla 'Blue Sky'	H. m. 'Blaumeise'	Hydrangea macrophylla Teller Weiss	H. macrophylla 'Libelle'
Hydrangea macrophylla 'Blue Tit'	H. m. 'Blaumeise'	Hydrangea macrophylla v acuminata	H. serrata 'Bluebird'
Hydrangea macrophylla 'Blue Wave'	H. macrophylla 'Mariesii Perfecta'	Hydrangea macrophylla v thunbergii	H. serrata v thunbergii
		Hydrangea macrophylla Vulcan	H. m. 'Vulcain'
H. macrophylla 'Bluebird' misapplied	H. serrata 'Bluebird'	Hydrangea mandarinorum -Diels	H. heteromalla -D.Don
Hydrangea macrophylla 'Cordata'	H. arborescens	Hydrangea maritima -Howarth-Booth	H. mac v normalis
H. macrophylla 'Geoffrey Chadbund'	H. macrophylla 'Mowe'	Hydrangea maritima 'Sea Foam'	H. macrophylla 'Sea Foam'
H. macrophylla 'James Grant'	H. m. 'Grant's Choice'		
Hydrangea macrophylla 'Lady Fujiyo'	H. m. 'Frau Fujiyo'	Hydrangea nivea -Michx.	H. arborescens ssp radiata
H. macrophylla 'Lady Mariko'	H. m. 'Frau Mariko'		
H. macrophylla 'Lady Nobuko'	H. m. 'Frau Nabuko'	H. opuloides -(Lam.) h. ex Savi	H. macrophylla
H. macrophylla 'Lady Taiko Blue'	H. m. 'Taiko' blue	Hydrangea petiolaris -Sieb. & Zucc.	H. anomala ssp petiol.
H. macrophylla 'Lady Taiko Pink'	H. m. 'Taiko' pink	Hydrangea platanifolia h.	H. quercifolia -Bartr.
Hydrangea macrophylla 'Lilacina'	H. macrophylla 'Mariesii Lilacina'	Hydrangea quercifolia 'Flore Pleno'	H. q. 'Snow Flake'
		Hydrangea radiata -Walt.	H. arborescens ssp r.
H. macrophylla 'Mandschurica'	H. macrophylla 'Nigra'	Hydrangea rehderana -Schneid.	H. aspera -D.Don
H. macrophylla 'Mariesii Alba'	H. m. 'White Wave'	Hydrangea robusta h.	H. heteromalla 'Snowcap'
H.macrophylla 'Mariesii Grandiflora'	H. m. 'White Wave'		
Hydrangea macrophylla 'Mini Hornli'	H. macrophylla 'Hornli'	Hydrangea sargentiana -Rehd.	H. aspera ssp sargent.
Hydrangea macrophylla 'Pax'	H. m. 'Nymphe'	Hydrangea scandens -Maxim.	H. anomala ssp petiolaris
Hydrangea macrophylla 'Preziosa'	H. 'Preziosa'		
H. macrophylla 'Teller Variegated'	H. m. 'Tricolor'	H scandens -Poepp.not Ser. Maxim.	H. serratifolia

Synonym	Current Name
Hydrangea serrata 'Acuminata'	H. serrata 'Bluebird'
Hydrangea serrata 'Belle Deckle'	H. ser. 'Blue Deckle'
Hydrangea serrata 'Preziosa'	H. 'Preziosa'
Hydrangea sinensis	H. scandens ssp chinensis
Hydrangea strigosa -Rehd.	H. aspera ssp strigosa
Hydrangea strigosa v macrophylla	H. aspera ssp strigosa
Hydrangea tiliifolia	H. anomala ssp petiol.
Hydrangea umbellata	H. scandens ssp chin.
Hydrangea villosa	H. aspera Villosa Gr.
Hydrangea virens -(Thunb.) Sieb.	H. scandens -(L.f.) Ser.
Hydrangea xanthoneura -Diels.	H. heteromalla f xant.
Hydrilla verticillata	Elodea nuttallii
Hydrocleis	Hydrocleys
Hydrocleys commersonii	H. nymphoides
Hydrocotyle asiatica	Centella asiatica
Hydrocotyle ranunculoides	H. americana
Hydroglossum japonicum	Lygodium japonicum
Hydrophyllum atranthum	H. virginianum
Hydrosme -Schott	Amorphophallus - Blume
Hylotelephium	Sedum
Hylotelephium roseum	Sedum alboroseum
Hylotelephium sieboldii 'Variegatum'	Sedum spathulifolium 'Cape Blanco'
Hymenanthera	Melicytus
Hymenanthera angustifolia -DC.	Melicytus angustifolius
Hymenanthera crassifolia -Hook. f.	Melicytus crassifolius
Hymenanthera dentata -DC.	Melicytus angustifolius
Hymenanthera dentata v alpina	Melicytus alpinus
Hymenanthera dent. v angustifolia	Melicytus angustifolius
Hymenanthera obovata -Kirk	Melicytus obovatus
Hymenocallis calathina	H. narcissiflora
Hymenocallis occidentalis	H. caroliniana
Hymenolepis parviflora	Athanasia parviflora
Hymenoxys acaulis	Tetraneuris acaulis
Hymenoxys acaulis v caespitosa	Tet. acaulis v caespit.
Hymenoxys grandiflora	Tetraneuris grandifl.
Hypericum 'Citrinum'	H. olympicum f uniflorum 'Citrinum'
Hypericum 'Elstead'	H. x inodorum 'Elstead'
Hypericum 'Gold Penny'	H. androsaemum 'Dart's Golden Penny'
Hypericum 'Hidcote Gold'	H. 'Hidcote'
Hypericum 'Mrs Brabazon'	H. androsaemum 'Gladys Brabazon'
Hypericum 'Sungold'	H. kouytchense
Hypericum 'Variegatum'	H. x moserianum 'Tricolor'
H. androsaemum 'Orange Flair'	H. x inodorum 'Orange Flair'
H. androsaemum 'Variegatum'	H. androsaemum 'Gladys Brabazon'
Hypericum angustifolium -Lowe	H. perforatum -L.
Hypericum aureum -Batr. not Lour.	H. frondosum
Hypericum bacciferum	H. androsaemum
Hypericum bacciforme	H. androsaemum
Hypericum beanii 'Gold Cup'	H. x cyathiflorum 'Gold Cup'
Hypericum calcaratum h.	H. forrestii
Hypericum cernuum -D.Don	H. oblongifolium - Choisy
Hypericum chinense -L.	H. monogynum -L.
Hypericum commutatum	H. perforatum -L.
Hypericum cuneatum	H. pallens
Hypericum dimoniei -Velen.	H. olympicum -L.
Hypericum dyeri h. not Rehd.	H. stellatum -N.Robson
Hypericum elatum -Ait.	H. x inodorum -Mill.
H. empetrifolium 'Prostatum'	H. empetrifolium ssp tortuosum
H. empetrifolium v prostatum	H. em. ssp tortuosum
Hm empetrifolium v tortuosum	H. em. ssp tortuosum
Hypericum floridum	H. androsaemum
Hypericum foliosissimum	H. perforatum -L.
Hypericum fragile h.	H. olympicum f minus
Hypericum garrettii - Craib	H. hookeranum
Hypericum grandiflorum	H. kouytchense
Hypericum hircinum v minor -Lav.	H. hircinum ssp minus
Hypericum hircinum v pumilum	H. hircinum ssp minus
Hypericum hookeranum h. in part	H. lobbii -N.Robson
Hypericum inodorum -Willd. not Mill.	H. xylosteifolium
H. kouytchense -sensu Rehd.not Levl.	H. wilsonii -N.Robson
Hypericum kouytchense h. not Levl.	H. acmosepalum
Hypericum lasianthum -L.	Gordonia lasianthus
Hypericum leschenaultii misapplied	H. 'Rowallane'
Hypericum leschenaultii misapplied	H. addingtonii
Hypericum lineolatum	H. perforatum -L.
H. lysimachioides h.not Wall.	H. stellatum -N.Robson
Hypericum macrocalyx	H. olympicum -L.
Hypericum multiflorum h.	H. x inodorum -Mill.
Hypericum nachitschevanicum	H. perforatum -L.
H. oblongifolium -sensu Hook. f.	H. lobbii -N.Robson
H. oblong. -sensu Wall not Choisy	H. hookeranum
Hypericum oblongifolium h.	H. acmosepalum
H. olympicum 'Grandiflorum'	H. o. f uniflorum
Hypericum patulum 'Hidcote'	H. 'Hidcote'
Hypericum patulum 'Sungold'	H. kouytchense
Hypericum patulum f forrestii	H. forrestii
Hypericum patulum v forrestii	H. forrestii
Hypericum patulum v forrestii h. in part not Chittenden H. kouytchense -Levl.	
H. patulum v grandiflorum h.	H. kouytchense -Levl.
Hypericum patulum v henryi -Rehd.	H. pseudohenryi
Hypericum patulum v henryi	H. beanii -N.Robson
H. patulum v oblongifolium -Koehne	H. hookeranum
H. patulum v uralum -(D.Don)Koehne	H. uralum -D.Don
Hypericum penduliflorum h.	H. kouytchense -Levl.
Hypericum persistens -F.Schneider	H. x inodorum -Mill.
Hypericum plasonii	H. perforatum -L.
Hypericum polyphyllum	H. olympicum f minus

Synonym	Current Name	Synonym	Current Name
Hypericum polyphyllum 'Citrinum'	H. olympicum f minus 'Sulphureum'	Hyssopus recticaulis	H. officinalis
		Hyssopus ruber	H. officinalis
H. polyphyllum 'Grandiflorum'	H. olymp. f uniflorum	Hyssopus schleicheri	H. officinalis
Hypericum polyphyllum 'Sulphureum'	H. olympicum f minus 'Sulphureum'	Hyssopus vulgaris	H. officinalis
		Iberis amoena	I. umbellata
Hypericum polyphyllum 'Variegatum'	H. olympicum f minus 'Variegatum'	Iberis bursa-pastoris	Capsella bursa-past.
H. pseudopetiolatum v yakusimense	H. kiusianum v yakusimense	Iberis campestris	Lepidium campestre
		Iberis candolleana	I. pruitii Candolleana Group
Hypericum quadrangulum -Linnaeus	H. tetrapterum	Iberis commutata	I. sempervirens
Hypericum reptans h.	H. olympicum f minus	Iberis corymbosa	I. umbellata
Hypericum rhodoppeum -Frivaldsky	H. cerastioides ssp mueselianum	Iberis hortensis	I. umbellata
		Iberis jordanii	I. pruitii
Hypericum rogersii	H. 'Rowallane'	Iberis pulchra	I. umbellata
Hypericum splendens -Sm.	H. frondosum	Iberis pygmaea	I. sempervirens 'Pygmaea'
Hypericum stenophyllum	H. perforatum -L.		
Hypericum triflorum -Bl.	H. leschenaultii -Choisy	Iberis roseopurpurea	I. umbellata
Hypericum veronense	H. perforatum -L.	Iberis saxatilis candolleana	I. pruitii Candolleana Group
Hypericum vulgare	H. perforatum -L.		
H. x inodorum 'Albury Purple'	H. androsaceum 'Albury Purple'	Iberis sempervirens Little Gem	I. sempervirens 'Weisser Zwerg'
H. x moserianum 'Variegatum'	H. x mos. 'Tricolor'	Iberis sempervirens Schneeflocke	I. s. 'Snowflake'
Hypericum x penduliflorum h.	H. kouytchense -Levl.	Iberis sempervirens Snowdrift	I. sempervirens 'Zwergschneeflocke'
Hypericum yakusimense	H. kiusianum v yakus.		
Hypocyrta	Nematanthus	Iberis vermiculata -Willd.	I. saxatilis -L.
Hypocyrta radicans	Nematanth. gregarius	Ibidium cernuum	Spiranthes cernua
Hypocyrta strigillosa	Nemat. strigillosus	Ictodes -Big.	Symplocarpus
Hypoestes sanguinolenta misapplied	H. phyllostachya	Idria columnaris	Fouquieria columnaris
Hypopeltis aculeata	Polystichum aculeatum	Ilex 'Dazzler'	I. cornuta 'Dazzler'
Hypopeltis hastulata	Polystichum setiferum	Ilex 'Pyramidalis'	I. aq. 'Pyramidalis'
Hypopeltis lonchitis	Polystichum lonchitis	Ilex altaclarensis	I. x altaclerensis
Hypopetis prolifera	Polystichum proliferum	I. aquifolium 'Argentea Mediopicta'	I. aq. 'Silver Milkmaid'
Hypoxis parvula	x Rhodohypoxis baurii x Rhodoxis hybrida	Ilex aquifolium 'Argentea Pendula'	I. aquifolium 'Argentea Marginata Pendula'
Hypoxis rooperi	H. hemerocallidea	Ilex aquifolium 'Argentea Regina'	I. aq. 'Silver Queen'
Hypoxis stellata	H. capensis	Ilex aquifolium 'Argentea Variegata'	I. aquifolium 'Argentea Marginata'
Hypoxis x Rhodohypoxis	x Rhodoxis		
Hypsela longiflora	H. reniformis	I. aq. 'Aurea Marginata Ovata'	I. aq. 'Ovata Aurea'
Hyssopus alopecuroides	H. officinalis -L.	Ilex aquifolium 'Aurea Ovata'	I. aq. 'Ovata Aurea'
Hyssopus altissimus	H. officinalis -L.	Ilex aquifolium 'Aurea Regina'	I. aq. 'Golden Queen'
Hyssopus anethiodorus	Agastache foeniculum	I. aq. 'Aureovariegata Pendula'	I. aquifolium 'Weeping Golden Milkmaid'
Hyssopus angustifolius	H. officinalis -L.		
Hyssopus aristatus	H. officinalis ssp arist.	Ilex aquifolium 'Bicolor'	I. aq. 'Aurifodina'
Hyssopus beugesiacus	H. officinalis	Ilex aquifolium 'Calamistrata'	I. aquifolium 'Crispa'
Hyssopus canescens	H. officinalis ssp can.	Ilex aquifolium 'Clouded Gold'	I. aq. 'Flavescens'
Hyssopus caucasicus	H. officinalis	I.aquifolium 'Crispa Aureomaculata'	I. aquifolium 'Crispa Aureopicta'
Hyssopus cinerascens	H. officinalis		
Hyssopus decumbens	H. officinalis	I. aquifolium 'Fructu Luteo' -Dallim.	I. aq. 'Bacciflava'
Hyssopus fischeri	H. officinalis	I.aq. 'Heterophylla Aureomarginata'	I. aq. 'Pyramidalis Aureomarginata'
Hyssopus montanus	H. officinalis		
Hyssopus myrtifolius	H. officinalis	Ilex aquifolium 'Latispina Major'	I. aq. 'Monstrosa'
H. officinalis ssp angustifolius	H. officinalis	Ilex aquifolium 'Latispina Minor'	I. aquifolium 'Hastata'
Hyssopus orientalis	H. officinalis	Ilex aquifolium 'Laurifolia Variegata'	I. aq. 'Laurifolia Aurea'
Hyssopus polycladus	H. officinalis	Ilex aquifolium 'Muricata'	I. aq. 'Aurifodina'
Hyssopus pubescens	H. officinalis	I. aq. 'Myrtifolia Aureovariegata'	I. aquifolium 'Myrtifolia

Synonym	Current Name	Synonym	Current Name
	Aurea Maculata'	Ilex nobilis -Gumbleton	I. kingiana -Cockerell
Ilex aquifolium 'N.F.Barnes'	I. x altaclerensis	Ilex nummarioides -Franch. & Sav.	I. crenata 'Mariesii'
	'N.F.Barnes'	Ilex oblata -(W.E.Evans) Comber	I. nothofagifolia
Ilex aquifolium 'Pendula Mediopicta'	I. aquifolium 'Weeping	Ilex pedunculosa f continentalis	I. pedunculosa
	Golden Milkmaid'	Ilex perado 'Aurea'	I. x altaclerensis
Ilex aquifolium 'Polycarpa Laevigata'	I. aq. 'J.C. van Tol'		'Belgica Aurea'
Ilex aquifolium 'Polycarpa'	I. aq. 'J.C. van Tol'	Ilex perado h. not Ait.	I. x altaclerensis
Ilex aquifolium 'Silver King'	I. aq. 'Silver Queen'	Ilex perado latifolia	I. per. ssp platyphylla
Ilex aquifolium 'Silver Sentinel'	I. x altaclerensis	Ilex perado v maderensis	I. perado h.
	'Belgica Aurea'	Ilex perado v platyphylla	I. per. ssp platyphylla
Ilex aquifolium 'Tortuosa'	I. aquifolium 'Crispa'	Ilex pernyi v veitchii	I. bioritsensis
Ilex aquifolium 'W.J.Bean'	I. x altaclerensis	Ilex platyphylla -Webb & Berth	I. per. ssp platyphylla
	'W.J.Bean'	Ilex poneantha	I. kusanoi
Ilex aquifolium 'Waterer's Gold'	I. aq. 'Watereriana'	Ilex prinoides -Ait.	I. decidua -Walt.
Ilex aquifolium Moonlight holly	I. aq. 'Flavescens'	Ilex radicans -Nakai	I. crenata v paludosa
Ilex aquifolium v altaclerense -Loud.	I. x altaclerensis	Ilex radicans v paludosa -Nakai	I. crenata v paludosa
Ilex aquifolium v balearica h.	I. x altacl. 'Balearica'	Ilex sieboldii -Miq.	I. serrata
Ilex aquifolium v platyphylla -Dallim.	I. perado ssp platyp.	Ilex verticillata 'Compacta'	I. verticillata 'Nana'
Ilex balearica h.	I. x altacl. 'Balearica'	Ilex verticillata 'Red Sprite'	I. verticillata 'Nana'
Ilex bioritensis v ciliospinosa	I. ciliospina -Loes.	I. x altacl. 'Maderensis Variegata'	I. aquifolium
Ilex bronxensis	I. verticillata		'Maderensis Variegata'
Ilex caroliniana -Mill.	I. cassine -L.	Ilex x altaclerensis 'Nobilis'	I. x altacl. 'Hodginsii'
Ilex cassine -Walt. not L.	I. myrtifolia -Walt.	Ilex x altaclerensis 'Shepherdii'	I. x altacl. 'Hodginsii'
Ilex cassine v myrtifolia	I. vomitoria -Ait.	Ilex x altaclerensis 'Silver Sentinel'	I. x altaclerensis
Ilex castaneifolia h.	I. x koehneana		'Belgica Aurea'
	'Chestnut Leaf'	Ilex x topelii	I. x attenuata
Ilex chinensis misapplied	I. purpurea	Ilex yunnanensis f gentilis -Loes.	I. yunnanensis
Ilex corallina v pubescens -S.Y.Hu	I. corallina	Iliamna	Sphaeralcea
Ilex crenata 'Aureovariegata'	I. crenata 'Variegata'	Illicium religiosum -Sieb. & Zucc.	I. anisatum -L.
Ilex crenata 'Bullata'	I. crenata 'Convexa'	Ilyphilos triandrus	Elatine triandra
Ilex crenata 'Compacta'	I.c. 'Bennett's Compact'	Ilysanthes	Lindernia
Ilex crenata 'Fructo Luteo'	I. cr. f watanabeana	Impatiens 'Salmon' (Fiesta Series)	I. walleriana (Fiesta S)
Ilex crenata 'Fukarin'	I. cr. 'Shiro-fukarin'		'Sparkler Salmon'
Ilex crenata 'Luteovariegata'	I. crenata 'Variegata'	Impatiens 'Salmon' (Fiesta Series)	I. walleriana (Fiesta S)
Ilex crenata 'Snowflake'	I. cr. 'Shiro-fukarin'		Fiesta Ole Salmon
Ilex crenata f latifolia	I. cr. v latifolia	Impatiens biflora	I. capensis
Ilex crenata v mutchagara	I. mutchagara -Mak	Impatiens fulva	I. capensis
Ilex crenata v nummularioides	I. crenata 'Mariesii'	Impatiens giorgii	I. balsamina
Ilex crenata v nummularioides	I. crenata 'Mariesii'	Impatiens hawkeri	I. schlecheteri
Ilex curtissii	I. decidua	Impatiens holstii	I. walleriana
Ilex dubia -not Weber	I. amelanchier	Impatiens maculata	I. capensis
Ilex fastigiata	I. verticillata	Impatiens New Guinea Group	I. schlecheteri
Ilex ferox	I. aquifolium 'Ferox'	Impatiens nortonii	I. capensis
Ilex franchetiana -Loes.	I. fargesii	Impatiens oliveri	I. sodenii
Ilex furcata -(Lind).	I. cornuta	Impatiens petersiana	I. walleriana
Ilex hascombensis	I. aq. 'Hascombensis'	Impatiens roylei	I. glandulifera
Ilex heterophyllus -G.Don	Osmanthus heterophyl.	Impatiens sultani	I. walleriana
Ilex insignis -Hook. f. not Heer	I. kingiana -Cockerell	Impatiens sultani	Impatiens walleriana
Ilex japonica-Thunb.	Mahonia japonica	Imperata arundinacea v europaea	I. cylindrica
Ilex leucoclada -(Maxim.) Mak.	I. integra v leucoclada	Imperata cylindrica 'Red Baron'	I. cylindrica 'Rubra'
Ilex maderensis -Lam.	I. perado h.	Imperata sacchariflora	Miscanthus saccharif.
Ilex maderensis h. not Lam.	I. x altaclerensis	Incarvillea brevipes	I. mairei
Ilex mariesii	I. crenata 'Mariesii'	Incarvillea delavayi 'Alba'	I. delavayi 'Snowtop'
Ilex melanotricha -Merrill	I. fargesii ssp melan.	Incarvillea emodi	I. arguta
Ilex microcarpa -Lindl. ex Paxt.	I. rotunda v microc.	Incarvillea grandiflora brevipes	I. mairei

127

Synonym	Current Name	Synonym	Current Name
Incarvillea koopmannii	I. olgae	Ipomoea versicolor	I. lobata
I. mairei v mairei f multifoliata	I. zhongdianensis	Ipomoea violacea h.	I. tricolor
I. mairei v mairei f multifoliata	I. zhongdianensis	Ipomoea x sloteri	I. x multifida
Indigofera brachyodon	Indigastrum parviflorum	Iridodictyum danfordiae	I. danfordiae
		Iridodictyum reticulatum	Iris reticulata
Indigofera dosua -Lindl. not D.Don	I. heterantha -Wall. ex Brandis (1874)	Iris 'Angel's Tears'	I. histrioides 'Angel's Tears'
I. gerardiana -Wall. ex Baker (1876)	I. heterantha -Wall. ex Brandis (1874)	Iris 'Bollinger'	I. 'Hornpipe'
		Iris 'Cambridge Blue'	I. 'Monspur Cambridge Blue'
Indigofera incarnata -(Willd.) Nakai	I. decora -Lindl.		
Indigofera macrostachya -not Vent	I. kirilowii -Palib.	Iris 'Campbellii'	I. lutescens 'Campbellii'
Indigofera oxycarpa	Indigastrum parviflorum	Iris 'Chain White'	I. 'Chain Wine'
		Iris 'Die Braut'	I. 'Bride'
Indigofera parviflora	Indigastrum parviflor.	Iris 'Elegant'	I. laevigata 'Weymouth Elegant'
Indigofera pratensis v coriacea	I. scabrella		
Indigofera rubra	I. pulchella	Iris 'Galathea'	I. ensata 'Galathea'
Indigofera violacea	I. pulchella	Iris 'Gerald Derby'	I. x robusta 'Gerald Derby'
Indocalamus solidus	Bonia solida		
Inga pulcherrima (unv)	Calliandra tweedii	Iris 'Hokkaido'	I. ensata 'Perry's Hokkaido'
Inula 'Golden Beauty'	Buphthalmum salicifolium 'Golden Wonder'		
		Iris 'Martyn Rix'	I. confusa 'Martyn Rix'
Inula afghanica h.	I. magnifica	Iris 'Moonlight Waves'	I. ensata 'Moonlight Waves'
Inula candensis	Conyza candensis		
Inula dysenterica	Pulicaria dysenterica	Iris 'Nancy Lindsay'	I. lutescens 'Nancy Lindsay'
Inula glandulosa	I. orientalis		
Inula japonica	I. britannica v chinensis	Iris 'Pacific Coast Hybrids'	I. Californian Hybrids
		Iris 'Peacock'	I. ensata 'Peacock'
Inula macrocephala misapplied	I. royleana	Iris 'Princess Beatrice'	I. pallida ssp pallida
Inula squarrosa	I. conyza	Iris 'Reginae'	I. variegata v reginae
Inula vulgaris	I. conyza	Iris 'Rose Queen'	I. ensata 'Rose Queen'
Iochroma tubulosa	I. cyanea	Iris 'Smooth Orange'	I. 'Orange Chariot'
Iochroma violaceum h.	I. cyaneum 'Trebah'	Iris 'Snowdrift'	I. laevigata 'Snowdrift'
Iochroma warscewiczii	I. grandiflorum	Iris 'The Bride'	I. 'Bride'
Ioxylon pomiferum -Raf.	Maclura pomifera	Iris 'The Rocket'	I. 'Rocket'
Ipomoea acuminata	I. indica	Iris 'Walter Butt'	I. unguicularis 'Walter Butt'
Ipomoea affinis	I. purpurea		
Ipomoea bona-nox	I. alba	Iris anglica	I. latifolia
Ipomoea brasiliensis	I. pes-caprae ssp bras.	Iris arenaria	I. humilis
Ipomoea chanetii	I. purpurea	Iris aurea	I. crocea
Ipomoea coccinea v hederifolia	I. hederifolia	Iris balkana	I. reichenbachii Balkana Group
Ipomoea diversifolia	I. purpurea		
Ipomoea gerrardiana	I. purpurea	Iris barnumae polakii	I. polakii
Ipomoea glandulifera	I. purpurea	Iris biglumis	I. lactea
Ipomoea hirsutula	I. purpurea	Iris brandzae	I. sintenisii ssp brand.
Ipomoea hispida	I. purpurea	Iris bucharica h.	I. orchioides -Carr.
Ipomoea imperialis	I. nil	Iris caerulea	I. albomarginata
Ipomoea jalapa	I. purga	Iris canadensis	I. hookeri
Ipomoea learii	I. indica	Iris chamaeiris	I. lutescens
Ipomoea mexicana	I. purpurea	Iris chrysographes 'Rubra'	I. chrys. 'Rubella'
Ipomoea palmata	I. cairica	Iris colchica	I. graminea
Ipomoea pilossissima	I. purpurea	Iris cretensis	I. unguicularis ssp cre.
Ipomoea rubrocaerulea	I. tricolor	Iris cuprea	I. fulva
I. rubrocaerulea 'Heavenly Blue'	I. tricolor 'Heavenly Blue'	Iris elegantissima	I. iberica ssp elegantissima
Ipomoea tuberosa	Merremia tuberosa	Iris ewbankiana	I. acutiloba ssp

Synonym	Current Name	Synonym	Current Name
	lineolata	Iris sibirica cream	I. s. 'Primrose Cream'
Iris extremorientalis	I. sanguinea	Iris sieboldii	I. sanguinea
Iris flavissima	I. humilis	Iris sindjarensis	I. aucheri
Iris florentina v albicans	I. florentina alba	Iris sisyrinchium	Gynandriris sisyrinch.
Iris foetidissima chinensis	I. foetidissima v citrina	Iris spuria ssp ochroleuca	I. orientalis -Mill.
Iris foliosa	I. brevicaulis	Iris stylosa	I. unguicularis
Iris germanica v florentina	I. 'Florentina'	Iris tauri	I. stenophylla
Iris gormanii	I. tenax	Iris thunbergii	I. sanguinea
Iris graminifolia	I. kerneriana	Iris tolmeiana	I. missouriensis
Iris halophila	I. spuria ssp halophila	Iris tuberosa	Hermodactylus tuber.
Iris hispanica h.	I. xiphium	Iris unguicularis v lazica	I. lazica
Iris histrioides 'Angel's Tears'	I. histr. 'Angel's Eye'	Iris urmiensis	I. barnumae f urmiens.
Iris illyrica	I. pallida	Iris violacea	I. spuria ssp
Iris jordana	I. atrofusca		musulmanica
Iris kaempferi	I. ensata	Iris virginica 'De Luxe'	I. x robusta 'Dark
Iris klattii	I. spuria ssp		Aura'
	musulmanica	Iris wilsonii 'Gelbe Mantel'	I. 'Gelbe Mantel'
Iris laevigata 'Elegant'	I. laevigata	Iris xiphioides	I. latifolia
	'Weymouth Elegant'	Isatis banatica	I. tinctoria
Iris laevigata 'Midnight'	I. laevigata 'Weymouth	Isatis campestris	I. tinctoria
	Midnight'	Isatis dalmatica	I. tinctoria
Iris laevigata 'Purity'	I. l. 'Weymouth Purity'	Isatis dasycarpa	I. tinctoria
Iris laevigata 'Rose Queen'	I. ensata 'Rose Queen'	Isatis heterocarpa	I. tinctoria
Iris laevigata 'Surprise'	I. laevigata 'Weymouth	Isatis indigotica	I. tinctoria
	Surprise'	Isatis lasiocarpa	I. tinctoria
Iris laevigata 'Weymouth' I.	I. 'Weymouth Blue'	Isatis maeotica	I. tinctoria
Iris mellita	I. suaveolens	Isatis maritima	I. tinctoria
Iris mellita v rubromarginata	I. suaveolens	Isatis pilosa	I. tinctoria
Iris nepalensis	I. decora	Isatis praecox	I. tinctoria
Iris nertschinskia	I. sanguinea	Isatis yezoensis	I. tinctoria
Iris ochroleuca	I. orientalis -Mill.	Ischarum -(Blume) Reich.	Biarum -Schott
Iris orchioides h.	I. bucharica -Foster	Ismene	Hymenocallis
Iris orientalis -Thunb.	I. sanguinea	Isoloma	Kohleria
Iris orientalis 'Alba'	I. sanguinea 'Alba'	Isomeris	Cleome
Iris pallida 'Aurea Variegata'	I. pallida 'Variegata'	Isopogon anemonifolius f simplicifolia	I. anemonifolius
Iris pallida 'Aurea'	I. pallida 'Variegata'	Isopogon anemonifolius v glaber	I. anemonifolius
Iris pallida v dalmatica	I. pallida ssp pallida	Isopogon anemonifolius v pubescens	I. anemonifolius
Iris pumila ssp attica	I. attica	Isopogon anemonifolius v pubiflorus	I. anemonifolius
Iris purpurea	I. galatica	Isopogon anemonifolius v tenuifolius	I. prostratus
Iris rubromarginata	I. suaveolens	Isopogon attenuatus v angustatus	I. attenuatus
	'Rubromarginata'	Isopogon buxifolius v typicus	I. buxifolius v buxifolius
Iris rudskyi	I. variegata	Isopogon confertus	I. anethifolius
Iris serbica	I. reichenbachii	Isopogon cornigerus	I. teretifolius
Iris setosa 'Hookeri'	I. hookeri	Isopogon cornu-damae	I. ceratophyllus
Iris setosa 'Kirigamini'	I. setosa 'Hondoensis'	Isopogon eriophorus	I. anethifolius
Iris setosa dwarf	I. hookeri	Isopogon globosus	I. anethifolius
Iris setosa ssp canadensis	I. hookeri	Isopogon scaber	I. asper
Iris setosa v nana	I. hookeri	Isopogon spathulatus v linearis	I. buxifolius v linearis
Iris shrevei	I. virginica v shrevei	Isopogon tridactylidis	I. anemonifolius
Iris sibirica 'Alba'	I. 'Sibirica Alba'	Isopogon virgulatus	I. anethifolius
Iris sibirica 'Baxteri'	I. 'Sibirica Baxteri'	Isopyrum grandiflorum	Paraquilegia
Iris sibirica 'Clouded Moon'	I. s. 'Forncett Moon'		anemonoides
Iris sibirica 'Redflare'	I. s. 'Melton Red Flare'	Isopyrum microphyllum	Paraquilegia microph.
Iris sibirica 'Snow Queen'	I. sanguinea 'Snow	Isopyrum ohwianum	I. nipponicum v
	Queen'		sarmentosum

Synonym	Current Name	Synonym	Current Name
Isopyrum trifolium	Coptis trifolia	Jasminum officinale 'Variegatum'	J. officinale 'Argenteovariegatum'
Isotoma axillaris	Laurentia axillaris		
Isotoma fluviatilis	Pratia pedunculata	Jasminum primulinum -Hemsl.	J. mesnyi -Hance
Itea virginica Swarthmore form	I. v. 'Henry's Garnet'	Jasminum pubigerum -D.Don	J. humile f wallichianum
Ixia Bird of Paradise	I. 'Paradijsvogel'		
Ixia Blauwe Vogel	I. 'Blue Bird'	Jasminum reevesii h.	J. humile 'Revolutum'
Ixia chinensis	Belamcanda chinensis	Jasminum revolutum -Sims	J. humile 'Revolutum'
Ixiolirion ledebourii	I. tataricum Ledebourii Group	Jasminum rex	J. nobile ssp rex
		Jasminum sambac 'Flore Pleno'	J. sambac 'Grand Duke of Tuscany'
Ixiolirion montanum	I. tataricum		
Ixiolirion pallasii	I. tataricum	Jasminum sambac 'Trifoliatum'	J. sambac 'Grand Duke of Tuscany'
Jacaranda acutifolia misapplied	J. mimosifolia		
Jacaranda ovalifolia	J. mimosifolia	Jasminum sieboldianum -Bl.	J. nudiflorum -Lindl.
Jacea alata	Centaurea montana	Jasminum suavissimum	J. simplicifolium ssp suavissimum
Jacea communis	Centaurea jacea		
Jacea debauxii	Centaurea jacea	Jasminum trifoliatum -Moench	J. azoricum
Jacea decipiens	Centaurea jacea	Jasminum triumphans	J. humile 'Revolutum'
Jacea jungens	Centaurea jacea	Jasminum v revolutum	J. humile 'Revolutum'
Jacea nigra	Centaurea nigra	Jasminum volubile	J. simplicifolium ssp australiense
Jacea pratensis	Centaurea jacea		
Jacea scabiosa	Centaurea scabiosa	Jasminum wallichianum -Lindl.	J. humile f wallichian.
Jacea segetalis	Centaurea cyanus	Jateorhiza calumba	J. palmata
Jacea segetum -(Hill) Lam.	Centaurea cyanus	Jeffersonia bartonis	J. diphylla
Jacea subjacea	Centaurea jacea	Jeffersonia binata	J. diphylla
Jacea tomentosa	Centaurea jacea	Jonopsidium acaule	Ionopsidium acaule
Jacksonia anomala	Leptosema anomalum	Josephia	Dryandra
Jacksonia petrophiliodes	Leptosema anomalum	Jovibarba globolifera ssp hirta	J. hirta
Jacobinia 'Carnea'	Justicia carnea	Jovibarba hirta ssp allionii	J. allionii
Jacobinia coccinea	Pachystachys coccinea	Juanulloa aurantiaca	J. mexicana
Jacobinia pauciflora	Justicia rizzinii	Jubaea spectabilis -H.B.K.	J. chilensis
Jacobinia pohliana	Justicia carnea	Juglans alba v odorata	Carya glabra
Jacobinia spicigera	Justicia spicigera	Juglans aquatica -Michx. f.	Carya aquatica
Jacobinia suberecta	Dicliptera suberecta	Juglans cathayensis -Dode	J. mandshurica
Jacobinia velutina	Justicia carnea	Juglans cinerea x ailanthifolia	J. x bixbyi
Jacquemontia violacea	J. pentantha	Juglans cordiformis -Maxim.	J. ailanthifolia v cordif.
Jaimenostia -Guin. & Gom.Mor.	Typhonium -Schott	Juglans fallax	J. regia -L.
Jankaea	Jancaea	Juglans fraxinifolia -Lam.	Pterocarya fraxinifolia
Jasione amethystina	J. crispa ssp ameth.	Juglans glabra	Carya glabra
Jasione humilis	J. crispa ssp amethystina	Juglans illinoensis -Wangenh.	Carya illinoinensis
		Juglans intermedia v pyriformis	J. x intermedia -Carr.
Jasione jankae	J. heldreichii	Juglans laciniosa -Michx. f. major -(Torr). Heller	Carya laciniosa Juglans J. elaeopyren
Jasione laevis Blue Light	J. laevis 'Blaulicht'		
Jasione perennis	J. laevis	Juglans microcarpa ssp major	J. elaeopyren
Jasminum affine -Lindl.	J. officinale f affine	Juglans myrsticaeformis -Michx. f.	Carya myristiciformis
Jasminum capense -Thunb.	J. angulare	Juglans nana -Engelm.	J. microcarpa -Berl.
Jasminum diversifolium -Kobuski	J. subhumile	Juglans obcordata	Carya glabra
Jasminum farreri -Gilmour	J. humile f farreri	Juglans ovalis -Wangenh.	Carya ovalis
Jasminum fluminense h.	J. azoricum	Juglans ovata -Mill.	Carya ovata
Jasminum grandiflorum h.	J. officinale f affine	Juglans pyriformis -Muhl.	Carya glabra
Jasminum heterophyllum -Roxb.	J. subhumile	Juglans regia v intermedia -Carr.	J. x intermedia -Carr.
Jasminum humile v glabrum	J. h. f wallichianum	Juglans rupestris -Engelm.	J. microcarpa -Berl.
Jasminum nitidum	J. laurifolium f nitidum	Juglans rupestris v major -Torr.	J. elaeopyren
Jasminum nudiflorum 'Argenteum'	J. n. 'Mystique'	Juglans sieboldiana -not Goeppert	J. ailanthifolia -Carr.
J. officinale 'Aureovariegatum'	J. officinale 'Aureum'	Juglans sinensis	J. regia
Jasminum officinale 'Grandiflorum'	J. officinale f affine	Juglans tomentosa -Poir	Carya tomentosa

130

Synonym	Current Name	Synonym	Current Name
Juncus decipiens 'Spiralis'	J. d. 'Curly-Wurly'	Juniperus communis v suecica	J. c. Suecica Group
Juncus glaucus	J. inflexus -L.	Juniperus conferta	J. rigida ssp conferta
Juncus griscomii	J. effusus -L.	Juniperus conferta v maritima	J. taxifolia
Juncus polyanthemus	J. effusus -L.	Juniperus coxii -A.B.Jacks	J. recurva v coxii
Juncus pylaei	J. effusus -L.	J. davurica 'Expansa Albopicta'	J. chinensis 'Expansa
Juncus zebrinus	Schoenoplectus		Variegata'
	lacustris ssp taber	J. davurica 'Expansa Variegata'	J.c.'Expansa Variegata'
	naemontani 'Zebrinus'	Juniperus davurica 'Expansa'	J. chinensis 'Parsonsii'
Juniperus 'Densa Spartan'	J. chinensis 'Spartan'	Juniperus densa -Gord.	J. squamata -D.Don
Juniperus 'Grey Owl'	J. virginiana 'Grey Owl'	Juniperus fargesii -Komar.	J. squamata v fargesii
Juniperus 'Hetzii'	J. virginiana 'Hetz'	Juniperus hibernica h.	J. communis
Juniperus 'Kaizuka Variegata'	J. 'Variegated Kaizuka'		'Hibernica'
Juniperus 'Pyramidalis Variegata'	J. chinensis 'Variegata'	Juniperus horizontalis 'Blue Moon'	J. horiz. 'Blue Chip'
Juniperus 'Stricta Variegata'	J. ch. 'Variegated'	Juniperus horizontalis 'Blue Rug'	J. horizontalis 'Wiltonii'
Juniperus 'Sulphur Spray'	J. virginiana 'Sulphur	Juniperus horizontalis 'Montana'	J. communis v mont.
	Spray'	J. horizontalis 'Plumosa Compacta'	J. horizontalis
Juniperus canadensis	J. communis v		'Andorra Compact'
	depressa	Juniperus horizontalis 'Venusta'	J. virginiana 'Venusta'
Juniperus chinensis 'Albovariegata'	J. chinensis 'Variegata'	Juniperus horizontalis v saxatilis	J. communis v
Juniperus chinensis 'Armstrongii'	J. x pfitzeriana		communis
	'Armstrongii'	Juniperus lemeean -Levl. & Blin	J. squamata v fargesii
Juniperus chin. 'Densa Spartan'	J. chinensis 'Spartan'	Juniperus litoralis -Maxim.	J. conferta -Parl.
Juniperus chin. 'Excelsa Stricta'	J. ch. 'Pyramidalis'	Juniperus macropoda -Boiss.	J. excelsa v
J. chinensis 'Japonica Oblonga'	J. chinensis 'Oblonga'		polycarpos
J. chinensis 'Kaizuka Variegata'	J. chinensis	Juniperus nana -Willd.	J. communis v mont.
	'Variegated Kaizuka'	Juniperus nipponica -Maxim.	J. rigida ssp nipponica
Juniperus chinensis 'Kuriwao Gold'	J. x pfitzeriana	Juniperus pachyphlaea -Torr.	J. deppeana v pachyp.
	'Kuriwao Gold'	Juniperus procumbens -not Sieb.	J.chinensis v sargentii
Juniperus chinensis 'Pfitzeriana'	J. x pfitzeriana	Juniperus prostrata -Pers.	J. horizontalis -Moench
J. chinensis 'Pyramidalis Variegata'	J. chinensis 'Variegata'	J. pseudosabina -not Fisch. & Mey.	J. wallichiana -Parl.
J. chinensis 'Stricta Variegata'	J. chinensis 'Variegata'	Juniperus pyriformis -A.Murr.	J. occidentalis -Hook.
Juniperus chin. 'Sulphur Spray'	J. x pfitzeriana	Juniperus recurva 'Nana'	J. recurva 'Densa'
	'Sulphur Spray'	Juniperus recurva v viridis	J. rec. 'Embley Park'
Juniperus chinensis 'Torulosa'	J. chinensis 'Kaizuka'	Juniperus sabina 'Knap Hill'	J. x pfitzeriana
J. chinensis v procumbens -Endl.	J. procumbens		'Wilhelm Pfitzer'
Juniperus chinensis v sargentii	J. sargentii	Juniperus sabina 'Mountaineer'	J. scopulorum
Juniperus communis 'Gelb'	J. communis 'Schnever		'Mountaineer'
	dingen Goldmachangel'	Juniperus sabina 'Tripartita'	J. virginiana
J. communis 'Golden Showers'	J. c. 'Schneverdingen		'Tripartita'
	Goldmachangel'	Juniperus sabina Blue Danube	J. sabina 'Blau Donau'
J. communis 'Hibernica Variegata'	J. communis	J. sabina v cupressifolia -Ait. (also been known as J.sabina of	
	'Constance Franklin'	which it is a dwarf form)	J. s. Cupressifolia Gr.
Juniperus communis 'Prostrata'	J. c. 'Hornibrookii'	Juniperus sabina v hudsonica	J. horizontalis -Moench
Juniperus communis 'Stricta'	J. c. 'Hibernica'	Juniperus sabina v procumbens	J. horizontalis -Moench
J. communis 'Suecica Aurea'	J. c. 'Gold Cone'	Juniperus sabina v prostrata -Loud	J. horizontalis -Moench
Juniperus communis f suecica	J. c. Suecica Group	Juniperus sabinoides -Griseb.	J. foetidissima -Willd.
Juniperus communis ssp depressa	J. c. v depressa	Juniperus sanderi	Thuja orientalis
Juniperus communis ssp nana	J. c. v montana -Ait.		'Sanderi'
Juniperus communis v alpina	J. c. v montana	Juniperus sargentii	J. chinensis v sargent.
Juniperus communis v canadensis	J. c. v depressa	Juniperus seravshanica -Komar.	J. excelsa v
J. c. v fastigiata -Parl. in part	J. c. Suecica Group		polycarpos
J. communis v hemispherica	J. c. v communis	Juniperus sheppardii v torulosa	J. chinensis 'Kaizuka'
Juniperus communis v jackii -Rehd.	J. c. v montana	Juniperus sibirica -Burgsdf.	J. communis v mont.
Juniperus communis v nipponica	J. rigida ssp nipponica	Juniperus sphaerica -Lindl.	J. chinensis -L.
Juniperus communis v saxatilis	J. c. v montana -Ait.	J. squamata 'Blue Star Variegated'	J. sq. 'Golden Flame'

Synonym	Current Name	Synonym	Current Name
Juniperus squamata 'Blue Swede'	J. sq. 'Hunnetorp'	Kalimeris yomena 'Variegata'	K. yomena 'Shogun'
Juniperus squamata 'Forrestii'	J. pingii 'Forrestii'	Kalmia carolina -Small	K. angustifolia v carol.
Juniperus squamata 'Glassell'	J. pingii 'Glassell'	Kalmia glauca -Ait.	K. microphylla
Juniperus squamata 'Loderi'	J. pingii v wilsonii	Kalmia glauca v microphylla -Hook.	K. microphylla
Juniperus squamata 'Pygmaea'	J. pingii 'Pygmaea'	Kalmia lucida h.	K. latifolia -L.
Juniperus squamata 'Wilsonii'	J. pingii v wilsonii	Kalmia occidentalis -Sm.	K. microphylla
Juniperus squamata v fargesii	J. squamata	Kalmia polifolia 'Glauca'	K. microphylla
Juniperus suecica -Mill.	J. comm. Suecica Gr.	Kalmia polifolia v microphylla	K. microphylla
Juniperus utahensis -(Engel). Lemm.	J. osteosperma	Kalopanax pictus	K. septemlobus
Juniperus uvifera -D.Don	Libocedrus uvifera	Kalopanax ricinifolius	K. septemlobus
Juniperus virginiana 'Dundee'	J. virginiana 'Hillii'	Karos carvi	Carum carvi
Juniperus virginiana 'Helle'	J. chinensis 'Spartan'	Kennedya	Kennedia
Juniperus virginiana 'Keteleeri'	J. chinensis 'Keteleeri'	Kentia acuminata	Carpentaria acuminata
J. virginiana 'Pyramidiformis Hillii'	J. virginiana 'Hillii'	Kentia belmoreana	Howea belmoreana
Juniperus virginiana 'Skyrocket'	J. scopulorum 'Skyrocket'	Kentia canterburyana	Hedyscepe canterb.
		Kentia forsteriana	Howea forsteriana
J. virginiana 'Sulphur Spray'	J. x pfitzeriana 'Sulphur Spray'	Kentia joannis	Veitchia joannis
		Kentranthus	Centranthus
Juniperus virginiana v scopulorum	J. scopulorum -Sarg.	Kentrophyllum lanatum	Carthamnus lanatus
Juniperus x gracilis 'Blaauw'	J. chinensis 'Blaauw'	Kermadecia	Grevillea
Juniperus x media	J. x pfitzeriana	Kerria japonica 'Flore Pleno'	K. japonica 'Pleniflora'
Juniperus x media -Van Melle	J. x pfitzeriana	Kerria japonica 'Variegata'	K. japonica 'Picta'
Juniperus x media 'Armstrongii'	J. x pfitzeriana 'Armstrongii'	Kerria japonica (single)	K. japonica 'Simplex'
		Kerria japonica double-flowered	K. japonica 'Pleniflora'
Juniperus x media 'Hetzii'	J. virginiana 'Hetz'	Keteleeria fabri -Mast.	Abies delavayi (fabri ?)
Juniperus x pfitzeriana 'Blaauw'	J. chinensis 'Blaauw'	Kigelia pinnata	K. africana
Juniperus x pfitzeriana 'Blue Cloud'	J. virginiana 'Blue Cloud'	Kitaibelia	Kitaibela
		Kitchingia	Kalanchoe
J. x pfitzeriana 'Globosa Cinerea'	J.ch. 'Globosa Cinerea'	Klanderia chlorantha	Prostanthera chloran.
J. x pfitzeriana 'Old Gold Carbery'	J. x pfitzeriana 'Carbery Gold'	Kleinia articulata	Senecio articulatus
		Kleinia repens	Senecio serpens
Juniperus x pfitzeriana 'Pfitzeriana'	J. x pfitzeriana 'Wilhelm Pfitzer'	Kleinia rowleyanus	Senecio rowleyanus
		Knautia borderei	K. arvensis
Juniperus x pfitzeriana 'Sea Green'	J. x pfitz. 'Mint Julep'	Knautia indivisa	K. arvensis
Juno bucharica	Iris bucharica	Knautia ligerina	K. arvensis
Juno magnifica	Iris magnifica	Knautia pannonica	K. arvensis
Jurinea ceratocarpa	Saussurea ceratocar.	Kniphofia 'C.M.Prichard' misapplied	K. rooperi
Jurinea macrocephala	J. dolomiaea	Kniphofia 'Light of the World'	K. triangularis ssp tri. 'Light of the World'
Jurinella	Jurinea		
Jurtsevia richardsonii	Anemone richardsonii	Kniphofia 'Nobilis'	K. uvaria 'Nobilis'
Jussiaea	Ludwigia	Kniphofia alooides	K. uvaria
Justicia brandegeeana 'Lutea'	J. brandegeeana 'Yellow Queen'	Kniphofia elegans	K. schimperi
		Kniphofia galpinii misapplied	K. triangularis ssp tri.
Justicia coccinea	Pachystachys coccinea	Kniphofia macowanii	K. triangularis ssp tri.
Justicia floribunda	J. rizzinii	Kniphofia nelsonii -Mast.	K. triangularis ssp tri.
Justicia ghiesbreghtiana h.	J. spicigera	Kniphofia sparsa	K. gracilis
Justicia guttata	J. brandegeeana	K. thomsonii v snowdenii misapplied	K. thomsonii v thoms.
Justicia pauciflora	J. rizzinii	Kniphofia tuckii -Baker	K. ensifolia
Justicia pohliana	J. carnea	Kochia	Bassia
Justicia suberecta	Dicliptera suberecta	Kochia cheelii	Maireana cheelii
Kaempferia ovalifolia	K. parishii	Kochia trichophylla	Bassia scoparia f tric.
Kalanchoe schweinfurthii	K. laciniata	Kodda -P. Adans.	Pistia -L.
Kalanchoe somaliensis	K. marmorata	Koeleria cristata	K. macrantha
Kalanchoe tubiflora	K. delagoensis	Koellia flexuosa	Pycnanthemum tenuifolium
Kalanchoe zimbabwensis	K. lateritia		

132

Synonym	Current Name	Synonym	Current Name
Koelreuteria apiculata	K. paniculata	Lamium garganicum ssp reniforme	L. garg. ssp striatum
Koelreuteria chinensis	K. paniculata	Lamium grandiflorum	L. maculatum
Koelreuteria japonica	K. paniculata	Lamium grenieri	L. maculatum
Koelreuteria paniculata v apiculata	K. paniculata	Lamium hirsutum	L. maculatum
Koelreuteria paullinoides	K. paniculata	Lamium laevigatum	L. maculatum
Kohleria digitaliflora	K. warscewiezii	Lamium luteum	L. galeobdolon
Kohlrauschia saxifraga	Petrorhagia saxifraga	Lamium maculatum 'Gold Leaf'	L. maculatum 'Aureum'
Korolkowia sewerzowii	Fritillaria sewerzowii	Lamium maculatum 'Golden Nuggets'	L. maculatum 'Aureum'
Kreidon chinensis	Conioselinum chinense	Lamium maculatum 'Shell Pink'	L. maculatum 'Roseum'
Kunda -Raf.	Amorphophallus - Blume	Lamium melissifolium	L. maculatum
		Lamium mutabile	L. maculatum
Kunzea podantha	Leptospermum oligandrum	Lamium niveum	L. maculatum
		Lamium niveum h.	L. album
+ Laburnocytisus adamii	+ Laburnocytisus 'Adamii'	Lamium pallidiflorum	L. maculatum
		Lamium parietariaefolium	L. album
Laburnum adamii -(Poiteau) Kirchn.	+ Laburnocy. 'Adamii'	Lamium petiolatum	L. album
L. anagyroides 'Semperflorens'	L. anagyr. 'Autumnale'	Lamium rubrum	L. maculatum
Laburnum vulgare -Bercht. & Presl	L. anagyroides -Med.	Lamium rugosum	L. maculatum
Laburnum vulgare watereri -Kirchn.	L. x watereri	Lamium sibiricum	Leonurus sibirica -L.
Laburnum x vossii h.	L. x watereri 'Vossii'	Lamium stoloniferum	L. maculatum
Lachenalia 'Tricolor'	L. aloides	Lamium tomentosum	L. maculatum
Lachenalia angustifolia	L. contaminata	Lamium vulgatum	L. maculatum
Lachenalia glaucina	L. orchioides v glauc.	Lampranthus aberdeenensis	Delosperma aberdeen.
Lachenalia pendula	L. bulbifera	Lampranthus deltoides	Oscularia deltoides
Lachenalia tricolor	L. aloides	Lampranthus edulis	Carpobrotus edulis
Lachnanthes tinctoria	L. caroliana	Lampranthus lehmannii	Delosperma lehmannii
Lacinaria	Liatris	Lampranthus oscularis	Oscularia deltoides
Lactuca alpina	Cicerbita alpina	Lampranthus pallidus	Delosperma pallidum
Lactuca bourgaei	Cicerbita bourgaei	Lamprocapnos spectabilis	Dicentra spectabilis
Lactuca elongata	L. canadensis	Lantana aculeata	L. camara
Lactuca integrifolia -Big.	L. canadensis	Lantana aculeata f varia	L. camara f varia
Lactuca longifolia	L. canadensis	Lantana antillana	L. camara
Lactuca multifida	L. biennis	Lantana armata	L. camara
Lactuca plumieri	Cicerbita plumieri	Lantana camara Cloth of Gold	L. camara 'Drap d'Or'
Lactuca sagittifolia	L. canadensis	Lantana camara Goldmine	L. camara 'Mine d'Or'
Lactuca sanguinea -Big.	L. hirsuta	Lantana corcea	L. camara
Lactuca scariola -L.	L. serriola -L.	Lantana delicatissima	L. montevidensis
Lactuca steelei	L. canadensis	Lantana flava	L. camara
Lactuca terrae-novae	L. biennis	Lantana glandulosissima	L. camara
Laelia majalis	L. speciosa	Lantana hirsuta	L. camara
Lamiastrum	Lamium	Lantana horrida	L. camara
Lamiastrum galeobdolon	Lamium galeobdolon	Lantana mista	L. camara
Lamium affine	L. maculatum	Lantana moritziana	L. camara
Lamium album 'Aureovariegatum'	L. album 'Goldflake'	Lantana nivea	L. cam. white-flowered
Lamium album v maculatum	L. maculatum	Lantana polyacantha	L. camara
Lamium barbatum	L. album	Lantana salvifolia -L.	Buddleja saviifolia
Lamium brachyodon	L. album	Lantana sanguinea	L. camara
Lamium capitatum	L. album	Lantana scabrida	L. camara
Lamium cardiaca	Leonurus cardiaca -L.	Lantana scandens	L. camara
Lamium dumeticola	L. album	Lantana scorta	L. camara
Lamium foliosum	L. maculatum	Lantana sellowiana	L. montevidensis
Lamium galeobdolon 'Variegatum'	L. gal. ssp montanum 'Florentinum'	Lantana tiliifolia	L. camara
		Lantana viburnoides	L. camara
Lamium galeobdolon Silver Carpet	L. g. 'Silberteppich'	Lantana x hybrida h.	L. camara
Lamium garganicum ssp pictum	L. garg. ssp striatum	Lapageria alba -Gay	L. rosea v albiflora

Synonym	Current Name	Synonym	Current Name
Lapathum	Rumex		limbosperma
Lapeirousia cruenta	Anomatheca laxa	Lastraea standishii	Arachniodes standishii
Lapeirousia laxa	Anomatheca laxa	Lastraea thelypteris	Thelypteris palustris
Lapeirousia viridis	Anomatheca viridis	Lastrea abbreviata	Dryopteris affinis
Lappa bardana	Arctium lappa	Lastrea aemula	Dryopteris aemula
Lappa bardana major	Arctium lappa	Lastrea chrysocarpa	Dryopteris pseudofilix-mas
Lappa edulis	Arctium lappa		
Lappa glabra	Arctium lappa	Lastrea cristata	Dryopteris cristata
Lappa intermedia	Arctium minus	Lastrea decursive-pinnata	Phegopteris d.-pinnata
Lappa lappa	Arctium lappa	Lastrea dilatata	Dryopteris dilatata
Lappa major	Arctium lappa	Lastrea dryopteris	Gymnocarpium dryop.
Lappa minor	Arctium minus	Lastrea erythrosora	Dryopteris erythroso.
Lappa nemorosa	Arctium minus	Lastrea filix-femina	Athyrium filix-femina
Lappa officinalis	Arctium lappa	Lastrea filix-mas	Dryopteris filix-mas
Lappa officinalis ssp nemorosa	Arctium minus	Lastrea foenisecii	Dryopteris aemula
Lappa tomentosa	Arctium tomentosum	Lastrea goldiana	Dryopteris erythroso.
Lappa vulgaris	Arctium lappa	Lastrea marginalis	Dryopteris marginale
Lapsana crispa	L. communis -L.	Lastrea oreopteris	Oreopteris
Lapsana macrocarpa	L. communis -L.		limbosperma
Lapsana pubescens	L. communis -L.	Lastrea phegopteris	Phegopteris connectilis
Lardizabala biternata	L. funaria	Lastrea propinqua	Dryopteris oreades
Larix amabilis -Nelson	P. amabilis	Lastrea robertiana	Gymnocarpium robert.
Larix americana -Michx.	L. laricina	Lastrea sieboldii	Dryopteris sieboldii
Larix americana v pendula	L. x pendula	Lastrea spinosa	Dryopteris carthus.
Larix chinensis -Beiss.	L. potaninii -Batal.	Lastrea spinulosa	Dryopteris carthus.
Larix dahurica -Turcz.	L. gmelinii	Lastrea thelypteris	Thelypteris palustris
Larix europaea -DC.	L. decidua -Mill.	Lastreopsis decomposita	L. calantha
Larix europaea -Middendorf.	L. sibirica	Lastreopsis shepherdii	L. acuminata
Larix europaea pendula -Laws.	L. decidua 'Pendula'	Lathyrus aleuticus	L. japonicus
Larix gmelini	L. gmelinii	Lathyrus azureus misapplied	L. sativus
Larix griffithii -Hook. f.	L. griffithiana -Carr.	Lathyrus clymenum articulatus	L. articulatus
Larix intermedia	L. sibirica	Lathyrus cyaneus misapplied	L. vernus
Larix japonica -Reg.	L. gmelinii v japonica	Lathyrus fremontii h.	L. laxiflorus
Larix kamtschatica -(Rupr.) Carr.	L. gmelinii v japonica	Lathyrus gmelinii 'Aureus'	L. aureus
Larix kurilensis -Mayr.	L. gmelinii v japonica	Lathyrus inermis	L. laxiflorus
Larix larix	L. decidua -Mill.	Lathyrus laetiflorus v vestitus	L. vestitus
Larix leptolepis	L. kaempferi	L. latifolius 'White Pearl' misapplied	L. latifolius 'Albus'
Larix microcarpa -(Lamb.) Desf.	L. laricina	Lathyrus latifolius Pink Pearl	L. lat. 'Rosa Perle'
Larix olgensis -Henry	L. gmelinii v olgensis	Lathyrus latifolius Weisse Perle	L. lat. 'White Pearl'
Larix russica -(Endl). Trautv.	L. sibirica -Ledeb.	Lathyrus luteus -(L) Peterm.	L. gmelinii
Larix sudetica	L. decidua -Mill.	Lathyrus luteus 'Aureus'	L. aureus
Larix sukaczevii	L. sibirica	Lathyrus luteus h.	L. aureus
Larix thibetica -Franch.	L. potaninii -Batal.	Lathyrus macranthus	L. palustris -L.
Larix x eurolepis	L. x marschlinsii	Lathyrus magelanthus	L. latifolius -L.
Lasiagrostis	Stipa	Lathyrus magellanicus	L. nervosus
Lasiandra macrantha	Tibouchina urvilleana	Lathyrus montanus	L. linifolius v montanus
Lasierpa hispidula	Gaultheria hispidula	Lathyrus myrtifolius	L. palustris -L.
Lasiopetalum ledifolium	Boronia ledifolia	Lathyrus pilosus	L. palustris -L.
Lasioptera campestris	Lepidium campestre	Lathyrus sativus v azureus	L. sativus
Lasius -Hass.	Lasia -Lour.	Lathyrus sibthorpii	L. undulatus
Lastraea aemula	Dryopteris aemula	Lathyrus vernus aurantiacus	L. aureus
Lastraea cristata	Dryopteris cristata	Laurelia serrata	L. sempervirens
Lastraea dilatata	Dryopteris dilatata	Laurentia	Isotoma
Lastraea filix-mas	Dryopteris filix-mas	Laurocerasus officinalis	Prunus laurocerasus
Lastraea montana	Oreopteris	Laurocerasus undulata	Prunus undulata

Synonym	Current Name
Laurus aestivalis -L.	Lindera benzoin
Laurus benzoin -L.	Lindera benzoin
Laurus camphora -L.	Cinnamomum camphor.
Laurus canariensis -not Willd.	L. azorica
Laurus nobilis v undulata -Meissn.	L. nobilis 'Crispa'
Laurus pseudobenzoin -Michx.	Lindera benzoin
Laurus sericea -Bl.	Neolitsea sericea
Laurus umbellata -Thunb.	R. umbellata
Laurustinus	Viburnum tinus
Lavandula 'Alba'	L. angustifolia 'Alba'
Lavandula 'Alba'	L. x intermedia 'Alba'
Lavandula 'Cornard Blue'	L. 'Sawyers'
Lavandula 'Hidcote Blue'	L. angustifolia 'Hidcote'
Lavandula 'Jean Davis'	L. angustifolia 'Jean Davis'
Lavandula 'Loddon Pink'	L. ang. 'Loddon Pink'
Lavandula 'Rosea'	L. angustifolia 'Rosea'
Lavandula 'Silver Edge'	L. x int. Walberton's Silver Edge
Lavandula angustifolia 'Alba Nana'	L. ang. 'Nana Alba'
L. angustifolia 'Bowles' Grey'	L. ang. 'Bowles' Early'
L. angustifolia 'Bowles' Variety'	L. ang. 'Bowles' Early'
L. angustifolia 'Miss Donnington'	L. ang. 'Bowles' Early'
Lavandula dentata silver	L. dentata v candicans
Lavandula heterophylla h.	L. x allardii
Lavandula officinalis -Chaix	L. angustifolia -Mill.
Lavandula pterostoechas pinnata	L. pinnata
Lavandula spica	L. angustifolia -Mill.
Lavandula spica	L. latifolia
Lavandula spica	L. x intermedia
Lavandula spica 'Hidcote Purple'	L. angustifolia 'Hidcote'
Lavandula spica v angustifolia -L. f.	L. angustifolia -Mill.
Lavandula spica v latifolia -L. f.	L. angustifolia
Lavandula stoechas 'Papillon'	L. st.ssp pedunculata
Lavandula stoechas v albiflora	L. stoechas f leucantha
Lavandula vera -DC.	L. angustifolia -Mill.
Lavandula vera misapplied	L. x intermedia Dutch Group
Lavatera 'Peppermint Ice'	L. thuringiaca 'Ice Cool'
Lavatera 'Pink Frills'	L. olbia 'Pink Frills'
Lavatera 'Variegata'	L. x clementii 'Wembdon Variegated'
Lavatera arborea 'Rosea'	L. x clementii 'Rosea'
Lavatera bicolor -(Rouy) Stapf	L. maritima -Gouan
Lavatera cachemirica	L. cachemiriana
Lavatera maritima ssp bicolor -Rouy	L. maritima -Gouan
Lavatera olbia 'Rosea'	L. x cementii 'Rosea'
Lawsonia alba	L. inermis
Layia douglasii	L. glandulosa
Layia elegans	L. platyglossa
Lazarum -A. Hay.	Typhonium -Schott
Lechenaultia	Leschenaultia
Ledebouria adlamii	L. cooperi
Ledebouria violacea	L. socialis
Ledum buxifolium -Berg.	Leiophyllum buxifolium
Ledum columbianum -Piper	L. glandulosum ssp columbianum
Ledum decumbens -(Ait.) Lodd.	L. palustre ssp decum.
Ledum hypoleucum	L. palustre f dilatatum
Ledum latifolium -Jacq	L. groenlandicum
Ledum pacificum -Small	L. groenlandicum
Ledum palustre f decumbens	L. palustre ssp decum.
Ledum palustre ssp groenlandicum	L. groenlandicum
Ledum palustre v decumbens -Ait.	L. palustre ssp decum.
Ledum thymifolium -Lam.	Leiophyllum buxifolium
Leea coccinea	L. guineensis
Leersia hackelii	L. oryzoides
Leersia sayanuka	L. oryzoides
Leiophyllum serpyllifolium -DC.	L. buxifolium
Leiophyllum thymifolium	L. buxifolium
Leleba multiples -(Lour.) Nakai	Bambusa multiplex
Lemaireocereus euphorbioides	Neobuxbaumia euphor.
Lemaireocereus thurberi	Stenocereus thurberi
Lembotropis	Cytisus
Lemna polyrhiza	Spirodela polyrhiza
Lens esculenta	L. culinaris
Leonotis leonotis	L. ocymifolia
Leontice albertii	Gymnospermium alber.
Leontice altaica	Bongardia chrysogonum
Leontice chrysogonum	Bongardia chrysogon.
Leontice thalictroides	Caulophyllum thalictr.
Leontice triphylla	Achlys triphylla
Leontodon glaber	L. autumnalis
Leontodon pratensis	L. autumnalis
Leontodon taraxacum	Taraxacum officinale
Leontopodium aloysiodorum	L. haplophylloides
Leontopodium nivale	L. alpinum ssp nivale
Leontopodium palibinianum	L. ochroleucum v campestre
Leontopodium sibiricum	L. leontopodioides
Leontopodium tataricum	L. discolor
Leontopodium umbellatum	L. alpinum
Leonurus artemisia	L. japonicus
Leonurus galeobdolon	Lamium galeobdolon
Leonurus glaucescens	L. cardiaca
Leonurus heterophyllus	L. sibiricus
Leonurus tataricus	L. cardiaca
Leonurus villosus	L. cardiaca
Leopoldia comosa	Muscari comosum
Leopoldia spreitzenhoferi	Muscari spreitzenh.
Leopoldia tenuiflora	Muscari tenuiflorum
Lepachis pinnata	Ratibida pinnata
Lepachys columnifera	Ratibida columnifera
Lepia	Lepidium
Lepidanthus phyllanthoides -Nutt.	Andrachne phyllanth.
Lepidium accedens	L. campestre
Lepidium bursa-pastoris	Capsella bursa-past.
Lepidium campicola	L. campestre
Lepidium denticulatum	L. campestre

Synonym	Current Name	Synonym	Current Name
Lepidium didymum	Coronopus didymus	Leucanthemum mawii	Rhodanthemum
Lepidium draba	Cardaria draba		gayanum
Lepidium errabundum	L. campestre	Leucanthemum maximum misapplied	L. x superbum
Lepidium vagum	L. campestre	Leucanthemum maximum uliginosum	Leucanthemella
Leptandra virginica	Veronicastrum virg.		serotina
Leptilon canadense	Conyza candense	Leucanthemum nipponicum	Nipponanthemum nipp.
Leptinella hispida	Cotula hispida	Leucanthemum paludosum	Chrysanthemum palud.
Leptinella pectinata v sericea	L. albida	Leucanthemum vulgare May Queen	L. vulgare 'Maikonigin'
Leptinella reptans	L. scariosa	Leucanthemum x superbum 'Everest'	L. x s. 'Mount Everest'
Leptopetion -Schott	Biarum -Schott	L. x superbum 'Little Princess'	L. x superbum
Leptopogon furcatus	Andropogon gerardii		'Silberprinzesschen'
Leptospermum abnorme	L. brachyandrum	L. x superbum 'Tizi-n-Test'	Rhodanthemum cat.
Leptospermum citratum	L. petersonii		'Tizi-n-Test'
Leptospermum cunninghamii	L. myrtifolium	L. x superbum Sunshine	L. x s. 'Sonnenschein'
Leptospermum ericoides	Kunzea ericoides	Leucocasia -Schott	Colocasia -Schott
Leptospermum eriocalyx	L. parvifolium	Leucocoma dasycarpa	Thalictrum dasyc.
Leptospermum flavescens -Sm.	L. polygalifolium	Leucojum hiemale	L. nicaeense
L. flavescens misapplied	L. glaucescens	Leucopogon colensoi -Hook. f.	Cyathodes colensoi
Leptospermum floribundum	L. scoparium	Leucopogon parviflorus	Cyathodes parviflora
Leptospermum humifusum -Schauer	L. rupestre -Hook. f.	Leucospermum conocarpum	L. conocarpodendron
Leptospermum imbricatum	Triplarina imbricata	Leucospermum nutans	L. cordifolium
L. lanigerum 'Cunninghamii'	L. myrtifolium	Leucothamnus montanus	Thomasia montana
L. lanigerum 'Silver Sheen'	L. myrtifolium 'Silver Sheen'	Leucothamnus polyspermus	Thomasia rugosa
		Leucothoe acuminata -(Ait.) G.Don	Agarista populifolia
Leptospermum leucodendron	Melaleuca leucadendra	Leucothoe catesbaei h.	L. walteri
Leptospermum longifolium	L. parviflorum	Leucothoe chlorantha -not DC.	L. grayana -Maxim.
Leptospermum oligandrum	Kunzea podantha	Leucothoe editorum	L. walteri
Leptospermum phylicoides	Kunzea ericoides	Leucothoe populifolia	Agarista populifolia
Leptospermum podanthum	L. oligandrum	Leucothoe spicata -(Wats.) D.Don	L. racemosa
Leptospermum porophyllum	L. polygalifolium	Leucothoe walteri	L. fontanesiana
Leptospermum prostratum	L. rupestre	Leuzea centaureoides	Stemmacantha centau.
Leptospermum pubescens -Lam.	L. lanigerum -(Ait.) Sm.	Levisticum levisticum	L. officinale
Leptospermum rodwayanum	L. grandiflorum	Levisticum paludapifolium	L. officinale
L. scoparium v prostratum h.	L. rupestre -Hook. f.	Levisticum persicum	L. officinale
Leptosyne calliopsidea	Coreopsis calliopsidea	Lewisia longifolia	L. cotyledon v cotyled.
Leptosyne gigantea	Coreopsis gigantea	Lewisia nevadensis bernardina	L. nevadensis
Leptosyne maritima	Coreopsis maritima	Lewisia pygmaea ssp longipetala	L. longipetala
Lespedeza bicolor v alba -Bean	L. thunbergii 'Albiflora'	Lewisia Rainbow mixture	L. cotyledon
L. bicolor v intermedia f albiflora	L. thunbergii 'Albiflora'		'Regenbogen'
Lespedeza hedysaroides	L. juncea	Leymus giganteus	L. racemosus
Lespedeza japonica -Bailey	L. thunbergii 'Albiflora'	Leymus hispidus	Elymus hispidus
Lespedeza sericea	L. cuneata	Lhotzkya	Calytrix
Lespedeza sieboldii -Miq.	L. thunbergii	Liatris callilepis	L. spicata
Lespedeza tiliifolia	Desmodium elegans	Liatris scabra	L. aspera
Leucaena leucocephala	L. latisiliqua	Liatris scariosa	L. aspera
Leucantha cyanus	Centaurea cyanus	Liatris spheroidea	L. aspera
Leucanthemopsis hosmariensis	Rhodanthemum hosm.	Liatris spicata callilepis	L. spicata
Leucanthemopsis radicans	L. pectinata	Liatris spicata Goblin	L. spicata 'Kobold'
Leucanthemum arcticum	Arctanthemum arc.	Libertia chilensis	L. formosa
Leucanthemum atlanticum	Rhodanthemum atlan.	Libertia laurencei	L. pulchella
Leucanthemum catananche	Rhodanthemum cat.	Libocedrus chilensis -(D.Don) Endl.	Austrocedrus chilensis
Leucanthemum corymbosum	Tanacetum corymbos.	Libocedrus decurrens -Torr.	Calocedrus decurrens
Leucanthemum hosmariensis	Rhodanthemum hosm.	Libocedrus doniana -(Hook.) Endl.	L. plumosa
Leucanthemum ircutianum	L. vulgare	Libocedrus formosana -Florin	Calocedrus formosana
Leucanthemum leucanthemum	L. vulgare	Libocedrus macrolepis	Calocedrus macrolepis

Synonym	Current Name	Synonym	Current Name
Libocedrus tetragona -(Hook.) Endl.	L. uvifera	Lilium 'Mr.Ruud'	L. 'Ruud'
Libonia	Justicia	Lilium 'Prominence'	L. 'Firebrand'
Libonia floribunda	Justicia rizzinii	Lilium 'Royal Gold'	L. regale 'Royal Gold'
Licuala muelleri	L. ramsayi	Lilium 'Uchida Kanoka'	L. speciosum 'Uchida'
Ligularia clivorum	L. dentata	Lilium 'White American'	L. longiflorum 'White
Ligularia oblongata	Cremanthodium oblong.		American'
Ligularia reniformis	Cremanthodium renif.	Lilium 'White Pixie'	L. 'Snow Crystal'
Ligularia sibirica v speciosa	L. fischeri	Lilium 'Yellow Giant'	L. 'Joanna'
Ligularia smithii	Senecio smithii	Lilium pyrenaicum v aureum	L. pyr. v pyrenaicum
Ligularia tangutica	Sinacalia tangutica	Lilium pyrenaicum yellow	L. pyr. v pyrenaicum
Ligularia tussilaginea	Farfugium japonicum	Lilium Red Knight (Red Night according to RHS dictionary,	
Ligularia x palmatiloba	L. x yoshizoeana	though the PF lists this separately)	L. 'Roter Cardinal'
	'Palmatiloba'	Lilium shastense	L. kelleyanum
Ligusticum acutilobum	Angelica acutiloba	Lilium szovitsianum	L. monadelphum
Ligusticum carvi	Carum carvi	Lilium tenuifolium	L. pumilum
Ligusticum chinense	Conioselinum chinense	Lilium thunbergianum	L. maculatum
Ligusticum foeniculum	Foeniculum vulgare	Lilium tigrinum	L. lancifolium
Ligusticum gingidium	Angelica sylvestris (A.	Lilium willmottiae	L. davidii v willmottiae
	montana -(J.R.&G.Forst) Cock.	Lilium 'Aristo'	L. 'Orange Aristo'
Ligusticum ibukicola	Angelica acutiloba	Lilium 'Delta'	L. leichtlinii 'Delta'
Ligusticum levisticifolium	Levisticum officinale	Lilium 'Elite'	L. 'Gibraltar'
Ligusticum levisticum	Levisticum officinale	Lilium 'Le Reve'	L. 'Joy'
Ligusticum monnieri	Cnidium monnieri	Lilium 'Marhan'	L. x dalhansonii
Ligusticum podagraria	Aegopodium podagr.		'Marhan'
Ligusticum vaginatum	Conioselinum vaginat.	Lilium 'Mr.Ed'	L. 'Ed'
Ligustrina pekinensis -(Rupr). Dieck	Syringa reticulata ssp	Lilium albanicum	L. pyrenaicum ssp
	pekinensis		carniolicum v albanic.
Ligustrum acuminatum -Koehne	L. tschonoskii	Lilium auratum 'Gold Band'	L. au. v platyphyllum
Ligustrum brachystachyum -Decne.	L. quihoui -Carr.	Lilium canadense v flavum	L. canadense
Ligustrum chenaultii	L. compactum	Lilium canadense v rubrum	L. canad. v coccineum
Ligustrum formosanum -Rehd.	L. pricei -Hayata	Lilium carniolicum	L. pyrenaicum ssp
L. ibota -Sieb. & Zucc. (1846)	L. obtusifolium		carniolicum
Ligustrum insulare -Decne.	L. vulgare 'Insulense'	Lilium cordatum	Cardiocrinum cordatu.
Ligustrum insulense -Decne.	L. vulgare 'Insulense'	Lilium cordifolium	Cardiocrinum cordat.
Ligustrum ionandrum -Diels	L. delavayanum -Hariot	Lilium giganteum	Cardiocrinum gigant.
Ligustrum italicum -Mill.	L. vulgare v italicum	Lilium heldreichii	L. chalcedonicum
Ligustrum japonicum 'Coriaceum'	L. j. 'Rotundifolium'	Lilium longiflorum 'Mount Carmel'	L. longiflorum 'Carmel'
L. ovalifolium 'Aureomarginatum'	L. ovalifolium 'Aureum'	Lilium maculatum v davuricum	L. dauricum
Ligustrum ovalifolium 'Variegatum'	L. oval. 'Argenteum'	Lilium martagon v dalmaticum	L. m. v cattaniae
Ligustrum ovalifolium multiflorum	L. sinense 'Multiflorum'	Lilium ponticum	L. pyrenaicum ssp pon.
Ligustrum pekinensis	Syringa reticulata ssp	Lilium x maculatum v davuricum	L. dauricum
	pekinensis	Lilium x marhan 'J.S.Dijt'	L. 'Jacques S.Dijt'
Ligustrum prattii -Koehne	L. delavayanum	Lilloa -Speg.	Synandrospadix -Engl.
Ligustrum regelianum -Koehne	L. obtusifolium v regel.	Limnanthemum nymphoides	Nymphoides peltata
Ligustrum sinense floribundum	L. sinense 'Multiflorum'	Limnanthemum peltatum	Nymphoides peltata
Ligustrum sinense v multiflorum	L. sinense 'Multiflorum'	Limnetis glomerata	Dactylis glomerata
Ligustrum sinense v stauntonii	L. stauntonii -DC.	Limnocharis humboldtii	Hydrocleys nymphoides
Ligustrum suspensum	Forsythia suspensa	Limnonesis -Klot.	Pistia -L.
Ligustrum texanum	L. japonicum 'Texanum'	Limodorum autumnale	Spiranthes cernua
Ligustrum vulgare 'Fastigiatum'	L. vulgare 'Pyramidale'	Limonium dumosum	Goniolimon tataricum v
Ligustrum vulgare 'Sempervirens'	L. vulgare v italicum		angustifolium
Ligustrum vulgare v insulense	L. vulgare 'Insulense'	Limonium globulariifolium	L. ramosissimum
Ligustrum vulgare v sempervirens	L. vulgare v italicum	Limonium latifolium	L. platyphyllum
Ligustrum x vicaryi	L. 'Vicaryi'	Limonium reticulata	L. bellidifolium
Ligustrum yunnanense -Henry	L. compactum -Brandis	Limonium speciosum	Goniolimon incanum

Synonym	Current Name	Synonym	Current Name
Limonium spicata	Psylliostachys spicata	L. styraciflua 'Aurea Variegata'	L. styr. 'Variegata'
Limonium suworowii	Psylliost. suwororii	Liquidambar styraciflua 'Aurea'	L. styr. 'Variegata'
Limonium tataricum	Goniolimon tataricum	Liriodendron figo -Lour.	Michelia figo
Limonium tetragonum	L. dregeanum	Liriodendron tulipifera 'Pyramidale'	L. tul. 'Fastigiatum'
Linanthastrum	Linanthus	Liriodendron tulipifera v chinense	L. chinense
Linaria 'Globosa Alba'	Cymbalaria muralis 'Globosa Alba'	Liriope 'Big Blue'	L. muscari 'Big Blue'
		Liriope exiliflora Silvery Sunproof	L. ex. 'Ariaka-janshige'
Linaria aequitriloba	Cymbalaria aequitrilob.	Liriope graminifolia misapplied	L. muscari
Linaria cymbalaria	Cymbalaria muralis	Liriope graminifolia v densiflora	L. muscari
Linaria genistifolia ssp dalmatica	L. dalmatica	Liriope hyacinthifolia	Reineckea carnea
Linaria glareosa	Chaenorhinum glareos.	Liriope muscari 'Alba'	L. m. 'Monroe White'
Linaria glutinosa	L. bipunctata	Liriope muscari 'Evergreen Giant'	L. muscari gigantea
Linaria grandiflora	L. dalmatica	L. muscari 'Majestic' misapplied	L. exiliflora
Linaria hepaticifolia	Cymbalaria hepaticifol.	Liriope platyphylla	L. muscari
Linaria linaria	L. vulgaris	Liriope spicata 'Silver Dragon'	L. spicata 'Gin-ryu'
Linaria minor	Chaenorrhinum minus	Liriopsis fuscata -(Andr.) Spach	Michelia figo
Linaria origanifolia	Chaenorrhinum originif.	Liriosma ovata	Dulacia inopiflora
Linaria pallida	Cymbalaria pallida	Lisianthus russelianus	Eustoma grandiflorum
Linaria pilosa	Cymbalaria pilosa	Lithagrostis lacryma-jobi	Coix lacryma-jobi
Linaria praetermissa	Chaenorrhinum minus	Lithodora graminifolia	Moltkia suffruticosa
Linaria purpurea 'Alba'	L. purpurea 'Springside White'	Lithodora x intermedia	Moltkia x intermedia
		Lithophragma bulbiferum	L. glabrum
L. purpurea 'Radcliffe Innocence'	L. purpurea 'Springside White'	Lithops bella	L. karasmontana ssp bella
Linaria tristis 'Lurida'	L. tr. v lurida 'Toubkal'	Lithops hookeri	L. turbiniformis
Linaria viscida	Chaenorrhinum minus	Lithops kuibisensis	L. schwantesii
Lindelofia anchusiflora h.	L. longiflora	Lithops schwantesii v kuibisensis	L. schwantesii
Lindelofia anchusoides misapplied	L. longiflora	Lithospermum arvense	Buglossoides arvensis
Lindelofia spectabilis	L. longiflora	Lithospermum diffusum -Lag.	Lithodora diffusa
Lindera cercidifolia -Hemsl.	L. obtusiloba -Blume	Lithospermum doerfleri	Moltkia doerfleri
Lindera cercidifolia h.	L. praetermissa	Lithospermum graminifolium -Viv.	Moltkia suffruticosa
Lindera hypoglauca -Maxim.	L. umbellata -Thynb.	L. officinale ssp erythrorhizon	L. erythrorhizon
Lindera membranacea -Maxim.	L. umbellata -Thynb.	Lithospermum oleifolium	Lithodora oleifolia
L. triloba h.not (Sieb & Zucc.) Blume	L. obtusiloba -Blume	Lithospermum petraeum	Moltkia petraea
Linnaea americana	L. borealis ssp americ.	Lithospermum prostratum -Loisel.	Lithodora diffusa
Linnaea engleriana	Abelia engleriana	Lithospermum purpureocaeruleum	Buglossoides purpuro.
Linnaea schumannii	Abelia schumannii	Lithospermum rosmarinifolium	Lithodora rosmarinif.
Linnaea umbellata	Abelia umbellata	Lithospermum x intermedium	Moltkia x intermedia
Linosyris vulgaris	Aster linosyris	Lithospermum zahnii	Lithodora zahnii
Linum alpinum	L. perenne ssp alpinum	Litobrochia endlicheriana	Pteris zahlbruckeriana
Linum bulgaricum	L. tauricum	Litocarpus cordifolia	Aptenia cordifolia
Linum monogynum 'Nelson'	L. monog. v diffusum	Litsea aestivalis -(L.) Fern.	Lindera benzoin
Linum perenne Blue Sapphire	L. per. 'Blau Saphir'	Litsea glauca -Sieb.	Neolitsea sericea
Linum salsoloides	L. suffruticosum ssp salsoloides	Littaea geminiflora -Tagliabue	Agave geminiflora
		Livistona oliviformis	L. chinensis
Linum sibiricum	L. perenne	Lizeron arvensis	Convolvulus arvensis
Lippia canescens	Phyla nodiflora v can.	Lloydia graeca	Gagea graeca
Lippia chamaedrifolia	Verbena peruviana	Loasa lateritia	Caiophora lateritia
Lippia citriodora -(Ortega) H.B.K.	Aloysia triphylla	Loathoe pomeridiana	Chlorogalum pomerid.
Lippia nodiflora	Phyla nodiflora	Lobeira macdougallii	Nopalxochia macdoug.
Lippia repens	Phyla nodiflora	Lobelia 'Cinnabar Deep Red'	L. 'Fan Tiefrot'
Liquidambar acerifolia -Maxim.	L. formosana -Hance	Lobelia 'Cinnabar Rose'	L. 'Fan Zinnoberrosa'
Liquidambar formosana v monticola	L. form. Monticola Gr.	Lobelia 'Flamingo'	L. 'Pink Flamingo'
Liquidambar imberbe -Ait.	L. orientalis -Mill.	Lobelia 'Hadspen Purple'	L. x gerardii 'Hadspen Purple'
Liquidambar peregrina -L.	Comptonia peregrina		

Synonym	Current Name	Synonym	Current Name
Lobelia 'Zinnoberrosa'	L. 'Fan Zinnoberrosa'	Lochnera rosea	Catharanthus roseus
Lobelia angulata	Pratia angulata	Lomandra dura	L. multiflora ssp dura
Lobelia bellidifolia	L. erinus	Lomandra endlicheri	L. nigricans
Lobelia benguellensis	L. erinus	Lomandra glauca ssp collina	L. collina
Lobelia bracteolata	L. erinus	Lomandra glauca ssp nana	L. nana
Lobelia cavanillesii	L. laxiflora	Lomandra longifolia ssp exilis	L. longifolia
Lobelia Compliment Blue	L. 'Kompliment Blau'	Lomandra longifolia ssp hystrix	L. hystrix
Lobelia Compliment Deep Red	L. 'Kompliment Tiefrot'	Lomandra longifolia ssp longifolia	L. longifolia
Lobelia Compliment Purple	L. 'Kompliment Purpur'	Lomandra micrantha v soraria	L. mic. ssp tuberculata
Lobelia Compliment Scarlet	L. 'Kompliment Scharlach'	Lomandra montana	L. spicata
		Lomandra tropica ssp arnhemica	L. tropica
Lobelia erinoides	L. erinus	Lomaria	Blechnum
Lobelia erinus 'Richardii'	L. richardsonii	Lomaria acuminata	Blechnum norfolkianum
Lobelia Fan Deep Red	L. 'Fan Tiefrot'	Lomaria aggregata	Blechnum chambersii
Lobelia Fan Deep Rose	L. 'Fan Orchidrosa'	Lomaria alpina	Blechnum penna-marina
Lobelia filiformis	L. erinus		
Lobelia fulgens Saint Elmo's Fire	L. fulgens 'Elmfeuer'	Lomaria antarctica	B. penna-marina
Lobelia graminea -Lam.	L. cardinals ssp gram.	Lomaria blechnoides	Blechnum ambiguum
Lobelia lacustris	L. dortmanna	Lomaria capense v scabrum	Blechnum camfieldii
Lobelia lavandulacea	L. erinus	Lomaria gibba	Blechnum gibbum
Lobelia lydenburgensis	L. erinus	Lomaria lanceolata	Blechnum norfolkianum
Lobelia nuda	L. erinus	Lomaria magellanica	Blechnum chilense
Lobelia pedunculata	Pratia pedunculata	Lomaria norfolkianum	Blechnum norfolkianum
Lobelia perpusilla	Pratia perpusilla	Lomaria procera v paludosa	Blechnum minus
Lobelia phyllostachya	L. cardinals	Lomaria spicant	Blechnum spicant
Lobelia physaloides	Pratia physaloides	Lomaria vulcanica	Blechnum vulcanicum
Lobelia radicans	L. chinensis	Lomatia arguta	L. myricoides
Lobelia repens	Pratia repens	Lomatia densa	L. myricoides
Lobelia rosulata	L. erinus	Lomatia fallacina	L. myricoides
Lobelia schrankii	L. erinus	Lomatia fraseri v fraseri	L. fraseri
Lobelia secunda	L. erinus	Lomatia fraseri v pinnatipartita	L. fraseri
Lobelia senegalensis	L. erinus	Lomatia fraseri v velutina	L. fraseri
Lobelia splendens	L. cardinals	Lomatia ilicifolia -R.Br.	L. arborescens
Lobelia strictiflora	L. kalmii	Lomatia ilicifolia -R.Br.	L. arborescens
Lobelia taccada	Scaevola taccada	Lomatia longifolia -R.Br.	L. myricoides
Lobelia transvaalensis	L. erinus	Lomatia obliqua	L. hirsuta -(Lam.) Diels
Lobelia treadwellii	Pratia angulata 'Treadwellii'	Lomatia polymorpha v cinerea -R.Br.	L. polymorpha
		Lomatia polymorpha v rufa -R.Br.	L. polymorpha
Lobelia vedrariensis	L. x gerardii 'Vedrariensis'	Lomatia silaifolia f angustifolia	L. silaifolia
		Lomatia silaifolia f latifolia	L. silaifolia
Lobelia wildii	L. erinus	L. silaifolia h. in part not (Sm.) R.Br.	L. tinctoria
Lobivia arachnacantha	Echinopsis arachnac.	Lomatia silaifolia v divaricata	L. silaifolia
Lobivia aurea	Echinopsis aurea	Lomatia silaifolia v induta	L. silaifolia
Lobivia backebergii	Echinopsis backebergii	Lomatia silaifolia v pinnata	L. silaifolia
Lobivia bruchii	Echinopsis bruchii	Lomatia silaifolia v stenoloba	L. silaifolia
Lobivia caespitosa	Echinopsis maximiliana	Lomatia silaifolia v typica	L. silaifolia
Lobivia cinnabarina	Echinopsis cinnabarina	Lomatium graveolens	Anethum graveolens
Lobivia densispina	Echinopsis kuehnrichii	Lomatium kingii	Anethum graveolens
Lobivia ferox	Echinopsis ferox	Lomatophyllum citreum	L. occidentale v citr.
Lobivia huascha	Echinopsis huascha	Lonas inodora	L. annua
Lobivia pentlandii	Echinopsis pentlandii	Lonicera 'Clavey's Dwarf'	L. x xylosteoides 'Clavey's Dwarf'
Lobivia pygmaea	Rebutia pygmaea		
Lobivia silvestrii	Echin. chamaecereus	Lonicera 'Dropmore Scarlet'	L. x brownii 'Dropmore Scarlet'
Lobularia halimifolia -not(Bois.)Steud.	L. maritima		
Lobularia strigulosa	L. maritima	Lonicera 'Early Cream'	L. caprifolium

Synonym	Current Name	Synonym	Current Name
Lonicera 'Gold Flame'	L. x heckrottii 'Gold Flame'	Lonicera x americana misapplied	L. x italica
		L. x brownii 'Fuchsioides' misapplied	L. x brownii 'Dropmore Scarlet'
Lonicera aureoreticulata h.	L. japonica 'Aureoreticulta'	Lonicera xerocalyx -Diels	L. deflexicalyx v xeroc.
Lonicera brachypoda -DC.	L. japonica v repens	Lonicera yunnanensis	Dipelta yunnanensis
Lonicera brachypoda v repens -Sieb.	L. japonica v repens	Lonicera zabelii -h.	L. tatarica 'Zabelii'
Lonicera bracteata -Royle	L. hispida v bracteta	Lonicera zabelii -Rehd.	L. korolkowii v zabelii
Lonicera caprifolium f pauciflora	L. x italica	Lophanthus anisatus	Agastache foeniculum
Lonicera caroliniana	L. sempervirens -L.	Lophanthus rugosus	Agastache rugosa
Lonicera chinensis -Wats.	L. japonica v repens	Lophiolepis dubia	Cirsium vulgare
Lonicera ciliosa v occidentalis	L. ciliosa -(Pursh) Poir.	Lophion aduncum	Voila adunca
Lonicera delavayi -Franch.	L. similis v delavayi	Lophocereus schottii	Pachycereus schottii
Lonicera diervilla -L.	Diervilla lonicera -Mill.	Lophodium spinosum	Pachycereus schottii
Lonicera diversifolia -Wall.	L. quinquelocularis	Lopholoma alpestris	Centaurea scabiosa
Lonicera etrusca v brownii -Reg.	L. x brownii	Lopholoma scabiosa	Centaurea scabiosa
Lonicera flexuosa -Thunb.	L. japonica v repens	Lophomyrtus x ralphii 'Gloriosa'	L. x ralphii 'Variegata'
Lonicera germanica	L. periclymenum -L.	Lophomyrtus x ralphii 'Tricolor'	L. x ralphii 'Sundae'
Lonicera gibbiflora -Maxim.	L. chrysantha	Lophophora echinata	L. williamsii
Lonicera giraldii misapplied	L. acuminata	Lophophora lutea	L. williamsii
Lonicera glauca -Hill	L. dioica -L.	Lorinseria areolata	Woodwardia areolata
Lonicera glaucohirta	L. periclymenum v gl.	Loropetalum chinense 'Burgundy'	L. chinense f rubrum
Lonicera grata -Ait.	L. x americana	Loropetalum indicum -K.Tong	L. chinense
Lonicera henryi v subcoriacea	L. henryi	Lotus dorycnium -L.	Lotus pentaphyllus ssp pentaphyllus
Lonicera hispida v chaetocarpa	L. chaetocarpa		
Lonicera insularis	L. morrowii	Lotus mascaensis misapplied	L. sessilifolius
Lonicera japonica 'Peter Adams'	L. j. 'Horwood Gem'	Lotus pedunculatus	L. uliginosus
Lonicera japonica 'Variegata'	L. j. 'Aureoreticulata'	Lotus siliquosus	L. maritimus
Lonicera japonica v chinensis	L. japonica v repens	Lotus suffruticosus	L. pentaphyllus ssp pentaphyllus
Lonicera japonica v flexuosa	L. japonica v repens		
L. japonica v repens 'Red Coral'	L. japonica 'Superba'	Luetkea sibbaldioides -Bong.	L. pectinata
L. korolkowii v zabelii misapplied	L. tatarica 'Zabelii'	Luffa aegyptica	L. cyclindrica
Lonicera ledebourii -Eschs.	L. involucrata v ledeb.	Lunaria biennis	L. annua
Lonicera ligustrina v yunnanensis	L. nitida -Wils.	Lunaria inodora	L. annua
Lonicera nitida 'Silver Lining'	L. pileata 'Silver Lining'	Lunaria ovalis	L. annua
Lonicera nitida Maygreen	L. nitida 'Maigrun'	Lupinus 'Dwarf Lulu'	L. 'Lulu'
Lonicera occidentalis -(Lindl.) Hook.	L. ciliosa -(Pursh) Poir.	Lupinus cruckshankii	L. mutabilis crucksh.
Lonicera odora	L. periclymenum -L.	Lupinus lyallii	L. lepidus v lobbii
Lonicera orientalis v caucasica	L. caucasica -Pall.	Lupinus pilosus	L. varius ssp orientalis
L. periclymenum 'Belgica' misapplied	L. x italica	Luzula maxima	L. sylvatica
Lonicera periclymenum 'Florida'	L. p. 'Serotina'	Luzula maxima 'Aurea'	L. sylvatica 'Aurea'
Lonicera periclymenum 'Late Red'	L. p. 'Serotina'	Luzula sylvatica 'A. Rutherford'	L. s. 'Taggart's Cream'
Lonicera pileata v yunnanensis	L. nitida -Wils.	Luzula sylvatica 'Aureomarginata'	L. sylvatica 'Marginata'
Lonicera pilosa -Maxim.	L. strophiophora	Lycaste candida	L. brevispatha
Lonicera pubescens -Sweet	L. hirsuta -Eaton	Lycaste gigantea	L. longipetala
Lonicera rupicola	L. syringantha	Lycaste virginalis	L. skinneri
Lonicera sachalinensis	L. maximowiczii v sac.	Lychnis agrostemma	Agrostemma githago
L. sempervirens 'Dropmore Scarlet'	L. x brownii 'Dropmore Scarlet'	Lychnis coeli-rosi	Silene coeli-rosi
		L. coronaria 'Abbotswood Rose'	L. x walkeri 'Abbotswood Rose'
Lonicera spinosa v albertii	L. albertii -Reg.		
Lonicera sullivantii -A. Gray	L. prolifera	Lychnis dioica	Silene dioica
Lonicera syringantha	L. rupicola v syringan.	Lychnis flos-jovis 'Minor'	L. flos-jovis 'Nana'
Lonicera tenuipes -Nakai	L. gracilipes	Lychnis githago	Agrostemma githago
Lonicera translucens -Carr.	L. quinquelocularis f translucens	Lychnis kubotae	x Lycene kubotae
		Lychnis lagascae	Petrocoptis pyrenaica ssp glaucifolia
Lonicera virgniana	L. sempervirens -L.		

Synonym	Current Name	Synonym	Current Name
Lychnis segetalis	Agrostemma githago	Machaeranthera pattersonii	M. bigelovii
Lychnis viscaria 'Flore Pleno'	L. v. 'Splendens Plena'	Machaerocereus eruca	Stenocereus eruca
Lychnis viscaria alpina	L. viscaria	Machilus ichangensis -Rehd. & Wils.	Persea ichangensis
Lychnis yunnanensis alba	L. yunnanensis	Macleaya cordata misapplied	M. x kewensis
Lycianthes rantonnettii	Solanum rantonnettii	Maclura aurantiaca -Nutt.	M. pomifera
Lycium barbarum v chinense	L. barbarum -L.	Maclura tricuspidata -Carr.	Cudrania tricuspidata
Lycium boerhaavifolium -L.	Grabowskia boerhaavi.	Macrobriza maxima	Briza maxima -L.
Lycium chinense -Mill.	L. barbarum -L.	Macrocarpium chinense	Cornus chinensis
Lycium chinense v ovatum	L. barbarum -L.	Macrodiervilla	Weigela
Lycium chinense v rhombifolium	L. barbarum -L.	Macropiper crocatum	Piper ornatum
Lycium europaeum h. not L.	L. barbarum -L.	Macrotomia benthamii	Arnebia benthamii
Lycium grevilleanum -Miers	L. chinense -Bert.	Macrotomia echioides	Arnebia pulchra
Lycium halimifolium -Mill.	L. barbarum -L.	Macrotomia euchroma	Arnebia euchroma
Lycium halimifolium v lanceolatum	L. barbarum -L.	Macrozamia corallipes	M. spiralis
Lycium halimifolium v subglobosum	L. barbarum -L.	Macrozamia cylindrica	M. macleayi
Lycium lanceolatum -Veillard	L. barbarum -L.	Macrozamia dyeri	M. riedlei
Lycium mediterraneum -Dun.	L. europaeum -L.	Macrozamia fearnsidae	M. fearnsidei
Lycium megistocarpum -Dun.	L. barbarum -L.	M. pauli-guilielmi ssp flexuosa	M. flexuosa
Lycium ovatum -Veillard	L. barbarum -L.	M. pauli-guilielmi ssp plurinervia	M. machinii
Lycium rhombifolium -Dipp.	L. barbarum -L.	Magnolia 'Pickard's Sundew'	M. 'Sundew'
Lycium salicifolium -Mill.	L. europaeum -L.	Magnolia 'Schmetterling'	M. x soul. 'Pickard's
Lycium trewianum -Roem. & Schult.	L. barbarum -L.		Schmetterling'
Lycium vulgare -Dun.	L. barbarum -L.	Magnolia acuminata 'Miss Honeybee'	M. a. v subcordata
Lyconia cayculata	Chamaedaphne calycul.		'Miss Honeybee'
Lycoperdon gemmatum	L. perlatum	Magnolia acuminata v cordata	M. acuminata v
Lycopsis	Anchusa		subcordata
Lycopus angustifolius	L. americanus	Magnolia ashei	M. macrophylla ssp
Lycopus bracteatus	L. americanus		ashei
Lycopus heterophyllus	L. americanus	Magnolia auriculata -Bartr.	M. fraseri -Walt.
Lycopus longifolius	L. americanus	Magnolia campbellii ssp mollicomata	M. campbellii ssp moll.
Lycopus pauciflorus	L. americanus	Magnolia coatesii h.	M. 'Charles Coates'
Lycopus pensylvanicus	L. americanus	Magnolia compressa -Maxim.	Michelia compressa
Lycopus prealtus	L. americanus	Magnolia conspicua -Salisb.	M. denudata
Lycopus sinuatus	L. americanus	Magnolia cordata -Michx.	M. acuminata v
Lygodium scandens	L. japonicum		subcordata
Lygos monosperma -(L.)Heywood	Retama monosperma	Magnolia cordata 'Miss Honeybee'	M. acuminata v subcor
Lygos sphaerocarpa -(L.) Heywood	Retama sphaerocarpa		data 'Miss Honeybee'
Lyonia formosa -(Wall.) Hand.-Mazz.	Pieris formosa	Magnolia cylindrica misapplied	M. 'Pegasus'
Lyonia marginata -D.Don	L. lucida -(Lam.)	Magnolia denudata v elongata	M. sprengeri v elong.
	K.Koch	Magnolia denudata v purpurascens	M. sprengeri v diva
Lyonia paniculata -Nutt.	L. ligustrina -(L.) DC.	Magnolia discolor -Venten.	M. liliiflora
Lyonothamnus aspleniifolius -Greene	L. floribundus ssp asp.	Magnolia foetida -(L.) Sarg.	M. grandiflora -L.
L. floribundus v aspleniifolius	L. floribundus ssp asp.	Magnolia fuscata -Andr.	Michelia figo
Lysimachia ciliata 'Purpurea'	L. ciliata 'Firecracker'	Magnolia glauca -L.	M. virginiana -L.
Lysimachia japonica 'Minuta'	L. j. 'Minutissima'	Magnolia glauca v major -Sims	M. x thompsoniana
Lysimachia leschenaultii	L. atropurpurea	Magnolia glauca v thompsoniana	M. x thompsoniana
Lysimachia lyssii	L. congestiflora	Magnolia grandiflora 'Exoniensis'	M. gran. 'Exmouth'
Lysimachia punctata 'Variegata'	L. punctata 'Alexander'	Magnolia grandiflora 'Lanceolata'	M. gran. 'Exmouth'
Lysimachia punctata misapplied	L. verticillaris	Magnolia halliana -Parsons	M. stellata
Lysimachia punctata verticillata	L. verticillaris	Magnolia heptapeta	M. denudata
Lysistigma -Schott	Taccarum -Brongn.	Magnolia hypoleuca	M. obovata -Thunb.
Lythrum salicaria Firecandle	L. s. 'Feuerkerze'	M. hypoleuca -not Sieb. & Zucc.	M. officinalis
Lythrum tomentosum -not D.C.	L. salicaria -L.	Magnolia insignis -Wall.	Manglietia insignis
Lythrum verticillatum	Decodon verticillatus	Magnolia kobus 'Norman Gould'	M. stellata 'Norman
Maackia hupehensis -Takeda	M. chinensis -Takeda		Gould'

Synonym	Current Name	Synonym	Current Name
Magnolia kobus v loebneri	M. x loebneri	Mahonia toluacensis -Bean	M. 'Heterophylla'
Magnolia kobus v stellata	M. stellata	Maianthemum dilatatum	M. bifolium v
Magnolia macrophylla ssp ashei	M. ashei		kamtschaticum
Magnolia mollicomata -W.W.Sm.	M. campbellii ssp molli.	Maianthemum racemosum	Smilacina racemosa
Magnolia nicholsoniana	M. wilsonii	Maianthemum stellatum	Smilacina stellata
Magnolia obovata -Diels	M. officinalis	Mairrania alpina	Arctous alpina
Magnolia obovata -Thunb.	M. hypoleuca	Mairrania uva-ursi	Arctostaphylos uva-u.
Magnolia obovata -Willd. not Thunb.	M. liliiflora -Desrouss.	Majorana hortensis	Origanum majorana
Magnolia parviflora -not Blume	M. wilsonii	Majorana onites	Origanum onites
Magnolia parviflora v wilsonii	M. sieboldii -K.Koch	Malus 'Admiration'	M. 'Adirondack'
Magnolia pumila -Andre	M. coco	Malus 'Aldenhamensis'	M. x purpurea
Magnolia purpurea -Curtis	M. liliiflora -Desrouss.		'Aldenhamensis'
Magnolia pyramidata	M. fraseri v pyramid.	Malus 'Echtermeyer'	M. x gloriosa
Magnolia quinquepeta	M. liliiflora		'Oekonomierat
Magnolia salicifolia 'W.B.Clarke'	M. 'W.B.Clarke'		Echtermeyer'
Magnolia sinensis	M. sieboldii ssp sinen.	Malus 'Golden Hornet'	M. x zumi 'Golden
Magnolia sprengeri diva -Stapf	M. sprengeri v diva		Hornet'
Magnolia sprengeri elongata	M. sprengeri v elong.	Malus 'Hillieri'	M. x schiedeckeri
Magnolia taliensis -W.W.Sm.	M. wilsonii		'Hillieri'
Magnolia thurberi	M. kobus -DC.	Malus 'Kaido'	M. x micromalus
Magnolia tomentosa -Thunb.	M. stellata	Malus 'Magdeburgensis'	M. x magdeburgensis
Magnolia tsarongensis -W.W.Sm.	M. globosa	Malus 'Profusion'	M. x moerlandsii
Magnolia umbrella -Desrouss.	M. tripetala -L.		'Profusion'
Magnolia virginiana v foetida -L.	M. grandiflora -L.	Malus 'Red Jade'	M. x schiedeckeri 'Red
Magnolia wilsonii f. nicholsoniana	M. wilsonii		Jade'
Magnolia wilsonii f. taliensis	M. wilsonii	Malus 'Red Siberian'	M. x robusta 'Red
Magnolia x highdownensis	M. wilsonii		Siberian'
Magnolia x kewensis 'Kewensis'	M. x k. 'Kew Clone'	Malus 'Yellow Siberian'	M. x robusta 'Yellow
Magnolia x lennei	M. x soulangeana		Siberian'
	'Lennei'	Malus acerba -Merat	M. sylvestris -(L.) Mill.
M. x soulangeana 'Alba Superba'	M. x soulangeana 'Alba'	Malus communis -Poir. in part	M. domestica - Borkh.
Magnolia x soulangeana 'Nigra'	M. liliiflora 'Nigra'	Malus coronaria 'Flore Pleno'	M. c. 'Charlottae'
M. x soulangeana 'Pickard's Sundew'	M. 'Sundew'	Malus crataegifolia	M. florentina
Magnolia x soulangeana 'Red Lucky'	M. 'Hong Yur'	Malus diversifolia	M. fusca
M. x soulangeana 'Rubra' misapplied	M. x s. 'Rustica Rubra'	Malus docynioides -Schneid.	Docynia rufifolia
Magnolia x watsonii	M. x weiseneri	Malus domestica 'American Mother'	M. domestica 'Mother'
Magnolia yulan -Desf.	M. denudata	Malus domestica 'Balsam'	M. domestica 'Green
Maguirea -A. D. Hawkes	Dieffenbachia -Schott		Balsam'
Mahonia 'Aldenhamensis'	M. x wagneri	M. domestica 'Bewley Down Pippin'	M. domestica 'Crimson
	'Aldenhamensis'		King'
Mahonia 'Undulata'	M. x wagneri	Malus domestica 'Blenheim Red'	M. d. 'Red Blenheim'
	'Undulata'	Malus domestica 'Boston Russet'	M. d. 'Roxbury Russet'
Mahonia acanthifolia	M. napaulensis	Malus domestica 'Delbards'	M.d. Jubilee (Delbards)
Mahonia aquifolium 'Fascicularis'	M. x wagneri 'Pinnacle'	M. dom. 'Doctor Kidds Orange Red'	M. domestica 'Kidd's
Mahonia aquifolium 'Heterophylla'	M. 'Heterophylla'		Orange Red'
Mahonia aquifolium 'Moseri'	M. x wagneri 'Moseri'	M. domestica 'Dumeller's Seedling'	M. d. 'Dummellor's
Mahonia bealei	M. japonica Bealei Gr.		Seedling'
Mahonia eutriphylla	M. trifolia	Malus domestica 'Early Victoria'	M. d. 'Emneth Early'
Mahonia fascicularis -DC.	M. x wagneri 'Pinnacle'	Malus domestica 'Early Worcester'	M. d. 'Tydeman's Early
Mahonia glumacea	M. nervosa		Worcester'
Mahonia japonica 'Hiemalis'	M. japonica 'Hivernant'	Malus domestica 'Echtermeyer'	M. x gloriosa
Mahonia nana -(Greene) Fedde	M. repens		'Oekonomierat
Mahonia neubertii v ilicifolia	x Mahoberberis neub.		Echtermeyer'
Mahonia pinnata misapplied	M. x wagneri 'Pinnacle'	M. domestica 'Emperor Alexander'	M. d. 'Alexander'
Mahonia schiedeana -Schlecht	M. trifolia	Malus domestica 'Epicure'	M. d. 'Laxton's Epicure'

Synonym	Current Name	Synonym	Current Name
Malus domestica 'Flamenco'	M. domestica 'Obelisk'	Malus spectabilis v plena -Bean	M. spectabilis
Malus domestica 'Forfar'	M. d. 'Dutch Mignonne'	Malus sylvestris v paradisiaca	M. pumila -Mill.
Malus domestica 'Fortune'	M.d. 'Laxton's Fortune'	Malus theifera -Rehd.	M. hupehensis
Malus domestica 'Gala Royal'	M. d. 'Royal Gala'	Malus toringoides	M. bhutanica
Malus domestica 'Green Roland'	M. domestica 'Greenup's Pippin'	Malus x purpurea 'Pendula'	M. x gl. 'Oekonomierat Echtermeyer'
M. domestica 'Isaac Newton's Tree'	M. d. 'Flower of Kent'	Malus x purpurea f eleyi	M. x purpurea 'Eleyi'
Malus domestica 'Jackson's'	M. d. 'Crimson King'	Malus x zumi 'Calocarpa'	M. x zumi v calocarpa
Malus domestica 'John Toucher's'	M. d. 'Crimson King'	Malva bicolor	Lavatera maritima
M. domestica 'Jonagold Crowngold'	M. d. 'Crowngold'	Malva capensis	Anisodontea capensis
Malus domestica 'Jubilee'	M. d.a 'Royal Jubilee'	Malva crispa	M. verticillata 'Crispa'
Malus domestica 'Laxton's Epicure'	M. domestica 'Epicure'	Malva involucrata	Callirhoe involucrata
Malus domestica 'Laxton's Fortune'	M. domestica 'Fortune'	Malva montana	M. verticillata
Malus domestica 'Mondial Gala'	M. d. 'Gala Mondial'	Malva moschata 'Romney Marsh'	Althaea officinalis 'Romney Marsh'
Malus domestica 'Port Wine'	M. domestica 'Harry Master's Jersey'	Malvastrum capense	Anisodontea capensis
Malus domestica 'Red Jonagold'	M. d. 'Jonagored'	Malvastrum capensis	Anisodontea capensis
M. domestica 'Reine des Reinettes'	M. domestica 'King of the Pippins'	Malvastrum coccineum	Sphaeralcea coccinea
		Malvastrum peruvianum	Modiolastrum peruv.
M. d. 'Saint Edmund's Russet'	M. domestica 'Saint Edmund's Pippin'	Malvastrum x hypomadarum	Anisodontea x hypom.
		Malvaviscus arboreus v mexicanus	M. arboreus
M. domestica 'Sir Isaac Newton's'	M. d. 'Flower of Kent'	Malvaviscus conzattii	M. arboreus v drummondii
M. domestica 'Snell's Glass Apple'	M. d. 'Glass Apple'		
Malus domestica 'Sour Natural'	M. d. 'Langworthy'	Malvaviscus grandiflorus	M. arb. v drummondii
Malus domestica 'Stone's'	M. d. 'Loddington'	Malvaviscus mollis	M. arboreus
Malus domestica 'Superb'	M. d. 'Laxton's Superb'	Malvaviscus penduliflorus	M. arboreus
Malus domestica 'Wellington'	M. domestica 'Dumellor's Seedling'	Mamillopsis senilis	Mammillaria senilis
		Mammillaria centricirrha	M. magnimamma
M. d. 'Wellspur Red Delicious'	M. d. 'Wellspur'	Mammillaria conoidea	Neolloydia conoidea
Malus domestica 'Woodbine'	M. d. 'Northwood'	Mammillaria dealbata	M. haageana
Malus domestica 'Wyatt's Seedling'	M. d. 'Langworthy'	Mammillaria shurliana	M. blossfeldiana
Malus domestica Crispin	M. domestica 'Mutsu'	Mandevilla suaveolens -Lindl.	M. laxa
Malus domestica Katy	M. domestica 'Katja'	Mandevilla tweediana	M. laxa
Malus domestica Miel d'Or	M. d. 'Honeygold'	Mandevilla x amabilis 'Alice du Pont'	M. x amoena 'Alice du Pont'
Malus domestica Swiss Orange	M. domestica 'Schweizer Orange'		
Malus floribunda purpurea -Barbier	M. x purpurea	Manettia bicolor	M. luteorubra
Malus floribunda v atrosanguinea	M. x atrosanguinea	Manettia inflata	M. luteorubra
Malus niedzwetzkyana	M. pumila 'Niedzwetzkyana'	Manfreda	Agave
		Maranta leuconeura 'Erythroneura'	M. leu. v erythroneura
Malus pashia v sikkimensis -Wenzig	M. sikkimensis	Maranta leuconeura 'Kerchoveana'	M. leu. v kerchoveana
Malus Perpetu	M. 'Evereste'	Maranta leuconeura 'Massangeana'	M. leu. v massangeana
M. pumila -authors, in part, not Mill.	M. domestica - Borkh.	Maranta makoyana	Calathea makoyana
Malus pumila h.	M. sylvestris	Marginatocereus marginatus	Stenocereus marginat.
Malus pumila v domestica	M. domestica - Borkh.	Margyricarpus setosus	M. pinnatus
Malus pumila v niedzwetskyana	M. p. 'Niedzwetskyana'	Margyricarpus setosus	M. pinnatus
Malus pumila v paradisiaca	M. pumila -Mill.	Mariscus	Cyperus
Malus ringo -Sieb.	M. prunifolia v rinki	Mariscus mariscus	Cladium mariscus
Malus rivularis -(Hook.) Roem.	M. fusca	Markhamia platycalyx	M. lutea
Malus sargentii	M. toringo ssp sargen.	Marlea platanifolium -Sieb. & Zucc.	Alangium platanifolium
Malus sieboldii -(Reg.) Rehd.	M. toringo	Marniera chrysocardium	Epiphyllum chrysoc.
Malus sieboldii 'Calocarpa'	M. x zumi v calocarpa	Marrubium candidissimum	M. incanum
Malus sieboldii v zumi	M. x zumi	Marsdenia erecta -(L.) R.Br.	Cionura erecta Marsea
Malus sinensis -Dum.-Cours.	Pseudocydonia sinens.	canadensis	Conyza canadensis
Malus spectabilis v kaido -Sieb.	M. x micromalus -Mak.	Martynia	Proboscidea
		Mascarena	Hyophorbe

Synonym	Current Name
Masdevallia bella	Dracula bella (unv)
M. elephantipes v pachysepala	M. mooreana
Masdevallia ignea	M. militaris
Massovia -K. Koch	Spathiphyllum -Schott
Matricaria arctica	Arctanthemum arct.
Matricaria chamomilla	M. recutita
Matricaria coronata	M. recutita
Matricaria corymbosa	Tanacetum corymbos.
Matricaria courrantiana	M. recutita
Matricaria eximia	Tanacetum parthenium
Matricaria inodora	Tripleurospermum maritimum
Matricaria kochiana	M. recutita
Matricaria leucanthemum	Leucanthemum vulgare
Matricaria maritima	Tripleurospermum ma.
Matricaria parthenium	Tanacetum parthenium
Matricaria patens	M. recutita
Matricaria pusilla	M. recutita
Matricaria pyrethroides	M. recutita
Matricaria salina	M. recutita
Matricaria segetum	Glebionis segetum
Matricaria suaveleons	M. recutita
Matteuccia intermedia	Onoclea intermedia
Matteuccia pensylvanica	M. struthiopteris
Matthiola annua	M. incana
Matthiola fenestralis	M. incana
Matthiola glabra	M. incana
Matthiola glabrata	M. incana
Matthiola graeca	M. incana
Matthiola rupestris	M. incana
Matthiola simpliciulis	M. incana
Matthiola thessala	M. fruticulosa
Matthiola undulata	M. incana
Matthiolaria	Matthiola
Matucana aurantiaca	Oreocereus aurantiac.
Matucana haynei	Oreocereus haynei
Matucana intertexta	Oreocereus intertexta
Maurandia	Maurandya
Maurandya 'Pink Ice'	Lophospermum scandens 'Pink Ice'
Maurandya 'Red Dragon'	Lophospermum 'Red Dragon'
Maurandya erubescens	Lophospermum erub.
Maurandya lophantha	Lophosperm. scandens
Maurandya lophospermum	Lophosperm. scandens
Maxillaria meleagris	M. cucullata
Maximiliana vitifolium	Cochlospermum vitifol.
Maytenus chilensis -DC.	M. boaria -Mol.
Mazus rugosus	Mazus reptans
Meconopsis 'Blue Ice'	M. 'Lingholm' fertile
Meconopsis 'James Cobb'	M. integrifolia ssp inte grifolia 'Wolong'
Meconopsis baileyi	M. betonicifolia
Meconopsis cambrica 'Rubra'	M. c.'Frances Perry'
Meconopsis grandis -GS 600	M. George Sherriff Gr.

Synonym	Current Name
Meconopsis grandis misapplied	M. George Sherriff Gr.
Meconopsis horridula v racemosa	M. racemosa v racem.
Meconopsis nudicaulis	Papaver nudicaule
Meconopsis wallichii	M. napaulensis
M. x sheldonii misapplied sterile	M. Infertile Blue Group
Medicago echinus	M. intertexta
Megadenus capitatus	Eleocharis elliptica
Megadenus palustris	Eleocharis palustris
Megalodonta beckii	Bidens beckii
Megalodonta nudata	Bidens beckii
Megalonium	Aeonium
Megapterum	Oenothera
Megasea	Bergenia
Megotigea -Raf.	Helicodiceros -Schott
Meibomia canadensis	Desmodium canadensis
Meibomia michauxii	Desmod. rotundifolium
Meibomia nudiflora	Desmodium nudiflorum
Meibomia rotundifolia	Desmod. rotundifolium
Meistera cernua -Sieb. & Zucc.	Enkianthus cernuus
Melaleuca acacioides ssp alsophila	M. alsophila
Melaleuca acacioides v angustifolia	M. acacioides
Melaleuca acerosa	M. systena
Melaleuca angulata	M. suberosa
Melaleuca arenaria	M. tuberculata v aren.
Melaleuca armillaris v tenuifolia	M. diosmatifolia
Melaleuca brachyphylla	M. microphylla
Melaleuca brachystachya	M. subfalcata
Melaleuca callistemonea	M. lateritia
Melaleuca calycina ssp dempta	M. dempta
Melaleuca canaliculata	M. pentagona
Melaleuca canescens	M. incana
M. cardiophylla v longistaminea	M. longistaminea
Melaleuca cardiophylla v parviflora	M. coronicarpa
Melaleuca carinata	M. calycina
Melaleuca chlorantha	M. diosmifolia
Melaleuca coccinea eximia	M. eximia
Melaleuca coccinea ssp penicula	M. penicula
Melaleuca concava	M. acuminata ssp websteri
Melaleuca cordata v ovata	M. conothamnoides
Melaleuca coronata	M. thymifolia
Melaleuca corrugata	M. fulgens ssp corrug.
Melaleuca costata	Angophora costata
Melaleuca crassifolia	M. lateriflora
Melaleuca crassifolia	M. laxiflora
Melaleuca crosslandiana	M. nervosa
Melaleuca cuneata	M. leptospermoides
Melaleuca cupressina	M. thyoides
Melaleuca curvifolia	M. lanceolata
Melaleuca curvifolia	M. sieberi
Melaleuca cuspidata	Conothamnus trinervis
M. cuticularis v brachyphylla	M. halmaturorum
Melaleuca cylindrica	M. diosmatifolia
Melaleuca cymbifolia	M. halmaturorum
Melaleuca daleana	M. bracteata

Synonym	Current Name	Synonym	Current Name
Melaleuca decussata v ovoides	M. decussata	Melaleuca longicoma	M. macronychia
Melaleuca deltoidea	M. cucullata	Melaleuca magnifica	Asteromyrtus magnif.
Melaleuca densa v dorrien-smithii	M. densa	Melaleuca maidenii	M. quiquinervia
Melaleuca discolor	M. thymifolia	Melaleuca mimosoides	M. leucadendra
Melaleuca divaricata	M. violacea	Melaleuca minutifolia ssp monantha	M. monantha
Melaleuca drummondii	M. hamata	Melaleuca monticola	M. bracteata
Melaleuca elachophylla	M. depauperata	Melaleuca myrtifolia	M. squarrosa
Melaleuca elegans	M. decussata	Melaleuca neglecta	M. brevifolia
M. eleuterostachya v abietana	M. adnata	Melaleuca nervosa f latifolia	M. nervosa
Melaleuca epacridioides	M. densa	Melaleuca nervosa f pendulina	M. fluviatilis
Melaleuca eremaea	M. trichophylla	Melaleuca nesophylla	M. nesophila
Melaleuca eriantha	M. leptospermoides	Melaleuca nodosa v tenuifolia	M. nodosa
Melaleuca ericaefolia	M. armillaris	Melaleuca nummularia	M. elliptica
Melaleuca ericifolia v erubescens	M. diosmatifolia	Melaleuca oligantha	M. thymifolia
Melaleuca erubescens	M. diosmatifolia	Melaleuca orara	M. brevifolia
Melaleuca eruciformis	M. blaeriifolia	Melaleuca ornata	M. seriata
Melaleuca exarata	M. suberosa	Melaleuca ottonis	M. squamea
Melaleuca fasciculiflora	M. brevifolia	Melaleuca parviflora -Lindl.	M. lateriflora
Melaleuca foliosa	M. diosmifolia	Melaleuca parviflora -Otto	M. thymifolia
Melaleuca fraseri	M. diosmatifolia	Melaleuca parviflora v latifolia	M. sieberi
Melaleuca genistifolia	M. decora	Melaleuca parviflora v leiostachya	M. lanceolata -Otto
Melaleuca genistifolia v coriacea	M. bracteata	Melaleuca parviflora v pubescens	M. lanceolata -Otto
Melaleuca glaucocalyx	M. bracteata	Melaleuca pauciflora	M. biconvexa
Melaleuca gnidiifolia	M. thymifolia	Melaleuca pentagona v subulifolia	M. pentagona
Melaleuca gunniana	M. ericifolia	Melaleuca pinifolia	M. ericifolia
Melaleuca gunniana v capitata	M. ericifolia	Melaleuca polygaloides	M. incana
Melaleuca hakeacea	M. teretifolia	Melaleuca preissiana v leiostachya	M. lanceolata -Otto
Melaleuca hakeoides	M. glomerata	Melaleuca propinqua	M. densa
M. halmaturorum ssp cymbifolia	M. halmaturorum	Melaleuca pubescens	M. lanceolata -Otto
Melaleuca halmaturorum v enervis	M. halmaturorum	Melaleuca punicea	Petraeomyrtus pun.
M. halmaturorum v tuberculifera	M. halmaturorum	Melaleuca quinquenervia	M. viridiflora v
Melaleuca heliophila	M. ericifolia		rubriflora
Melaleuca howeana	M. ericifolia	Melaleuca saligna	M. cajuputi
Melaleuca hypochondriaca	M. incana	Melaleuca semiteres	M. teretifolia
Melaleuca juniperina	M. nodosa	Melaleuca seorsiflora	M. lanceolata -Otto
Melaleuca juniperoides	M. nodosa	Melaleuca serpyllifolia	M. thymifolia
Melaleuca lanceolata	M. deanei	Melaleuca smithii	M. quinquenervia
M. lanceolata ssp occidentalis	M. lanceolata -Otto	Melaleuca splendens	M. fulgens ssp fulgens
Melaleuca lanceolata ssp planifolia	M. lanceolata -Otto	Melaleuca squamea v glabra	M. squamea
Melaleuca lateriflora v elliptica	M. lateriflora	Melaleuca squarrosa v glabrata	M. squarrosa
Melaleuca lehmannii	M. viminea	Melaleuca steedmanii	M. fulgens
Melaleuca leptoclada	M. pauciflora	Melaleuca stenostachya v pendula	M. saligna
Melaleuca leucadendra f ruscifolia	M. arcana	M. styphelioides v squamophoia	M. squamophloia
Melaleuca leucadendra v albida	M. quiquinervia	Melaleuca tamariscina ssp irbyana	M. irbyana
M. leucadendra v angustifolia	M. quiquinervia	M. tamariscina ssp pallescens	M. pallescens
Melaleuca leucadendra v coriacea	M. quiquinervia	Melaleuca tenella	M. incana ssp tenella
M. leucadendra v mimosoides	M. leucadendra	Melaleuca tenuifolia	M. nodosa
Melaleuca leucadendra v minor	M. cajuputi	Melaleuca tenuissima	M. microphylla
Melaleuca leucadendra v nervosa	M. nervosa	Melaleuca ternifolia	M. ericifolia
Melaleuca leucadendra v parvifolia	M. deanei	Melaleuca tetragona	M. decussata
Melaleuca leucadendra v saligna	M. saligna	Melaleuca tomentosa	M. incana
Melaleuca linariifolia v alternifolia	M. alternifolia	Melaleuca viminalis	Callistemon viminalis
M. linariifolia v trichostachya	M. trichostachya	Melaleuca viminea v major	M. viminea
Melaleuca linariifolia v typica	M. linariifolia	Melaleuca violacea v petiolata	M. platycalyx
Melaleuca loguei	M. lasiandra	Melaleuca viridiflora v angustifolia	M. quinquinervia

Synonym	Current Name	Synonym	Current Name
Melaleuca viridiflora v rubriflora	M. quinquinervia	Mentha flexuosa	M. arvensis
Melaleuca waeberi	M. pentagona	Mentha glabra	M. arvensis
Melaleuca websteri	M. acuminata ssp web.	Mentha glabrior	M. arvensis
Melanchrysum rigens	Gazania rigens	Mentha hirsuta	M. aquatica
Melandrium	Vaccaria	Mentha incana	M. longifolia
Melandrium elisabethae	Silene elisabethae	Mentha insularis	M. suaveolens
Melandrium keiskei	Silene keiskei	Mentha lanata	M. arvensis
Melandrium rubrum	Silene dioica	Mentha macrostachya	M. suaveolens
Melasphaerula graminea	M. ramosa	Mentha maculata	M. arvensis
Melia australis	M. azedarach	Mentha nemerosa v alopecuroides	M. x villosa f alopec.
Melia azedarach v japonica	M. azedarach	Mentha nigricans	M. x piperita
Melia japonica	M. azedarach	Mentha odorata	M. x piperita f citrata
Melianthium cochinchinensis	Asparagus cochinchin.	Mentha piperita v citriodora	M. x piperita f citrata
Melianthium luteum	Chionographis japonica	Mentha pulegiformis	M. arvensis
Melica effusa	Milium effusum	M. pulegium 'Dwarf Pennyroyal'	M. pulegium
Melilotus arvensis	M. officinalis		'Cunningham Mint'
Melilotus vulgaris	M. officinalis	Mentha rotundifolia -(L.) Hudson	M. x villosa
Meliosma cuneifolia -Franch.	M. dillenifolia ssp cun.	Mentha rotundifolia 'Bowles'	M. x villosa f alopec
Meliosma dilatata -Diels	M. parviflora -Lecomte		uroides Bowles' Mint
Meliosma oldhamii Miq.	M. pinnata v oldhamii		
Meliosma parvifolia h.	M. parviflora -Lecomte	Mentha rotundifolia misapplied	M. suaveolens
Meliosma pendens -Rehd. & Wils.	M. dilleniifolia ssp	Mentha rubra v raripila	M. x smithiana
	flexuosa	Mentha sylvestris -L.	M. longifolia
Meliosma stewardii -Merr.	M. myriantha ssp ste.	Mentha tenuifolia	M. arvensis
Meliosma tenuis -Maxim.	M. dillenifolia ssp ten.	Mentha viridis	M. spicata
Melissa acinos	Acinos arvensis	Mentha x gentilis	M. x gracilis
Melissa arvensis	Acinos arvensis	Mentha x gentilis 'Aurea'	M. x gracilis 'Variegata'
M. officinalis 'Variegata' misapplied	M. officinalis 'Aurea'	Mentha x gentilis 'Variegata'	M. x gracilis 'Variegata'
Melissa vulgaris	Clinopodium vulgare	Mentha x gracilis 'Aurea'	M. x gracilis 'Variegata'
Melocactus actinacanthus	M. matanzanus	Mentzelia aurea	M. lindleyi
Melocactus communis	M. intortus	Menyanthes crista-galli	Nephrophyllidium c-gal.
Melocactus macrodiscus	M. zehntneri	Menziesia alba	Daboecia cantabrica f
Melocactus oaxacensis	M. curvispinus		alba
Menispermum carolinum -L.	Coccolus carolinus	Menziesia alba lasiophylla	M. ciliicalyx v
Menispermum palmatum	Jateorhiza palmata		purpurea
Menispermum trilobum -Thunb.	Coccolus orbiculatus	Menziesia aleutica -Spreng.	Phyllodoce aleutica
Menomphalus scabiosa	Centaurea scabiosa	Menziesia bryantha -(L.) Swartz	Bryanthus gmelinii
Mentha 'Eau de Cologne'	M. x piperita f citrata	Menziesia caerulea	Phyllodoce caerulea
Mentha 'Sayakaze'	M. arvensis v piperas	Menziesia ciliicalyx lasiophylla	M. cil. v purpurea
	cens 'Sayakare'	Menziesia empetriformis -Sm.	Phyllodoce empetrif.
		Menziesia glanduliflora -Hook.	Phyllodoce glanduliflor.
Mentha angustifolia -Corb.	M. x villosa	Menziesia globularis -Salisb.	M. pilosa -(Michx.)
Mentha angustifolia -Host	M. arvensis		Juss. (ferruginea?)
Mentha aquatica krause minze	M. aquatica v crispa	Menziesia intermedia -Hook.	P. x intermedia
Mentha austriaca	M. arvensis	Menziesia lasiophylla -Nakai	M.ciliicalyx v purpurea
Mentha borealis	M. arvensis	Menziesia multiflora -Maxim.	M. ciliicalyx v multifl.
Mentha Bowles' Mint	M. x villosa v	Menziesia polifolia	Daboecia cantabrica
	alopecuroides	Menziesia purpurea h.	M.ciliicalyx v purpurea
Mentha canadensis	M. arvensis	Meratia praecox	Chimonanthus praecox
Mentha cardiaca	M. x gracilis	Merendera bulbocodium	M. montana
Mentha citrata	M. x piperita f citrata	Merendera caucasica	M. trigyna
Mentha cordifolia	M. x villosa	Merendera eichleri	M. trigyna
Mentha corsica	M. requienii	Merendera pyrenaica	M. montana
Mentha crispa L. (1753)	M. spicata v crispa	Merendera raddeana	M. trigyna
Mentha crispa L. (1763)	M. aquatica v crispa	Meriolix	Oenothera
Mentha elata	M. arvensis	Mertensia asiatica	M. simplicissima

Synonym	Current Name	Synonym	Current Name
Mertensia maritima ssp asiatica	M. simplicissima		quinquinervia
Mertensia pterocarpa	M. sibirica	Metrosideros decora	Melaleuca decora
Mertensia pulmonarioides	M. virginica	Metrosideros floribunda	Angophora floribunda
Merxmuellera	Rytidosperma	Metrosideros glomulifera	Syncarpia glomulifera
Meryta sinclairii 'Variegata'	M. sinclairii 'Moonlight'	Metrosideros gummifera	Eucalyptus gummifera
Mesembryanthemum 'Basutoland'	Delosperma nubigenum	Metrosideros hispida	Angophora hispida
Mesembryanthemum acinaciforme	Carpobrotus acinacif.	Metrosideros hypericifolia	Melaleuca hypericifolia
Mesembryanthemum blandum	Lampranthus blandus	Metrosideros hyssopifolia	Melaleuca linariifolia
Mesembryanthemum brownii	Lampranthus brownii	Metrosideros juniperina	Melaleuca nodosa
Mesembryanthemum cordifolium	Aptenia cordifolia	Metrosideros linearis -Sm.	Callistemon linearis
Mesembryanthemum criniflorum	Dorotheanthus	Metrosideros lucida	M. umbellata
	bellidiformis	Metrosideros nodosa	Melaleuca nodosa
M. derenbergianum	Ebracteola derenberg.	Metrosideros pallidus -Bonpl.	Callistemon pallidus
Mesembryanthemum edule	Carpobrotus edulis	Metrosideros pungens	Melaleuca nodosa
Mesembryanthemum multiradiatum	Lampranthus roseus	Metrosideros quinquinervia	Melaleuca quinquiner.
Mesembryanthemum ornatulum	Delosperma ornatulum	Metrosideros salicifolia -Gaertn.	Eucalyptus crebra
Mesembryanthemum putterillii	Ruschia putterillii	Metrosideros salignus -Sm.	Callistemon salignus -
Mesembryanthemum tricolor	Dorotheanthus	M. salignus v viridiflorus	Callistemon viridiflorus
	gramineus	Metrosideros speciosa -Sims	Callistemon speciosus -
Mespilus amelanchier -L.	Amelanchier ovalis	Metrosideros tomentosa	M. excelsa
Mespilus amelanchier v canadensis	Amelanchier canadens.	Metrosideros villosa	M. sclerocarpa
Mespilus arborea -Michx. f.	Amelanchier arborea	Metrosideros viminalis	Callistemon viminalis
Mespilus arbutifolia v melanocarpa	Aronia melanocarpa	Metrosideros viridiflorus -Sims	Callistemon viridiflorus
Mespilus canadensis -L.	Amelanchier canadens.	Meum foeniculum	Foeniculum vulgare
Mespilus canadensis v obovalis	Amelanchier obovalis	Meum piperitum	Foeniculum vulgare
Mespilus canadensis v oligocarpa	Amelanch. bartramiana	Meyenia erecta	Thunbergia erecta
Mespilus cotoneaster -L.	Cotoneaster	Meyenia fasciculata -Schlecht.	Cestrum fasciculatum
	integerrimus -Med.	Michelia excelsa -Blume	M. doltsopa
Mespilus crenulata -D.Don	Pyracantha crenulata	Michelia fuscata - (Andr.) Wall.	M. figo -(Lour.) Spreng
Mespilus flabellata -Spach	Crataegus flabellata	Michelia sinensis	M. wilsonii
Mespilus fontanesiana -Spach	Crataegus fontanes.	Microcasia -Becc.	Bucephalandra -Schott
Mespilus grandiflora -Smith	+ Crataegomespilus	Microcoelum	Lytocaryum
	grandiflora	Microculcas -A. Peter	Gonatopus
Mespilus japonica -Thunb.	Eriobotrya japonica	Microglossa albescens -(DC.)C.B.Cl.	Aster albescens
Mespilus lobata -Poir.	+ Crataegomespilus	Microlaena	Ehrharta
	grandiflora	Micromeles japonica	Sorbus japonica
Mespilus oliveriana -Dum. Cours.	Crataegus oliveriana	Micromeria arkansana	Calamintha arkansana
Mespilus phaenopyrum L. f.	Crataegus phaenopyr.	Micromeria corsica	Acinos corsicus
Mespilus pruinosa -Wendl.	Crataegus pruinosa	Micromeria douglasii	M. chamissonis
Mespilus prunifolia -Lam.	Crataegus persimilis	Micromeria glabella	Calamintha arkansana
	'Prunifolia'	Micromeria pygmaea	Satureja montana
Mespilus pyracantha -L.	Pyracantha coccinea	Micromeria rupestris	M. thymifolia
Mespilus racemiflorus -Desf.	Cotoneaster racemifl.	Microseris ringens h.	Leontodon rigens
Mespilus smithii -Smith	+ Crataegomespilus	Microsorum diversifolium	Phymatosorus diversif.
	grandiflora	Mikania ternata	M. dentata
Mespilus tanacetifolia -Lam.	Crataegus tanacetifolia	Miliarium effusum	Milium effusum
Metapanax	Pseudopanax	Milium confertum	Milium effusum
Metasequoia glyptostroboides 'Fastigiata'		M. effusum 'Bowles' Golden Grass'	M. effusum 'Aureum'
	M. glyptostroboides	Milium schmidtianum -C. Koch	Milium effusum
	'National'	Milium transsilvanicum -Schur	Milium effusum
Metrosideros anomala	Angophora hispida	Milium virgatum	Panicum virgatum
Metrosideros armillaris	Melaleuca armillaris	Milla caerulea	Androstephium
Metrosideros calycina	Melaleuca thymifolia		caeruleum
Metrosideros citrinus -Curt.	Callistemon citrinus	Miltonia phalaenopsis	Miltoniopsis phalaenop.
Metrosideros coriacea	Melaleuca	Miltonia roezlii	Miltoniopsis roezlii

147

Synonym	Current Name	Synonym	Current Name
Mimetes lyrigera	M. cucullatus		'Nanus Variegatus'
Mimosa alata	Acacia alata	Miscanthus yakushimensis	M. s. 'Little Kitten'
Mimosa arborea -Forssk.	Albizia julibrissin	Miscanthus yakushimensis	M. sinensis 'Yaku-jima'
Mimosa biflora	Acacia biflora	Mnemion cornutum	Viola cornuta
Mimosa binervia	Acacia binervia	Mnium	Plagiomnium
Mimosa brownei	Acacia brownii	Mohria carolina	Halesia carolina
Mimosa decurrens -Wendl.	Acacia decurrens	Mohrodendron carolinum	Halesia carolina
Mimosa farnesiana	Acacia farnesiana	Molinia altissima	M. caerulea ssp
Mimosa floribunda -Vent.	Acacia longifolia v flor.		arundinacea
Mimosa juniperina -Vent.	Acacia decurrens	Molinia litoralis	M. c. ssp arundinacea
Mimosa longifolia -Andr.	Acacia longifolia	Molopospermum circutarium	M. peloponnesiacum
Mimosa sophorae -Labill.	Acacia longifolia v sop.	Moltkia graminifolia -(Viv.) Nyman	M. suffruticosa
Mimosa verticillata -L'Herit.	Acacia verticillata	Molucella frutescens -L.	Ballota frutescens
Mimulus 'Andean Nymph'	M. naiandinus	Momordica elateria	Ecballium elaterium
Mimulus 'Wine Red'	M. bifidus 'Verity	Momordica lanata	Citrullus lanatus
	Purple'	Monarda 'Libra'	M. 'Balance'
Mimulus aurantiacus orange	M. au. v puniceus	Monarda 'Pisces'	M. 'Fishes'
Mimulus bifidus 'Wine'	M. bif. 'Verity Purple'	Monarda 'Scorpio'	M. 'Scorpion'
Mimulus glutinosus	M. aurantiacus	Monarda 'Snow Maiden'	M. 'Schneewittchen'
Mimulus glutinosus -Wendl.	M. aurantiacus -Curt.	Monarda 'Snow White'	M. 'Schneewittchen'
Mimulus glutinosus atrosanguineus	M. aurantiacus v	Monarda 'Snow Witch'	M. 'Schneewittchen'
	puniceus	Monarda austromontana	M. citriodora ssp au.
Mimulus glutinosus luteus	M. aurantiacus	Monarda Blue Stocking	M. 'Blaustrumpf'
Mimulus langsdorffii	M. guttatus	Monarda Bowman	M. 'Sagittarius'
Mimulus luteus 'Variegatus'	M. luteus 'Gaby'	Monarda bradburiana	M. bradburyana
M. luteus 'Variegatus' misapplied	M. guttatus 'Richard	Monarda Firecrown	M. 'Feuerschopf'
	Bish'	Monarda Gemini	M. 'Twins'
Mimulus puniceus	M. aurantiacus v pun.	Monarda Prairie Night	M. 'Prarienacht'
Mimulus radicans	Mazus radicans	Mondo japonicum	Ophiopogon japonicus
Mimulus Red Emperor	M. 'Roter Kaiser'	Monolepis chenopodioides	M. nuttalliana
Mimulus sp -Mac&W 5257	M. 'Andean Nymph' -	Monopsis lutea	Lobelia lutea
	Mac&W 5257	Montbretia	Crocosmia
Mimulus x bartonianus	M. x harrisonii	Montia australasica	Neopaxia australasica
Mimulus yellow hose in hose	M. 'Orkney Gold'	Montia californica	Claytonia nevadensis
Mina	Ipomoea	Montia parvifolia	Naiocrene parvifolia
Mina lobata	Ipomoea lobata	Montia perfoliata	Claytonia perfoliata
Minuartia caucasica	M. circassica	Montia sibirica	Claytonia sibirica
Minuartia gerardii	M. verna ssp verna	Montia spathulata	Claytonia exigua
Minuartia parnassica	M. stellata	Moraea bicolor	Dietes bicolor
M. verna ssp caespitosa 'Aurea'	Sagina subulata v	Moraea chinensis	Belamcanda chinensis
	glabrata	Moraea glaucopsis	M. aristata
Minuartia verna ssp gerardii	M. verna ssp verna	Moraea herbertii	Cypella herbertii
Mirabilis uniflora	M. jalapa	Moraea iridioides	Dietes iridioides
Miscanthus floridulus misapplied	M. x giganteus	Moraea longifolia	Hexaglottis longifolia
Miscanthus sinensis 'Afrika'	M. oligostachyus	Moraea longifolia -Sweet	M. fugax
	'Afrika'	Moraea pavonia v lutea	M. bellendenii
Miscanthus sinensis 'Giganteus'	M. floridulus	Moraea robinsoniana	Dietes robinsoniana
Miscanthus sinensis 'Vittatus'	M. s. 'Variegatus'	Moraea spathacea	M. spathulata
Miscanthus sinensis Silver Feather	M. s. 'Silberfeder'	Morisia hypogaea	M. monanthos
M. s. v condensatus 'Central Park'	M. s. v condensatus	Morocarpus foliosus	Chenopodium foliosum
	'Cosmo Revert'	Morus acidosa -Griff	M. australis -Poir
M. s. v condensatus 'Emerald Giant'	M. s. v condensatus	Morus acidosa -Griff.	M. australis -Poir.
	'Cosmo Revert'	Morus alba 'Globosa'	M. alba 'Nana'
M. s. v purpurascens misapplied	M. 'Purpurascens'	Morus alba 'Skeletoniana'	M. alba 'Laciniata'
M. tinctorius 'Nanus Variegatus' mi.	M. oligostachyus	Morus alba f skeletoniana -Schneid.	M. alba 'Laciniata'

148

Synonym	Current Name	Synonym	Current Name
Morus alba laciniata -not K.Koch	M. alba 'Laciniata'	Muscarimia ambrosiacum	Muscari muscarimi
Morus alba v latifolia -Bur.	M. alba v multicaulis	Muscarimia macrocarpum	Muscari macrocarpum
Morus alba v mongolica -Bur.	M. mongolica	Musella lasiocarpa	Musa lasiocarpa
Morus alba v stylosa -(Ser.) Bur.	M. australis -Poir.	Mussaenda phillippica 'Aurorae'	M. 'Aurorae'
Morus bombycis	M. alba	Mutisia gayana -Remy	M. oligodon
Morus indica -Roxb. not L.	M. australis -Poir.	Mutisia hookeri -Meyen	M. subulata f
Morus kagayamae -Koidz	M. bombycis		rosmarinifolia
Morus multicaulis -Perrotet	M. alba v multicaulis	Mutisia linariifolia -Remy	M. subulata f rosmar.
Morus nigra 'King James'	M. nigra 'Chelsea'	Mutisia linearifolia -Hook.	M. subulata f rosmar.
Morus norwegica	Rubus chamaemorus	Mutisia retusa -Remy	M. spinosa v pulchella
Morus papyrifera -L.	Broussonetia papyr.	Mutisia retusa v glaberrima -Phil.	M. spinosa
Morus stylosa -Ser.	M. australis -Poir.	Myagrum sativum	Camelina sativa
Morus tatarica -Pall.	M. alba v tatarica	Myginda myrtifolia -Nutt.	Gyminda myrtifolia
Moschatella adoxa	Adoxa moschatellina -L.	Myoporum acuminatum v acumin.	M. acuminatum
Moschatellina adoxa	Adoxa moschatellina -L.	M. acuminatum v angustifolium	M. acuminatum
Mucuna deeringiana	M. pruriens v utilis	M. acuminatum v parviflorum	M. acuminatum
Muehlenbeckia axillaris misapplied	M. complexa	Myoporum betcheanum v pubescens	M. betcheanum
Muehlenbeckia complexa 'Nana'	M. axillaris -Walp.	Myoporum cunninghamii	M. acuminatum
Muehlenbeckia microphylla -Col.	M. complexa v microp.	Myoporum dampieri	M. acuminatum
Muehlenbeckia muricatula -Col.	M. ephedroides v muri.	Myoporum debile	Eremophila debilis
Muehlenbeckia nana h.	M. axillaris	Myoporum debile	Eremophila debilis
Muehlenbeckia platyclados	Homalocladium platyc.	Myoporum desertii	Eremophila deserti
Muehlenbeckia trilobata -Col.	M. complexa v trilobat.	Myoporum desertii	Eremophila deserti
Muehlenbeckia varians -Meissn.	M. complexa v trilobat.	Myoporum ellipticum	M. boninense ssp
Mulgedium	Cicerbita		australe
Mulgedium alpinum	Cicerbita alpina	Myoporum humile	M. parvifolium
Mulgedium plumieri	Cicerbita plumieri	Myoporum perforatum h.	M. laetum
Murraya exotica	M. paniculata	Myoporum refractum	M. brevipes
Musa arnoldiana	Ensete ventricosum	Myoporum salsoides	M. cordifolium
Musa cavendishii	M. acuminata 'Dwarf	Myoporum serratum v glandulosum	M. viscosum
	Cavendish'	Myosotidium nobile	M. hortensia
Musa coccinea	M. uranoscopus	Myosotis adpressa	M. scorpioides
Musa ensete	Ensete ventricosum	M. alpestris h. not F. W. Schmidt	M. sylvatica
Musa hookeri	M. sikkimensis	Myosotis annua	M. arvensis
Musa japonica h.	M. basjoo	Myosotis aspera	M. arvensis
Musa nana -auct.	M.a.'Dwarf Cavendish'	Myosotis collina	M. arvensis
Musa nana -Lour.	M. acuminata	Myosotis coronaria	M. scorpioides
Musa uranoscopus misapplied	M. coccinea	Myosotis decora	M. colensoi
M. x paradisiaca 'Dwarf Cavendish'	M. acuminata 'Dwarf	Myosotis densiflora	M. sylvatica
	Cavendish'	Myosotis hamosa	M. arvensis
Musa x sapientum	M. x paradisiaca	Myosotis hirta	M. scorpioides
Muscari ambrosiacum	M. muscarimi	Myosotis intermedia	M. arvensis
M. armeniacum 'Baby's Breath'	M. neglectum 'Baby's	Myosotis laxiflora	M. scorpioides
	Breath'	Myosotis macrantha	M. sylvatica
Muscari chalusicum	M. pseudomuscari	Myosotis montana	M. sylvatica
Muscari comosum 'Monstrosum'	M. com. 'Plumosum'	Myosotis monticola	M. arvensis
Muscari lingulatum	M. aucheri	Myosotis multiflora	M. scorpioides
Muscari moschatum	M. muscarimi	Myosotis myriantha	M. sylvatica
Muscari moschatum v flavum	M. macrocarpum	Myosotis oblongata	M. sylvatica
Muscari muscarimi v flavum	M. macrocarpum	Myosotis palustris	M. scorpioides
Muscari paradoxum	Bellevalia paradoxa	Myosotis perennis	M. scorpioides
Muscari pycnantha	Bellevalia paradoxa	Myosotis popovii	M. sylvatica
Muscari racemosum	M. neglectum	Myosotis praecox	M. scorpioides
Muscari tubergenianum	M. aucheri	Myosotis rupicola	M. alpestris
	'Tubergenianum'	Myosotis sylvatica alba	M. sylvatica f lactea

Synonym	Current Name	Synonym	Current Name
Myrceugenella apiculata	Luma apiculata		eleuterostachya
Myrceugenella chequen	Luma chequen	Myrtoleucodendron ellipticum	Melaleuca elliptica
Myrceugenia apiculata	Luma apiculata	Myrtoleucodendron erianthum	Melal. leptospermoides
Myrcia lechleriana -Miq.	Amomyrtus luma -	Myrtoleucodendron ericifolium	Melaleuca ericifolia
	Legr. & Kausel in part	Myrtoleucodendron fasciculiflorum	Melaleuca brevifolia
Myrica asplenifolia	Comptonia peregrina	Myrtoleucodendron filifolium	Melaleuca filifolia
Myrica asplenifolia -(L.) Ait.	Comptonia peregrina v	Myrtoleucodendron foliolosum	Melaleuca foliolosa
	asplenifolia -L.	Myrtoleucodendron fulgens	Melaleuca fulgens
Myrica carolinensis -Mill.	M. cerifera -L.	Myrtoleucodendron genistifolium	Melaleuca decora
M. carolin. -some authors, not Mill.	M. pensylvanica	Myrtoleucodendron gibbosum	Melaleuca gibbosa
Myrica cerifera v latifolia -Ait.	M. pensylvanica	Myrtoleucodendron glaberrimum	Melaleuca glaberrima
Myrica palustris	M. gale	Myrtoleucodendron globiferum	Melaleuca globifera
Myrica palustris -Lam.	M. gale -L.	Myrtoleucodendron glomeratum	Melaleuca glomerata
Myrica peregrina	Comptonia peregrina	Myrtoleucodendron hakeoides	Melaleuca glomerata
Myriophyllum brasiliense	M. aquaticum	Myrtoleucodendron hamulosum	Melaleuca hamulosa
Myriophyllum humile	M. verticillatum	Myrtoleucodendron holosericeum	Melaleuca holosericea
Myriophyllum pinnatum	M. verticillatum	Myrtoleucodendron huegelii	Melaleuca huegelii
Myriophyllum proserpinacoides	M. aquaticum	Myrtoleucodendron hypericifolium	Melaleuca hypericifolia
Myriopteris covillei	Cheilanthes covillei	Myrtoleucodendron incanum	Melaleuca incana
Myriopteris gracillima	Cheilanthes gracillima	Myrtoleucodendron lasiandrum	Melaleuca lasiandra
Myriopteris tomentosa	Cheilanthes tomentosa	Myrtoleucodendron lateriflorum	Melaleuca lateriflora
Myrmecophila tibicinis	Schomburgkia tibicinis	Myrtoleucodendron leiocarpum	Melaleuca leiocarpa
Myroxylon balsamum v pereirae	M. pereirae	Myrtoleucodendron leiopyxe	Melaleuca leiopyxis
Myroxylon peruiferum	M. pereirae	Myrtoleucodendron leptocaldum	Melaleuca pauciflora
Myroxylon toluiferum	M. balsamum	Myrtoleucodendron linariifolium	Melaleuca linariifolia
Myrrhis chaerophylloides	Anthriscus sylvestris	Myrtoleucodendron linophyllum	Melaleuca linophylla
Myrrhodes sylvestris	Anthriscus sylvestris	Myrtoleucodendron longicomum	Melal. macronychia
Myrsine africa v retusa -(Ait.) A.DC.	M. africana -L.	Myrtoleucodendron macronychium	Melale. macronychia
Myrsine retusa -Ait.	M. africana -L.	Myrtoleucodendron megacephalum	Melaleuca megaceph.
Myrtoleucodendron acacioides	Melaleuca acacioides	Myrtoleucodendron micromerum	Melaleuca micromera
Myrtoleucodendron acerosum	Melaleuca systena	Myrtoleucodendron microphyllum	Melaleuca microphylla
Myrtoleucodendron acuminatum	Melaleuca acuminata	Myrtoleucodendron minutifolium	Melaleuca minutifolia
Myrtoleucodendron adnatum	Melaleuca adnata	Myrtoleucodendron nesophilum	Melaleuca nesophila
Myrtoleucodendron alsophilum	Melaleuca alsophila	Myrtoleucodendron nodosum	Melaleuca nodosa
Myrtoleucodendron armillare	Melaleuca armillaris	Myrtoleucodendron oldfieldii	Melaleuca oldfieldii
Myrtoleucodendron basicephalum	Melaleuca basicephala	Myrtoleucodendron parviflorum	Melaleuca lateriflora
Myrtoleucodendron blaeriifolium	Melaleuca blaeriifolia	Myrtoleucodendron pauciflorum	Melaleuca pauciflora
M. brachystachyum	Melaleuca subfalcata	Myrtoleucodendron pauperiflorum	Melaleuca pauperiflora
Myrtoleucodendron calothamnoides	Melaleuca calothamn.	Myrtoleucodendron pentagonum	Melaleuca pentagona
Myrtoleucodendron calycinum	Melaleuca calycina	Myrtoleucodendron polycephalum	Melaleuca polycephala
Myrtoleucodendron cardiophyllum	Melaleuca cardiophylla	Myrtoleucodendron pulchelllum	Melaleuca pulchella
Myrtoleucodendron confertum	Melaleuca lecenantha	Myrtoleucodendron pustulatum	Melaleuca pustulata
Myrtoleucodendron cordatum	Melaleuca cordata	Myrtoleucodendron quadifarium	Melaleuca quadrifaria
Myrtoleucodendron crassifolium	Melaleuca lateriflora	Myrtoleucodendron radula	Melaleuca radula
Myrtoleucodendron cucullatum	Melaleuca cucullata	Myrtoleucodendron rhaphiophyllum	Melaleuca rhapiophylla
Myrtoleucodendron cylindra	Melaleuca diosmatifolia	Myrtoleucodendron scabrum	Melaleuca scabra
Myrtoleucodendron cymbifolium	Melaleuca halmatorum	Myrtoleucodendron seorsiflorum	Melaleuca lanceolata
Myrtoleucodendron deanei	Melaleuca deanei	Myrtoleucodendron seriatum	Melaleuca seriata
Myrtoleucodendron decussatum	Melaleuca decussata	Myrtoleucodendron sparsiflorum	Melaleuca sparsiflora
Myrtoleucodendron densum	Melaleuca densa	Myrtoleucodendron spathulatum	Melaleuca spathulata
Myrtoleucodendron depauperatum	Melaleuca depauperata	Myrtoleucodendron squameum	Melaleuca squamea
Myrtoleucodendron diissitiflorum	Melaleuca dissitiflora	Myrtoleucodendron squarrosum	Melaleuca squarrosa
Myrtoleucodendron diosmifolium	Melaleuca diosmifolia	Myrtoleucodendron styphelioides	Melaleuca styphel.
Myrtoleucodendron elachophyllum	Melaleuca depauperata	Myrtoleucodendron subfalcatum	Melaleuca subfalcata
M. eleuterostachyum	Melaleuca	Myrtoleucodendron subtrigonum	Melaleuca subfalcata

Synonym	Current Name	Synonym	Current Name
Myrtoleucodendron tamariscinum	Melaleuca tamariscina	Narcissus 'Albus Plenus Odoratus'	N. poeticus 'Plenus'
Myrtoleucodendron teretifolium	Melaleuca teretifolia	Narcissus 'Campernellii Plenus'	N. x odorus 'Double Campernelle'
Myrtoleucodendron thymifolium	Melaleuca thymifolia		
Myrtoleucodendron thymoides	Melaleuca thymoides	Narcissus 'Capax Plenus'	N. 'Eystettensis'
Myrtoleucodendron thyoides	Melaleuca thyoides	Narcissus 'Codlins and Cream'	N. 'Sulphur Phoenix'
Myrtoleucodendron trichophyllum	Melaleuca trichophylla	Narcissus 'Compressus'	N. x intermedius 'Compressus'
Myrtoleucodendron uncinatum	Melaleuca uncinata		
Myrtoleucodendron urceolare	Melaleuca urceolaris	Narcissus 'Double Campernelle'	N. x odorus 'Double Campernelle'
Myrtoleucodendron vimineum	Melaleuca viminea		
Myrtoleucodendron violaceum	Melaleuca violacea	Narcissus 'Golden Bells'	N. bulbocodium 'Golden Bells'
Myrtoleucodendron wilsonii	Melaleuca wilsonii		
Myrtus 'Glanleam Gold'	Luma apiculata 'Glanleam Gold'	Narcissus 'Grand Monarque'	N. tazetta ssp lacticol or 'Grand Monarque'
Myrtus 'Traversii'	Lophomyrtus x ralphii 'Traversii'	Narcissus 'Joy Bishop'	N. romieuxii 'Joy Bishop'
Myrtus acmenoides	Gussia acmenoides	Narcissus 'Joy'	Narcissus 'Jolity'
Myrtus apiculata	Luma apiculata	Narcissus 'Julia Jane'	N. romieuxii 'Julia Jane'
Myrtus baumannii	Uromyrtus baumannii		
Myrtus bidwillii	Gossia bidwillii	Narcissus 'L'Amour'	N. 'Madelaine'
Myrtus bullata -A.Cunn. not Salisb.	Lophomyrtus bullata	Narcissus 'Lobularis'	N. pseudonarcissus 'Lobularis'
Myrtus bullata 'Gloriosa'	Lophomyrtus x ralphii 'Variegata'	N. 'Paper White Grandiflorus'	N. papyraceus
Myrtus chequen -(Mol.) Spreng.	Luma chequen	Narcissus 'Paper White'	N. papyraceus
M. communis 'Jenny Reitenbach'	M. com. ssp tarentina	Narcissus 'Queen Anne's Double'	N. 'Eystettensis'
Myrtus communis 'Microphylla'	M. com. ssp tarentina	Narcissus 'Royal Command'	N. 'Royal Decree'
Myrtus communis 'Nana'	M. com. ssp tarentina	Narcissus 'Urchin'	N. 'Pzaz'
Myrtus communis 'Tricolor'	M. com. 'Variegata'	Narcissus 'Van Sion'	N. 'Telamonius Plenus'
Myrtus decaspermoides	Gossia inophloia	Narcissus alpestris	N. pseudonarcissus ssp moschatus
Myrtus dulcis	Austromyrtus dulcis		
Myrtus fragrantissima	Gossia fragrantissima	Narcissus Angel's Tears	N. triand. v triandrus
Myrtus gonoclada	Gossia gonoclada	Narcissus baeticus	N. assoanus v praelongus MS 656
Myrtus hillii	Gossia hillii		
Myrtus inophloia	Gossia inophloia	N. bulbocodium ssp romieuxii	N. romieuxii
Myrtus lechleriana -(Miq.) Sealy	Amomyrtus luma -Legr. & Kausel in part	Narcissus bulbocodium ssp vulgaris	N. bulbocodium ssp bu.
		Narcissus bulbocodium tananicus	N. tananicus
Myrtus luma	Luma apiculata	N. bulbocodium v mesatlanticus	N. romieuxii ssp romieuxii v mesatlanti.
Myrtus metrosideros	Uromyrtus metrosid.		
Myrtus monosperma	Gossia lucida	Narcissus campernellii	N. x odorus
Myrtus nummularia -Poir.	Myrteola nummularia	Narcissus canaliculatus -Gussonne	N. tazetta ssp lacticolor
Myrtus obcordata -(Raoul) Hook.f.	Lophomyrtus obcordat.		
Myrtus opaca	Gossia hillii	Narcissus citrinus	N. bulbocodium ssp bulbocodium v citrinus
Myrtus pubiflora	Gossia pubiflora		
Myrtus racemulosa	Gossia bidwillii	Narcissus concolor -(Haworth) Link	N. triandrus ssp triandrus v concolor
Myrtus racemulosa v conferta	Gossia bidwillii		
Myrtus shepherdii	Gossia shepherdii	Narcissus gracilis	N. x tenuior
Myrtus sunshinensis	Uromyrtus sunshinen.	Narcissus graellsii	N. bulbocodium ssp bulbocodium v graellsii
Myrtus ugni -Mol.	Ugni molinae -Turcz.		
Myrtus x ralphii -Hook.f.	Lophomyrtus x ralphii	Narcissus hellenicus	N. poeticus v hellenic.
Naegelia cinnabarina	Smithiantha cinnabar.	Narcissus henriquesii	N. jonquilla v henrique.
Naegelia zebrina	Smithiantha zebrina	Narcissus juncifolius	N. assoanus
Nageia falcata -(Thunb). O.Kuntze	Afrocarpus falcatus	Narcissus lobularis -Schultes	N. obvallaris
Nageia nagi -(Thunb). O.Kuntze	Podocarpus nagi	Narcissus marvieri	N. rupicola ssp marv.
Nananthus rubrolineata	Aloinopsis rubrolineata	Narcissus minimus h.	N. asturiensis
Nananthus schooneesii	Aloinopsis schooneesii	Narcissus minor v pumilus 'Plenus'	N. 'Rip van Winkle'
Nandina domestica 'Nana'	N. d. 'Pygmaea'	Narcissus nanus	N. minor

Synonym	Current Name	Synonym	Current Name
Narcissus Old Pheasant's Eye	N. poeticus v recurvus	Nemesia caerulea 'Joan Wilder'	N. caerulea lilac/blue
N. poeticus Old Pheasant's Eye	N. poeticus v recurvus	Nemesia denticulata 'Confetti'	N. denticulata
N. pseudonarcissus ssp gayi	N. gayi	Nemesia foetens	N. caerulea
N. pseudonarcissus ssp moschatus	N. moschatus	Nemesia fruticans misapplied	N. caerulea
N. pseudonarcissus ssp nevadensis	N. nevadensis	Nemesia umbonata h.	N. caerulea lilac/blue
N. pseudonarcissus ssp obvallaris	N. obvallaris	Nemopanthus collinus -(Alex). Clark	Ilex collina
N. pseudonarcissus ssp pallidiflorus	N. pallidiflorus	Nemophila insignis	N. menziesii
Narcissus pulchellus	N. triandrus ssp triandrus v pulchellus	Neobesseya asperispina	Escobaria asperispina
		Neobesseya macdougallii	Ortegocactus macdou.
Narcissus pumilus	N. minor v pumilus	Neoceis microcephala	Senecio glomeratus
Narcissus requienii	N. assoanus	Neoceis tomentosa	Senecio quadridentat.
Narcissus rifanus	N. romieuxii ssp romieuxii v rifanus	Neochamaelea pulverulenta	Cneorum pulverulent.
		Neochilena chilensis	Neoporteria chilensis
Narcissus tazetta aureus	N. aureus	Neochilenia mitis h.	Neoporteria napina
Narcissus tazetta ssp papyraceus	N. papyraceus	Neocodon carpaticus	Campanula carpatica
Narcissus tenuifolius	N. bulbocodium ssp bulbocodium v tenuif.	Neodypsis decaryi	Dypsis decaryi
		Neodypsis leptocheilos	Dypsis leptocheilos
Narcissus triandrus v albus	N. trian. v triandrus	Neolepia campestris	Lepidium campestre
Narcissus triandrus v concolor	N. concolor	Neolitsea glauca -(Sieb.) Koidz.	N. sericea -(Bl.) Koidz
Narcissus v plenus odoratus'	N. poeticus 'Plenus'	Neolloydia mcdowellii	Thelocactus mcdowellii
Narcissus watieri	N. rupicola ssp watieri	Neopanax	Pseudopanax
Narcissus x odorus 'Rugulosus'	N. 'Rugulosus'	Neopanax arboreum -(L.f.) Allan	Pseudopanax arboreus
Narcissus zaianicus	N. romieuxii ssp albidus v zaianicus	Neopanax laetum -(Kirk) Allan	Pseudopanax laetus
		Neopaxia australasica blue-leaved	N. aus. 'Kosciusko'
N. zaianicus lutescens S&F 374	N. romieuxii ssp albidus v zaianicus f lutescens SF 374	Neopaxia australasica bronze-leaved	N. australasica 'Ohau'
		Neopaxia australasica green-leaved	N. aus. 'Great Lake'
		Neopaxia australasica grey	N. aus. 'Kosciusko'
Narcissus zaianicus v albus MS 168	N. romieuxii ssp albidus v zaianicus f albus MS 168	Neoporteria litoralis	N. subgibbosa
		Neoporteria mitis	N. napina
		Neoregelia carolinae 'Tricolor'	N. carolinae f tricolor
Nardostachys jatamansi	N. grandiflora	Neoregelia concentrica 'Plutonis'	N. conc. v plutonis
Nasella tenuissima	Stipa tenuissima	Neottia pubescens	Goodyera pubescens
Nasturtium armoracia	Armoracia rusticana	Nepenthes rafflesiana x ampullaria	N. x hookeriana
Nasturtium globosum	Rorippa globosa	Nepeta 'Blue Beauty'	N. sibirica 'Souvenir d'Andre Chaudron'
Naumburgia thyrsiflora	Lysimachia thyrsiflora		
Nautilocalyx tessellatus	N. bullatus	Nepeta 'Souvenir d'Andre Chaudron'	N. sibirica 'Souvenir d'Andre Chaudron'
Neanthe bella	Chamaedorea elegans		
Nebrownia -Kuntze.	Schismatoglottis	Nepeta argolica	N. sibthorpii
Nectaroscordum dioscoridis	N. siculum ssp bulgaricum	Nepeta calaminthoides	N. cataria
		Nepeta citriodora -Dum.	N. cataria 'Citriodora'
Nectolis vitellina	Salix alba	Nepeta glechoma 'Variegata'	Glechoma hederacea 'Variegata'
Negundo cissifolium -Sieb. & Zucc.	Acer cissifolium		
Neillia bracteata -(Rydb.) Bean	Physocarpus bracteat.	Nepeta hederacea 'Variegata'	Glechoma hederacea 'Variegata'
Neillia capitata -(Pursh) Greene	Physocarpus capitatus		
Neillia longiracemosa -Hemsl.	N. thibetica	Nepeta incana	Caryopteris incana
Neillia malvacea	Physocarpus malvac.	Nepeta lanceolata	N. nepetella
Neillia opulifolia	Physocarpus opulifol.	Nepeta laurentii	N. cataria
Neillia ribesioides -Rehd.	N. sinensis v ribesioid.	Nepeta macrantha	N. sibirica
Neillia torreyi	Physocarpus malvaceus	Nepeta macrura	N. cataria
		Nepeta minor	N. cataria
Nelumbium speciosum	N. nucifera	Nepeta mollis	N. cataria
Nematanthus gregarius 'Variegatus'	N. gr. 'Golden West'	Nepeta mussinii h.	N. x faassenii
Nematanthus radicans	N. gregarius	Nepeta mussinii Spreng.	N. racemosa
Nematostigma paniculata	Libertia paniculata	Nepeta pannonica	N. nuda
Nemesia 'Tapestry'	N. 'Pastel'	Nepeta reichenbachiana	N. racemosa

Synonym	Current Name	Synonym	Current Name
Nepeta ruderalis	N. cataria	Nigella elegans	N. damascena
Nepeta tatarica	N. sibirica	Nigella involucrata	N. damascena
Nepeta vulgaris	N. cataria	Nigella multifida	N. damascena
Nephrodium abbreviatum	Dryopteris affinis	Nigella romana	N. damascena
Nephrodium acrostichoides	Polystichum acrostich.	Nigella taurica	N. damascena
Nephrodium aemulum	Dryopteris aemula	Nigritella	Gymnadenia
Nephrodium bissetianum	Dryopteris bissetiana	Nigromnia globosa	S. globosa
Nephrodium calanthum	Lastreopsis calantha	Nintooa japonica -(Thunb.) Sweet	Lonicera japonica
Nephrodium cristatum	Dryopteris cristata	Niphobolus lingua	Pyrrosia lingua
Nephrodium dilatatum	Dryopteris dilatata	Nipponocalamus chino	Pleiobastus chino
Nephrodium dryopteris	Gymnocarpium dryop.	Nipponocalamus simonii	Pleiobastus simonii
Nephrodium erythrosorum	Dryopteris erythroso.	Noccaea	Thlaspi
Nephrodium expansum	Dryopteris expansa	Nolana atriplicifolia	N. paradoxa
Nephrodium goldianum	Dryopteris erythroso.	Nolana grandiflora	N. paradoxa
Nephrodium jordani	Dryop. carthusiana	Nolina recurvata	Beaucarnea recurvata
Nephrodium lanosum	Cheilanthes vestita	Nolina stricta	Beaucarnea stricta
Nephrodium marginale	Dryopteris marginale	Nolina tuberculata	N. recurvata
Nephrodium microsorum	Lastreopsis calantha	Nomocharis mairei	N. pardanthina
Nephrodium phegopteris	Phegopteris connectilis	Nomocharis nana	Lilium nanum
Nephrodium plumula	Polystichum munitum	Nomocharis oxypetala	Lilium oxypetalum
Nephrodium punctilobulum -Michx.	Dennstaedtia punctilob.	Nomochlaena atropurpurea	Pellaea atropurpurea
Nephrodium sieboldii	Dryopteris sieboldii	Nopalea cochenillifera	Opuntia cochenillifera
Nephrodium spinulosum	Dryop. carthusiana	Nordmannia cordifolia	Trachystemon
Nephrodium thelypteris	Thelypteris palustris		orientalis
Nephrodium tokyoense	Dryopteris tokyoensis	Notelaea excelsa	Picconia excelsa
Nephrolepis exaltata 'Aurea'	N. ex. 'Golden Boston'	Nothochelone	Penstemon
Nephthytis	Syngonium	Nothofagus antarctica 'Prostrata'	N. ant. 'Benmore'
Nephthytis triphylla h.	Syngon. podophyllum	Nothofagus cliffortioides	N. solderi v
Nerine bowdenii 'Fenwick's Variety'	N. b. 'Mark Fenwick'		cliffortioides
Nerine bowdenii 'Variegata'	N. b. 'Mollie Cowie'	Nothofagus nervosa	N. alpina
Nerine corusca 'Major'	N. sarniensis v corus.	Nothofagus procera -Oerst.	N. nervosa
Nerine crispa	N. undulata	Nothofagus procera misapplied	N. x alpina
Nerium indicum	N. oleander	Notholaena	Cheilanthes
Nerium obesum	Adenium obesum	Notholirion hyacinthinum	N. bulbiferum
Nerium odorum	N. oleander	Nothopanax	Polyscias
Nerium oleander 'Monca'	N. olean. 'Casablanca'	Nothopanax arboreum (L.f.) Seem.	Pseudopanax arboreus
Nerium oleander 'Monta'	N. oleander 'Tangier'	Nothopanax davidii -(Franch.) Harms	Pseudopanax davidii
Nerium oleander 'Monvis'	N. oleander 'Ruby Lace'	Nothopanax laetum -(Kirk) Cheesem.	Pseudopanax laetus
Nerium oleander 'Mrs Roeding'	N. o. 'Carneum Plenum'	Nothopothos -Kuntze	Anadendrum -Schott
Nesaea salicifolia -H.B.K.	Heimia salicifolia	Nothoscordum fragrans	N. gracile
Nesaea verticillata	Decodon verticillatus	Nothoscordum neriniflorum	Caloscordum neriniflo.
Neurosoria pteroides	Cheilanthes nitida	Notocactus apricus	Parodia concinna
Nicodemia madagascariensis	Buddleja madagascar.	Notocactus brevihamatus	Parodia brevihamatus
Nicolaia elatior	Etlingera elatior	Notocactus claviceps	Parodia claviceps
Nicotiana affinis	N. alata	Notocactus conncinnus	Parodia concinna
Nicotiana decurrens	N. alata	Notocactus graessneri	Parodia graessneri
Nidularium carolinae	Neoregelia carolinae	Notocactus haselbergii	Parodia haselbergii
Nidularium flandria	Neoregelia c. 'Flandria'	Notocactus leninghausii	Parodia leninghausii
	(Meyendorffii Group)	Notocactus magnifica	Parodia magnifica
Nierembergia caerulea	N. linariifolia	Notocactus mammulosus	Parodia mammulosa
Nierembergia frutescens	N. scoparia	Notocactus mutabilis	Parodia mutabilis
Nierembergia hippomanica	N. linariifolia	Notocactus ottonis	Parodia ottonis
Nierembergia rivularis	N. repens	Notocactus penicillata	Parodia penicillata
Nigella bourgaei	N. damascena	Notocactus rutilans	Parodia rutilans
Nigella caerulea	N. damascena	Notocactus scopa	Parodia scopa

Synonym	Current Name	Synonym	Current Name
Notocactus submammulosus	Parodia submammul.	Ocimum basilicum 'Licorice'	O. basilicum 'Horapha'
Nuphar lutea ssp variegata	N. variegata	Ocimum basilicum 'Thai'	O. basilicum 'Horapha'
Nuphar luteum	N. lutea	Ocimum basilicum v citriodorum	O. x citriodorum
Nuttallia	Oemleria	Ocimum canum	O. americanum
Nuttallia involucrata	Callirhoe involucrata	Ocimum frutescens	Perilla frutescens
Nyctocereus serpentinus	Peniocereus serpentin.	Ocimum sanctum	O. tenuiflorum
Nymphaea 'Albatros' misapplied	N. 'Hermine'	Ocimum suave	O. gratissimum
Nymphaea 'Apple Blossom Pink'	N. 'Marliacea Carnea'	Ocimum viride	O. gratissimum
Nymphaea 'Exquisita'	N. 'Odorata Exquisita'	Odontoglossum bictoniense	Lemboglossum bicton.
Nymphaea 'Hollandia' misapplied	N. 'Darwin'	Odontoglossum cervantessii	Lemboglossum cervan.
N. 'Laydekeri Rosea' misapplied	N. 'Laydekeri Rosea Prolifera'	Odontoglossum cordatum	Lemboglossum cordat.
		Odontoglossum grande	Rossioglossum grande
Nymphaea 'Luciana'	N. 'Odorata Luciana'	Odontoglossum rossii	Lemboglossum rossii
N. 'Mrs Richmond' misapplied	N. 'Fabiola'	Odontoglossum stellatum	Lemboglossum stellat.
Nymphaea 'Occidentalis'	N. alba ssp occidental.	Odontoglossum triumphans	Lemb. spectatissimum
Nymphaea 'Odorata Alba'	N. odorata	Odontospermum maritimum	Asteriscus maritimus
Nymphaea 'Odorata William B.Shaw'	N. 'W.B.Shaw'	Oenanthe japonica	O. javanica
N. 'Perry's Yellow Sensation'	N. 'Yellow Sensation'	Oenothera acaulis 'Lutea'	O. acaulis 'Aurea'
Nymphaea 'Pygmaea Alba'	N. tetragona	Oenothera berlandieri	O. speciosa 'Rosea'
Nymphaea 'Rembrandt' misapplied	N. 'Meteor'	Oenothera berlandieri 'Childsii'	O. speciosa 'Rosea'
Nymphaea 'Sunrise'	N. 'Odorata Sulphurea Grandiflora'	Oenothera childsii	Oenothera speciosa
		Oenothera cinaeus	O. fruticosa ssp glauca
Nymphaea 'Tuberosa Flavescens'	N. 'Marliacea Chromatella'	Oenothera erythrosepala	O. glazioviana
		Oenothera Fireworks	O. fruticosa 'Fyrverkeri'
Nymphaea 'Turicensis'	N. 'Odorata Turicensis'		
Nymphaea colorata	N. capensis	Oenothera fraseri	O. fruticosa ssp glauca
Nymphaea odorata 'Pumila'	N. odorata v minor	Oenothera fruticosa Fireworks	O. frut. 'Fyrverkeri'
Nymphaea pygmaea	N. tetragona	Oenothera fruticosa Highlight	O. frut. 'Hoheslicht'
Nymphaea tetragona 'Alba'	N. tetragona	O. fruticosa ssp glauca Solstice	O. fruticosa ssp glauca 'Sonnenwende'
Nymphaea tuberosa 'Rosea'	N. 'Rosea'		
Nymphaea x helvola	N. 'Pygmaea Helvola'	Oenothera glabra -Miller	O. biennis
Nyssa candidans -Michx.	N. ogeche -Marsh.	Oenothera glauca	O. fruticosa ssp glauca
Nyssa multiflora -Wangenh.	N. sylvatica -Marsh.	Oenothera hookeri	O. elata ssp hookeri
Nyssa uniflora -Wangenh.	N. aquatica -L.	Oenothera lamarckiana	O. glazioviana
Nyssa uniflora -Wangenh.	N. grandidentata	Oenothera linearis	O. fruticosa
Nyssa uniflora -Wangenh.	N. tomentosa -Michx.	Oenothera mexicana	O. laciniata
Nyssa villosa -Michx.	N. sylvatica -Marsh.	Oenothera missouriensis	O. macrocarpa
Oakesia	Uvularia	Oenothera muricata	O. biennis
Oakesiella	Uvularia	Oenothera odorata -Hook. & Arn.	O. biennis
Obione billardierei	Atriplex billardierei	Oenothera odorata 'Sulphurea'	O. stricta 'Sulphurea'
Obione confertifolia -Torr.	Atriplex confertifolia	Oenothera odorata misapplied	O. stricta
Obione elegans	Atriplex elegans	Oenothera pumila	O. perennis
Obione portulacoides -L.	Halimione portulacoid.	Oenothera speciosa v childsii	O. speciosa
Obione truncata	Atriplex truncata	Oenothera taraxacifolia	O. acaulis
Ochagavia lindleyana	O. carnea	Oenothera tetragona	O. fruticosa ssp glauca
Ochetophila trinervis -Poepp.	Disaria trinervis	Oenothera tetragona 'Sonnenwende'	O. fruticosa ssp glauca 'Sonnenwende'
Ochna japonica	O. serrulata		
Ochna multiflora	O. serrulata	Oenothera tetragona v fraseri	O. fruticosa ssp glauca
Ochna serratifolia h.	O. serrulata	Oenothera youngii h.	O. fruticosa ssp glauca
Ocimum americanum 'Meng Luk'	O. americanum	Olea europaea 'Pyramidalis'	O. europaea v europaea 'Cipressino'
Ocimum americanum 'Spice'	O. 'Spice'		
Ocimum basilicum 'Anise'	O. basilicum 'Horapha'	Olea fragrans -Thunb.	Osmanthus fragrans
Ocimum basilicum 'Glycyrrhiza'	O. basilicum 'Horapha'	Olea ilicifolia -Hassk.	Osman. heterophyllus
Ocimum basilicum 'Holy'	O. tenuiflorum	Olea japonica -Sieb.	Osmanthus x fortunei
Ocimum basilicum 'Lettuce Leaf'	O. basilicum v crispum	Olearia 'Zennorencis'	O. x mollis

Synonym	Current Name	Synonym	Current Name
	'Zennorencis'	Onoclea augescens	O. sensibilis
Olearia albida misapplied	O. 'Talbot de Malahide'	Onoclea germanica	Matteuccia
Olearia albiflora h.	O. albida -Hook.		struthiopteris
Olearia alpina -Buchan.	O. lacunosa -Hook. f.	Onoclea obtusilobata	O. sensibilis
Olearia alpina (Hook. f.) W.M.Curtis	O. tasmanica	Onoclea orientalis	Matteuccia orientalis
Olearia arborescens v angustifolia	O. cheesemanii	Onoclea struthiopteris	Matt. struthiopteris
Olearia arborescens v capillaris	O. capillaris -Buchan.	Ononis cenisia	O. cristata
Olearia aspera	Minuria macrorhiza	Ononis hircina -Jacq	O. arvensis
Olearia cunninghamii h.	O. cheesemanii	Onopordon	Onopordum
Olearia cymbifolia -Hook.	O. nummulariifolia v cymbifolia	Onopordum arabicum	O. nervosum
		Onopordum ramosum	O. acanthium
Olearia dentata -Hook. f.	O. macrodonta -Baker	Onopordum viride	O. acanthium
Olearia dentata h.	O. rotundifolia	Onopordum vulgare	O. acanthium
Olearia feruginea h.	O. rotundifolia	Onosma cinerea	O. alborosea
Olearia flocjtonae	O. flocktoniae	Onosma echioides	O. taurica
Olearia forsteri -Hook.f.	O. paniculata	Onychium densum	Aspidotis densa
Olearia gunniana -(DC.) Hook.f.	O. phlogopappa	Operculina tuberosa	Merremia tuberosa
Olearia gunniana v splendens	O. phlogopappa Splendens Group	Ophelia chirata	Swertia chirata
		Ophioglossum japonicum	Lygodium japonicum
Olearia insignis	Pachystegia insignis	Ophione -Schott	Dracontium -L.
Olearia lineata -(Kirk) Ckn.	Olearia virgata v linea.	Ophiopogon 'Black Dragon'	O. planiscapus
Olearia lyrata	O. lirata -(Sims) Hutch.		'Nigrescens'
Olearia myrsinoides h.	O. erubescens	Ophiopogon 'Black Knight'	O. plan. 'Nigrescens'
Olearia nitida -(Hook.f.) Hook. f.	O. arborescens	Ophiopogon 'Gin-ryu'	Liriope spicata 'Gin-ryu'
Olearia oleifolia	O. 'Waikariensis'		
Olearia phlogopappa 'Rosea'	O. phlogopappa 'Comber's Pink'	Ophiopogon graminifolius	Liriope muscari
		O. intermedius 'Variegatus'	O. intermedius 'Argeomarginatus'
Olearia ramulosa v communis	O. ramulosa		
Olearia rani h.	O. cheesemanii	O. jaburan 'Argenteovittatus'	O. jaburan 'Vittatus'
Olearia semidentata misapplied	O. 'Henry Travers'	Ophiopogon jaburan 'Javanensis'	O. jaburan 'Vittatus'
Olearia stellulata 'Splendens'	O. phlogopappa Splendens Group	Ophiopogon jaburan 'Variegatus'	O. jaburan 'Vittatus'
		Ophiopogon planiscapus 'Arabicus'	O. plan. 'Nigrescens'
Olearia stellulata h. not DC.	O. phlogopappa	O. planiscapus 'Ebony Knight'	O. plan. 'Nigrescens'
Olearia stellulata v frostii	O. frostii	Ophiopogon spicatus	Liriope spicata
Olearia tomentosa h.	O. rotundifolia	Ophrys aranifera	O. sphegodes
Olearia traversii 'Variegata'	O. tr. 'Tweedledum'	Ophrys cernua	Spiranthes cernua
Olearia tridens	Minuria tridens	Ophrys fuciflora	O. holoserica
Olearia waikariensis h.	O. 'Waikariensis'	Ophrys speculum	O. vernixia
Olearia waikensis h.	O. 'Waikariensis'	Oplismenus africanus 'Variegatus'	O. 'Variegatus'
Olearia x mollis h.	O. ilicifolia x O. moschata	Oplismenus hirtellus	O. africanus
		Oporinia autumnalis	Leontodon autumnalis
Olearia x scilloniensis h.	O. stelluta -De Candolle	Opulaster bracteatus -Rydb.	Physocarpus bracteat.
Oligogynium -Engl.	Nephthytis -Schott	Opulaster intemedius -Rydb.	Physoc. opulifolius
Oligoneuron	Solidago	Opulaster opulifolius -Rydb.	Physoc. opulifolius
Oligosporus dracunculus	Artemisia dracunculus	Opuntia compressa	O. humifusa
Oligostachyum lubricum	Semiarundinaria lubri.	Opuntia engelmannii	O. ficus-indica
Oliveranthus elegans	Echeveria harmsii	Opuntia engelmannii h.	O. phaeacantha
Omphalodes cornifolia	O. lojkae	Opuntia hystricina	O. erinacea
Omphalodes linifolia alba	O. linifolia	Opuntia linguiformis	O. lindheimeri
Omphalodes lusitanica	O. nitida	Opuntia megacantha	O. ficus-indica
Omphalogramma rockii	O. vinciflorum	Opuntia monacantha	O. vulgaris
Oncidium papilio	Psychopsis papilio	Opuntia rhodantha	O. polycantha
Oncostema	Scilla	Opuntia rufida	O. microdasys v rufida
Onobrychis sativa	O. viciifolia	Orchiodes pubescens	Goodyera pubescens
Onobrychis vulgaris	O. viciifolia	Orchis elata	Dactylorhiza elata

Synonym	Current Name	Synonym	Current Name
Orchis foliosa	Dactylorhiza foliosa	Oryza oryzoides	Leersia oryzoides
Orchis fuchsii	Dactylorhiza fuchsii	Oryzopsis hymenoides	Achnatherum hymen.
Orchis laxiflora	Anacamptis laxiflora	Oryzopsis lessoniana	Anemanthele lessonian.
Orchis maculata	Dactylorhiza maculata	Oscularia deltoides	Lampranthus deltoides
Orchis maderensis	Dactylorhiza foliosa	Osmanthus aquifolium -Sieb.	O. heterophyllus
Orchis majalis	Dactylorhiza majalis	O. aquifolium v ilicifolius latifolius h.	O. x fortunei -Carr.
Orchis morto	Anacamptis morto	Osmanthus forrestii -Rehd.	O. yunnanensis
Oreastrum alpigenum	Oreostemma alpigenum	O. heterophyl. 'Argenteomarginatus'	O. heterophyllus 'Variegatus'
Oreocallis 'Wickhamii'	Alloxylon flammeum		
Oreocallis pinnata	Alloxylon pinnatum	O. heterophyllus 'Aureovariegatus'	O.h. 'Aureomarginatus'
Oreocereus peruviana	Oroya peruviana	Osmanthus heterophyllus 'Aureus'	O.h. 'Aureomarginatus'
Oreochorte yunnanensis	Anthriscus sylvestris	O. heterophyllus 'Aureus' mis.	O. h. all gold
Oreocome candollei	Selinum wallichianum	Osmanthus heterophyllus Tricolor	O. h. 'Goshiki'
Oreodoxa regia	Roystonea regia	Osmanthus ilicifolius -(Hassk.) Carr	O. heterophyllus
Origanum angelicum	O. vulgare	Osmanthus ilicifolius v latifolius h.	O. x fortunei -Carr.
Origanum barcense	O. vulgare	Osmanthus x fortunei 'Variegatus'	O. heterophyllus 'Latifolius Variegatus'
Origanum caespitosum	O. vulgare 'Nanum'		
Origanum capitatum	O. vulgare	Osmaronia	Oemleria
Origanum creticum	O. vulgare ssp hirtum	Osmunda asiatica	O. cinnamomea
Origanum dilatatum	O. vulgare	Osmunda cinnamomea v fokiensis	O. cinnamomea
Origanum elegans	O. vulgare	Osmunda crispa	Cryptogramma crispa
Origanum flexuosum	Pycnanthemum tenuifolium	Osmunda interrupta	O. claytoniana
		Osmunda lunaria	Botrychium lunaria
Origanum floridum	O. vulgare	Osmunda nipponica -Mak.	O. japonica
Origanum heracleoticum -L.	O. vulgare ssp hirtum	Osmunda regalis Undulata Group	O. reg. Cristata Group
Origanum heracleoticum h.	O. x applei	Osmunda spicant	Blechnum spicant
Origanum hortensis	O. majorana	Osmunda struthiopteris	Matteuccia struth.
Origanum kopatdaghense	O. vulgare ssp gracile	Osmunda virginianum	Botrychium virginian.
Origanum nutans	O. vulgare	Osmundastrum cilaytonianum	Osmunda claytoniana
Origanum pulchellum	O. x hybridinum	Osmundastrum cinnamomeum	Osmunda cinnamomea
Origanum sipyleum sp Mac.&W5882	Nepeta phyllochlamys	Osteomeles anthyllidifolia f subrotunda	
Origanum tournefortii	O. calcaratum		O. subrotunda -K.Koch
Origanum villosum	Thymus villosus	O. anthyllidifolia -some, not Lindl.	O. schweriniae
Origanum vulgare 'Curly Gold'	O. v. 'Aureum Crispum'	Osteospermum 'African Queen'	O. 'Nairobi Purple'
Origanum vulgare 'Humile'	O. vulgare 'Compactum'	Osteospermum 'Blackthorn Seedling'	O. jucundum 'Blackthorn Seedling'
Origanum vulgare 'Variegatum'	O. vulgare 'Gold Tip'		
Ornithogalum balansae	O. oligophyllum	Osteospermum 'Bloemhoff Belle'	O. 'Nairobi Purple'
Ornithogalum caudatum	O. longibracteatum	Osteospermum 'Brickell's Hybrid'	O. 'Chris Brickell'
Ornithogalum chloranthum	O. nutans	Osteospermum 'Coconut Ice'	O. 'Croftway Coconut Ice'
Ornithogalum nanum	O. sigmoideum		
Ornithogalum sibthorpii	O. sigmoideum	Osteospermum 'Killerton Pink'	O. jucundum 'Killerton Pink'
Ornithogalum tenuifolium	O. orthophyllum		
Ornus europaea -Pers.	Fraxinus ornus -L.	Osteospermum 'Langtrees'	O. juc. 'Langtrees'
Ornus xanthoxyloides -G.Don	Fraxinus xanthoxyl.	Osteospermum 'Merriments Joy'	O. jucundum 'Merriments Joy'
Orobus aurantiacus h.	Lathyrus aureus		
Orobus aureus	Lathyrus aureus	Osteospermum 'Pale Face'	O. 'Lady Leitrim'
Orobus vernus	Lathyrus vernus	Osteospermum 'Peggyi'	O. 'Nairobi Purple'
Orontium majus	Antirrhinum majus	Osteospermum 'Port Wine'	O. 'Nairobi Purple'
Orostachys malacophylla	O. aggregata	Osteospermum 'Prostratum'	O. 'White Pim'
Orothamnus vauvilliersii -Decne.	Cassinia vauvilliersii	Osteospermum 'Silver Spoons'	O. 'Croftway Silverspoons'
Oroya neoperuviana	O. peruviana		
Orphanidesia gaultherioides	Epigaea gaultherioides	Osteospermum 'Starshine'	O. ecklonis 'Starshine'
Orthostemon sellowianus -Berg	Acca sellowiana	Osteospermum 'Tauranga'	O. 'Whirlygig'
Orthotropis	Chorizema	Osteospermum 'Tresco Peggy'	O. 'Nairobi Purple'
Oryza clandestina	Leersia oryzoides	Osteospermum 'Tresco Purple'	O. 'Nairobi Purple'

Synonym	Current Name	Synonym	Current Name
Osteospermum 'Wine Purple'	O. 'Nairobi Purple'	Paederota ageria	P. lutea
Osteospermum barberae h.	O. jucundum	Paeonia 'Flight of Cranes'	P. suffruticosa
Osteospermum caulescens h.	O. 'White Pim'		'Renkaku'
O. ecklonis v prostratum	O. 'White Pim'	Paeonia 'Floral Rivalry'	P. suffr. 'Hana-kisoi'
Ostrya virginica -Willd.	O. virginiana	Paeonia 'General MacMahon'	P. lactiflora 'Augustin
Ostrya vulgaris -Willd.	O. carpinifolia -Scop.		d'Hour'
Osyris japonica -Thunb.	Helwingia japonica	Paeonia 'Green Dragon Lying on a Chinese Inkstone'	
Osyris rhamnoides	Hippophae rhamnoides		P. suffruticosa 'Qing
Othonna gregorii	Senecio gregorii		Long Wo Mo Chi'
Othonna gypsicola	Senecio gypsicola	Paeonia 'Hei Hua Kui'	P. suffr. 'Hei Hua Kui'
Othonna rigens	Gazania rigens	Paeonia 'Isani Gidui'	P. lactiflora 'Isami-jishi'
Othonnopsis	Othonna	Paeonia 'Joseph Rock'	P. rockii
Otosma -Raf.	Zantedeschia -Spreng.	Paeonia 'Kinkaku'	P. x lemoinei 'Souvenir
Ourisia elegans	O. coccinea		de Maxime Cornu'
Oxalis cernua	Oxalis pes-caprae	Paeonia 'Kinko'	P.x lem. 'Alice Harding'
Oxalis deppei	O. tetraphylla	Paeonia 'Kinshi'	P. x lem. 'Chromatella'
Oxalis enneaphylla x adenophylla	O. 'Matthew Forrest'	Paeonia 'Kintei'	P. x lem. 'L'Esperance'
Oxalis floribunda h.	O. articulata	Paeonia 'Magnificent Flower'	P. suffr. 'Hana-daijin'
Oxalis inops	O. depressa	Paeonia 'Mrs Gwyn Lewis'	P. 'Duchesse de
Oxalis lactea double form	O. magellanica 'Nelson'		Nemours'
Oxalis magellanica 'Flore Pleno'	O. magellanica 'Nelson'	Paeonia 'Sheriff's Variety'	P. delavayi v ludlowii
Oxalis perdicaria	O. lobata	Paeonia 'Sunshine'	P. pereg. 'Otto Froebel'
Oxalis purpurea v bowiei	O. bowiei	Paeonia 'Victor Hugo'	P. lacti. 'Felix Crousse'
Oxalis regnellii	O. triangularis ssp	Paeonia albiflora	P. lactiflora
	papilionacea	Paeonia anomala ssp veitchii	P. veitchii
Oxalis rosea -Jacquin	O. articulata	Paeonia arborea -Donn ex K.Koch	P. suffruticosa -Andr.
Oxalis rosea h.	O. rubra	Paeonia arietina	P. mascula ssp arietin.
Oxalis speciosa	O. purpurea	Paeonia banatica	P. officinalis ssp banat.
Oxalis squamosoradicosa	O. laciniata	Paeonia Bird of Rimpo	P. suffruticosa 'Rimpo'
Oxalis vespertilionis -Torr. & A.Gr.	O. drummondii	Paeonia Blue and Purple Giant	P. suffruticosa 'Zi Lan
Oxalis vespertilionis -Zuccarini	O. latifolia		Kui'
Oxyanthe phragmites	Phragmites australis	Paeonia caucasica	P. mascula ssp mascul.
Oxycoccus hispidulus	Gaultheria hispidula	Paeonia commutata	P. officinalis
Oxycoccus macrocarpus	Vaccinum macrocarp.	Paeonia corallina	P. mascula ssp mascul.
Oxycoccus maderense -Link	Vaccinum oxycoccus	Paeonia Crimson Red	P. suffr. 'Hu Hong'
Oxycoccus palustris -Pers.	Vaccinum oxycoccus	Paeonia daurica	P. mascula ssp
Oxycoccus quadripetala -Gilib.	Vaccinum oxycoccos		triternata
Oxylobium carinatum	Chorizema carinatum	Paeonia decora	P. peregrina
Oxylobium genistoides	Chorizema gensitoides	P. delavayi Drizzling Rain Cloud	P. suffr. 'Shiguregumo'
Oxylobium obtusifolium	Chorizema obtusifolium	Paeonia delavayi Potaninii Group	P. del. v angustiloba f
Oxylobium spathulatum	Chorizema spathulatum		angustiloba
Oxypetalum caeruleum	Tweedia caerulea	Paeonia foemina	P. officinalis
Oxyria reinformis	O. dignya	Paeonia Fragrance and Beauty	P. suffruticosa 'Lan
Oxys acetosella	Oxalis acetosella		Tian Yu'
Ozodia foeniculacea	Foeniculum vulgare	Paeonia humilis	P. officinalis ssp
Pachistema	Paxistima		microcarpa
Pachypharynx acuminata	Atriplex paludosa ssp	Paeonia japonica misapplied	P. lactiflora
	cordata	Paeonia kevachensis	P. mascula ssp mascul.
Pachystachys cardinalis	P. coccinea	Paeonia laciniata	P. 'Smouthii'
Pachystegia	Olearia	P. lactiflora 'General Macmahon'	P. lactiflora 'Augustin
Pachystema	Paxistima		d'Hour'
Pachystima	Paxistima	Paeonia lactiflora 'President Taft'	P. lactiflora 'Reine
Padus laurocerasus	Prunus laurocerasus		Hortense'
Padus napaulensis	Prunus napaulensis	Paeonia lithophila	P. tenuifolia ssp lithop.
Paederia chinensis -Hance	P. scandens	Paeonia lobata 'Fire King'	P. peregrina

Synonym	Current Name	Synonym	Current Name
Paeonia lobata 'Sunshine'	P. pereg. 'Otto Froebel'	Paeonia suffruticosa Moon World	P. suffr. 'Gessekai'
Paeonia ludlowii	P. delavayi v ludlowii	Paeonia suffruticosa Palace of Gems	P. s. 'Shugyo-kuden'
Paeonia lutea -Franch.	P. delavayi v lutea -	Paeonia suffruticosa Pride of Taisho	P. s. 'Taisho-no-hokori'
Paeonia lutea v ludlowii	P. delavayi v ludlowii	P. suffr. Seven Gods of Fortune	P. s. 'Sitifukujin'
Paeonia mollis	P. officinalis ssp villosa	Paeonia suffruticosa ssp rockii	P. rockii
Paeonia moutan -Sims	P. suffruticosa -Andr.	Paeonia suffruticosa The Sun	P. suffruticosa 'Taiyo'
Paeonia nemoralis	P. officinalis	Paeonia suffruticosa Twilight	P. suffr. 'Higurashi'
Paeonia officinalis 'Paradoxa Rosea'	P. off. 'Anemoniflora Rosea'	Paeonia suffruticosa Wisteria at Kamada	P. s. 'Kamada-fuji'
		Paeonia tomentosa	P. wittmanniana
Paeonia officinalis mascula	Paeonia mascula	Paeonia White Phoenix	P. suffr. 'Feng Dan Bai'
Paeonia officinalis ssp humilis	P. officinalis ssp microcarpa	Paeonia x smouthii	P. 'Smouthii'
		Paeonia Yao's Yellow	P. 'Yao Huang'
Paeonia papaveracea -Andr.	P. suffruticosa	Paeonia Yellow Flower of Summer	P. 'Huang Hua Kui'
Paeonia paradoxa	P. o. ssp microcarpa	Paliurus aculeata -Lam.	P. spina-christi -Mill.
P. Peony with the Purple Roots	P. suffr. 'Shou an Hong'	Paliurus aubletii	P. ramosissimus
Paeonia peregrina 'Sunshine'	P. pereg. 'Otto Froebel'	Paliurus australis -Gaertn.	P. spina-christi -Mill.
Paeonia potaninii	P. delavayi v angustilo ba f angustiloba	Pallenis spinosus	Asteriscus spinosus
		Panax arboreum -L.f.	Pseudopanax arboreus
Paeonia promiscua	P. officinalis	Panax arboreum v laetum -Kirk	Pseudopanax laetus
Paeonia pubens	P. officinalis	Panax davidii -Franch.	Pseudopanax davidii
Paeonia rockii	P. suffr. ssp rockii	Panax divaricatus -Sieb. & Zucc.	Eleutherococcus divar.
Paeonia rockii hybrid	P. Gansu Mudan Group	Panax ferox -Kirk	Pseudopanax ferox
Paeonia romanica	P. peregrina	Panax innovans	Pseudopanax innovans
Paeonia Rouge Red	P. suffr. 'Zhi Hong'	Panax longissimum -Hook. f.	Pseudopanax crassifolius
Paeonia russoi	P. mascula ssp russoi		
Paeonia Shandong Red Lotus	P. suffr. 'Lu He Hong'	Panax sessiliflorum -Rupr. & Maxim.	Eleutherococcus sess.
Paeonia sinensis	P. lactiflora	Pandanus odoratissimus	P. tectorius
Paeonia suffruticosa 'Joseph Rock'	P. suffr. ssp rockii	Pandorea jasminoides 'Alba'	P. jasminoides 'Lady Di'
Paeonia suffruticosa 'Kinkaku'	P. x lemoinei 'Souvenir de Maxime Cornu'	Pandorea jasminoides 'Variegata'	P. jasm. 'Charisma'
		Pandorea lindleyana	Clytostoma callistegioides
Paeonia suffruticosa 'Kinshi'	P. x lemoinei 'Alice Harding'	Pandorea ricasoliana	Podranea ricasoliana
P. suffruticosa 'Rock's Variety'	P. rockii	Panicum buchingeri	P. virgatum
P. suffruticosa Best-shaped Red	P. s. 'Zhuan Yuan Hong'	Panicum giganteum	P. virgatum
Paeonia suffruticosa Bird of Rimpo	P. suffruticosa 'Rimpo'	Panicum glaberrimum	P. virgatum
P. suffr. Black Dragon Brocade	P. s. 'Kokuryu-nishiki'	Panicum havardii	P. virgatum
P. suffr. Black Flower Chief	P. s. 'Hei Hua Kui'	Panicum ichnanthoides	P. virgatum
P. suffr. Brocade of the Naniwa	P. suff. 'Naniwa-nishiki'	Panicum violaceum	P. miliaceum 'Violaceum'
Paeonia suffruticosa Charming Age	P. suffruticosa 'Howki'		
P. s. Cherries of Imperial Palace	P. s. 'Gosho-zakura'	Panicum virgatum 'Haense Herms'	P. virg. 'Hanse Herms'
Paeonia suffruticosa Double Cherry	P. suffr. 'Yae-zakura'	Panzeria sibirica h.	Leonurus sibiricus -L.
P. suffruticosa Eternal Camellias	P. s. 'Yachiyo-tsubaki'	Papaver alpinum ssp burseri	P. burseri
Paeonia suffruticosa Five Continents	P. suffr. 'Godaishu'	Papaver alpinum ssp rhaeticum	P. rhaeticum
Paeonia suffruticosa Flight of Cranes	P. suffr. 'Renkaku'	Papaver bracteatum	P. orientale v bracta.
Paeonia suffruticosa Floral Rivalry	P. suffr. 'Hana-kisoi'	Papaver commutatum 'Ladybird'	P. commutatum
P. s. Flying Swallow Lady in Red	P. suffruticosa 'Fei Yan Hong Zhuang'	Papaver heldreichii	P. spicatum
		Papaver miyabeanum tatewakii	P. miyabeanum
P. suffruticosa Jewel in the Lotus	P. suffr. 'Tama-fuyo'	Papaver nanum 'Flore Pleno'	P. lateritium 'Fireball'
P. suffruticosa Jewelled Screen	P. suffr. 'Tama-sudare'	P. nudicaule Garden Gnome Group	P. nudicaule Gartenzwerg Series
P. suffruticosa Kamada Brocade	P. s. 'Kamada-nishiki'		
P. suffruticosa King of Flowers	P. suffruticosa 'Kaow'	P. orientale 'Mrs Marrow's Plum'	P. or. 'Patty's Plum'
P. suffruticosa King of White Lions	P. suffr. 'Hakuojisi'	P. orientale 'Nanum Flore Pleno'	P. lateritium 'Fireball'
Paeonia suffruticosa Knight's Dance	P. suffr. 'No-kagura'	P. orientale Princess Victoria Louise	P. orientale 'Prinzessin Victoria Louise'
Paeonia suffruticosa Lotus Green	P. suffr. 'He Hua Lu'		
P. suffruticosa Magnificent Flower	P. suffr. 'Hana-daijin'	Papaver orientale Stormtorch	P. or. 'Sturmfackel'

Synonym	Current Name	Synonym	Current Name
Papaver rhoeas Fairy Wings	P. rh. 'Mother of Pearl'	Passiflora 'Mavis Mastics'	P. x viol.'Tresederi'
P. rupifragum 'Dble Tangerine Gem'	P. rupifr. 'Flore Pleno'	Passiflora 'Purple Passion'	P. edulis f edulis
Papyrus antiquorum	Cyperus papyrus	Passiflora amethystina misapplied	P. 'Amethyst'
Papyrus papyrifera	Broussonetia papyr.	Passiflora antioquiensis misapplied	P. x exoniensis
Parabenzoin	Lindera	Passiflora banksii	P. aurantia
Parachampionella	Strobilanthes	Passiflora chinensis	P. caerulea
Parahebe 'Greencourt'	P. catarractae 'Delight'	Passiflora fulgens	P. coccinea
Parahebe bidwillii -of most authors	Parahebe decora	Passiflora ianthina -Mast.	P. umbilicata
P. catarractae 'Porlock Purple'	P. catarractae 'Delight'	Passiflora incana	P. seemannii
Parahebe densifolia	Chionhebe densifolia	Passiflora lowei	P. ligularis
Parahebe diffusa	P. catarractae	Passiflora mayana	P. caerulea
Parahebe olsenii	P. hookeriana v olsenii	Passiflora menispermifolia	P. pilosa
Paraquilegia adoxoides	Semiaquilegia adoxoid.	Passiflora obtusifolia	P. coriacea
Paraquilegia grandiflora	P. anemonoides	Passiflora onychina	P. amethystina -Mikan
Parasenecio auriculata	Cacalia auriculata	Passiflora princeps -Lodd.	P. racemosa
Parasenecio delphinifolia	Cacalia delphinifolia	Passiflora retipetala	P. cyanea
Parasenecio farfarifolia	Cacalia farfarifolia	Passiflora sanguinea	P. vitifolia
Parasenecio hastata orientalis	Cacalia hastata orient.	Passiflora serrata	P. serratodigitata
Parasenecio hastata tanakae	Cacalia hastata tanak.	Passiflora velutina	P. coccinea
Parasenecio kiusiana	Cacalia kiusiana	Passiflora x alatocaerulea	P. x belotii
Parasenecio nikomontana	Cacalia nikomontana	P. x belotii 'Imperatrice Eugenie'	P. x belotii
Parasenecio peltifolia	Cacalia peltifolia	Passiflora x caerulea racemosa	P. x violacea
Paraserianthes distachya	P. lophantha	Passiflora x caeruleoracemosa	P. x violacea
Parasyringa	Ligustrum	Passiflora x innesii	P. x decaisneana
Pardanthus chinensis	Belamcanda chinensis		'Innesii'
Parietaria officinalis	P. judaica	Passiflora x tresederi	P. x viol. 'Tresederi'
Parochetus communis misapplied	P. africanus	Passiflora x violacea 'Lilac Lady'	P. x viol. 'Tresederi'
Parodia liliputana	Blossfeldia liliputana	Pastinaca anethum	Anethum graveolens
Parodia sanguiniflora	P. microsperma	Pastinaca graveolens	Anethum graveolens
Paronychia nivea	P. capitata	Pastinacea sphondylium	Heracleum sphondyli.
Paronychia serpyllifolia	P. kapela ssp serpyllif.	Patrinia palmata	P. triloba v palmata
Parrotia jacquemontiana -Decne.	Parrotiopsis jacquem.	Pauella -Ramam. & Sebastine.	Theriophonum -Blume
Parrotia persica 'Variegata'	P. per. 'Lamplighter'	Paullinia japonica -Thunb.	Vitis japonica
Parrotiopsis involucrata	Parrotiopsis jacquem.	Paullinia sorbilis	P. cupana
Parrya menziesii	Phoenicaulis	Paulownia fargesii -Osborn	P. tomentosa 'Lilacina'
	cheiranthoides	Paulownia fargesii h.	P. tomentosa 'Lilacina'
Parthenocissus henryi v glaucescens	Cayratia thomsonii	Paulownia imperialis -Sieb & Zucc	P. tomentosa Paulownia
P. himalayana 'Purpurea'	P. himal. v rubrifolia	imperialis v lanata -Dode	P. tomentosa
Parthenocissus hirsuta	P. quinquefolia	Paulownia lilacina -Sprague	P. tomentosa 'Lilacina'
Parthenocissus muralis	P. quinquefolia	Paulownia recurva -Rehd.	P. tomentosa Paulownia
Parthenocissus pubescens	P. quinquefolia	tomentosa v lanata	P. tomentosa
P. quinquefolia incisa h.	P. inserta v laciniata	Paurotis wrightii	Acoelorraphe wrightii
P. quinquefolia v laciniata -Planch.	P. inserta v laciniata	Pavetta caffra	Pavetta capensis
Parthenocissus semicordata	P. himalayana	Pavia alba -Poir.	Aesculus parviflora
Parthenocissus sinensis	Vitis piasezkii	Pavia bicolor -Raf.	Aesculus flava
Parthenocissus striata	Cissus striata	Pavia californica -(Spach) Hartw.	Aesculus californica
Parthenocissus thomsonii	Cayratia thomsonii	Pavia edulis -Poit.	Aesculus parviflora
Pasania densiflora	Lithocarpus densiflor.	Pavia flava -(Sol.) Moench	Aesculus flava
Pasania edulis -Mak.	Lithocarpus edulis	Pavia fulva -Raf.	Aesculus flava
Pasania glabra -(Thunb.) Oerst.	Lithocarpus glaber	Pavia indica -Wall. ex Camb.	Aesculus indica
Paspalum effusum	Milium effusum	Pavia lutea	Aesculus flava
Passiflora 'Empress Eugenie'	P. x belotii	Pavia macrostachya -Michx.	Aesculus parviflora
Passiflora 'Lavender Lady'	P. 'Amethyst'	Pavia macrostachys -(Pers.) Loisel.	Aesculus parviflora
Passiflora 'Lilac Lady'	P. x violacea	Pavia mutabilis -Spach	Aesculus x mutabilis
	'Tresederi'	Pavia parviflora -(Walt.) Raf.	Aesculus parviflora

Synonym	Current Name	Synonym	Current Name
Pavia rubicunda	Aesculus x carnea	Pelargonium 'Frosty Petit Pierre'	P. 'Variegated Kleine Liebling'
Paviana flava	Aesculus flava		
Pavonia multiflora h.	P. x gledhillii	Pelargonium 'Frosty' misapplied	P. 'Variegated Kleine Liebling'
Pavonia x intermedia	P. x gledhillii		
Pawia hippocastanum -(L.) Kuntze	Aesculus hippocast.	Pelargonium 'Golden Well Sweep'	P. crispum 'Golden Well Sweep'
Pawia octandra	Aesculus flava		
Pawia parviflora -(Walt.) Kuntze	Aesculus parviflora	Pelargonium 'Gooseberry Leaf'	P. grossularioides
Pawia rubicunda -(Loisel.) Kuntze	Aesculus x carnea	Pelargonium 'Grandma Fischer'	P. 'Grossmutter Fischer'
Pawia turbinata -(Blume) Kuntze	Aesculus turbinata		
Paxistima myrsinites -(Pursh) Raf.	P. myrtifolia	P. 'Greengold Petit Pierre'	P. 'Greengold Kleine Liebling'
Pectinaria pillansii	Stapeliopsis pillansii		
Pelargonium 'A Happy Thought'	P. 'Happy Thought'	Pelargonium 'H. Guinier'	P. 'Charles Gounod'
Pelargonium 'Aurore'	P. 'Unique Aurore'	P. 'Hillscheider Amethyst'	P. 'Amethyst'
Pelargonium 'Balcon Lilas'	P. 'Roi des Balcons Lilas'	Pelargonium 'Jackie Gall'	P. 'Jackie'
		Pelargonium 'Joan of Arc'	P. 'Jeanne d'Arc'
Pelargonium 'Balcon Rose'	P. 'Hederinum'	Pelargonium 'Karrooense'	P. quercifolium
Pelargonium 'Balcon Rouge'	P. 'Roi des Balcons Imperial'	Pelargonium 'King of Balcon'	P. 'Hederinum'
		Pelargonium 'L'Enfer'	P. 'Mephistopheles'
Pelargonium 'Balcon Royale'	P. 'Roi des Balcons Imperial'	Pelargonium 'Lady Alice of Valencia'	P. 'Grenadier'
		P. 'Lavender Mini Cascade'	P. 'Lilac Mini Cascade'
Pelargonium 'Ballerina'	P. 'Carisbrooke'	Pelargonium 'Lemon Crisp'	P. crispum
P. 'Beauty of Eastbourne' mis.	P. 'Lachskonigin'	Pelargonium 'Lilac Cascade'	P. 'Roi des Balcons Lilas'
Pelargonium 'Berryl Bodey'	P. 'Mrs L.R.Bodey'		
Pelargonium 'Black Butterfly'	P. 'Brown's Butterfly'	Pelargonium 'Lilac Domino'	P. 'Telston's Prima'
Pelargonium 'Black Vesuvius'	P. 'Red Black Vesuvius'	Pelargonium 'Liverbird'	P. 'Harlequin Miss Liver Bird'
Pelargonium 'Blue Beard'	P. 'Barbe Bleu'		
Pelargonium 'Blue Spring'	P. 'Blauer Fruhling'	Pelargonium 'Lord Baden-Powell'	P. 'Colonel Baden-Powell'
Pelargonium 'Bluebeard'	P. 'Barbe Bleu'		
Pelargonium 'Brook's Purple'	P. 'Royal Purple'	Pelargonium 'Lord de Ramsay'	P. 'Tip Top Duet'
Pelargonium 'Cal'	P. 'Salmon Irene'	Pelargonium 'Madame Guinier'	P. 'Charles Gounod'
Pelargonium 'Cardinal'	P. 'Kardinal'	Pelargonium 'Madame Margot'	P. 'Hederinum Variegatum'
Pelargonium 'Carnival' (Regal)	P. 'Marie Vogel'		
Pelargonium 'Cerise Carnation'	P. 'Mrs H.J.Jones'	Pelargonium 'Marble Sunset'	P. 'Wood's Surprise'
P. 'Chocolate Tomentosum'	P. 'Chocolate Peppermint'	P. 'Meshed Pink Gay Baby'	P. 'Laced Sugar Baby'
		Pelargonium 'Mexicanerin'	P. 'Rouletta'
Pelargonium 'Clorinda Variegated'	P. 'Variegated Clorinda'	Pelargonium 'Miriam Basey'	P. 'Dwarf Miriam Baisey'
Pelargonium 'Countess Mariza'	P. 'Grafin Mariza'	Pelargonium 'Monsieur Ninon' h.	P. 'Madame Auguste Nonin'
P. 'Countess of Scarborough'	P. 'Lady Scarborough'		
Pelargonium 'Crocodile'	P. 'The Crocodile'	Pelargonium 'Mrs Henry Cox'	P. 'Mr Henry Cox'
Pelargonium 'Dark Presidio'	P. 'Dark Mabel'	Pelargonium 'Petit Pierre'	P. 'Kleine Liebling'
Pelargonium 'Deacon Finito'	P. 'Finito'	Pelargonium 'Pink Capitatum'	P. 'Pink Capricorn'
Pelargonium 'Deacon Golden Mist'	P. 'Golden Mist'	Pelargonium 'Pink Cascade'	P. 'Hederinum'
Pelargonium 'Decora Lavender'	P. 'Decora Lilas'	Pelargonium 'Pink Gay Baby'	P. 'Sugar Baby'
Pelargonium 'Decora Mauve'	P. 'Decora Lilas'	Pelargonium 'Pink Mini Cascade'	P. 'Rosa Mini Cascade'
Pelargonium 'Double Henry Jacoby'	P. 'Double Jacoby'	Pelargonium 'Princess of Balcon'	P. 'Roi des Balcons Lilas'
Pelargonium 'Duke of Edinburgh'	P. 'Hederinum Variegatum'		
		Pelargonium 'Purple Ball'	P. 'Purpurball'
Pelargonium 'Dwarf Miriam Read'	P. 'Dwarf Miriam Baisey'	Pelargonium 'Purple Light'	P. 'Purple Gem'
		Pelargonium 'Red Silver Cascade'	P. 'Mutzel'
Pelargonium 'Easter Greeting'	P. 'Ostergruss'	Pelargonium 'Roi des Balcons Rose'	P. 'Hederinum'
Pelargonium 'Emma Hossle'	P. 'Frau Emma Hossle'	Pelargonium 'Roi des Balcons'	P. 'Hederinum'
Pelargonium 'Filicifolium'	P. denticulatum 'Filicifolium'	Pelargonium 'Rote Mini Cascade'	P. 'Red Mini Cascade'
		Pelargonium 'Salmon Queen'	P. 'Lachskonigin'
Pelargonium 'Fragrans'	P. Fragrans Group	Pelargonium 'Snowflake'	P. 'Atomic Snowflake'

Synonym	Current Name	Synonym	Current Name
Pelargonium 'Sofie'	P. 'Decora Rose'	Pellaea mucronata	P. atropurpurea
Pelargonium 'Stellar Arctic Star'	P. 'Arctic Star'	Pellaea spiculata	P. atropurpurea
Pelargonium 'Stellar Grenadier'	P. 'Grenadier'	Pellionia	Elatostema
P. 'Stellar Hannaford Star'	P. 'Hannaford Star'	Pellionia daveauana	Elatostema repens
Pelargonium 'Summertime'	P. 'Deacon	Pellionia pulchra	Elatostema pulchra
	Summertime'	Pellionia repens	Elatostema repens
Pelargonium 'Susan Baldwin'	P. 'Salmon Kovalevski'	Peltandra alba	P. saggitifolia
Pelargonium 'Sussex Lace'	P. 'White Mesh'	Peltandra luteospadix	P. virginica
Pelargonium 'The Culm'	P. 'Culm'	Peltandra tharpii	P. virginica
Pelargonium 'The Czar'	P. 'Czar'	Peltandra undulata	P. virginica
Pelargonium 'The Dart'	P. 'Dart'	Peltiphyllum	Darmera
Pelargonium 'Unique Mons Ninon'	P. 'Monsieur Ninon'	Peltiphyllum peltatum	Darmera peltata
Pelargonium 'Variegated Fragrans'	P. 'Fragrans	Pennellianthus	Penstemon
	Variegatum' (Frag. Gr.)	P. alopecuroides Autumn Wizard	P. alopecuroides
P. 'Variegated Petit Pierre'	P. 'Variegated Kleine		'Herbstzauber'
	Liebling'	Pennisetum compressum	P. alopecuroides
Pelargonium 'Ville de Paris'	P. 'Hederinum'	Pennisetum japonicum	P. alopecuroides
Pelargonium acerifolium -L'Heritier	P. cucullatum ssp	Pennisetum longistylum h.	P. villosum
	strigifolium	Pennisetum rueppellii	P. setaceum
Pelargonium acerifolium h.	P. vitifolium	P. 'Apple Blossom' misapplied	P. 'Thorn'
Pelargonium asperum -Ehr.ex Willd.	P. 'Graveolens'	Penstemon 'Barbara Barker'	P. 'Beech Park'
Pelargonium Balcon Imperial	P. 'Roi des Balcons	Penstemon 'Bisham Seedling'	P. 'White Bedder'
	Imperial'	Penstemon 'Blue Spring'	P. heterophylla 'Blue
Pelargonium canescens	P. 'Blandfordianum'		Springs'
Pelargonium Cascade Lilac	P. 'Roi des Balcons	Penstemon 'Burford Purple'	P. 'Burgundy'
	Lilas'	Penstemon 'Burford Seedling'	P. 'Burgundy'
Pelargonium Cascade Pink	P. 'Hederinum'	Penstemon 'Burford White'	P. 'White Bedder'
Pelargonium Cascade Red	P. 'Red Cascade'	Penstemon 'Candy Pink'	P. 'Old Candy Pink'
Pelargonium coriandrifolium	P. myrrhifolium v	Penstemon 'Catherine de la Mare'	P. heteroph. 'Catherine
	coriandrifolium		de la Mare'
P. echinatum 'Miss Stapleton'	P. 'Miss Stapleton'	Penstemon 'Cherry Ripe' misapplied	P. 'Cherry'
P. fissifolium 'Creamy Nutmeg'	P. 'Creamy Nutmeg'	Penstemon 'Cottage Garden Red'	P. 'Windsor Red'
P. fissifolium 'Snowy Nutmeg'	P. 'Fragrans Varie	Penstemon 'Drinkwater Red'	P. 'Drinkstone'
	gatum' (Fragrans Gr.)	Penstemon 'Firebird'	P. 'Schoenholzeri'
Pelargonium glaucum	P. lanceolatum	Penstemon 'Garden Red'	P. 'Windsor Red'
P. karrooense 'Graham Rice'	P. 'Grollie's Cream'	Penstemon 'Garnet'	P. 'Andenken an
Pelargonium Lila Compakt-Cascade	P. 'Decora Lilas'		Friedrich Hahn'
Pelargonium Pearl Necklace	P. 'Perlenkette'	Penstemon 'John Nash' misapplied	P. 'Alice Hindley'
Pelargonium Pinto Series	P. Pulsar Series	Penstemon 'June'	P. 'Pennington Gem'
P. quercifolium 'Fair Ellen'	P. 'Fair Ellen'	Penstemon 'Lord Home'	P. 'George Home'
Pelargonium rogersianum	P. worcesterae	Penstemon 'Mrs Morse'	P. 'Chester Scarlet'
Pelargonium Snow Queen	P. 'Schneekonigin'	Penstemon 'Myddleton Red'	P. 'Myddleton Gem'
Pelargonium Sophie Cascade	P. 'Decora Rose'	Penstemon 'Phare'	P. 'Le Phare'
P. tomentosum 'Chocolate'	P. 'Chocolate	Penstemon 'Phyllis'	P. 'Evelyn'
	Peppermint'	Penstemon 'Pink Bedder'	P. 'Hewell Pink Bedder'
Pelargonium tricolor h.	P. 'Splendide'	Penstemon 'Pink Bedder'	P. 'Sutton's Pink
Pelargonium violareum h.	P. 'Splendide'		Bedder'
Pelargonium viscosum	P. glutinosum	Penstemon 'Purple and White'	P. 'Countess of
Pelargonium x fragrans	P. Fragrans Group		Dalkeith'
Pelargonium x schottii	P. 'Schottii'	Penstemon 'Purpureus Albus'	P. 'Countess of
Pelargonium x stapletoniae	P. 'Miss Stapleton'		Dalkeith'
Pellaea alabamensis	Cheilanthes alabamen.	Penstemon 'Roy Davidson'	P. procerus 'Roy
Pellaea atropurpurea v cristata	P. atropurpurea		Davidson'
Pellaea densa	Aspidotis densa	Penstemon 'Royal White'	P. 'White Bedder'
Pellaea hastata	P. calomelanos	Penstemon 'Ruby'	P. 'Schoenholzeri'

Synonym	Current Name	Synonym	Current Name
Penstemon 'Sissinghurst Pink'	P. 'Evelyn'	Penstemon sonomensis	P. newberryi ssp son.
Penstemon 'Snow Storm'	P. 'White Bedder'	Penstemon tall pink	P. 'Welsh Dawn'
Penstemon 'Snowflake'	P. 'White Bedder'	Penstemon taosensis	P. crandallii ssp taos.
P. 'Sour Grapes' misapplied	P. 'Stapleford Gem'	Penstemon ternatus	Keckiella ternata
P. 'Souvenir d'Andre Torres' mis.	P. 'Chester Scarlet'	Penstemon tusharensis	P. caespitosus ssp
Penstemon 'Threave Pink'	P. 'Pink Endurance'		suffruticosus
Penstemon 'True Sour Grapes'	P. 'Sour Grapes' -	Penstemon virgatus ssp arizonicus	P. deaveri
	M.Fish	Pentapera sicula -(Guss). Klotsch	Erica sicula -Guss.
Penstemon albertinus	P. humilis	Pentaphylloides fruticosa	P. fruticosa -L.
Penstemon alpinus ssp brandegeei	P. brandegeei	Pentaphylloides glabrata	P. fruticosa v davurica
Penstemon antirrhinoides	Keckiella antirrhinoid.	Pentapterygium	Agapetes
P. antirrhinoides ssp microphyllum	Keckiella antirrhi	Pentas carnea	P. lanceolata
	noides ssp microphyll.	Peperomia 'Princess Astrid'	P. orba
Penstemon arizonicus	P. whippleanus	Peperomia hederifolia	P. griseoargentea
Penstemon bradburii	P. grandiflorus	Peperomia magnoliifolia	P. obtusifolia
Penstemon bridgesii	P. rostriflorus		Magnoliifolia Group
Penstemon caeruleus	P. angustifolius	Peperomia nummulariifolia	P. rotundifolia
Penstemon caespitosus 'Claude Barr' misapplied (purple-fl)		Peperomia pulchella	P. verticillata
	P. procumbens 'Claude Barr'	Peperomia resediflora	P. fraseri
P. caespitosus ssp suffruticosus	P. tusbarensis	Peperomia sandersii	P. argyreia
P. campanulatus pulchellus	P. campanulatus	Peperomia verschaffeltii	P. marmorata
P. campanulatus roseus misapplied	P. kunthii	Peplis americana	Elatine americana
Penstemon coccineus h.	P. barbatus ssp cocc.	Peramium pubescens	Goodyera pubescens
Penstemon cordifolius	Keckiella cordifolia	Pereskia amapola	P. nemerosa
Penstemon crassifolius -Lindl.	P. fruticosus	Pereskia grandiflorus	P. grandifolia
Penstemon cristatus	P. eriantherus	Pereskia sacharosa h.	P. nemerosa
Penstemon davidsonii ssp menziesii	P. davidsonii v menz.	Perezia microcephala	Acourtia microcephala
Penstemon diffusus	P. serrulatus	Pericalymma teretifolium	Kunzea pauciflora
Penstemon digitalis 'Purpureus'	P.digitalis 'Husker Red'	Perilla frutescens v nankinensis	P. frutescens v crispa
Penstemon douglasii -Hook.	P. fruticosus	Perilla macrostachya	P. frutescens
P. fruticosus ssp cardwellii -(Howell) Piper		Perilla urticifolia	P. frutescens
	P. cardwellii -Howell	Periploca laevigata ssp angustifolia	P. angustifolia -Labill.
Penstemon fruticosus ssp scouleri	P. fruticosus v scoul.	Periploca laevigata v angustifolia	P. angustifolia -Labill.
P.f. v cardwellii -(Howell) Krautter	P. cardwellii -Howell	Pernettya	Gaultheria
Penstemon fruticosus v douglasii	P. fruticosus P.	Pernettya empetrifolia -(Lam.)Gaud.	Gaultheria pumila
heterophyllus 'True Blue'	P. heterophyllus	Pernettya prostrata	Gaultheria myrsinoides
P. heterophyllus ssp australis	P. australis	Persea carolinensis -Nees	P. borbonia
Penstemon kunthii	P. campanulatus	Persea gratissima -Gaertn. f.	P. americana -Mill.
Penstemon lewisii -Benth.	P. fruticosus	Persica davidiana -Carr.	Prunus davidiana
Penstemon mackayanus	P. hirsutus	Persicaria affinis 'Dimity'	P. affinis 'Superba'
P. menziesii -Hook. nom illegit.	P. davidsonii v menzi.	Persicaria alata	P. nepalensis
Penstemon menziesii ssp davidsonii	P. davidsonii -Greene	Persicaria amplexicaulis 'Arun Gem'	P. amplex. v pendula
Penstemon menziesii v douglasii	P. fruticosus	Persicaria filiformis	P. virginiana
Penstemon menziesii v newberryi	P. newberryi -A.Gr.	Persicaria japonica	Fallopia j. v compacta
Penstemon menziesii v robinsonii	P. newberryi -A.Gr.	Persicaria polystachya	P. wallichii
Penstemon menziesii v scouleri	P. fruticosus v scoul.	Persicaria scoparia	Polygonum scoparium
Penstemon newberryi ssp berryi	P. berryi	Persicaria sphaerostachya -Meiss.	P. macrophylla
Penstemon newberryi v rupicola	P. rupicola	Petalostemon	Dalea
Penstemon pubescens	P. hirsutus	Petamenes	Gladiolus
Penstemon pulchellus -Greene	P. procerus v	Petasites jap. v gig. 'Variegatus'	P. japonicus v gigan
	formosus		teus 'Nishiki-buki'
Penstemon pulchellus -Lindley	P. campanulatus	Petasites palmatus	P. frigidus v palmatus
Penstemon roezlii -Reg.	P. laetus ssp roezlii	Petrocallis lagascae	P. pyrenaica
Penstemon roezlii h.	P. newberryi f humilior	Petrophila	Petrophile
Penstemon scouleri -Lindl.	P. fruticosus v scoul.	Petrophila adiantifolia	P. diversifolia

Synonym	Current Name	Synonym	Current Name
Petrophile argyrotricha	P. biloba	Petroselinum filiforme	Apium filiforme
Petrophile bakersiana	P. pedunculata	Petroselinum hortense	P. crispum
Petrophile chrysotricha	P. biloba	Petroselinum sativum	P. crispum
Petrophile colorata	P. squamata	Petroselinum tuberosum	P. crispum v tuberos.
Petrophile crassifolia	P. teretifolia	Petunia Million Bells Series	Calibrachoa Million
Petrophile cunninghamii	P. squamata		Bells Series
P. cunninghamii v brachyphylla	P. squamata	Petunia Superbells Series	Calibrachoa Superbells
P. cunninghamii v cunninghamii	P. squamata		Series
Petrophile cunninghamii v gracilis	P. squamata	Peucedanum anethum	Anethum graveolens
Petrophile cunninghamii v major	P. squamata	Peucedanum cartilaginomarginatum	Angelica crucifolia
Petrophile dasyclada	P. striata	Peucedanum decursivum	Angelica decursiva
Petrophile dubia	Isopogon dubius	Peucedanum graveolens	Anethum graveolens
Petrophile ericifolia f subglabra	P. ericifolia	Peucedanum kingii	Anethum graveolens
Petrophile ericifolia v glabriflora	P. phylicoides	Peucedanum litorale	Kitagawia litoralis
Petrophile ericifolia v scabriuscula	P. scabriuscula	Peucedanum makinoi	Angelica crucifolia
Petrophile falcata	P. linearis	Peucedanum officinale	Conioselinum chinense
Petrophile fucifolia	P. pulchella	Peucedanum sowa	Anethum graveolens
Petrophile glabriflora	P. phylicoides	Phaca alpina	Astragalus alpinus
Petrophile glanduligera	P. serruriae	Phaca astragalina	Astragalus alpinus
Petrophile gracilis	P. squamata	Phaedranthus	Distictis
P. heterophylla v angustifolia	P. heterophylla	Phaedranthus buccinatorius	Distictis buccinatoria
P. heterophylla v heterophylla	P. heterophylla	Phaeomeria magnifica	Nicolaia elatior
P. heterophylla v intermedia	P. heterophylla	Phaeomeria speciosa	Nicolaia elatior
Petrophile heterophylla v latifolia	P. heterophylla	Phaiophleps biflora	Olsynium biflorum
Petrophile inconspicua	Isopogon inconspicuus	Phaiophleps nigricans	Sisyrinchium striatum
Petrophile intricata	P. divaricata	Phaius maculatus	Phaius flavus
Petrophile linearis v anceps	P. anceps	Phalangium liliago	Anthericum liliago
Petrophile linearis v microcephala	P. linearis	Phalaridantha arundinacea	Phalaris arundinacea
Petrophile longifolia v caulescens	P. longifolia	Phalaris arundinacea 'Elegantissima'	P. arundinacea v picta
Petrophile longifolia v longifolia	P. longifolia		'Picta'
Petrophile longifolia v lorea	P. longifolia	Phalaris arundinacea 'Picta'	P. arund. v picta 'Picta'
Petrophile longifolia v tenuifolia	P. filifolia	Phalaris arundinacea 'Tricolor'	P. arund. v picta 'Picta'
Petrophile media v brevifolia	P. brevifolia	P. arund. v picta 'Mervyn Feesey'	P. aru. v picta 'Feesey'
Petrophile media v juncifolia	P. juncifolia	Phalaris eruciformis	Beckmannia erucif.
Petrophile media v media	P. media	Phalaris glomerata	Dactylis glomerata
Petrophile media v typica	P. media	Phalaris japonica	P. arundinacea
Petrophile obtusifida	P. pedunculata	Phalaris oryzoides	Leersia oryzoides
Petrophile propinqua	P. squamata	Phalaris picta	P. arund. v picta 'Picta'
Petrophile propinqua v propinqua	P. squamata	Phalaris tuberosa v stenoptera	P. aquatica
Petrophile propinqua v sericiflora	P. squamata	Phalaroides arundinacea	Phalaris arundinacea
Petrophile pulchella v canescens	P. canescens	Phalaroides japonica	Phalaris arundinacea
Petrophile pulchella v sessilis	P. sessilis	Phalerocarpus serpyllifolia	Gaultheria hispidula
Petrophile pulchella v typica	P. pulchella	Phanera	Bauhinia corymbosa
Petrophile rhoifolia	P. diversifolia	Phanerophlebia caryotidea	Cyrtomium caryotid.
Petrophile semifurcata v planifolia	P. incurvata	Phanerophlebia falcata	Cyrtomium falcatum
P. semifurcata v semifurcata	P. semifurcata	Phanerophlebia falcatum v fortunei	Cyrtomium fortunei
Petrophile seminuda v indivisa	P. seminuda	Phanerophlebia fortunei	Cyrtomium fortunei
Petrophile seminuda v seminuda	P. seminuda	Pharbitis	Ipomoea
Petrophile stylaris	P. striata	Pharbitis hispida	Ipomoea purpurea
Petrophile trifida	Isopogon trilobus	Pharbitis learii	Ipomoea indica
Petrophile triternata	P. drummondii	Pharbitis purpurea	Ipomoea purpurea
Petrophyton	Petrophytum	Phaseolus caracalla	Vigna caracalla
Petrophytum elatius	P. caespitosum	Phegopteris calcarea	Gymnocarpium
Petroselinum anatolicum	P. crispum		robertianum
Petroselinum crispum 'Italian'	P. cr. v neapolitanum	Phegopteris dryopteris	Gymnocarpium dryop.

Synonym	Current Name	Synonym	Current Name
Phegopteris phegopteris	P. connectilis	Philodendron bipinnatifidum	P. selloum
Phegopteris polypodioides	P. connectilis	Philodendron elegans	P. angustisectum
Phegopteris robertiana	Gymnocarpium robert.	Philodendron epipremnum	Epipremnum pinnatum
Phegopteris vulgaris	Phegopteris connectilis	Philodendron hastatum h.	P. domesticum
Phegopyrum esculentum	Fagopyrum esculentum	Philodendron laciniatum	P. pedatum
Phellodendron amurense h. in part	P. amurense v lavallei	Philodendron micans	P. scandens f micans
Phell. amurense v japonicum	P. japonicum -Maxim.	Philodendron oxycardium	P. scandens f oxycard.
Phellodendron japonicum h. in part	P. amurense v lavallei	Philodendron panduriforme	P. bipennifolium
Phellodendron lavallei -Dode	P. amurense v lavallei	Philodendron pertusum	Monstera deliciosa
Phellodendron sachalinense	P. amurense v sachali.	Philodendron sellowianum	P. imbe
Phellodendron sinense -Dode	P. chinense v glabriusculum	Philodendron sodiroi	P. ornatum
		Philodendron trifoliatum	Syngonium auritum
Pherosphaera fitzgeraldii	Microstrobos fitzg.	Philodendrum -Schott	Philodendron -Schott
Pherosphaera hookeriana -Hook.	Microstr. niphophilus	Philonotion -Schott	Schismatoglottis
Philadelphus 'Innocence Variegatus'	P. 'Innocence'	Philotria angustifolia	Elodea nuttallii
Philadelphus 'Souvenir de Billiard'	P. insignis	Philotria canadensis	Elodea canadensis
Philadelphus acuminatus -Lange	P. satsumi	Philotria linearis	Elodea canadensis
Philadelphus billiardii -Koehne	P. insignis -Carr.	Philotria minor	Elodea nuttallii
P. brachybotrys v purpurascens	P. purpurascens	Philotria nuttallii	Elodea nuttallii
Philadelphus caucasicus 'Aureus'	P. coronarius 'Aureus'	Philotria occidentalis	Elodea nuttallii
P. coronarius 'Bowles' Variety'	P. cor. 'Variegatus'	Phlebodium	Polypodium
P. coronarius 'Foliis Aureus'	P. coronarius 'Aureus'	Phlomis balearica -Chodat	P. italica -L.
Philadelphus delavayi v calvescens	P. purpurascens	Phlomis rotundifolia -Mill.	P. italica -L.
Philadelphus floribundus -Schrad.	P. x cymosus	Phlomis samia -Boissier	P. russeliana
Philadelphus grandiflorus -Willd.	P. inodorus v grandifl.	Phlomis samia ssp maroccana	P. bovei ssp marocc.
Philadelphus grandiflorus h. in part	P. pubescens -Loisel.	Phlomis sibirica	Leonurus sibiricus -L.
P. grandiflorus v floribundus -Gary	P. pubescens -Loisel.	Phlomis viscosa misapplied	P. russeliana
Philadelphus laniger -Ait.	Leptospermum lanig.	Phlox 'Chattahoochee'	P. divaricata ssp laphamii
Philadelphus latifolius	P. pubescens -Loisel.		
Philadelphus maculatus h.	P. mexicanus 'Rosa Syringa'	Phlox 'Daniel's Cushion'	P. subulata 'McDaniel's Cushion'
Philadelphus mandschuricus -Nakai	P. schrenkii -Rupr.	Phlox 'Louisiana'	P. divaricata 'Loiusiana Purple'
Philadelphus pallidus	P. coronarius -L.	Phlox 'Millstream'	P. x procumbens 'Millstream'
P. pekinensis v brachybotrys	P. brachybotrys		
P. pekinensis v brachybotrys	P. brachybotrys	Phlox 'Mrs Campbell'	P. paniculata 'Elizabeth Campbell'
Philadelphus pubescens v intectus	P. intectus		
Philadelphus pubescens v intectus	P. intectus -Beadle	Phlox 'Pink Ridge'	P. stolonifera 'Pink Ridge'
P. pubescens v verrucosus	P. pubescens		
Philadelphus satsumanus	P. satsumi	Phlox amoena 'Variegata'	P. x procumbens 'Variegata'
Philadelphus Silver Showers	P. 'Silberregen'		
Philadelphus speciosus -Schrad.	P. inodorus v grandifl.	Phlox amoena h.	P. x procumbens
Philadelphus subcanus v wilsonii	P. subcanus -Koehne	Phlox bernardina	P. dolicantha
Philadelphus verrucosus -Schrad.	P. pubescens -Loisel.	Phlox borealis	P. sibirica ssp borealis
Philadelphus wilsonii -Koehne	P. subcanus -Koehne	Phlox brittonii	P. subulata
Philadelphus x falconeri -Sarg.	P. 'Falconeri'	Phlox caespitosa ssp condensata	P. condensata
Philadelphus x lemoinei 'Erectus'	P. 'Erectus'	Phlox caespitosa ssp pulvinata	P. pulvinata
Philadelphus x splendens -Rehd.	P. splendens	Phlox camlaensis	P. nivalis 'Camla'
Philesia buxifolia -Lam.	P. magellanica -Gmel.	Phlox canadensis	P. divaricata
Phillyrea decora -Boiss. & Bal.	Osmanthus decorus	Phlox canescens	P. hoodii
Phillyrea latifolia v ilicifolia	P. latifolia v spinosa	Phlox covillei	P. condensata
Phillyrea laurifolia h.	Osmanthus decorus	Phlox depressa	P. multiflora ssp depr.
Phillyrea media -L.	P. latifolia -L.	Phlox douglasii 'Tycoon'	P. subulata 'Tamaongalei'
Phillyrea vilmoriniana -Boiss.	Osmanthus decorus		
Philodendron andraeanum	P. melanochrysum	Phlox douglasii Lilac Queen	P. doug. 'Lilakonigin'
Philodendron auritum h.	Syngonium auritum		

164

Synonym	Current Name	Synonym	Current Name
Phlox drummondii 'Twinkle'	P. dru. 'Sternenzauber'	Phormium 'Rainbow Chief'	P. 'Maori Chief'
Phlox maculata 'Avalanche'	P. mac. 'Schneelawine'	Phormium 'Rainbow Maiden'	P. 'Maori Maiden'
Phlox mesoleuca	P. nana ssp ensifolia	Phormium 'Rainbow Queen'	P. 'Maori Queen'
Phlox Mexican Hybrids	P. nana	Phormium 'Rainbow Sunrise'	P. 'Maori Sunrise'
P. paniculata 'Amethyst' misapplied	P. panic. 'Lilac Time'	Phormium colensoi -Hook. f.	P. cookianum -Le Jolis
Phlox paniculata 'Count Zeppelin'	P. pan. 'Graf Zeppelin'	P. cookianum 'Alpinum Purpureum'	P. tenax 'Nanum
Phlox paniculata 'Darwin's Choice'	P. pan. 'Norah Leigh'		Purpureum'
P. paniculata 'Eclaireur' misapplied	P. p. 'Duesterlohe'	Phormium hookeri -Gunn ex Hook. f.	P. cookianum spp hook.
Phlox paniculata 'Etoile de Paris'	P. pan. 'Toits de Paris'	Phormium tenax 'Rainbow Queen'	P. 'Maori Queen'
Phlox paniculata 'Fujiyama'	P. pan. 'Mount Fuji'	Phormium tenax 'Rainbow Sunrise'	P. 'Maori Sunrise'
Phlox paniculata 'Latest Red'	P. paniculata 'Spatrot'	Photinia arbutifolia	Heteromeles salicifolia
Phlox paniculata 'Miss Jill'	P. x arendsii 'Miss Jill'	Photinia crenato-serrata -Hance	P. crenato-serrata -
Phlox paniculata 'Miss Jill'	P. x arendsii 'Miss Jill'	Photinia glabra 'Pink Lady'	P. glabra 'Parfait'
Phlox paniculata 'Miss Jo-Ellen'	P. x ar. 'Miss Jo-Ellen'	Photinia glabra 'Red Robin'	P. x fraseri 'Red Robin'
Phlox paniculata 'Miss Jo-Ellen'	P. x ar. 'Miss Jo-Ellen'	Photinia glabra 'Robusta'	P. x fraseri 'Robusta'
Phlox paniculata 'Miss Karen'	P. x ar. 'Miss Karen'	Photinia glabra 'Roseomarginata'	P. glabra 'Parfait'
Phlox paniculata 'Miss Karen'	P. x ar. 'Miss Karen'	Photinia glabra 'Rubens'	P. x fraseri 'Rubens'
Phlox paniculata 'Miss Margie'	P. x ar. 'Miss Margie'	Photinia glabra 'Variegata'	P. glabra 'Parfait'
Phlox paniculata 'Miss Margie'	P. x ar. 'Miss Margie'	Photinia glaucescens -Lindl.	P. nussia
Phlox paniculata 'Miss Mary'	P. x ar. 'Miss Mary'	Photinia glomerata misapplied	P. prionophylla
Phlox paniculata 'Miss Mary'	P. x ar. 'Miss Mary'	Photinia japonica	Eriobotrya japonica
Phlox paniculata 'Miss Wilma'	P. x ar. 'Miss Wilma'	Photinia koreana	P. villosa f
Phlox paniculata 'Miss Wilmer'	P. x ar. 'Miss Wilmer'		maximowicziana
Phlox paniculata 'Mount Fujiyama'	P. pan. 'Mount Fuji'	Photinia salicifolia -Presl.	P. arbutifolia -Lindl.
Phlox paniculata 'Nicky'	P. p. 'Duesterlohe'	Photinia serrulata -Lindl.	P. serratifolia
P. paniculata 'Orange Perfection'	P. p. 'Prince of Orange'	Photinia subumbellata -Rehd.&Wils.	P. parvifolia
Phlox paniculata 'Spitfire'	P. paniculata 'Frau	Photinia variabilis -Hemsl.	Photinia villosa
	Alfred von Mauthner'	Phragmites altissimus	P. australis ssp altis.
P. pan. 'Toits de Paris' misapplied	P. pan. 'Cool of the	Phragmites australis giganteus	P. australis ssp altis.
	Evening'	Phragmites berlandieri	P. australis
Phlox paniculata July Glow	P. paniculata 'Juliglut'	Phragmites communis	P. australis
Phlox paniculata Lavender Cloud	P. p. 'Lavendelwolke'	Phragmites dioicus	P. australis
Phlox paniculata Snowdrift	P. pan. 'Schneerausch'	Phragmites karka	P. australis
Phlox reptans	P. stolonifera	Phragmites macer	Hakonechloa macra
Phlox setacea	P. subulata	Phragmites phragmites	P. australis
Phlox subulata 'Beauty of Ronsdorf'	P. subulata	Phragmites vulgaris	P. australis
	'Ronsdorfer Schone'	Phrygia major	Centaurea scabiosa
Phlox subulata 'Blue Eyes'	P. s. 'Oakington Blue	Phrygia nigra	Centaurea nigra
	Eyes'	Phusicarpos linearis	Hovea linearis
P.subulata 'Bressingham Blue Eyes'	P. subulata 'Oakington	Phusicarpos longifolius	Hovea longifolia
	Blue Eyes'	Phygelius 'Golden Gate'	P. aequalis 'Yellow
Phlox subulata 'Camla'	P. nivalis 'Camla'		Trumpet'
Phlox subulata 'Candy Stripe'	P. sub. 'Tamaongalei'	Phygelius aequalis 'Aureus'	P. a. 'Yellow Trumpet'
Phlox subulata 'Drumm'	P. sub. 'Tamaongalei'	Phygelius aequalis 'Cream Trumpet'	P. a. 'Yellow Trumpet'
Phlox subulata 'G. F. Wilson'	P. subulata 'Lilacina'	Phygelius aequalis 'Indian Chief'	P. x rectus 'African
Phlox subulata 'Kimono'	P. sub. 'Tamaongalei'		Queen'
Phlox subulata 'Mikado'	P. sub. 'Tamaongalei'	Phygelius aequalis albus	P. a. 'Yellow Trumpet'
Phlox subulata 'Snow Queen'	P. subulata 'Maischnee'	Phygelius aequalis x capensis	P. x rectus
Phlox subulata May Snow	P. subulata 'Maischnee'	Phygelius capensis coccineus	P. capensis
Phlox tumulosa	P. griseola	Phygelius capensis x aequalis	P. x rectus
P. virginiana v spec. 'Rose Bouquet'	P. virginiana v spe	Phygelius x rectus 'Winton Fanfare'	P. x rectus
	ciosa 'Bouquet Rose'		'Winchester Fanfare'
Phodina	Callisia	Phylica pubescens	P. plumosa
Phoenix humilis	P. loureirii	Phylica superba h.	P. arborea
Pholidia scaberula	Eremophila scaberula	Phyllanthus nivosus	Breynia disticha

Synonym	Current Name	Synonym	Current Name
Phyllitis fernaldiana	Asplenium scolopendrium	Phyllostachys puberula	P. nigra v henonis
		P. puberula v nigro-punctata	P. nigra f punctata
Phyllitis ruta-muraria	Asplen. ruta-muraria	Phyllostachys pubescens	P. edulis f pubescens
Phyllitus japonica ssp americana	Asplenium scolopendr.	P. pubescens 'Heterocycla'	P. edulis v heterocycla
Phyllitus scolopendrium	Asplenium scolopendr.	P. pubescens 'Kikkochiku'	P. edulis v heterocycla
Phyllocactus biformis	Disocactus biformis	Phyllostachys purpurata	P. heteroclada
Phyllocactus eichlamii	Disocactus eichlamii	Phyllostachys quiloi -A.&C.Riv.	P. bambusoides
Phyllocladus rhomboidalis	P. aspleniifolius	Phyllostachys reticulata h.	P. bambusoides
Phyllodoce alata	Acacia alata	Phyllostachys ruscifolia	Shibataea kumasasa
P. aleutica ssp glanduliflora white	P. aleutica sso grandi flora 'Flora Slack'	Phyllostachys sulphurea	P. bamb. 'Holochrysa'
		P. sulphurea v viridis 'Mitis'	P. suphurea f viridis
Phyllodoce amabilis -Stapf	P. nipponica -Makino	Phyllostachys viridis	P. suphurea f viridis
Phyllodoce caerulea japonica	P. nipponica	Phyllotaenium -Andre	Xantosoma -Schott
P. empetriformis v amabilis	P. nipponica -Makino	Phyllyrea decora -Boiss. & Bal.	Osmanthus decorus
Phyllodoce erecta -(Lindl.) Drude	x Phyllothamus erect.	Phyllyrea decora 'Latifolia'	Osmanthus decorus
Phyllodoce glanduliflora -Hook.	P. aleutica ssp gland.	Phyodina	Callisia
Phyllodoce hybrida -Nakai	P. x alpina -Koidz.	Physalis edulis	P. peruviana
Phyllodoce hybrida -Rydb.	P. x intermedia	Physalis franchetii	P. alkekengi v franch.
Phyllodoce nipponica v amabilis	P. nipponica -Makino	Physianthus albens -Mart.	Araujia sericifera
Phyllodoce nipponica v tsugifolia	P. nip. v oblono-ovata	Physocarpus intermedius	P. opulifolius
Phyllodoce pallasiana -D.Don	P. aleutica	Physocarpus ribesifolius 'Aureus'	P. opulifolius 'Luteus'
Phyllodoce pseudopetriformis h.	P. x intermedia 'Fred Stoker'	Physolobium macrophyllum	Kennedia macrophylla
		Physostegia 'Snow Queen'	P. virginiana 'Summer Snow'
Phyllodoce taxifolia -Salisb.	P. caerulea		
Phyllodoce tsugifolia -Nakai	P. nip. v oblono-ovata	Physostegia Schneekrone	P. vir. 'Crown of Snow'
P. tsugifolia v oblongo-ovata	P. nip. v oblono-ovata	Physostegia speciosa	P. virginiana v spec.
Phyllostachys 'Bory'	P. nigra 'Boryana'	Phyteuma balbisii	P. cordatum
Phyllostachys 'Henon'	P. nigra v henonis	Phyteuma comosum	Physoplexis comosa
Phyllostachys 'Sulphurea'	P. sulphurea	Phyteuma halleri	P. ovatum
Phyllostachys aurea 'Violascens'	P. violascens	Phytolacca arborea -Moq.	P. dioica
Phyllostachys aureocaulis	P. aureosulcata f aure.	Phytolacca clavigera	P. polyandra
Phyllostachys aureocaulis	P. vivax f aureocaulis	Phytolacca decandra	P. americana
Phyllostachys aureosulcata	P. aureos. f pekinensis	Phytolacca thyrsiflora	P. americana
Phyllostachys bambusoides 'Allgold'	P. bamb. 'Holochrysa'	Picea abies 'Argentea'	P. abies 'Finedonensis'
P. bambusoides 'Sulphurea'	P. bamb. 'Holochrysa'	Picea abies 'Excelsa'	P. abies -(L.) Karsten
P. bambusoides 'Violascens'	P. violascens	Picea abies 'J. W. Daisy's White'	P. glauca 'J. W. Daisy's White'
Phyllostachys bambusoides v aurea	P. aurea		
P. bambusoides v castilloni	P. bamb. 'Castillonis'	Picea abies 'Pendula'	P. abies 'Inversa'
Phyllostachys boryana	P. nigra 'Boryana'	Picea abies 'Prostrata'	P. a. 'Pseudoprostrata'
Phyllostachys castillonis -Mitf.	P. bamb. 'Castillonis'	Picea abies 'Veitchii'	P. abies 'Gregoryana Veitchii'
Phyllostachys congesta h.	P. atrovaginata		
Phyllostachys edulis f pubescens	P. edulis	Picea abies 'Will's Dwarf'	P. abies 'Wills Zwerg'
Phyllostachys edulis f pubescens	P. edulis -H. de Leh.	Picea ajanensis -Fisch.	P. jezoensis
Phyllostachys edulis subconvexa	P. viridiglaucescens	Picea alba -Link.	P. glauca
Phyllostachys elegans	P. viridiglaucescens	Picea albertiana -S.Brown	P. abies v albertiana
Phyllostachys henonis -Mitf.	P. nigra v henonis	Picea ascendens -Patschke	P. brachytyla
P. heteroclada 'Solid Stem' misap.	P. purpurata 'Straight Stem'	Picea asperata v retroflexa	P. retroflexa -Mast.
		Picea bicolor -(Maxim.) Carr.	Picea alcockiana -Carr.
Phyllostachys heterocycla	P. edulis v heterocycla	Picea canadensis	P. glauca
P. heterocycla f pubescens	P. edulis -H. de Leh.	Picea complanata -Mast.	P. brachytyla
Phyllostachys mitis h.	P. edulis -H. de Leh.	Picea concolor -Gord.	Abies concolor
P. nidularia smooth sheath	P. nidularia f glabrovaginata	Picea excelsa -Link	P. abies -(L.) Karsten
		Picea glauca 'Albertiana Conica'	P. abies v albertiana 'Conica'
Phyllostachys nigra 'Punctata'	P. nigra f punctata		
Phyllostachys nigra v punctata	P. nigra f punctata	Picea glauca 'J.W.Daisy's White'	P.a.'J.W.Daisy's White'

Synonym	Current Name	Synonym	Current Name
Picea glauca ssp engelmannii	P. engelmannii	Pimelea bowmanii	P. leptospermoides
Picea hondoensis -Mayr	P. jezoensis ssp hond.	Pimelea coarctata h.	P. prostrata
Picea kosteri 'Glauca'	P. pungens 'Koster'	Pimelea laevigata -Gaertn.	P. prostrata
Picea likiangensis v balfouriana	P. lik. v rubescens	P. lehmanniana v ligustrinoides	P. rara
Picea likiangensis v purpurea	P. purpurea	Pimelea longistyla	P. angustifolia
Picea lowiana -Gord.	Abies lowiana	Pimelea nervosa	P. angustifolia
Picea morinda -Link.	P. smithiana	Pimelea sylvestris v aeruginosa	P. aeruginosa
Picea nigra -(Ait). Link	P. mariana	Pimelea tenuis	P. angustifolia
Picea nordmanniana -(Steven) Loud.	Abies nordmanniana	Pimelea thymifolia	P. curviflora v curvifl.
Picea obovata v schrenkiana	P. schrenkiana	Pimpinella aromatica	P. anisum
Picea omorika 'Gnom'	P. x mariorika 'Gnom'	Pimpinella leptophylla	Cyclospermum leptop.
Picea orientalis 'Aureospicata'	P. orientalis 'Aurea'	Pimpinella magna 'Rosea'	P. major 'Rosea'
Picea orientalis 'Nana Gracilis'	P. orientalis 'Gracilis'	Pimpinella podagraria	Aegopodium podagr.
Picea orientalis 'Weeping Dwarf'	P. orientalis 'Pendula'	Pimpinella sisarum	Sium sisarum
Picea pachyclada -Patschke	P. brachytyla	Pinellia pinnatisecta	P. tripartita
Picea parryana -Sarg.	Picea pungens-Engelm.	Pinellia tubifera	P. ternata
Picea pungens 'Glauca Globosa'	P. pungens 'Globosa'	Pinguicula caudata	P. moranensis v caud.
Picea pungens 'Prostrata'	P. p. 'Glauca Prostrata'	Pinus abies -L.	Picea abies
Picea retroflexa -Mast.	P. asperata v retr.	Pinus abies v nordmanniana	Abies nordmanniana
Picea rubra -(Du Roi) Link.	P. rubens -Sarg.	Pinus alba -Ait.	Picea glauca
Picea sargentiana -Rehd. & Wils.	P. brachytyla	Pinus albicaulis 'Nana'	P. alb. 'Noble's Dwarf'
Picea sitchensis 'Papoose'	P. sitchensis 'Tenas'	Pinus araucana -Mol.	Araucaria araucana
Picea tianschanica -Rupr.	Picea schrenkiana	Pinus armandii v mastersiana	P. armandii -Franch.
Picea watsoniana -Mast.	P. wilsonii -Mast.	Pinus austriaca -Hoess.	P. nigra ssp nigra
Picea yunnanensis h.	P. likiangensis	Pinus balsamea L.	Abies balsamea
Picraenia excels	Picrasma excelsa	Pinus bracteata D.Don	Abies bracteata
Picrasma ailanthoides -Planch.	P. quassioides	Pinus brutia -Ten.	P. halepensis ssp brut.
Pieris forrestii -Harrow	Pieris formosa v forr.	Pinus canadensis	Tsuga canadensis
Pieris japonica 'Bert Chandler'	P. 'Bert Chandler'	Pinus cembra 'Aurea'	P. ce. 'Aureovariegata'
Pieris japonica 'Chandleri'	P. 'Bert Chandler'	Pinus cembra 'Columnaris'	P. cembra 'Stricta'
Pieris japonica 'Don'	P. japonica 'Pygmaea'	Pinus cembra 'Nana'	P. pumila 'Nana'
Pieris japonica 'Rosea Daisen Form'	P. japonica 'Daisen'	Pinus cembra v pumila -Pall.	P. pumila -(Pall.) Reg.
Pieris japonica 'Variegata' h.	P. japonica 'White Rim'	Pinus cembroides v monophylla	P. monophylla
Pieris japonica 'Wada's Pink'	P. j. 'Christmas Cheer'	Pinus chylla	P. wallichiana
Pieris lucida -(Lam.) Rehd	Lyonia lucida	Pinus cilicica -(Ant. & Kotschy)	Abies cilicica
Pieris macrocalyx -Anthony	Lyonia macrocalyx	Pinus concolor	Abies concolor
Pieris mariana -(L.) Benth & Hook.	Lyonia mariana	Pinus contorta 'Minima'	P. con. 'Spaan's Dwarf'
Pieris nitida -(Bartr.) Benth & Hook.	Lyonia lucida	Pinus cupressoides -Mol.	Fitzroya cupressoides
Pieris ovalifolia -(Wall.) D.Don	Lyonia ovalifolia	Pinus densiflora 'Ja-nome'	P. d. 'Oculus Draconis'
Pieris ovalifolia v elliptica	Lyonia ovalifolia v ellip.	Pinus densiflora 'Tagyosho'	P. d. 'Umbraculifera'
Pieris ovalifolia v lanceolata	Lyonia ovalifolia v lanc.	Pinus deodara -Roxb.	Cedrus deodara
Pieris taiwanensis	P. japonica	Pinus deodara v robusta -Laws.	Cedrus deo. 'Robusta'
Pieris taiwanensis -Hayata	P. japonica	Pinus devoniana -Lindl.	P. montezumae
	Taiwanensis Group	Pinus divaricata -(Ait.) Dum. Cours.	P. banksiana -Lamb.
Pieris taiwanensis 'Crispa'	P. japonica 'Crispa'	Pinus edgariana -Hartw.	P. muricata -D.Don
Pilea mollis	P. involucrata	Pinus edulis -Engelm.	P. cembroides v edulis
Pilea muscosa	P. microphylla	Pinus excelsa -Link	Picea abies
Pilgerodendron uviferum	Libocedrus uvifera	Pinus excelsa -Wall. ex D.Don	P. wallichiana
Pilocereus senilis	Cephalocereus senilis	Pinus filifolia -Lindl.	P. montezumae
Pilosocereus leucocephalus	P. palmeri	Pinus flexilis v albicaulis	P. albicaulis -Engelm.
Pimelea ammocharis v maitlandii	P. ammocharis	Pinus fraseri -Pursh	Abies fraseri
Pimelea angustifolia v calvescens	P. angustifolia	Pinus glauca -Moench	Picea glauca
Pimelea angustifolia v drummondii	P. angustifolia	Pinus gordoniana -Hartweg	P. montezumae -Lamb.
Pimelea angustifolia v major	P. angustifolia	Pinus grenvillaea -Lindl.	P. montezumae -Lamb.
Pimelea angustifolia v minor	P. angustifolia	Pinus griffithii -McClelland	P. wallichiana

Synonym	Current Name	Synonym	Current Name
Pinus heldreichii v leucodermis	P. heldreichii	Pinus orientalis -L.	Picea orientalis
Pinus himekomatsu -Miyabe & Kudo	P. parviflora	Pinus parryana -Gord.	P. ponderosa -Laws.
Pinus hudsonica -Poir.	P. banksiana -Lamb.	Pinus parviflora v pentaphylla	P. parviflora
Pinus inops -Soland.	P. virginiana -Mill.	Pinus patula v macrocarpa -Mast.	P. greggii -Engelm.
Pinus insignis -Dougl. ex Loud.	P. radiata -D.Don	Pinus pendula -Soland.	Larix x pendula
Pinus kaempferi -Lamb.	Larix kaempferi	Pinus pentaphylla -Mayr	P. parviflora
Pinus khasia -Royle	P. kesiya	Pinus ponderosa v arizonica	P. arizonica
Pinus koraiensis 'Compacta Glauca'	P. cembra 'Compacta Glauca'	Pinus ponderosa v jeffreyi	P. jeffreyi -Balf.
		Pinus pseudostrobus v oaxacana	P. oaxacana
Pinus lanceolata -Lamb.	Cunninghamia lanceola.	Pinus pumila 'Dwarf Blue'	P. pumila 'Glauca'
Pinus laricina -Du Roi	Larix laricina	Pinus pumila 'Saphir'	P. parviflora 'Saphir'
Pinus laricio -Poir.	P. nigra ssp laricio	P. pyrenaica -some authors in part	P. halepensis ssp brutia -(Ten.) Henry
Pinus laricio v calabrica -Loud.	P. nigra ssp laricio		
Pinus laricio v corsicana -Loud.	P. nigra ssp laricio	Pinus religiosa -H.B.K.	A. religiosa
Pinus laricio v heldreichii	P. heldreichii -Christ	Pinus rubra -Mill.	P. sylvestris -L.
Pinus laricio v leucodermis	P. heldreichii v leucod.	Pinus russelliana -Lindl.	P. montezumae -Lamb.
Pinus laricio v poiretiana -Ant.	P. nigra ssp laricio	Pinus salzmannii -Dun.	P. nigra ssp salzmannii
Pinus larix -L.	Larix decidua -Mill.	Pinus sibirica -Du Tour	P. cembra ssp sibirica
Pinus larix v russica -Endl.	Larix sibirica -Ledeb.	Pinus sinensis -Lamb.	P. massoniana -Lamb.
Pinus lasiocarpa -Hook.	Abies lasiocarpa	Pinus sinensis -Mayr.	P. tabuliformis -Carr.
Pinus leiophylla v chihuahuana	P. chihuahuana	Pinus sitchensis -Bongard	Picea sitchensis
Pinus leucodermis -Ant.	P. heldreichii	Pinus smithiana -Wall.	P. smithiana
Pinus leucosperma -Maxim.	P. tabuliformis -Carr.	Pinus spectabilis D.Don	Abies spec. v brevifolia
Pinus llaveana -Schiede	P. cembroides -Zucc.	Pinus strobus 'Nana'	P. strobus Nana Group
Pinus longaeva	P. aristata	Pinus strobus 'Nivea'	P. strobus 'Alba'
Pinus longifolia -Roxb. ex Lamb.	P. roxburghii -Sarg.	Pinus strobus 'Tortuosa'	P. strobus 'Contorta'
Pinus macrophylla -Lindl.	P. montezumae -Lamb.	Pinus strobus f nana	P. strobus Nana Group
Pinus magnifica	P. devoniana	Pinus sylvestris -Mill. not L.	P. pinaster -Ait.
Pinus mandschurica -Rupr.	P. koraiensis	Pinus sylvestris 'Aurea'	P. sylv. Aurea Group
Pinus maritima -Poir.	P. pinaster -Ait.	Pinus sylvestris 'Edwin Hillier'	P. sylv. 'Argentea'
Pinus massoniana -Sieb. & Zucc.	P. thunbergii -Parl.	Pinus sylvestris 'Jade'	P. sylvestris 'Iceni'
Pinus mastersiana -Hayata	P. armandii -Franch.	Pinus sylvestris 'Nana' misapplied	P. sylv. 'Watereri'
Pinus microcarpa -Lamb.	Larix laricina	Pinus sylvestris 'Pumila'	P. sylv. 'Watereri'
Pinus montana -Mill.	P. mugo -Turra	Pinus sylvestris 'Scott's Dwarf'	P. sylv. 'Nisbet's Gem'
Pinus montezumae v hartwegii	P. hartwegii -Lindl.	Pinus sylvestris f fastigiata	P. sylv. 'Fastigiata'
Pinus montezumae v hartwegii	P. hartwegii	Pinus sylvestris v divaricata -Ait.	P. banksiana -Lamb.
Pinus montezumae v rudis	P. rudis	Pinus sylvestris v maritima -Ait.	P. nigra ssp laricio
Pinus monticola 'Pygmy'	P. mon. 'Raraflora'	Pinus tabuliformis v yunnanensis	P. yunnanensis
Pinus mughus -Scop.	P. mugo ssp mugo	Pinus taxifolia -Lamb.	Pseudotsuga menziesii
Pinus mugo 'Carsten's Winter Gold'	P. mugo 'Winter Gold'	Pinus thunbergiana	P. thunbergii
Pinus mugo v mughus	P. mugo ssp mugo	Pinus thunbergii 'Yatsubusa'	P. thunb. 'Sayonara'
Pinus mugo v rostrata	P. mugo ssp uncinata	Pinus tuberculata -Gord.	P. attenuata -Lemm.
Pinus nigra -Ait.	P. mariana	Pinus uncinata	P. mugo ssp uncinata
Pinus nigra 'Pygmaea'	P. nigra ssp laricio 'Pygmaea'	Pinus venusta -Dougl.	Abies bracteata
		Pinus wilsonii -Shaw	P. tabuliformis -Carr.
Pinus nigra ssp maritima	P. nigra ssp laricio	Piper excelsum	Macropiper excelsum
Pinus nigra v austriaca	P. nigra ssp nigra	Piptanthus forrestii -Craib.	P. nepalensis -Sweet
Pinus nigra v calabrica	P. nigra ssp laricio	Piptanthus laburnifolius	P. nepalensis -Sweet
Pinus nigra v caramanica	P. nigra ssp pallasiana	Piscidia erythrina	P. piscipula
Pinus nigra v corsicana	P. nigra ssp laricio	Pisonia brunoniana	P. umbellifera
Pinus nigra v leucodermis	P. heldreichii v leucod.	Pistacia narbonensis -L.	P. vera -L.
Pinus nobilis -D.Don	Abies procera -Rehd.	Pistacia palaestina -Boiss.	P. terebinthus ssp pal.
Pinus nordmanniana -Steven	Abies nordmanniana	Pistacia reticulata -Willd.	P. vera -L.
Pinus nuttallii	Larix occidentalis	Pistacia trifolia -L.	P. vera -L.
Pinus omorika -Pancic	Picea omorika	Pittosporum 'Nanum Variegatum'	P. tobira 'Variegatum'

Synonym	Current Name	Synonym	Current Name
Pittosporum adaphniphylloides	P. daphniphylloides v adaphniphylloides	Platycerium grande h.	P. superbum
		Platycladus chengii	Thuja orientalis
Pittosporum chinense	P. tobira	Platycladus orientalis	Thuja orientalis
Pittosporum flavum -Hook.	Hymenosporum flavum	Platycladus stricta -Spach.	Thuja orientalis
Pittosporum fulvum -Rudge	P. revolutum -Ait. f.	Platycodon glaucum	P. grandiflorus
Pittosporum mayi h.	P. tenuifolium -Gaertn.	Platycodon grandiflorus 'Shell Pink'	P. grandiflorus
Pittosporum nigricans h.	P. tenuifolium		'Perlmutterschale'
P. tenuifolium 'John Flanagan'	P. 'Margaret Turnbull'	P. grandiflorus Mother of Pearl	P. grandiflorus
Pittosporum tenuifolium 'Sunburst'	P. ten. 'Eila Keightley'		'Perlmutterschale'
Plagianthus betulinus	P. regius	Platyloma atropurpurea	Pellaea atropurpurea
Plagianthus lyallii -(Hook.f.) Hook.f.	Hoheria lyallii -Hook.f.	Platylophus obscurus	Centaurea nigra
Plagiorhegma	Jeffersonia	Platyosprion platycarpum	Cladrastis platycarpa
Plagiorhegma dubium	Jeffersonia dubia	Plectranthus australis misapplied	P. verticillatus
Plagiospermum sinense -(Oliver)	Prinsepia sinensis	Plectranthus behrii	P. fruticosus
Planera acuminata -Lindl.	Zelkova serrata	Plectranthus coleoides 'Marginatus'	P. forsteri
Planera davidii -Hance	Hemiptelea davidii		'Marginatus'
Planera ricardii -Michx.	Zelkova carpinifolia	Plectranthus coleoides 'Variegatus'	P. madagascariensis
Planera ulmifolia -Michx	P. aquatica		'Variegated Mintleaf'
Plantago borealis	P. maritima	Plectranthus Swedish ivy	P. oertendahlii
Plantago bracteata	P. major	Plectranthus Swedish ivy	P. verticillatus
Plantago cynops -L.	P. sempervirens	Pleioblastus 'Gauntlettii'	P. argenteostriatus f
Plantago decipiens	P. maritima		pumilus
Plantago eriophora	P. lanceolata	Pleioblastus auricomus	P. viridistriatus
Plantago intermedia	P. major	Pleioblastus auricomus 'Vagans'	Sasaella ramosa
Plantago major 'Atropurpurea'	P. major 'Rubrifolia'	Pleioblastus chino chrysanthus	Sasa chrysantha
Plantago major 'Bowles' Variety'	P. major 'Rosularis'	Pleiobl. chino v argeteostriatus	P. argenteostriatus
Plantago major v asiatica	P. asiatica		'Okindake'
Plantago oliganthos	P. maritima	Pleioblastus chino v laydeckeri	P. chino 'Laydeckeri'
Plantago rosea	P. major 'Rosularis'	Pleioblastus distichus -(Mitf.)	P. pygmaeus v distich.
Plantago uniflora	Littorella uniflora	Pleioblastus fortunei	P. variegatus
Platanus californica -Benth.	P. racemosa -Nutt.	Pleioblastus glaber 'Albostriatus'	Sasaella masamuneana
Platanus californica h.	P. 'Augustine Henry'		f 'Albostriata'
Platanus cretica -Dode	P. orientalis v insularis	Pleioblastus humilis v pumilus	P. argenteostriatus f
Platanus cuneata -(Willd.)	P. orientalis 'Cuneata'		pumilus
Platanus cyprius h.	P. orientalis v insularis	Pleioblastus longifimbriatus	Sinobambusa
Platanus hispanica h. in part	P. occidentalis -L.		intermedia
Platanus intermedia h.	P. x hispanica	Pleiobl. simonii v heterophyllus	P. simonii 'Variegatus'
Platanus macrophylla h. in part	P. occidentalis -L.	Pleioblastus variegatus v viridis	P. argenteostriatus f
Platanus occidentalis h. not L.	P. x hispanica		glaber
Platanus occidentalis v hispanica	P. occidentalis -L.	Pleioblastus viridistriatus	P. auricomus
Platanus occidentalis v pyramidalis	P. x hispanica 'Pyramidalis'	Pleioblastus viridistriatus v vagans	Sasaella ramosa
		Pleione bulbocodioides Limprichtii Group	
Platanus orientalis 'Laciniata'	P. orientalis f digitata		P. limprichtii
Platanus orientalis v undulata -Ait.	P. orientalis 'Cuneata'	Pleione bulbocodioides Pricei Group	P.formosana Pricei Gr.
Platanus pyramidalis -Riv. ex Henry	P. x hisp. 'Pyramidalis'	Pleione chunii	P. aurita
Platanus racemosa h.	P. 'Augustine Henry'	Pleione pinkepankii	P. grandiflora
Platanus vulgaris v angulosa -Spach	P. occidentalis -L.	Pleione pogonioides -Rolfe	P. bulbocodioides
Platanus vulgaris v pyramidalis	P. x hisp. 'Pyramidalis'	Pleione pogonioides misapplied	P. pleionoides
Platanus x acerifolia	P. x hispanica	Pleione speciosa -Ames &Schltr.	P. pleionoides
Platanus x acerifolia h. in part	P. x hisp. 'Pyramidalis'	Pleione yunnanensis misapplied	P. bulbocodi. 'Yunnan'
Platanus x acerifolia v hispanica	P. x hispanica	Pleomele	Dracaena
Platanus x acerifolia v hispanica	P. x hispanica	Pleroma macrantha	Tibouchina urvilleana
Platanus x acerifolia v minor -Ten.	P. x hispanica	Plesmonium -Schott	Amorphophallus
Platanus x hybrida -Brot.	P. x hispanica	Pleurandra camforosma	Hibbertia fasciculata
Platycerium alcicorne h.	P. bifurcatum	Pleurandra cistiflora	Hibbertia cistiflora

Synonym	Current Name	Synonym	Current Name
Pleurandra diamesogenos	Hibbertia diameso.	Polanisia viscosa	Cleome viscosa
Pleurandra hemignosta	Hibbertia hemignosta	Polemonium 'Apricot Beauty'	P. carneum 'Apricot
Pleurandra hibbertioides	Hibbertia hibbertioides		Delight'
Pleuriarum -Nakai	Arisaema -Mart.	Polemonium 'Katie Daley'	P. 'Hopley's'
Pleuropterus cuspidatus	Fallopia japonica v	Polemonium acutifolium	P. caeruleum ssp
	compacta		villosum
Pleuropterus zuccarinii	Fallopia j. v compacta	P. acutifolium v nipponicum	P. caeruleum v nipp.
Pleurospa -Raf.	Montrichardia -Crueg.	Polemonium ambervicsii	P. pauciflorum ssp
Plumbago capensis	P. auriculata		hinckleyi
Plumbago indica rosea	P. indica	P. brandegeei ssp mellitum	P. brandegeei -Greene
Plumbago larpentiae -Lindl.	Ceratostigma	Polemonium caeruleum 'Humile'	P. 'Northern Lights'
	plumbaginoides -Bunge	P. caeruleum Himalayan misapplied	P. cashmerianum
Plumbago rosea	P. indica	P. caeruleum ssp amygdalinum	P. occidentale
Plumeria 'Singapore'	P. obtusa	Polemonium caeruleum v album	P. caeruleum ssp
Plumeria acuminata	P. rubra v acuminata		caeruleum f album
Pneumatopteris	Cyclosorus	P. caeruleum v grandiflorum	P. c. ssp himalayanum
Pneumonanthe andrewsii	Gentiana andrewsii	Polemonium caeruleum v lacteum	P. caeruleum ssp
Poa ariguensis	P. tricialis -L.		caeruleum f album
Poa callida	P. trivialis -L.	Polemonium confertum	P. viscosum
Poa maxima	Briza maxima -L.	Polemonium delicatum	P. pulcherrimum ssp
Poa trichodes	Eragrostis trichodes		delicatum
Poa woronowii	P. trivialis -L.	Polemonium flavum	P. foliosissimum v flav.
Podagraria aegopodium	Aegopodium podagrar.	P. foliosissimum misapplied	P. archibaldiae
Podocarpus 'Golden Dwarf'	Prumnopitys ferrug	P. foliosissimum v albiflorum	P. folios. v alpinum
	inea 'Golden Dwarf'	Polemonium mellitum	P. brandegeei -Greene
Podocarpus andinus -Endl.	Prumnopitys andina	Polemonium occidentale	P. caeruleum ssp
Podocarpus aspelifolius -Labill	Phyllocladus aspleniif.		amygdalinum
Podocarpus chilinus -Rich.	P. salignus -D.Don	P. pauciflorum silver-leaved	P. pauciflorum ssp
Podocarpus chinensis h.	P. macrophyllus		pauciflorum
Podocarpus cunninghamii -Col.	P. hallii	P. pauciflorum ssp typicum	P. pauc. ssp paucifl.
Podocarpus dacrydioides -A.Rich	Dacrycarpus dacrydi.	Polemonium pulchellum -Salisb.	P. reptans
Podocarpus excelsus	Dacryc. dacrydioides	Polemonium pulchellum -Turcz.	P. caeruleum
Podocarpus falcatus	Afrocarpus falcatus	Polemonium pulcherrimum 'Tricolor'	P. boreale
Podocarpus ferrugineus	Prumnopitys ferrugin.	P. pulcherrimum misapplied	P. boreale
Podocarpus gracilior	Afrocarpus gracilior	Polemonium reptans 'Album'	P. r. 'Virginia White'
Podocarpus hallii 'Aureus'	P. totara 'Aureus'	Polemonium reptans 'Dawn Flight'	P. 'Dawn Flight'
Podocarpus spicatus -Mirbel	Prumnopitys taxifolia	P. reptans 'Lambrook Manor'	P. 'Lambrook Mauve'
Podocarpus totara v hallii	P. hallii -Kirk	Polemonium reptans 'Pink Beauty'	P. 'Pink Beauty'
Podocytisus caramanicus -Boiss.	Laburnum caramanic.	Polemonium richardsonii -Graham	P. boreale
Podolobium aciculare	Chorizema aciculare	Polemonium richardsonii misapplied	P. 'Northern Lights'
Podophyllum diphyllum	Jeffersonia diphylla	Polemonium scopulinum	P. pulcherrimum ssp
Podophyllum emodi	P. hexandrum		delicatum
Podophyllum emodi v chinense	P. hex. 'Chinense'	Polemonium viscosum v eximium	P. eximium
Podophyllum japonicum	Ranzania japonica	Pollichia galeobdolon	Lamium galeobdolon
Podophyllum veitchii	P. delavayi	Polycampium lingua	Pyrrosia lingua
Podospadix -Raf.	Anthurium -Schott	Polycarpa maximowiczii -Lindl.	Idesia polycarpa
Poecilodermis	Brachychiton	Polygala 'Dalmaisiana'	P. x dalmaisiana
Pogonatherum saccharoideum	P. paniceum	Polygala chamaebuxus 'Purpurea'	P. cham. v grandiflora
Pogostemon patchouli	P. cablin	Polygala chamaebuxus 'Rhodoptera'	P. cham. v grandiflora
Pogostemon patchouly	P. cablin	P. chamaebuxus v rhodoptera	P. cham. v grandiflora
Poinciana gilliesii -Hook.	Caesalpinia gilliesii	Polygala myrtifolia 'Grandiflora'	P. x dalmaisiana
Poinciana pulcherrima	Caesalp. pulcherrima	Polygonatum 'Falcon'	P. humile
Poinciana regia	Delonix regia	Polygonatum canaliculatum	P. biflorum
Poinsettia pulcherrima	Euphorbia pulcherrima	Polygonatum commutatum	P. biflorum
Poiretia linearis	Hovea linearis	Polygonatum cyrtonema misapplied	Disporopsis pernyi

Synonym	Current Name	Synonym	Current Name
Polygonatum falcatum 'Variegatum'	P. odoratum v pluriflorum 'Variegatum'	Polygonum tinctorium	Persicaria tinctoria
		Polygonum vaccinifolium	Persicaria vaccinifolia
Polygonatum falcatum misapplied	P. humile	Polygonum virginianum	Persicaria virginiana
Polygonatum giganteum	P. biflorum	Polygonum viviparum	Persicaria vivipara
Polygonatum japonicum	P. odoratum	Polygonum weyrichii	Persicaria weyrichii
Polygonatum latifolium	P. hirtum	Polygonum zuccarinii	Fallopia ja. v compacta
P. multiflorum giganteum h.	P. biflorum	Polymnia uvedalia	Smallanthus uvedalius
Polygonatum multiflorum misapplied	P. x hybridum	Polypodium aculeatum	Polystichum aculeatum
P. odoratum 'Grace Barker'	P. x hyb. 'Striatum'	Polypodium aemulum	Dryopteris aemula
P. o. v pluriflorum 'Variegatum' mis.	P. falcatum 'Variegatum'	Polypodium aleuticum	P. glycyrrhiza
		Polypodium angulare	Polystichum setiferum
Polygonatum officinale	P. odoratum	Polypodium aspidioides v tropica	Lastreopsis rufescens
Polygonatum pluriflorum	P. graminifolium	Polypodium auritum	P. vulgare
Polygonatum polyanthemum	P. orientale	Polypodium australe	P. cambricum
Polygonatum pumilum	P. odoratum dwarf	Polypodium bissetianum	Dryopteris bissetiana
P. x hybridum 'Variegatum'	P. x hyb. 'Striatum'	Polypodium boreale	P. vulgare
Polygonum affine	Persicaria affinis	Polypodium bulbiferum	Cystopteris bulbifera
Polygonum amplexicaule	Persicaria amplexic.	Polypodium carthusianum	Dryopt. carthusiana
Polygonum aubertii -L.Henry	Fallopia baldschuanica	Polypodium commune	P. vulgare
Polygonum baldschuanicum -Reg.	Fallopia baldschuanica	Polypodium connectile	Phegopteris connectilis
Polygonum bistorta	Persicaria bistorta	Polypodium cristatum	Dryopteris cristata
Polygonum brunonis	Persicaria affine	Polypodium decursive-pinnata	Phegopteris d-pinnata
Polygonum buxifolium -Bieb.	Atraphaxis buxifolia	Polypodium dilatatum	Dryopteris dilatata
Polygonum campanulatum	Persicaria campanulat.	Polypodium dryopteris	Gymnocarpium dryopt.
Polygonum capitatum	Persicaria capitata	Polypodium falcatum	P. glycyrrhiza
Polygonum carneum	Persicaria bistorta ssp carnea	Polypodium falcatum	Cyrtomium falcatum
		Polypodium filix-femina	Athyrium filix-femina
Polygonum cereale	Fagopyrum esculentum	Polypodium filix-mas	Dryopteris filix-mas
Polygonum compactum	Fallopia japonica v co.	Polypodium fragile	Cystopteris fragilis
Polygonum crispulum -Sims	Atraphaxis buxifolia	Polypodium glycyrrhiza bifid	P. x coughlinii bifid
Polygonum cuspidatum	Fallopia japonica	Polypodium laciniatum	P. vulgare
Polygonum emarginatum	Fagopyrum esculentum	Polypodium lanceolatocristatum	Dryopt. carthusiana
Polygonum emodi	Persicaria emodi	Polypodium limbospermum	Oreopteris limbosper.
Polygonum equisetiforme h.	P. scoparium	Polypodium lingua	Pyrrosia lingua
Polygonum fagopyrum	Fagopyrum esculentum	Polypodium marginale	Dryopteris marginale
Polygonum filiforme	Persicaria virginiana	Polypodium montanum	Cystopteris montana
Polygonum flongisetum	Persicaria longiseta	Polypodium obtusatum	Woodsia obtusa
Polygonum frutescens -L.	Atraphaxis frutescens	Polypodium occidentale	P. glycyrrhiza
Polygonum macrophyllum	Persicaria macrophyll.	Polypodium officinale	P. vulgare
Polygonum milletii	Persicaria milletii	Polypodium palustre	Thelypteris palustris
Polygonum molle	Persicaria mollis	Polypodium penna-marina	Blechnum penna-marin.
Polygonum multiflorum	Fallopia multiflora	Polypodium phegopteris	Phegopteris connectilis
Polygonum odoratum	Persicaria odorata	Polypodium pinnatifidum	P. vulgare
Polygonum orientale	Persicaria orientalis	Polypodium robertianum	Gymnocarpium robert.
Polygonum oxyphyllum	Persic. amplexicaulis	Polypodium setiferum	Polystichum setiferum
Polygonum platycladum	Homalocladium platyc.	Polypodium spinosum	Dryopteris carthusiana
Polygonum polystachyum	Persicaria wallichii		
Polygonum reynoutria	Fallopia japonica v compacta	Polypodium spinulosum	Dryopt. carthusiana
		Polypodium thelypteris	Thelypteris palustris
Polygonum runciforme	Persicaria runcinata	P. vulgare 'Bifidocristatum'	P. v. 'Bifidomultifidum'
Polygonum sachalinense	Fallopia sachalinensis	P. vulgare 'Crispum Cristatum'	P. vulgare 'Congestum Cristatum'
Polygonum sphaerostachyum	Persicaria macrophylla	Polypodium vulgare 'Jean Taylor'	P. vulgare 'Congestum Cristatum'
Polygonum tataricum	Fagopyrum tataricum		
Polygonum tenuicaule	Persicaria tenuicaulis	Polypodium vulg. 'Longicaudatum'	P. glycyrrhiza

Synonym	Current Name	Synonym	Current Name
	'Longicaudatum'	Polystichum sieboldii	Dryopteris sieboldii
Polypodium vulg. ssp occidentale	P. glycyrrhiza	Polystichum spinosum	Dryopteris sieboldii
Polypodium vulgare ssp prionodes	P. interjectum	Polystichum spinulosum	Dryopt. carthusiana
Polypodium vulgare v attenuatum	P. interjectum	Polystichum tsus-simense	P. tsussimense
Polypodium vulgare v falcatum	P. glycyrrhiza	Polyxena pygmaea	P. ensifolia
Polypompholyx	Utricularia	Pomaderris argyrophylla ssp graniticola	
Polyspora axillaris -(Roxb.) Sweet	Gordonia axillaris		P. graniticola
Polystichum abbreviatum -Lowe	Dryopteris affinis	Pomaderris biaurita	P. obcordata
P. aculeatum 'Pulcherrimum'	P. setiferum	Pomaderris ericifolia	P. phylicifolia
	'Pulcherrimum Bevis'	Pomaderris humilis	P. aurea
Polystichum aculeatum v makinoi	P. makinoi	Pomaderris phyllirioides v nitidula	P. nitidula
P. aculeatum v nigro-palaceum	P. makinoi	Pongelion cacodendron	Ailanthus altissima
Polystichum aculeatum v proliferum	P. proliferum	Pongelion glandulosum	Ailanthus altissima
Polystichum adiantiforme	Lastreopsis calantha	Pontederia angustifolia	P. cordata
Polystichum aemulum	Dryopteris aemula	Pontederia lanceolata	P. cordata v lancifolia
Polystichum angulare	P. setiferum	Populus 'Carriereana'	P. x canadensis
Polystichum angustatum	Dryopt. carthusiana		'Carriereana'
Polystichum asperum	Polystichum lonchitis	Populus 'Eugenei'	P. x can. 'Eugenei'
Polystichum bissetianum	Dryopteris bissetiana	Populus 'Gelrica'	P. x can. 'Gelrica'
Polystichum braunii ssp andersonii	P. andersonii	Populus 'Henryana'	P. x can. 'Henryana'
Polystichum callipteris	Dryopt. carthusiana	Populus 'Lloydii'	P. x can. 'Lloydii'
Polystichum caryotideum	Cyrtomium caryotid.	Populus 'Marilandica'	P. x can. 'Marilandica'
Polystichum conifolium	Dryopt. carthusiana	Populus 'Pacheri'	P. x can. 'Pacheri'
Polystichum constantissimum	Dryopteris formosana	Populus 'Rumford'	P. x berolinensis
Polystichum cristatum	Dryopteris cristata		'Rumford'
Polystichum dilatatum	Dryopteris dilatata	Populus 'Tacatricho 32'	P. 'Balsam Spire'
Polystichum dryopteris	Gymnocarpium dryopt.	Populus 'TT 32'	P. 'Balsam Spire'
Polystichum falcatum	Cyrtomium falcatum	Populus alba 'Bolleana'	P. alba f pyramidalis
Polystichum falcatum v fortunei	Cyrtomium fortunei	Populus alba Rocket	P. alba 'Raket'
Polystichum filix-mas	Dryopteris filix-mas	Populus alba v canescens -Ait.	P. x canescens
Polystichum fortunei	Cyrtomium fortunei	Populus alba v nivea -Ait.	P. alba -L.
Polystichum goldieanum	Dryopteris erythros.	Populus alba v tomentosa	P. tomentosa -Carr.
Polystichum hoolepis v hikonensis	Dryopteris pacifica	Populus angulata	P. deltoides 'Carolin'
Polystichum japonicum	P. polyblepharum	Populus balsamifera x trichocarpa	P. 'Balsam Spire'
Polystichum jenningsii	P. andersonii	Populus betulaefolia -Pursh	P. nigra ssp betulifolia
Polystichum lobatum	P. aculeatum	Populus dilatata -Ait.	P. nigra 'Italica'
Polystichum lobatum v chinense	P. neolobatum	Populus fastigiata -Desf.	P. nigra 'Italica'
Polystichum macrophyllum	Cyrtomium macrophyll.	Populus gileadensis -Rouleau	P. x candicans
Polystichum marginale	Dryopteris marginale	Populus glauca -Haines	P. jacquemontii v glau.
Polystichum monotis	P. tsussimense	Populus hudsoniana -Michx. f.	P. nigra ssp betulifolia
Polystichum muelleri	Dryopt. carthusiana	Populus hybrida berolinensis	P. x berolinensis -Dipp.
Polystichum pacificum	Dryopteris pacifica	Populus monilifera -Ait.	P. deltoides -Marsh
Polystichum phegopteris	Phegopteris connectilis	Populus nigra 'Afghanica'	P. nigra 'Thevestina'
Polystichum plumula	P. munitum	Populus nigra 'Italica Aurea'	P. n. 'Lombardy Gold'
Polystichum proliferum h.	P. setiferum	Populus nigra 'Pyramidalis'	P. nigra 'Italica'
	Acutilobum Group	Populus nigra 'Thevestina'	P. nigra 'Afghanica'
Polystichum radicans -Presl.	P. proliferum	Populus nigra v italica -Muench.	P. nigra 'Italica'
P. sacrosanctum misapplied	Dryopteris bissetiana	Populus nigra v pyramidalis -Spach	P. nigra 'Italica'
P. setiferum 'Plumosodensum'	P. setiferum	Populus nigra v viadri	P. nigra
	'Plumosomultilobum'	Populus silvestrii -Pamp.	P. adenopoda -Maxim.
Polystichum setiferum angulare	P. setiferum	Populus tacamahaca -Mill.	P. balsamifera -L.
P. setiferum Percristatum Group	P. s. 'Cristatogracile'	Populus tremula 'Fastigiata'	P. tremula 'Erecta'
P. setiferum Proliferum Group	P. setiferum	Populus viadri -Rudiger	P. nigra
	Acutilobum Group	Populus violascens	P. lasiocarpa v tibetica
Polystichum setosum	P. discretum	P. x canadensis 'Serotina Aurea'	P. x canadensis 'Aurea'

Synonym	Current Name	Synonym	Current Name
P. x canadensis 'Serotina Erecta'	P. x canadensis 'Serotina de Selys'	P. fragiariformis ssp megalantha	P. megalantha
		Potentilla fruticosa 'Argentea Nana'	P. fruticosa 'Beesii'
Populus x canadensis 'Van Geertii'	P. x canadensis 'Aurea'	Potentilla fruticosa 'Blink'	P. fruticosa 'Princess'
Populus x candicans misapplied	P. x jackii	Potentilla fr. 'Donard Orange'	P. frut. 'Donard Gold'
Populus x charkoviensis	P. nig. 'Charkoviensis'	P. fruticosa 'Farreri Prostrata'	P. frut. v pyrenaica
Populus x eur(o)americana -Guinier	P. x canadensis	Potentilla fruticosa 'Farreri'	P. fruticosa 'Gold Drop'
Populus x jackii -Sarg.	P. x candicans	P. fruticosa 'Knap Hill Buttercup'	P. fruticosa 'Knap Hill'
Populus x jackii 'Gileadensis'	P. x candicans	Potentilla fruticosa 'Nana Argentea'	P. fruticosa 'Beesii'
Populus x petrowskyana -Schneid	P. x berolinensis 'Petrowskyana'	Potentilla fruticosa 'Nugget'	P. fr. 'Dart's Nugget'
		Potentilla fruticosa 'Rhodocalyx'	P. fruticosa v davurica 'Rhodocalyx'
Poria cocos	Wolfporia cocos		
Porphyroscias megaphylla	Angelica megaphylla	Potentilla fruticosa 'Sandvedana'	P. fruticosa 'Sandved'
Porphyrospatha -Engl.	Syngonium -Schott	Potentilla fruticosa glabra	P. fruticosa v davurica
Porteranthus trifoliatus	Gillenia trifoliata	Potentilla fruticosa Goldkugel	P. fruticosa 'Gold Drop'
Potamogeton lactucaceum	P. crispus	Potentilla fruticosa Moonlight	P. fruticosa 'Maanelys'
Potamopitys americana	Elatine americana	Potentilla fruticosa purdomii h.	P. fr. 'William Purdom'
Potamopitys triandra	Elatine triandra	Potentilla fruticosa v arbuscula h.	P. fruticosa 'Elizabeth'
Potentilla 'Beanii'	P. fruticosa 'Beanii'	P. fruticosa v dahurica 'Hersii'	P. fr. 'Snowflake'
Potentilla 'Everest'	P. fru. 'Mount Everest'	P. fruticosa v mandshurica h.	P. fruticosa 'Manchu'
Potentilla 'Gold Clogs'	P. aurea 'Goldklumpen'	Potentilla fruticosa v prostrata	P. frut. v pyrenaica
Potentilla 'Mandschurica'	P. fruticosa 'Manchu'	Potentilla fruticosa v rigida	P. frut. v arbuscula
Potentilla 'Monarch's Velvet'	P. thurberi 'Monarch's Velvet'	Potentilla fruticosa v vilmoriniana	P. frut.'Vilmoriniana'
		Potentilla fulgens	P. lineata
Potentilla 'Pyrenaica'	P. frutic. v pyrenaica	Potentilla glabra -Lodd.	P. fruticosa v davurica
Potentilla alpestris	P. crantzii	Potentilla glabra v veitchii	P. fruticosa v veitchii
Potentilla ambigua	P. cuneata	Potentilla glabrata -Schlecht.	P. fruticosa v davurica
Potentilla arbuscula -D Don	P. frutic. v arbuscula	Potentilla Glory of Nancy	P. recta 'Gloire de Nancy'
Potentilla arbuscula 'Beesii'	P. fruticosa 'Beesii'		
Potentilla arbuscula h.	P. fruticosa 'Elizabeth'	Potentilla gracilis ssp nuttallii	P. gracilis v glabrata
Potentilla argyrophylla	P. atrosanguinea v ar.	Potentilla indica	Duchesnea indica
P. argyrophylla atrosanguinea	P. atrosanguinea v argyrophylla	Potentilla insignis	P. atrosanguinea v argyrophylla
P. atrosanguinea v leucochroa	P. atrosanguinea v ar.	P.nepalensis 'Craigieburn Cochineal'	P. 'Craigieburn Cochineal'
Potentilla chrysocraspeda	P. aurea ssp chrysoc.		
Potentilla comarum	P. palustris	Potentilla parvifolia 'Buttercup'	P. frut. 'Buttercup'
Potentilla corsica	P. rupestris	Potentilla parvifolia 'Gold Drop'	P. fruticosa 'Gold Drop'
Potentilla crantzii 'Nana'	P. crantzii 'Pygmaea'	Potentilla parvifolia 'Klondike'	P. fruticosa 'Klondike'
Potentilla dahurica	P. fruticosa v dahurica	Potentilla prostrata -Lapeyr.	P. frut. v pyrenaica
Potentilla davurica -Nestl.	P. fruticosa v davurica	Potentilla recta 'Citrina'	P. recta v sulphurea
P. davurica 'Abbotswood Silver'	P. fruticosa 'Abbotswood Silver'	Potentilla recta 'Macrantha'	P. recta 'Warrenii'
		Potentilla tabernaemontani	P. neumanniana
Potentilla davurica 'Abbotswood'	P. frut. 'Abbotswood'	Potentilla ternata	P. aurea ssp chrysocraspeda
P. davurica 'Dart's Golddigger'	P. fruticosa 'Dart's Golddigger'		
		Potentilla thurberi 'White Queen'	P. 'White Queen'
Potentilla davurica 'Daydawn'	P. fruticosa 'Daydawn'	Potentilla tommasiniana	P. cinerea
Potentilla dav. 'Eastleigh Cream'	P. fr. 'Eastleigh Cream'	Potentilla tormentilla	P. erecta
Potentilla davurica 'Elizabeth'	P. fruticosa 'Elizabeth'	Potentilla tridentata	Sibbaldiopsis tridentat.
Potentilla davurica 'Hersii'	P. f. v davurica 'Hersii'	Potentilla veitchii -Wils.	P. fruticosa v veitchii
Potentilla davurica 'Manchu'	P. fruticosa 'Manchu'	Potentilla verna	P. neumanniana
Potentilla davurica 'Veitchii'	P. fruticosa v veitchii	Potentilla verna 'Pygmaea'	P. neumanniana 'Nana'
P. davurica Rhodocalyx Group	P. fruticosa v davurica 'Rhodocalyx'	Potentilla villosa	P. crantzii
		Potentilla warrensii	P. recta 'Warrenii'
P. davurica v mandschurica h.	P. fruticosa 'Manchu'	Potentilla willmottiae	P. nepalensis 'Miss Willmott'
Potentilla davurica v veitchii	P. fruticosa v veitchii		
Potentilla fragariiformis	P. megalantha	Potentilla x vilmoriniana	P. frut. 'Vilmoriniana'

Synonym	Current Name	Synonym	Current Name
Poterium	Sanguisorba	Primula allionii x pedemontana	P. x sendtneri
Poterium sanguisorba	Sanguisorba minor	Primula alpicola v luna	P. alpicola v alpicola
Potha -Kuntze	Pothos -L.	Primula altaica grandiflora	P. elatior ssp meyeri
Pothos celatocaulis	Rhaphidophora celatoc.	Primula americana	P. farinosa
Pothos foetidus	Symplocarpus foetidus	Primula amoena	P. elatior ssp meyeri
Pourthiaea arguta -Lav.	Photinia villosa v laevis	Primula anisodora	P. wilsonii v anisodora
Pourthiaea parvifolia -Pritz	Photinia parvifolia	P. auricula 'Guildersome Green'	P. auricula
Pourthiaea villosa -(Thunb). Decne	Photinia villosa		'Geldersome Green'
Pratia treadwellii	Pratia angulata	Primula auricula 'Kath Dryden'	P. allionii 'Kath Dryden'
	'Treadwellii'	Primula auricula ssp balbisii	P. auricula ssp ciliata
Presla arvensis	Equisetum arvense	P. Barnhaven Gold-laced Group	P. Gold-laced Group -
Presla hyemalis	Equisetum hyemale		Barnhaven Group
Presla limosa	Equisetum arvense	Primula Barnhaven Reds	P. Tartan Reds Group
Presla palustris	Equisetum palustre	Primula beluensis	P. x pubescens
Presla sylvatica	Equisetum sylvaticum		'Freedom'
Preslia cervina	Mentha cervina	Primula bhutanica	P. whitei 'Sherriff's
Primula 'Altaica'	P. elatior ssp meyeri		Variety'
Primula 'Bewerley White'	P. x pubescens	Primula bileckii	P. x forsteri 'Bileckii'
	'Bewerley White'	Primula brevicaula	P. chionantha ssp bre.
Primula 'Boothman's Ruby'	P. x pubescens	Primula bulleyana ssp beesiana	P. beesiana
	'Boothman's Variety'	Primula chrysopa	P. gemmifera v
Primula 'Dianne'	P. x forsteri 'Dianne'		zambalensis
Primula 'Double Lilac'	P. vulg. 'Lilacina Plena'	Primula columnae	P. veris
Primula 'Freedom'	P. x pubescens	Primula commutata	P. villosa
	'Freedom'	Primula cottica	P. villosa
Primula 'Garryard Guinevere'	P. 'Guinevere'	Primula crispa	P. glomerata
Primula 'Miniera'	P.x meridiana 'Miniera'	Primula edgeworthii	P. nana
Primula 'Quaker's Bonnet'	P. vulg. 'Lilacina Plena'	Primula glaucescens ssp calycina	P. glaucescens ssp
Primula 'Ravenglass Vermilion'	P. 'Inverewe'		glaucescens
Primula 'Snow Carpet'	P. 'Schneekissen'	Primula glutinosa -All.	P. allionii
Primula 'Snow Cushion'	P. 'Schneekissen'	Primula gracilipes 'Major'	P. bracteata
Primula 'Wedgwood'	P. x pubescens	Primula gracilipes 'Minor'	P. petiolaris
	'Wedgwood'	Primula graminifolia	P. chionantha
Primula 'Windrush'	P. x berninae	Primula halleri 'Longiflora'	P. halleri
	'Windrush'	Primula helodoxa	P. prolifera
Primula 'Winter White'	P. 'Gigha'	Primula helvetica 'Alba'	P. pubescens 'Alba'
Primula 'Wisley Crimson'	P. 'Wisley Red'	Primula hopeana	P. sikkimensis v hop.
Primula abchasica	P. vulgaris	Primula hyacinthina	P. bellidifolia ssp hyac.
Primula acaulis	P. vulgaris	Primula ianthina	P. prolifera
Primula allionii -JCA 4161/21	P. allionii 'Travellers' -	Primula intercedens	P. mistassinica
	JCA 4161/21	Primula intricata	P. elatior ssp intricata
Primula allionii -JCA 4161/22	P. allionii 'Jenny' -JCA	Primula involucrata	P. munroi
	4161/22	Primula kisoana	P. kisoana v shikokiana
Primula allionii -KRW	P. al. 'Ken's Seedling'	Primula leucophylla	P. elatior ssp leucop.
Primula allionii 'Aire Waves'	P. x loiseleurii 'Aire	Primula lichiangensis	P. polyneura
	Waves'	Primula littoniana	P. vialii
Primula allionii 'Clarence Elliott'	P. 'Clarence Elliott'	Primula longiflora	P. halleri
	(allionii hybrid)	Primula marginata 'Earl L. Bolton'	P. marginata 'El Bolton'
Primula allionii 'Elliott's Large'	P. allionii 'Edinburgh'	Primula marginata 'Holden Clough'	P. m. 'Holden Variety'
Primula allionii 'Elliott's Variety'	P. allionii 'Edinburgh'	Primula marginata 'Hyacinthia'	P. 'Hyacinthia'
Primula allionii 'Guiseppi's Form'	P. allionii 'Mrs Dyas'	Primula melanops	P. chionantha ssp mel.
Primula allionii 'Hemswell Blush'	P. 'Hemswell Blush'	Primula minima x glutinosa	P. x floerkeana
Primula allionii 'Hemswell Ember'	P. 'Hemswell Ember'	Primula minima x hirsuta	P. x forsteri
Primula allionii 'Pink Aire'	P. 'Pink Aire'	Primula minima x wulfeniana	P. x vochinensis
Primula allionii Hartside 383/12	P. al. 'Gilderdale Glow'	Primula mistassinica v macropoda	P. laurentiana

Synonym	Current Name	Synonym	Current Name
Primula nepalensis	P. tanneri ssp nepalen.	Prostanthera atroviolacea	P. clotteniana
Primula nivalis -Pallas	P. chionantha	Prostanthera baxteri v crassifolia	P. althoferi ssp longifolia
Primula nutans -Delavay	P. flaccida		
Primula obconica 'Apricot Brandy'	P. ob. 'Appleblossom'	Prostanthera baxteri v sericea	P. sericea
Primula oenensis	P. daonensis	Prostanthera coccinea	P. serpyllifolia ssp microphylla
Primula officinalis	P. veris		
Primula petiolaris misapplied	P. 'Redpoll'	P. coccinea v aspalathoides	P. aspalathoides
Primula petiolaris Sherriff's form	P. 'Redpoll'	Prostanthera empetrifolia	P. scutellarioides
Primula praenitens	P. sinensis	Prostanthera eriocalyx	P. aspalathoides
Primula rosea 'Delight'	P. rosea 'Micia Visser de Geer'	Prostanthera euphrasioides	P. cryptandroides
		Prostanthera hirtula v angustifolia	P. hirtula
Primula rotundifolia	P. roxburghii	Prostanthera hirtula v hirtula	P. hirtula
Primula rubra	P. erythra	Prostanthera incisa v pubescens	P. askania
Primula sibirica	P. nutans -Georgi	Prostanthera incisa v pubescens	P. incisa
Primula sibthorpii	P. vulgaris ssp sibt.	Prostanthera incisa v sieberi	P. incisa
Primula sinoplantaginea	P. chionantha ssp sino.	Prostanthera marifolia	P. junonis
Primula sinopurpurea	P. chionantha ssp sino.	P. melissifolia v parvifolia	P. melissifolia
Primula smithiana	P. prolifera	Prostanthera microphylla	P. serpyllifolia ssp mic.
Primula sorachiana	P. yuparensis	P. microphylla f aeruginosa	P. serpyllifolia ssp mic.
Primula uralensis	P. veris ssp macrocalyx	Prostanthera odoratissima	P. cryptandroides
		Prostanthera patula	P. aspalathoides
Primula vernalis	P. vulgaris	P. rotundifolia 'Chelsea Girl'	P. rotundifolia 'Rosea'
Primula villosa v cottica	P. villosa	Prostanthera sieberi	P. incisa
Primula viscosa -All.	P. latifolia	Prostanthera sieberi misapplied	P. melissifolia v parvifolia -Sealy
Primula vulgaris double white	P. vulgaris 'Alba Plena'		
Primula vulgaris green-flowered	P. vulgaris 'Viridis'	Prostanthera teretifolia	P. staurophylla
Primula wardii	P. munroi	Protasparagus setaceus	Asparagus setaceus
Primula warshenewskiana	P. involucrata ssp yargonensis	Protasparagus suaveolens	Asparagus suaveolens
		Protea acicularis	Petrophile acicularis
Primula x arctotis	P. x pubescens	Protea anemonifolia	Isopogon anemonifolius
Primula x chunglenta	P. x chungensis x pulverulenta	Protea anethifolia	Isopogon anethifolius
		Protea apifolia	Isopogon anemonifolius
Primula x deschmannii	P. x vochinensis	Protea barbata	P. speciosa
Primula x flagellicaulis	P. x polyantha	Protea barbigera	P. magnifica
Primula x juliana	P. x pruhonicensis	Protea dichotoma	Petrophile pulchella
Primula x pruhoniciana	P. x pruhonicensis	Protea diversifolia	Petrophile diversifolia
Primula x pubescens 'Carmen'	P. x pubescens 'Boothman's Variety'	Protea falcata	Petrophile linearis
		Protea filifolia	Petrophile filifolia
Primula x serrata	P. x vochinensis	Protea fucifolia	Petrophile pulchella
Primula x steinii	P. x forsteri	Protea furcellata	Isopogon anethifolius
Primula x variabilis	P. x polyantha	Protea mellifera	P. repens
Primula yargonensis	P. involucrata ssp yar.	Protea minor	P. longifolia
Primula yargonensis	P. munroi ssp yarg.	Protea pedunculata	Petrophile pedunculata
Prinos confertus	Ilex verticillatus	Protea pulchella	Petrophile pulchella
Prinos gronovii	Ilex verticillatus	Protea rangiferina	Isopogon anethifolius
Prinos padifolius	Ilex verticillatus	Protea squamata	Petrophile squamata
Prinos prunifolius	Ilex verticillatus	Protea teretifolia	Petrophile teretifolia
Prinos verticiilatus -L.	Ilex verticillatus	Protea tridactylidis	Isopogon anemonifolius
Proboscidea jussieui	P. louisianica	Protea trifida	Petrophile trifida
Proboscidea proboscidea	P. louisianica	Proteinophallus -Hook.f.	Amorphophallus -Blume
Prosartes	Disporum		
Prosopis chilensis	P. glandulosa	Prumnopitys elegans -Phil.	P. andina
Prostanthera albo-hirta	P. albohirta	Prumnopitys spicata -(Mirb). Mast.	P. taxifolia
Prostanthera arenicola	P. serpyllifolia ssp microphylla	Prunella gr. 'Little Red Riding Hood'	P. gr. 'Rotkappchen'
		Prunella incisa	P. vulgaris

Synonym	Current Name	Synonym	Current Name
Prunella x webbiana	P. grandiflora	Prunus cerasus f ranunculiflora	P. cerasus 'Rhexii'
Prunus 'Asano'	P. 'Geraldinae'	Prunus chamaecerasus -Jacq.	P. fruticosa -Pall.
Prunus 'Bendono'	P. 'Benden'	Prunus clarofolia	P. pilosiuscula
Prunus 'Blaze'	P. cerasifera 'Nigra'	Prunus communis -Huds.	P. domestica -L.
Prunus 'Blushing Bride'	P. 'Shogetsu'	Prunus conradinae	P. hirtipes
Prunus 'Cheals' Weeping'	P. 'Kiku-shidare-zakura'	Prunus dehiscens -Koehne	P. tangutica
		Prunus dielsiana v laxa	P. dielsiana
Prunus 'Cistena' -(Hansen)	P. x cistena	Prunus domestica 'Burbank's Giant'	P. d. 'Giant Prune'
Prunus 'Gioiko'	P. 'Gyoiko'	Prunus domestica 'Cropper'	P.d. 'Laxton's Cropper'
Prunus 'Hillieri Spire'	P. 'Spire'	Prunus domestica 'Delicious'	P. domestica 'Laxton's Delicious'
Prunus 'Hisakura'	P. 'Choshu-hizakura'		
Prunus 'Mount Fuji'	P. 'Shirotae'	P. domestica 'Denniston's Superb'	P. d. 'Imperial Gage'
Prunus 'Okumiyako' misapplied	P. 'Shogetsu'	Prunus domestica 'Early Orleans'	P. d. 'Monsieur Hatif'
Prunus 'Pink Star'	P. pendula 'Stellata'	Prunus domestica 'Early Prolific'	P. domestica 'Rivers' Early Prolific'
Prunus 'Pissardii Nigra'	P. cerasifera 'Nigra'		
Prunus 'Sekiyama'	P. 'Kanzan'	Prunus domestica 'Early Rivers'	P. domestica 'Rivers' Early Prolific'
Prunus 'Shidare-zakura'	P. 'Kiku-shidare-zakura'		
		P. domestica 'Laxton's Bountiful'	P. domestica 'Bountiful'
Prunus 'Shimidsu'	P. 'Shogetsu'	P. domestica 'Quetsche d'Alsace'	P. domestica German Prune Group
Prunus 'Shimizu-zakura'	P. 'Shogetsu'		
Prunus 'Takasago'	P. x sieboldii 'Caespitosa'	P. domestica 'Reine-Claude Doree'	P. domestica Reine-Claude Group
Prunus 'Wood's Variety'	P. cerasifera 'Woodsii'	Prunus domestica 'Willingham'	P. d. 'Willingham Gage' (Reine-Claude Group)
Prunus 'Yoshino Pendula'	P. x yedoensis 'Shidare-yoshino'		
		Prunus domestica Greengage Group	P. d. Reine-Claude Gr.
Prunus 'Yoshino'	P. x yedoensis	Prunus domestica Old Greengage	P. domestica 'Reine-Claude Vraie'
Prunus amygdalus -Batsch	P. dulcis		
Prunus amygdalus pollardii	P. x amygdalopersica 'Pollardii'	Prunus domestica ssp insititia	P. insititia
		Prunus domestica v myrolaban -L.	P. cerasifera -Ehrh.
Prunus amygdalus v persicoides	P. x amygdalopersica	Prunus glandulosa 'Rosea Plena'	P. glandulosa 'Sinensis'
Prunus ansu -(Maxim.) Komar	P. armeniaca v ansu	Prunus glandulosa v glabra -Koehne	P. glandulosa -Thunb.
Prunus armeniaca 'De Nancy'	P. armen. 'Gros Peche'	Prunus Hollywood	P. 'Trailblazer'
Prunus aspera -Thunb.	Aphananthe aspera	Prunus ilicifolia occidentalis	P. lyonii
Prunus avium 'Birchenhayes'	P. avium 'Early Birchenhayes'	Prunus insititia 'Golden Bullace'	P. in. 'White Bullace'
		Prunus insititia 'King of Damsons'	P. insititia 'Bradley's King Damson'
Prunus avium 'Bottlers'	P. avium 'Preserving'		
Prunus avium 'Cherokee'	P. avium 'Lapins'	Prunus insititia 'Mirabelle Petite'	P.i. 'Mirabelle de Metz'
Prunus avium 'Grandiflora'	P. avium 'Plena'	Prunus insititia 'Shropshire Damson'	P. i. 'Prune Damson'
Prunus avium 'May Duke'	P. x gondouinii 'May Duke'	Prunus integrifolia	P. lyonii
		Prunus iwagiensis -Koehne	P. nipponica -Matsum.
Prunus avium 'Merton Reward'	P. x gondouinii 'Merton Reward'	P. japonica -Sieb & Zucc. in part	P. glandulosa -Thunb.
		Prunus japonica 'Flore Roseoplena'	P. glandulosa 'Sinensis'
Prunus avium 'Multiplex'	P. avium 'Plena'	Prunus Korean Hill Cherry	P. x verecunda
Prunus avium 'Napoleon'	P. avium 'Bigarreau Napoleon'	Prunus korolkowii -Vilm.	P. cerasifera
		Prunus kurilensis -(Miyabe) Wils.	P. nipponica v kurilens.
Prunus bungei -Walp.	P. humilis -Bunge	P. laurocerasus 'Aureovariegata'	P. laurocerasus 'Taff's Golden Gleam'
Prunus cantabrigiensis -Stapf	P. pseudocerasus 'Cantabrigiensis'		
Prunus capollin -Zucc.	P. salicifolia	Prunus laurocerasus 'Macrophylla'	P. laurocerasus 'Latifolia'
Prunus capuli	P. salicifolia		
Prunus cerasifera 'Aspleniifolia'	P. c. 'Diversifolia'	Prunus laurocerasus 'Magnoliifolia'	P. l. 'Latifolia'
Prunus cerasifera 'Atropurpurea'	P. c. 'Pissardii'	Prunus laurocerasus 'Marbled White'	P. l. 'Castlewellan'
Prunus cerasifera 'Feketiana'	P. cerasifera 'Pendula'	P. laur. 'Schipkaensis Holland'	P. laurocerasus 'Schipka Holland'
Prunus cerasifera v blireana	P. x blireana -Andre		
Prunus cerasus 'James H Veitch'	P. 'Fugenzo'	P. laur. 'Variegata' misapplied	P. l. 'Castlewellan'
		Prunus laurocerasus Green Carpet	P. l. 'Grunerteppich'

Synonym	Current Name	Synonym	Current Name
Prunus lusitanica 'Angustifolia'	P. lus. 'Myrtifolia'	Prunus serrulata v sachalinensis	P. sargentii -Rehd.
Prunus lusitanica 'Pyramidalis'	P. lus. 'Myrtifolia'	Prunus serrulata v spontanea	P. jamasakura
Prunus macrophylla -Poir.	P. avium 'Decumana'	Prunus serrulata v spontanea	P. jamasakura
Prunus mume 'Beni-shidori'	P. mume 'Beni-chidori'	Prunus tibetica	P. serrula
Prunus mume 'Flore Pleno'	P. mume 'Alphandii'	Prunus triflora -Roxb.	P. salicina -Lindl.
Prunus mume 'Grandiflora'	P. armeniaca 'Flore Pleno'	Prunus triloba f multiplex	P. triloba 'Multiplex'
		Prunus triloba f simplex	P. triloba
Prunus mume 'Omoi-no-wac'	P. m. 'Omoi-no-mama'	Prunus vilmoriniana h.	P. scopulorum
Prunus mume 'Rosea Plena'	P. arm. 'Flore Pleno'	Prunus wallichii	P. undulata
Prunus mutabilis	P. jamasakura	Prunus x cistena 'Crimson Dwarf'	P. x cistena
Prunus mutabilis stricta h.	P. serrulata v hupehensis	Prunus x effusa -(Host) Schneid.	P. x goudouinii
		Prunus x hillieri 'Spire'	P. 'Spire'
Prunus myrobalana	P. cerasifera Myrobalan Group	Prunus x pollardii h.	P. x amygdalopersica 'Pollardii'
Prunus nana	P. tenella	P. x subhirtella 'Ibara Ito Sakura'	P. pendula 'Pendula Rubra'
Prunus nikkoensis -Koehne	P. nipponica -Matsum.		
Prunus padus 'Grandiflora'	P. padus 'Watereri'	P. x subhirtella 'Pendula Rubra'	P. pen. 'Pendula Rubra'
Prunus pauciflora	P. pseudocerasus	Prunus x subhirtella 'Pendula' h.	P. pen. 'Pendula Rosea'
Prunus pendula f ascendens	P. pendula v ascendens	Prunus x subhirtella 'Pink Star'	P. pendula 'Stellata'
Prunus persica 'Flore Roseoplena'	P. pers. 'Klara Mayer'	Prunus x subhirtella 'Plena'	P. x sub. 'Dahlem'
Prunus pilosiuscula v barbata	P. litigiosa -Schneid.	Prunus x subhirtella 'Stellata'	P. pendula 'Stellata'
Prunus pilosiuscula v media	P. litigiosa -Schneid.	Prunus x subhirtella v ascendens	P. pendula v ascendens
Prunus pissardii	P. cerasifera 'Pissardii'	Prunus x yedoensis 'Pendula'	P. x yedoensis 'Shidare-yoshino'
Prunus pissardii blireana fl.pl.	P. x blireana -Andre	Prunus x yedoensis 'Perpendens'	P.x y. 'Shidare-yoshino'
P. pseudocerasus v sachalinensis	P. sargentii -Rehd.	Prunus x yedoensis f perpendens	P.x y. 'Shidare-yoshino'
Prunus pseudocerasus v spontanea	P. jamasakura	Prunus yamadae	P. incisa f yamadae
Prunus pseudocerasus watereri h.	P. x sieboldii	Psalliota campestris	Agaricus campestris
Prunus puddum v tibetica -Batal.	P. serrula -Franch.	Psedera henryana	Parthenocissus henr.
Prunus pumila v besseyi	P. besseyi -Bailey	Psedera hirsuta	Parthenoc. quinquefolia
Prunus rehderiana -Koehne	P. litigiosa -Schneid.	Psedera tricuspidata	Partheno. tricuspidata
Prunus sachalinensis	P. sargentii -Rehd.	Pseudathyrium alpestre	Athyrium alpestre
Prunus seoulensis -Nakai	P. padus v commutata	Pseuderanthemum atropurpureum 'Tricolor'	
Prunus serotina v salicifolia	P. salicifolia		P. atrop. 'Variegatum'
Prunus serrula v tibetica	P. serrula -Franch.	Pseudocytisus -Kuntze	Vella
Prunus serrulata 'Alboplena'	P. serrulata	Pseudocytisus integrifolius	Vella pseudocytisus
Prunus serrulata 'Autumn Glory'	P. x verecunda 'Autumn Glory'	Pseudofumaria alba	Corydalis ochroleuca
		Pseudofumaria lutea	Corydalis lutea
Prunus serrulata 'Erecta'	P. 'Amanogawa'	Pseudofumaria ochroleuca	Corydalis ochroleuca
Prunus serrulata 'Grandiflora'	P. 'Ukon'	Pseudogynoxis chenopodiodes	Senecio confusus
Prunus serrulata 'Longipes'	P. 'Shogetsu'	Pseudohomalomena -A. D. Hawkes	Zantedeschia -Sprengl.
P. serrulata 'Miyako' misapplied	P. 'Shogetsu'	Pseudolarix fortunei -Mayr	P. amabilis
Prunus serrulata 'Rosea'	P. 'Kiku-shidare-zakura'	Pseudolarix kaempferi -Auct.	P. amabilis
		Pseudomuscari	Muscari
Prunus serrulata f affinis -Miyoshi	P. 'Jo-nioi'	Pseudopanax daviesii h.	P. laetus
Prunus serrulata f erecta	P. 'Amanogawa'	Pseudorhipsalis alata	Disocactus alatus
Prunus serrulata f fugenzo -Mak.	P. 'Fugenzo'	Pseudorhipsalis macrantha	Disocactus macranth.
Prunus serrulata f geraldiniae	P. 'Geraldinae'	Pseudosasa amabilis misapplied	Arundinaria gigantea
Prunus serrulata f luteioides	P. 'Asagi'	Pseudosasa japonica 'Variegata'	P. j. 'Akebonosuji'
Prunus serrulata f purpurascens	P. 'Kanzan'	Pseudosasa kurilensis	Sasa kurilensis
Prunus serrulata f rubida	P. 'Bendono'	Pseudosasa orthotropa	Sinobambusa orthot.
Prunus serrulata f sieboldii	P. x sieboldii	Pseudotsuga douglasii -(Lindl.)Carr.	P. menziesii
Prunus serrulata f tricolor	P. 'Gyoiko'	Pseudotsuga douglasii v glauca	P. menziesii v glauca
Prunus serrulata splendens h.	P. 'Choshu-hizakura'	Pseudotsuga glauca -(Mayr) Mayr	P. menziesii v glauca
Prunus serrulata v pubescens	P. verecunda	Pseudotsuga glauca 'Fletcheri'	P. menziesii 'Fletcheri'

Synonym	Current Name	Synonym	Current Name
Pseudotsuga glauca 'Nana'	P. menziesii 'Nana'	Pulmonaria officinalis rubra	P. rubra
Pseudotsuga taxifolia	P. menziesii	Pulmonaria picta	P. saccharata
Pseudozygocactus epiphylloides	Hatiora epiphylloides	Pulmonaria rubra v alba	P. r. v albocorollata
Psidium cattleyanum	P. littorale v longipes	Pulmonaria saccharata 'Blauhimmel'	P. 'Blauhimmel'
Psoralea linearis	Aspalathus linearis	Pulmonaria saccharata 'Picta'	P. saccharata
Psygmorchis pusilla	Oncidium pusillum	P. saccharata 'Sissinghurst White'	P. officinalis
Ptarmica	Achillea		'Sissinghurst White'
Ptelea angustifolia -Benth.	P. baldwinii	Pulmonaria saccharata 'White Barn'	P. 'Beth's Blue'
Ptelea crenulata -Greene	P. baldwinii v crenulat.	Pulmonaria suffruticosa -L.	Mertensia suffruticosa
Ptelea monophylla -Lam.	Cliftonia monophylla	Pulmonaria vallarsae 'Margery Fish'	P. 'Margery Fish'
Pteracanthus	Strobilanthes	Pulmonaria virginica -L.	Mertensia virginica
Pteretinodes struthiopteris	Matteucia struth.	Pulsatilla alpina ssp sulphurea	P. alpina ssp apiifolia
Pteretis nodulosa	Matteucia struth.	Pulsatilla bogenhardiana	P. vulgaris
Pteretis struthiopteris	Matteucia struth.	Pulsatilla halleri ssp grandis	P. vulgaris ssp grandis
Pteris alabamensis	Cheilanthes alabamens.	Pulsatilla lutea	P. alpina ssp apiifolia
Pteris argentea	Cheilanthes argentea	Pulsatilla nigella	P. vulgaris
Pteris atropurpurea	Pellaea atropurpurea	Pulsatilla nigricans	P. pratensis ssp nigri.
Pteris comans	P. zahlbruckeriana	Pulsatilla vulgaris 'Red Clock'	P. v. 'Rode Klokke'
Pteris endlicheriana	P. zahlbruckeriana	Pulsatilla vulgaris Rote Glokke	P. v. 'Rode Klokke'
Pteris hirsuta	Cheilanthes nudiuscula	Pulsatilla vulgaris White Swan	P. v. 'Weisse Schwan'
Pteris marginata	P. kingiana	Pultenaea nana	Chorizema nanum
Pteris quadriaurita	P. kingiana	Punica granatum 'Flore Pleno'	P. granatum 'Flore
Pteris scaberula	Paesia scaberula		Pleno Rubro'
Pteris spicata	Pellaea atropurpurea	Punica granatum 'Rubroplena'	P. granatum 'Flore
Pteris stelleri	Cryptogramma stelleri		Pleno Rubro'
Pteris trattinickiana	P. kingiana	Punica nana -L.	P. granatum v nana
Pteris tremula v kingiana	P. kingiana	Puschkinia libanotica	P. scilloides v libanot.
Pteris tripartita	P. kingiana	Puya caerulea	P. coerulea
Pterocactus kuntzei	P. tuberosus	Puya violacea	P. coerulea v violacea
Pterocarya caucasica -C.A.Mey	P. fraxinifolia	Pycnanthemum flexuosum	P. tenuifolium
Pterocarya caucasica -C.A.Mey	P. fraxinifolia Pterocarya	Pycnanthemum linifolium	P. tenuifolium
dumosa -Lav.	P. fraxinifolia v dum.	Pycnodoria cretica	Pteris cretica
Pterocarya sinensis -Rehd.	P. stenoptera	Pycnopteris sieboldii	Dryopteris sieboldii
Pterocephalus parnassi	P. perennis	Pygmaea	Chionohebe
Ptilotrichum pupureum	Alyssum purpureum	Pyracantha 'Golden Sun'	P. 'Soleil d'Or'
Ptilotrichum pyrenaicum	Alyssum pyrenaicum	Pyracantha 'John Stedman'	P. 'Stedman's'
Ptilotrichum spinosum -(L.) Boiss.	Alyssum spinosum -L.	Pyracantha 'Monrovia'	P. coccinea 'Lalandei'
Ptilotrichum spinosum 'Roseum'	Alyssum sp. 'Roseum'	Pyracantha 'Orange Giant'	P. coccinea 'Kasan'
Ptychosperma alexandrae	Archontophoenix alex.	Pyracantha 'Waterer's Orange'	P. 'Watereri'
Pueraria hirsuta	P. lobata	Pyracantha 'Yellow Sun'	P. 'Soleil d'Or'
Pueraria thunbergiana	P. lobata	Pyracantha crenulata v rogersiana	P. rogersiana
Pukateria littoralis -Raoul	Griselinia littoralis	Pyracantha fortuneana -(Maxim.) Li	P. crenato-serrata
Pulmonaria 'Highdown'	P. 'Lewis Palmer'	Pyracantha gibbsii -A.B.Jacks	P. atalantioides
Pulmonaria 'Mawson's Variety'	P. 'Mawson's Blue'	Pyracantha gibbsii 'Flava'	P. atalantioides 'Aurea'
Pulmonaria angustifolia 'Beth's Pink'	P. 'Beth's Pink'	Pyracantha x watereri	P. 'Watereri'
Pulmonaria angustifolia 'Blue Moon'	P. officinalis 'Blue Mist'	Pyracantha yunnanensis -Chitt.	P. crenato-serrata
Pulmonaria angustifolia 'Rubra'	P. rubra	Pyrenaria spectabilis	Tutcheria spectabilis
Pulmonaria azurea	P. angustifolia ssp az.	Pyrethropsis atlantica	Rhodanthemum atlant.
Pulmonaria grandiflora	P. saccharata	Pyrethropsis gayana	Rhodanthemum gayan.
Pulmonaria longifolia 'Coen Jansen'	P. longifolia 'Ankum'	Pyrethropsis hosmariense	Rhodanthemum hosm.
Pulmonaria longifolia 'Lewis Palmer'	P. 'Lewis Palmer'	Pyrethrum 'Brenda'	Tanacetum coccineum
Pulmonaria maculosa	P. officinalis		'Brenda'
Pulmonaria Milky Way	P. 'Milchstrasse'	Pyrethrum alpinum	Leucanthemopsis alp.
Pulmonaria montana	P. mollis	Pyrethrum arcticum	Arctanthemum arct.
Pulmonaria officinalis 'Bowles' Blue'	P. officinalis 'Blue Mist'	Pyrethrum balsamita	Tanacetum balsamita

Synonym	Current Name	Synonym	Current Name
Pyrethrum cinerariifolium	Tanacetum cinerariif.	Pyrus malus v mitis -Wallr.	Malus domestica
Pyrethrum coccineum	Tanacetum coccineum	Pyrus malus v paradisiaca -L.	Malus pumila -Mill.
Pyrethrum corymbosum	Tanacetum corymbos.	Pyrus malus v pumila -(Mill.) Henry	Malus pumila -Mill.
Pyrethrum diversifolium	Brachyscome diversif.	Pyrus malus v sylvestris -L.	Malus sylvestris
Pyrethrum leucanthemum	Leucanthemum vulgare	Pyrus maulei -(T.Moore) Mast.	Chaenomeles japonica
Pyrethrum majus	Tanacetum balsamita	Pyrus melanocarpa -(Michx.) Willd.	Aronia melanocarpa
Pyrethrum parthenium	Tanacetum parthenium	Pyrus niedzwetzkyana -Hemsl.	Malus pumila
Pyrethrum ptarmiciforum	Tanacetum ptarmiciflo.		'Niedwetzkyana'
Pyrethrum radicans	Leucanthemopsis	Pyrus pashia v kumaoni	P. pashia -D.Don
	pectinata	Pyrus prattii -Hemsl.	Malus prattii
Pyrethrum roseum	Tanacetum coccineum	Pyrus prunifolia -Willd.	Malus prunifolia
Pyrethrum segetum	Glebionis segetum	Pyrus pulcherrima	Malus floribunda
Pyrethrum tanacetifolium	Tanacet. corymbos.	Pyrus purpurea h.	Malus x purpurea
Pyrethrum tanacetum	Tanacetum balsamita	Pyrus pyrifolia '20th Century'	P. pyrifolia 'Nijisseiki'
Pyrocydonia danielii	+Pyrocydonia 'Danielii'	Pyrus ringo v kaido -(Sieb.) Wnzig	Malus x micromalus
Pyrola umbellata	Chimaphia umbellata	Pyrus rivularis -Hook.	Malus fusca
Pyronia danielii -(Daniel) Rehd.	+Pyrocydonia 'Danielii'	Pyrus rufifolia -Levl.	Docynia rufifolia
Pyrostegia ignea	P. venusta	Pyrus sanguinea -Pursh	Amelanchier sanguinea
Pyrrhocactus crispus	Neoporteria crispa	Pyrus sargentii -(Rehd.) Bean	Malus toringo ssp sar.
Pyrus alnifolia	Amelanchier alnifolia	Pyrus serotina -Rehd.	P. pyrifolia
Pyrus angustifolia -Ait.	Malus angustifolia	Pyrus sieboldii -Reg.	Malus toringo
Pyrus arbutifolia -L.	Aronia arbutifolia	Pyrus sikkimensis -Hook. f.	Malus sikkimensis
Pyrus aria	Sorbus aria	Pyrus sinensis -Decne. not Lindl.	P. ussuriensis -Maxim.
Pyrus baccata -L.	Malus baccata	Pyrus sorbus	Sorbus domestica
Pyrus bartramiana -Tausch	Amelanchier bartrami.	Pyrus soulardii -Bailey	Malus x soulardii
P. calleryana 'Cleveland Scarlet'	P. c. 'Chanticleer'	Pyrus spectabilis -Ait.	Malus spectabilis
Pyrus canadensis	Amelanchier canadens.	P. sp. floribunda scheideckeri	Malus x shceideckeri
Pyrus communis 'Chalk'	P. c. 'Crawford'	Pyrus spectabilis v kaido	Malus x micromalus
Pyrus communis 'Fertility Improved'	P.c. 'Improved Fertility'	Pyrus toringoides -(Rehd.) Osborn	Malus toringoides
Pyrus communis 'Sweet Huffcap'	P. c. 'Hellen's Early'	Pyrus transitoria -Batal.	Malus transitoria
Pyrus communis 'Triumph'	P. communis	Pyrus tschonskii -Maxim.	Malus tschonskii
	'Packham's Triumph'	Pyrus variolosa -G.Don	P. pashia -D.Don
Pyrus communis v cordata	P. cordata -Desv.	Pyrus x eleyi -(Bean) Hesse	Malus x purpurea
Pyrus communis v longipes	P. cossonii		'Eleyi'
Pyrus communis v pyraster	P. pyraster	Pyrus x eleyi -Bean	Malus x purp. 'Eleyi'
Pyrus commutata	Sorbus japonica	Pyrus x purpurea f eleyi	Malus x purp. 'Eleyi'
Pyrus coronaria -L.	Malus coronaria	Pyrus yunnanensis -Franch.	Malus yunnanensis
Pyrus coronaria v ioensis -Wood	Malus ioensis	Pyrus zumi -Matsum.	Malus x zumi
Pyrus crataegifolia -Savi	Malus florentina	Pyrus zumi 'Calocarpa'	Malus x z. v calocarpa
Pyrus cuneifolia -Guss.	P. amygdaliformis v c.	Pythion -Mart.	Amorphophallus
Pyrus cydonia -L.	Cydonia oblonga -Mill.	Pythonium -Schott	Amorphophallus
Pyrus delavayi -Franch.	Docynia delavayi	Pyxidium sylvestre	Amaranthus albus
Pyrus floribunda -Kirchn. not Lindl.	Malus floribunda	Qiongzhuea	Chimonobambusa
Pyrus floribunda atrosanguinea	Malus x atrosanguinea	Quamasia hyacinthina	Camassia scilloides
Pyrus floribunda scheideckeri h.	Malus x shceideckeri	Quamoclit coccinea	Ipomoea coccinea
Pyrus fusca -Raf.	Malus fusca	Quamoclit lobata	Ipomoea lobata
Pyrus germanica	Mespilus germanica	Quamoclit mina	Ipomoea lobata
Pyrus hupehensis -Pampan.	Malus hupehensis	Quamoclit pennata	Ipomoea quamoclit
Pyrus ioensis -(Wood) Bailey	Malus ioensis	Quassia cedron	Simaba cedron
Pyrus japonica -Sims not Thunb.	Chaenomeles speciosa	Quercus acuminata -not Roxb.	Q. muehlenbergii
Pyrus japonica -Thunb.	Chaenomeles japonica	Quercus aegilops -L.	Q. ithaburensis ssp
Pyrus kansuensis -Batal.	Malus kansuensis		macrolepis
Pyrus kumaoni -Decne.	P. pashia -D.Don	Quercus aegilops v pyrami	Q. ithaburensis
Pyrus longipes -Coss. & Durieu	P. cossonii -Rehd.	Quercus alba v minor -Marsh.	Q. stellata -Wnagenh.
Pyrus malus -L. in part	Malus domestica	Quercus ambigua -Michx. f.	Q. rubra -L.

Synonym	Current Name	Synonym	Current Name
Quercus ambrozyana	Q. x hispanica 'Ambrozyana'	Quercus hindsii -Benth.	Q. lobata -Nee
		Quercus hybrida -Ashe	Q. laurifolia -Michx.
Quercus annulata -Sm.	Q. glauca -Thunb.	Quercus hypoleuca -Engelm. not Miq.	Q. hypoleucoides
Quercus aquatica -Walt.	Q. nigra -L.	Quercus ilex 'Angustifolia'	Q. ilex 'Fordii'
Quercus aquifolioides -Rehd.&Wils.	Q. semecarpifolia -Sm.	Quercus incana -Roxb.	Q. leucotrichophora
Quercus armeniaca -Kotschy	Q. hartwissiana -Stev.	Quercus laevigata -Blume	Q. acuta -Thunb.
Quercus bambusifolia -Fort.	Q. myrsinifolia	Quercus lanuginosa -Lam.	Q. cerris -L.
Quercus banisteri -Michx.	Q. ilicifolia -Wangenh.	Quercus lanuginosa -Lam. nom illeg.	Q. pubescens -Willd.
Quercus borealis -Michx.	Q. rubra -L.	Quercus lanuginosa v virgiliana	Q. pubecens ssp pub.
Quercus borealis v maxima	Q. rubra -L.	Quercus liatungensis	Q. wutaishanica
Quercus brayi -Sm.	Q. muehlenbergii	Quercus lusitanica -Webb.	Q. faginea -Lam.
Quercus breweri	Q. garryana v breweri	Quercus lusitanica ssp baetica	Q. canariensis -Willd.
Quercus bungeana -Forbes	Q. variabilis -Blume	Quercus lusitanica v baetica	Q. faginea -Lam.
Quercus californica -Cooper	Q. kelloggii -Newberry	Quercus lusitanica v baetica -Webb	Q. canariensis -Willd.
Quercus calliprinos -Webb	Q. coccifera ssp callip.	Quercus macedonica -A.DC.	Q. trojana -Webb
Q. castaneifolia ssp aitchisonii	Q. castaneifolia	Quercus macrolepis	Q. ithaburensis ssp macrolepis
Quercus catesbaei -Michx.	Q. laevis -Walt.		
Quercus cerris 'Variegata'	Q. cerris 'Argenteovariegata'	Quercus mandanensis -Rydb.	Q. macrocarpa -Michx.
		Quercus maxima -(Marsh.) Ashe	Q. rubra -L.
Quercus cerris v ambrozyana	Q. x lucombeana 'Ambrozyana'	Quercus minor -(Marsh.) Sarg.	Q. stellata -Wangenh.
		Quercus mirbeckii -Durieu	Q. canariensis -Willd.
Quercus chinensis -Bunge not Abel	Q. variabilis -Blume	Quercus missouriensis	Q. velutina
Quercus chrysolepis v vaccinifolia	Q. vaccinifolia -Kell.	Quercus montana -Willd.	Q. prinus -L.
Quercus cinerea -Michx.	Q. incana -Bartr.	Quercus mysinifolia	Q. glauca
Quercus cleistocarpa -Seem.	Lithocarpus cleistocar.	Quercus nana -(Marsh.) Sarg.	Q. ilicifolia -Wangenh.
Quercus coccifera v calliprinos	Q. coccifera ssp callip.	Quercus nigra -Wangenh. not L.	Q. marilandica
Q. coccifera v pseudococcifera	Q. coccifera -L.	Quercus nobilis h. ex K.Koch	Q. falcata -Michx.
Quercus coccinea v micropcarpa	Q. ellipsoidalis -E.J.Hill	Quercus nuttallii	Q. texana
Quercus conferta -Kit.	Q. frainetto -Ten.	Quercus obtusa -(Willd.) Ashe	Q. laurifolia -Michx.
Quercus crispula -Blume	Q. mongolica v grosseserrata	Quercus obtusiloba -Michx.	Q. stellata -Wangenh.
		Quercus pachyphylla -Kurz	Lithocarpus pachyphyl.
Quercus cuneata -Wangenh.	Q. marilandica	Quercus pannonica -Booth ex Gord.	Q. frainetto -Ten.
Quercus cuspidata -Thunb.	Castanopsis cuspidata	Quercus pedunculata -Ehrh.	Q. robur -L.
Quercus daimio -K.Koch	Q. dentata -Thunb.	Quercus pedunculiflora	Q. robur ssp peduncul.
Quercus densiflora -Hook. & Arn.	Lithocarpus densiflor.	Quercus petraea 'Laciniata'	Q. petraea 'Insecata'
Quercus dielsiana -Seemen	Q. baronii -Skan	Quercus petraea 'Rubicunda'	Q. petraea 'Purpurea'
Quercus echinoides -R. Br.	Lithocarpus densi florus v echinoides	Quercus petraea 'Salicifolia'	Q. robur 'Holophylla'
		Quercus phellos v latifolia	Q. incana -Bartram
Quercus edulis -Mak.	Lithocarpus edulis	Quercus platanoides -Sudw.	Q. bicolor -Willd.
Quercus faginea ssp tlemcenensis	Q. faginea ssp broteroi	Quercus prinus -Engelm.	Q. montana
Quercus falcata v pagodifolia -Elliott	Q. pagoda -Raf.	Quercus prinus v acuminata -Roxb.	Q. muehlenbergii
Quercus falcata v triloba	Q. falcata -Michx.	Quercus prinus v monticola -Michx.	Q. prinus -L.
Quercus farnetto -Ten.	Q. frainetto -Ten.	Quercus prinus v palustris -Michx.	Q. michauxii -Nutt.
Quercus fruticosa -Brot.	Q. lusitanica -Lamarck	Quercus pseudococcifera -Desf.	Q. coccifera -L.
Quercus fulhamensis -Zab.	Q. x lucombeana 'Fulhamensis'	Quercus pseudococcifera -not Desf.	Q. coccifera ssp calliprinos
Quercus garryana v fruticosa	Q. garryana v breweri	Q. pseudosuber v tlemcenensis	Q. faginea ssp broteroi
Quercus glabra -not Thunb.	Lithocarpus edulis	Quercus pumila -Michaux	Q. montana
Quercus glabra -Thunb.	Lithocarpus glaber	Quercus pumila -Walt.	Q. phellos
Quercus glandulifera	Q. serrata	Quercus rhombica -Sarg.	Q. laurifolia -Michx.
Quercus grosseserrata -Blume	Q. mongolica v grosseserrata	Quercus robur -Spielart	Q. petraea
		Quercus robur 'Filicifolia'	Q. x rosacea 'Filicifolia'
Quercus haas -(Kotschy)	Q. pedunculiflora	Quercus robur 'Filicifolia' misapplied	Q. robur 'Pectinata'
Quercus hemisphaerica	Q. laurifolia -Michx.	Quercus robur 'Salicifolia Fastigiata'	Q. robur 'Salfast'
Quercus henryi -Seem.	Lithocarpus henryi	Quercus robur v virgiliana -Ten.	Q. pubecens ssp pub.

Synonym	Current Name	Synonym	Current Name
Quercus rubra v nana -Marsh.	Q. ilicifolia -Wangenh.	Racosperma auratiflorum	Acacia auratiflora
Quercus rubra v pagodifolia	Q. pagoda -Raf.	Racosperma auriculiforme	Acacia auriculiformis
Quercus schneckii -Britt.	Q. shumardii -Buckl.	Racosperma axillare	Acacia axillaris
Quercus serrata not Thunb.	Q. acutissima	Racosperma baeuerlenii	Acacia baeurlenii
Quercus serrata -Thunb.	Q. glandulifera	Racosperma baileyanum	Acacia baileyana
Quercus sessiliflora -Salisb.	Q. petraea	Racosperma bakeri	Acacia bakeri
Quercus sessilis -Ehre.	Q. petraea	Racosperma baueri	Acacia baueri
Quercus shumardii v schneckii	Q. shumardii -Buckl.	Racosperma beckleri	Acacia beckleri
Quercus sonomensis -A.DC.	Q. kelloggii -Newberry	Racosperma betchei	Acacia betchei
Quercus stranjensis -Turrill	Q. hartwissiana -Stev.	Racosperma binervatum	Acacia binervata -DC.
Quercus tauzin -Pers.	Q. pyrenaica -Willd.	Racosperma blakei	Acacia blakei
Quercus tinctoria -Michx.	Q. velutina -Lam.	Racosperma blakei ssp diphyllum	Acacia bl. sp diphylla
Quercus tinctoria v californica	Q. kelloggii -Newberry	Racosperma brachycarpum	Acacia brachycarpa
Quercus tlemcenensis	Q. faginea ssp broteroi	Racosperma brachypodum	Acacia brachypoda
Quercus toza -DC.	Q. pyrenaica -Willd.	Racosperma brassii	Acacia brassii
Quercus triloba -Michx.	Q. falcata -Michx.	Racosperma brownei	Acacia brownii
Quercus vibrayeana -Franch. & Sav.	Q. myrsinifolia	Racosperma brunioides	Acacia brunioides
Quercus virgiliana -(Ten.) Ten.	Q. pubecens ssp pub.	R. brunioides ssp graniticum	Acacia b. ssp granitica
Quercus wilsonii -Seem.	Lithocarpus	Racosperma burbidgeae	Acacia burbidgeae
	cleistocarpus	Racosperma burrowii	Acacia burrowii
Quercus x hybrida	Q. x rosacea	Racosperma buxifolium	Acacia buxifolia
Quercus x lucombeana	Q. x hispanica	Racosperma bynoeanum	Acacia bynoeana
Q. x lucombeana 'William Lucombe'	Q. x hispanica 'William Lucombe'	Racosperma caerulescens	Acacia caerulescens
		Racosperma calanthum	Acacia calantha
Quercus x ludoviciana v subfalcata	Q. x ludoviciana -Sarg.	Racosperma calcicola	Acacia calcicola
Quercus x subfalcata -Trelease	Q. x ludoviciana -Sarg.	Racosperma cambagei	Acacia cambagei
Quercus x turneri 'Pseudoturneri'	Q. x hispanica 'Pseudoturneri'	Racosperma canum	Acacia cana
		Racosperma caroleae	Acacia caroleae
Quillaya	Quillaja	Racosperma centrinervium	Acacia centrinervia
Quinaria hederacea	Parthenocissus quinquefolia	Racosperma chapmanii ssp australe	Ac. ch. ssp australis
		Racosperma chinchillense	Acacia chinchillensis
Quiongzhuea tumidinoda	Chimonobambusa tumidissinoda	Racosperma chippendalei	Acacia chippendalei
		Racosperma chishomii	Acacia chisholmii
Racosperma	Acacia	Racosperma cinncinnatum	Acacia cinncinnata
Racosperma accola	Acacia adunca	Racosperma crassiuscula v adunca	Acacia adunca
Racosperma acradenium	Acacia acradenia	Racosperma hamiltoniana	Acacia adunca
Racosperma adsurgens	Acacia adsurgens	Racosperma linearifolia	Acacia adunca
Racosperma adunca	Acacia adunca	Radicula armoracia	Armoracia rusticana
Racosperma ammobium	Acacia ammobia	Rajania quinata -Houtt.	Akebia quinata
Racosperma ammophilum	Acacia ammophila	Ramasetia -Hass.	Remusatia -Schott
Racosperma ancistrocarpum	Acacia ancistrocarpa	Ramonda pyrenaica	R. myconi
Racosperma aneurum	Acacia aneura	Ranunculastrum	Ranunculus
Racosperma angustum	Acacia angusta	Ranunculus acris 'Multiplex'	R. acris 'Flore Pleno'
Racosperma anomalum	Acacia anomala	Ranunculus albonaevum	R. bulbosus
Racosperma aphyllum	Acacia aphylla	Ranunculus anemonoides	Callianthemum anem.
Racosperma apretum	Acacia apreta	Ranunculus boreanus -Jord.	R. acris
Racosperma apricum	Acacia aprica	Ranunculus bulbiferum	R. bulbosus
Racosperma araneosum	Acacia araneosa	Ranunculus bulbosus 'Pleniflorus'	R. constantinopolitanus 'Plenus'
Racosperma argyreum	Acacia argyraea		
Racosperma armillatum	Acacia armillata	R. bulbosus 'Speciosus Plenus'	R. constantin. 'Plenus'
Racosperma armitii	Acacia armitii	Ranunculus bulbosus farreri	R. b. 'F.M.Burton'
Racosperma asperulaceum	Acacia asperulacea	Ranunculus cammarifolius	R. acris
R. ataxiphyllum ssp magnum	Acacia ata. ssp magna	Ranunculus ficaria 'Bowles Double'	R. fic. 'Double Bronze'
Racosperma attenuatum	Acacia attenuata	Ranunculus ficaria 'Bowles Double'	R. fic. 'Picton's Double'
Racosperma aulacocarpum	Acacia aulacocarpa	Ranunculus ficaria 'Cupreus'	R. f. v aurantiacus

Synonym	Current Name	Synonym	Current Name
Ranunculus ficaria 'E.A.Bowles'	R. ficaria 'Collarette'	Rapuntium kalmii	Lobelia kalmii
Ranunculus ficaria 'Holly'	R. ficaria 'Holly Green'	Razoumofskya americana	Arceuthobium americ.
Ranunculus ficaria anemone centred	R. ficaria 'Collarette'	Razoumofskya minuta	Arceuthobium pusillum
Ranunculus ficaria double cream	R. ficaria 'Double Mud'	Razoumofskya pusilla	Arceuthobium pusillum
Ranunculus ficaria double yellow	R. ficaria flore-pleno	Rebutia muscula	R. fiebrigii
Ranunculus ficaria ssp major	R.f.ssp chrysocephalus	Rebutia pulchra	R. rauschii
Ranunculus flagellifolius	R. repens	Rebutia violaciflora	R. minuscula
Ranunculus friesianus	R. acris	Rechsteineria	Sinningia
Ranunculus geranifolius	R. montanus	Rechsteineria leucotricha	Sinningia canescens
Ranunculus gouanii 'Plenus'	R. constantinopolitanus 'Plenus'	Rectophyllum -Post & Kuntze	Cercestis -Schott
		Rehmannia angulata	R. elata
Ranunculus hortensis	R. asiaticus	Reichardia decapetala	Caesalpinia decapetala
Ranunculus infestus	R. repens	Reinwardtia tetragyna	R. indica
Ranunculus intermedius	R. repens	Reinwardtia trigyna	R. indica
Ranunculus laetus	R. bulbosus	Rensselaeria -L. C. Beck	Peltandra -Raf.
Ranunculus lagascanus	R. repens	Restio subverticillatus	Ischyrolepis subvertic.
Ranunculus lucidus	R. repens	Retama sphaerocarpa -(L.) Boiss.	Genista sphaerocarpa
Ranunculus maccallai	R. acris	Retinispora -Sieb. & Zucc.	Chamaecyparis
Ranunculus napellifolius	R. acris	Retinispora -Zucc.	Chamaecyparis
Ranunculus oenanthifolius	R. repens	Reynoutria	Fallopia
Ranunculus pensylvanicus	R. repens	Reynoutria brachyphylla	Fallopia sachalinensis
Ranunculus pubescens	R. repens	Reynoutria cuspidatum	Fallopia japonica
Ranunculus rapaceus	R. bulbosus	Reynoutria henryi	Fallopia japonica
Ranunculus rectus	R. acris	Reynoutria sachalinensis	Fallopia sachalinensis
Ranunculus rupestris	R. spicatus	Reynoutria vivax	Fallopia sachalinensis
Ranunculus rutifolius	Callianthemum anemonoides	Rhamnoides hippophae	Hippophae rhamnoides
		Rhamnus alaternus 'Variegata'	R. alaternus 'Argenteovariegata'
Ranunculus scandinaicus	R. acris		
Ranunculus sennenii	R. bulbosus	Rhamnus alaternus v integrifolia	R. alaternus -L.
Ranunculus sparsipilum	R. bulbosus	Rhamnus alaternus v latifolia -Ait.	R. alaternus -L.
Ranunculus speciosus 'Flore Pleno'	R. constantinopolitanus 'Plenus'	Rhamnus cuneatus -Hook.	Ceanothus cuneatus
		Rhamnus hydriensis	R. cathartica -L.
Ranunculus speciosus 'Plenus'	R. constant. 'Plenus'	Rhamnus lineatus	Berchemia lineata
Ranunculus stipatus	R. acris	Rhamnus scandens -Hill.	Berchemia scandens
Ranunculus tomophyllus	R. acris	Rhamnus solutina	R. cathartica -L.
Ranunculus traunfellneri	R. alpestris	Rhamnus sylvatica	R. cathartica -L.
Ranunculus valdepubens	R. bulbosus	Rhamnus volubilis -L.f.	Berchemia scandens
Raoulia australis misapplied	R. hookeri	Rhamnus wikkor	R. cathartica -L.
Raoulia leontopodium	Leucogenes leontopod.	Rhaphidophora pinnata	R. celatocaulis
Raoulia lutescens	R. australis Lutescens Group -Hooker	Rhaphiolepis japonica -Sieb & Zucc.	R. umbellata
		Rhaphiolepis ovata -Briot	R. umbellata
Raoulia x Leucogenes	x Leucoraoulia	R. umbellata f integerrima -Hook.	R. umbellata
Raoulia x loganii	x Leucoraoulia loganii	Rhaphiolepis umbellata f ovata	R. umbellata
Rapanea chathmanica	Myrsine chathmanica	Rhaphiophallus -Schott	Amorphophallus
Rapanea nummularia	Myrsine nummularia	Rhaphithamnus cyanocarpus	R. spinosus
Raphanis magna	Armoracia rusticana	Rhapis flabelliformis	R. excelsa
Raphanistrum	Raphanus	Rhaponticum ciliatum	Centaurea nigra
Raphanus junceus	Brassica juncea	Rhaponticum cynaroides	Leuzea centauroides
Raphanus rusticanus	Armoracia rusticana	Rhaponticum jacea	Centaurea jacea
Raphidophora	Rhaphidophora	Rhazya orientalis	Amsonia orientalis
Raphiolepis -Lindl.	Rhaphiolepis	Rhektophyllum	Cercestis
Rapuntium bellidifolium	Lobelia erinus	Rheum 'Ace of Spades'	R. 'Ace of Hearts'
Rapuntium dortmanna	Lobelia dortmanna	Rheum emodi	R. australe
Rapuntium erinus -not Moench	Lobelia erinus	Rheum palmatum 'Atropurpureum'	R. p. 'Atrosanguineum'
Rapuntium inflatum	Lobelia inflatum	Rheum x cultorum	R. x hybridum

Synonym	Current Name	Synonym	Current Name
Rhipsalidopsis gaertneri	Hatiora gaertneri	Rhododendron 'Firefly'	R. 'Hexe'
Rhipsalidopsis rosea	Hatiora rosea	R. 'Fred Wynniatt Stanway'	R. 'Stanway'
Rhipsalis cassytha	R. baccifera	Rhododendron 'Glenn Dale Adorable'	R. 'Adorable'
Rhipsalis tucumanensis	R. floccosa	Rhododendron 'Gloria'	R. 'Bruns Gloria'
Rhodanthemum gayanum 'Flamingo'	R. gayanum	Rhododendron 'Gold Crown'	R. 'Gold Krone'
Rhodiola crassipes	R. wallichiana	Rhododendron 'Goldball'	R. 'Christopher Wren'
Rhodiola himalensis	R. 'Keston'	Rhododendron 'Golden Bouquet'	R. 'Goldbukett'
Rhodiola pachyclados	Sedum pachyclados	R. 'Golden Horn Persimmon'	R. 'Persimmon'
Rhodocactus grandifolius	Pereskia grandifolia	Rhododendron 'Golden Sunlight'	R. 'Directeur Moerlands'
Rhodochiton volubilis -Zucc.	R. atrosanguineus		
Rhodocistus berthelotianus -Spach	Cistus symphytifolius	Rhododendron 'Hardijzer's Beauty'	R. 'Hardijzer Beauty'
R. berthelotianus v leucophyllus	Cistus symphytifolius ssp leucophyllus	Rhododendron 'Hino-scarlet'	R. 'Campfire'
		Rhododendron 'Hot Shot'	R. 'Girard's Hot Shot'
Rhodocistus osbekiifolius -Webb	Cistus osbeckiifolius	Rhododendron 'I.M.S'	R. 'Irene Stead'
Rhododendron 'A.Bedford'	R. 'Arthur Bedford'	Rhododendron 'Iceberg'	R. 'Lodauric Iceberg'
Rhododendron 'A.J.Ivens'	R. 'Arthur J.Ivens'	Rhododendron 'Icecrean Flavour'	R. 'Flavour'
Rhododendron 'Analin'	R. 'Anuschka'	Rhododendron 'Icecrean Vanilla'	R. 'Vanilla'
Rhododendron 'Appleblossom'	R. 'Ho-o'	Rhododendron 'Indigo Diamant'	R. Diamant Gr. indigo
Rhododendron 'Arctic Tern'	x Ledodendron 'Arctic Tern'	Rhododendron 'J.M. de Montague'	R. 'The Hon. Jean Marie de Montague'
Rhododendron 'Balsaminiflorum'	R. indicum 'Balsaminiflorum'	R. 'Jean Marie Montague'	R. 'The Hon. Jean Marie de Montague'
Rhododendron 'Blue Steel'	R. fastigiatum 'Blue Steel'	Rhododendron 'Jenny'	R. 'Creeping Jenny'
		R. 'Jervis Bay' (Hawk Group)	R. 'Jervis Bay'
Rhododendron 'Bodartianum'	R. 'Boddaertianum'	Rhododendron 'King George' Loder	R. 'Loderi King George'
Rhododendron 'Centennial'	R. 'Washington State Centennial'	Rhododendron 'Koichiro Wada'	R. yakushimanum 'Koichiro Wada'
Rhododendron 'Checkmate'	R. 'Checkmate' (PJM Group)	R. 'Lady Bessborough Roberte'	R. 'Roberte'
Rhododendron 'Christmas Cheer'	R. 'Ima-shojo'	R. 'Lady Chamberlain Exbury'	R. 'Exbury Lady Chamberlain'
Rhododendron 'Congo'	R. 'Robin Hill Congo'	R. 'Lady Chamberlain Golden Queen'	R. 'Golden Queen'
Rhododendron 'Conroy'	R. cinnabarinum 'Conroy'	R. 'Lady Chamberlain Salmon Trout'	R. 'Salmon Trout'
Rhododendron 'Cornish Red'	R. Smithii Group	R. 'Lady Roseberry Pink Delight'	R. 'Pink Lady Roseberry'
R. 'Cottage Garden's Pride'	R. 'Mrs G W Leak'	Rhododendron 'Ledifolium Album'	R. x mucronatum
R. 'Countess of Derby' selfed	R. 'Trude Webster'	Rhododendron 'Ledifolium'	R. x mucronatum
Rhododendron 'County of York'	R. 'Catalode'	Rhododendron 'Linearifolium'	R. stenopetalum 'Linearifolium'
Rhododendron 'Crest' (Hawk Group)	R. 'Crest'		
Rhododendron 'Crimson Glory'	R. 'Natalie Coe Vitetti'	Rhododendron 'Macrostemon'	R. 'Macrostemum' (Obtusum Group)
R. 'Cunningham's Sulphur'	R. caucasicum 'Cunningham's Sulphur'	Rhododendron 'Melford Lemon'	R. 'Ilam Melford Lemon'
Rhododendron 'Cupcake'	R. 'Delp's Cupcake'	Rhododendron 'Merlin'	R. 'Hawk Merlin' (Hawk Group)
Rhododendron 'Damaris Logan'	R. 'Logan Damaris'		
Rhododendron 'Daybreak'R. 'Kirin'		Rhododendron 'Mikado'	R. kaempferi 'Mikado'
Rhododendron 'Diamant Purpur'	R. Diamant Gr. purple	Rhododendron 'Ming'	R. 'Ilam Ming'
Rhododendron 'Diamant Rot'	R. Diamant Group red	Rhododendron 'Mount Seven Star'	R. nakaharae 'Mount Seven Star'
Rhododendron 'Eastern Fire'	R. kaempferi 'Eastern Fire'	R. 'Mucronatum Amethystinum'	R. 'Amethystinum'
Rhododendron 'Elfenbein'	R. 'Bruns Elfenbein'	Rhododendron 'Mucronatum'	R. x mucronatum
Rhododendron 'Elizabeth Jenny'	R. 'Creeping Jenny'	Rhododendron 'Nakahari Orange'	R. nakaharae orange
Rhododendron 'Everlasting'	Kalmia latifolia x R. williamsianum 'Everlasting'	Rhododendron 'Nakahari-mariko'	R. nakaharae 'Mariko'
		R. 'Norbitonense Aureum'	R. 'Smithii Aureum'
		R. 'Norbitonense Broughtonianum'	R. 'Broughtonii Aureum'
Rhododendron 'Falcon'	R. 'Hawk Falcon'		
Rhododendron 'Fanny'	R. 'Pucella'	Rhododendron 'P.J.Mezitt'	R. 'Peter John Mezitt'

Synonym	Current Name	Synonym	Current Name
Rhododendron 'Palma'	R. parmulatum 'Palma'		glaucop. L&S 2764
Rhododendron 'Paris' (Naomi Group)	R. 'Paris'	Rhododendron brachysiphon	R. maddenii ssp madd.
Rhododendron 'Peach Blossom'	R. 'Saotome'	Rhododendron brachystylum	R. trichocladum
Rhododendron 'Pink Pearl' (Azalea)	R. 'Azuma-kagami'	Rhododendron bullatum	R. edgeworthii
Rhododendron 'Pioneer' selfed	R. 'Anna Baldsiefen'	Rhododendron caeruleum	R. rigidum
Rhododendron 'Polaris'	R. 'Hachmann's Polaris'	R. calostrotum red form	R. calostrotum 'Gigha'
Rhododendron 'Ponticum'	R. ponticum	Rhododendron calostrotum ssp riparium Rock's form R 178	
Rhododendron 'Ponticum' -(A)	R. luteum		R. saluense ssp riparioides R 178
Rhododendron 'Pulchrum Maxwellii'	R. 'Maxwellii'	R. calostrotum ssp riparium USDAPQ 03954/R 18453	
Rhododendron 'Purple Diamond'	R. Diamant Gr. purple	R. saluense ssp riparioides USDAPQ 03954/R 18453	
Rhododendron 'Queen Mother'	R. 'The Queen Mother'	R. calostrotum v calciphilum	R. calostrotum ssp
Rhododendron 'Red Diamond'	R. Diamant Group red		riparium Calciph. Gr.
Rhododendron 'Red Velvet'	R. 'Ilam Red Velvet'	Rhododendron caloxanthum	R. campylocarpum ssp
Rhododendron 'Rokoko'	R. 'Hachmann's Rokoko'		caloxanthum
Rhododendron 'Rosiflorum'	R. indicum	R. campylogynum 'Album'	R. 'Leucanthemum'
	'Balsaminiflorum'	R. campylogynum 'Beryl Taylor'	R. 'Beryl Taylor'
Rhododendron 'Roza Harrison'	R. 'Rosa Stevenson'	R. campylogynum v leucanthemum	R. 'Leucanthemum'
Rhododendron 'Roza Harrison'	R. 'Roza Stevenson'	Rhododendron cantabile	R. russatum
Rhododendron 'Satschiko'	R. 'Geisha Orange'	Rhododendron cardiobasis	R. orbiculare ssp card.
Rhododendron 'Silver Edge'	R. ponticum 'Silver	Rhododendron carolinianum	R. minus v minus
	Edge'		Carolinianum Group
Rhododendron 'Snowflake'	R. 'Kure-no-yuki'	Rhododendron chaetomallum	R. haematodes ssp
Rhododendron 'Solent Queen'	R. 'Solent Queen'		chaetomallum
	(Angelo Group)	Rhododendron chamaecistus -L	Rhodothamnus chamae.
Rhododendron 'Spring Dream'	R. 'Fruhlingstraum'	Rhododendron chameunum	R. saluenense ssp cha.
Rhododendron 'Spring Pearl'	R. 'Moerheim's Pink'	Rhododendron chapaense	R. maddenii ssp
Rhododendron 'Sugi-no-ito'	R. 'Kumo-no-ito'		crassum
Rhododendron 'Sunbeam'	R. 'Benifude'	Rhododendron charianthum	R. davidsonianum
Rhododendron 'Talavera'	R. 'Talavera' (Golden	Rhododendron charopoeum	R. campylogynum
	Oriole Group)		Charopoeum Group
Rhododendron 'Tangerine'	R. 'Fabia Tangerine'	Rhododendron chartophyllum	R. yunnanense
R. 'Thousand Butterflies'	R. 'One Thousand	Rhododendron chasmanthum	R. augustinii ssp chas.
	Butterflies'	Rhododendron chrysanthum	R. aureum
R. 'Tortoiseshell Champagne'	R. 'Champagne'	Rhododendron chryseum	R. rupicola v chryseum
Rhododendron adenophorum	R. adenogynum	Rhododendron chrysomanicum	R. Chrysomanicum Gr.
	Adenophorum Group	Rhododendron ciliatum 'Multiflorum'	R. 'Multiflorum'
R. adroserum USDAPI 52910	R. lukiangense R11275	Rhododendron ciliicalyx ssp lyi	R. lyi
Rhododendron aechmophyllum	R. yunnanense	R. cinnabarinum Conroy Group	R. cinnabarinum ssp
Rhododendron aemulorum	R. mallotum		cinnabarinum 'Conroy'
Rhododendron aeruginosum	R. campanulatum ssp	R. cinnabarinum v purpurellum	R. ci. ssp xanthocodon
	aeruginosum		Purpurellum Group
Rhododendron agapetum	R. kyawii Agapetum Gr.	Rhododendron coelicum F 21830	R. pocophorum v
Rhododendron apodectum	R. dichroanthum ssp		pocophorum F 21830
	apodectum	Rhododendron concatenans	R. c. ssp xanthocodon
R. arboreum 'Sir Charles Lemon'	R. 'Sir Charles Lemon'		Concatenans Group
Rhododendron argenteum	R. grande	Rhododendron concatenans -Hutch.	R. ci. ssp xanthocodon
Rhododendron artosquameum	R. oreotrephes		Concatenans Group
Rhododendron aucklandii	R. griffithianum	Rhododendron cookeanum	R. sikangense v sikang.
Rhododendron bakeri	R. cumberlandense		Cookeanum Group
Rhododendron bauhiniiflorum	R. triflorum v bauhiniif.	R. Cornish Early Red Group	R. Smithii Group
R. beanianum compact form	R. piercei	Rhododendron coryphaeum	R. praestans
Rhododendron bergii	R. augustinii ssp		Coryphaeum Group
	rubrum	Rhododendron cosmetum	R. saluense ssp
Rhododendron Blaue Donau	R. 'Blue Danube'		chameunum
R. brachyanthum -L&S 2764	R. glaucophyllum v	Rhododendron crassum	R. maddenii ssp crass.

Synonym	Current Name
Rhododendron crebreflorum	R. cephalanthum ssp cephalanthum Crebreflorum Group
Rhododendron cremastum	R. campylogynum Cremastum Group
Rhododendron cremastum	R. campylogynum Cremastum Group
Rhododendron croceum	R. wardii
Rhododendron cubittii	R. veitchianum Cubittii Group
Rhododendron cucullatum	R. roxieanum v cuculla.
Rhododendron cyclium	R. callimorphum
Rhododendron cyclium -Balf. & Forr.	R. callomorphum
Rhododendron dasycladum	R. selense ssp dasycl.
Rhododendron dauricum 'Album'	R. dauricum 'Hokkaido'
R. degronianum 'Metternianum'	R. de. ssp heptamerum v kyomaruense
Rhododendron delavayi	R. arboreum ssp dela.
Rhododendron deleiense	R. tephropeplum
Rhododendron desquamatum	R. rubiginosum Desquamatum Group
Rhododendron diaprepes	R. decorum ssp diapr.
R. dichroanthum ssp herpesticum	R. dichroanthum ssp scyphocalyx
Rhododendron dictyotum	R. traillianum v dicty.
Rhododendron didymum	R. sanguineum ssp didymum
Rhododendron dilatum	R. reticulatum
Rhododendron discolor	R. fortunei ssp discol.
Rhododendron doshongense	R. aganniphum v agan. Doshongense Group
Rhododendron drumonium	R. telmateium
Rhododendron dryophyllum	R. phaeochrysum v ph.
Rhododendron dryophyllum h.	R. phaeochrysum v levistratum
Rhododendron elaeagnoides	R. lepidotum
Rhododendron Electra Group	R.augustinii Electra Gr.
Rhododendron eriogynum	R. facetum
Rhododendron eritimum	R. anthosphaerum
Rhododendron erubescens	R. oreodoxa v fargesii Erubescens Group
Rhododendron euchaites	R. neriifolium ssp neri. Euchaites Group
R. eudoxum v eudoxum R10950	R. temenium v mesopolium R10950
Rhododendron eximium	R. falconeri ssp eximi.
Rhododendron exquisitum	R. oreotrephes Exquisitum Group
Rhododendron faberi ssp prattii	R. prattii
Rhododendron fargesii	R. oreodoxa v fargesii
Rhododendron fauriei	R. brachycarpum ssp fauriei
Rhododendron fictolacteum	R. rex ssp fictolacteum
Rhododendron fimbriatum	R.hippophaeoides v hip. Fimbriatum Group

Synonym	Current Name
Rhododendron Flava Group	R. Volker Group
R. forrestii ssp forrestii	R. chamaethomsonii v chamaeth. F 21723
Rhododendron fortunei 'Mrs Butler'	R.f. 'Sir Charles Butler'
Rhododendron fulvoides	R. fulvum ssp fulvoides
Rhododendron giganteum	R. protistum v gigant.
R. glaucophyllum v luteiflorum	R. luteiflorum
Rhododendron glaucum -Hook.	R. glaucophyllum
Rhododendron glischroides	R. glischrum ssp glischroides
Rhododendron globigerum	R. alutaceum v alut. Globigerum Group
Rhododendron glomerulatum	R. yungningense Glomerulatum Group
Rhododendron gratum	R. basilicum
Rhododendron groenlandicum	Ledum groenlandicum
Rhododendron gymnocarpum	R. microgynum Gymnocarpum Group
Rhododendron haematocheilum	R. oreodoxa
Rhododendron haematodes ssp chaetomallum KW21077	R. coelicum KW21077
Rhododendron hardingii	R. annae Hardingii Gr.
Rhododendron hardyi	R. augustinii ssp hard.
Rhododendron headfortianum	R. taggianum Headfortianum Group
Rhododendron heliolepis v fumidum	R. heliolepis v heliol.
Rhododendron hemidartum	R. pocophorum v hemi.
Rhododendron heptamerum	R. degronianum ssp he.
Rhododendron herpesticum	R. dichroanthum ssp scyphocalyx
R. hippophaeoides 'Bei-ma-shan'	R. hippop. 'Haba-shan'
Rhododendron houlstonii	R. fortunei ssp discol or Houlstonii Group
Rhododendron hylaeum -KW 6401	R. faucium -KW 6401
Rhododendron hypenanthum	R. anthopogon ssp hypenanthum
Rhododendron hypoglaucum	R. argyrophyllum ssp hypoglaucum
R. hypoglaucum 'Heane Wood'	R. argyrophyllum ssp hypogl. 'Heane Wood'
R. impeditum 'Blue Steel'	R. fastigiatum 'Blue Steel'
R. impeditum 'Moerheim'	R. 'Moerheim'
Rhododendron imperator	R. uniflorum v imperat.
R. indicum v eriocarpum	R. 'Gumpo'
Rhododendron iodes	R. alutaceum v iodes
Rhododendron irroratum R 72	R. lukiangense R 72
Rhododendron iteaphyllum	R. formosum v formo sum Iteaphyllum Group
Rhododendron japonicum	R. molle ssp japonicum
R. japonicum v japonicum -Schneider	R. degronianum ssp heptamerum
R. japonicum v pentamerum	R. degronianum ssp de.
Rhododendron kaempferi 'Damio'	R. kaempferi 'Mikado'
Rhododendron kaempferi 'Firefly'	R. 'Hexe'

Synonym	Current Name	Synonym	Current Name
Rhododendron keleticum	R. calostrotum ssp keleticum	Rhododendron nitens	R. calostrotum ssp riparium Nitens Group
Rhododendron Kewense Group	R. Loderi Group	Rhododendron nobleanum	R. Nobleanum Group
Rhododendron kingianum	R. arboreum ssp zeylanicum	Rhododendron nudiflorum	R. periclymenoides
		Rhododendron obovatum -Hook.	R. lepidotum
Rhododendron kiusianum 'Amoenum'	R. 'Amoenum'	R. obtusum f amoenum occidentale	R. 'Amoenum'
Rhododendron kotschyi	R. myrtifolium	Rhododendron obtusum f japonicum	R. kiusianum
R. lanatum Flinckii Group	R. flinckii	Rhododendron obtusum v kaempferi	R. kaempferi
Rhododendron leachiana	Kalmiopsis leachiana	Rhododendron oleifolium	R. virgatum ssp oleif.
Rhododendron ledifolium 'Bulstrode'	R. 'Bulstrode'	Rhododendron oporinum	R. heliolepis
R. ledifolium 'Magnificum'	R. 'Magnificum'	Rhododendron panteumorphum	R. x erythrocalyx Panteumorphum Group
Rhododendron ledifolium 'Ripense'	R. ripense		
Rhododendron ledoides	R. trichostomum Ledoides Group	Rhododendron patulum	R. pemakoense Patulum Group
R. lepidotum 'Reuthe's Purple'	R. 'Reuthe's Purple'	Rhododendron pennivenium	R. tanastylum v penniv.
Rhododendron litangense	R. impeditum	Rhododendron pentamerum	R. degronianum
Rhododendron litiense	R. wardii v wardii Litiense Group	Rhododendron peramoenum	R. arboreum ssp delavayi v peramoen.
R. lochiae misapplied variegated	R. viriosum	Rhododendron phaedropum	R. neriiflorum ssp pha.
Rhododendron lopsangianum	R. thomsonii ssp lopsangianum	Rhododendron phoenicodum	R. neriiflorum ssp ner. Phoenicodum Group
Rhododendron macranthum	R. indicum	Rhododendron pholidotum	R. heliolepis v brevis tylum Pholidotum Gr.
Rhododendron macrosmithii	R. argipeplum		
R. maculiferum ssp anwheiense	R. anwheiense	R. pleistanthum -R 11288	R. rigidum -R 11288
Rhododendron manipurense	R. maddenii ssp cras sum Otusifolium Group	R. pocophorum -KW 21075	R. coelicum -KW 21075
		Rhododendron pogonostylum	R. irroratum ssp pog.
R.mekongense v m. Rubroluteum Gr	R. viridescens Rubroluteum Group	Rhododendron polyandrum	R. maddenii ssp madd enii Polyandrum Group
R. mekongense v mekongense Viridescens Group		Rhododendron poukhanense	R. yedoense v poukha.
	R. viridescens	Rhododendron praecox	R. 'Praecox'
Rhododendron melinanthum	R. mekongense v melin.	Rhododendron praecox 'Emasculum'	R. 'Emasculum'
Rhododendron metternichii	R. degronianum ssp heptamerum	Rhododendron primulinum -Hemsl.	R. flavidum
		Rhododendron prostigiatum	R. 'Prostigiatum'
R. metternichii v angustifolium	R. makinoi	Rhododendron prostratum	R. saluense ssp chame unum Prostratum Gr.
R. metternichii v pentamerum	R. degronianum ssp degronianum	Rhododendron pruniflorum -KW7038	R. brachyanthum ssp hypolepidotum -KW
Rhododendron microleucum	R. orthocladum v microleucum	Rhododendron Psyche Group	R. Wega Group
Rhododendron micromeres	R. leptocarpum	Rhododendron punctatum	R. minus v minus Punctatum Group
Rhododendron mollicomum -F30940	R. hemitrichotum		
Rhododendron mollyanum	R. montroseanum	Rhododendron puralbum	R. wardii v puralbum
Rhododendron monosematum	R. pachytrichum v mo.	Rhododendron Queen Emma	R. 'Koningin Emma'
Rhododendron Morning Red	R. 'Morgenrot'	Rhododendron Queen Wilhelmina	R. 'Koningin Wilhelmina'
R. mucronatum v ripense	R. ripense		
R. mucronulatum v chejuense	R. mucr. v taquetii	Rhododendron radicans	R. calostrotum ssp keleticum Radicans Gr.
Rhododendron myiagrum	R. callimorphum v myi.		
Rhododendron myiagrum	R. callomorphum v myi.	Rhododendron ravum	R. cuneatum Ravum Gr.
Rhododendron myrtilloides	R. campylogynum Myrtilloides Group	Rhododendron recurvum	R. roxieanum v roxiea.
		R. repens v chamaethauma -Tagg.	R. chamaethomsonii v chamaethauma
R. neriiflorum ssp euchaites	R. neriiflorum Euchaites Group	R. repens v chamaethomsonii	R. chamaethomsonii
		Rhododendron rex ssp arizelum	R. arizelum
Rhododendron nigropunctatum	R. nivale ssp boreale Nigropunctatum Group	Rhododendron rhabdotum	R. dalhousieae v rhabd.
Rhododendron nilagiricum	R. arboreum ssp nilag.	Rhododendron rhombicum -Miq.	R. reticulatum
Rhododendron niphargum	R. uvariifolium	Rhododendron riparium -Ward	R. calostrotum ssp rip.

Synonym	Current Name	Synonym	Current Name
Rhododendron ririei -Guiz 75	R. haofui -Guiz 75		ctum Triplonaevium Gr.
Rhododendron roseotinctum	R. sanguineum ssp san.	Rhododendron tritifolium	R. alutaceum v russot
	v didymoides		inctum Tritifolium Gr.
	Roseotinctum Group	Rhododendron tsangpoense	R. charitopes ssp tsa.
Rhododendron roseum	R. prinophyllum	R. tsariense Poluninii Group	R. poluninii
Rhododendron roylei -Hook.	R. cinnabarinum ssp	Rhododendron tubiforme	R. glaucophyllum ssp
	cinn. Roylei Group		tubiforme
Rhododendron rubroluteum	R. viridescens	Rhododendron vellereum	R. principis Vellereum
	Rubroluteum Group		Group
Rhododendron rude	R. glischrum sso rude	Rhododendron viridescens -KW5829	R. mekongense v mek.
Rhododendron russotinctum	R. alutaceum v russot.		-KW 5829
R. saluense ssp riparioides	R. calostrotum ssp	Rhododendron viscosum 'Antilope'	R. 'Antilope'
	riparium Rock's form	Rhododendron viscosum 'Arpege'	R. 'Arpege'
R. sanguineum ssp roseotinctum	R. sanguineum ssp san.	Rhododendron wadanum -Mak.	R. reticulatum
	v didymoides	Rhododendron wilsoniae	R. latoucheae
	Roseotinctum Group	Rhododendron x arbutifolium	R. Arbutifolium Group
Rhododendron scintillans	R. polycladum	R. x hodconeri -LS&H 21296	R.hodgsonii
	Scintillans Group	Rhododendron x hodconeri -TSS 9	R. hodgsonii -TSS 9
Rhododendron scottianum	R. pachypodum	Rhododendron xanthinum	R. concinnum
Rhododendron scyphocalyx	R. dichroanthum ssp s.	Rhododendron xanthocodon	R. cinnabarinum ssp
Rhododendron setiferum	R. selense ssp setifer.		xanthocodon
Rhododendron shepherdii	R. kendrickii	Rhododendron xanthocodon -Hutch.	R. cinnabarinum ssp
Rhododendron sidereum -KW 13649	R. aff grande -KR13649		xanthocodon
Rhododendron silvaticum	R. lanigerum	R. yakishimanum FCC form	R. yakushimanum
Rhododendron silvaticum -Cowan	R. lanigerum		'Koichiro Wada'
Rhododendron Silver Cloud	R. 'Silberwolke'	R. yakushimanum ssp makinoi	R. makinoi
Rhododendron simulans	R. mimetes v simulans	R. yakushimanum ssp yakushim.	R. 'Ken Janeck'
Rhododendron sinense	R. molle	R. yungningense -F 29268	R. impeditum -F 29268
Rhododendron smithii	R. argipeplum	Rhododendron zeylanicum	R. arboreum ssp zeyl.
R. smithii Argipeplum Group	R. argipeplum	Rhodohypoxis 'Hebron Farm Biscuit'	Hypoxis parvula v
Rhododendron speciosum	R. flammeum		albiflora 'Hebron Farm
Rhododendron sphaeranthum	R. trichostomum		Biscuit'
Rhododendron spiciferum	R. scabrifolium v spic.	Rhodohypoxis 'Hebron Farm Cerise'	x Rhodoxis 'Hebron
Rhododendron stenaulum	R. moulmainense		Farm Cerise'
Rhododendron stenophyllum	R. makinoi	Rhodohypoxis 'Tetra White'	R. 'Helen'
Rhododendron stictophyllum	R. nivale ssp boreale	Rhodora	Rhododendron
	Stictophyllum Group	Rhodora deflexa -Griff.	Enkianthus deflexus
Rhododendron suberosum	R. yunnanense	Rhodostachys bicolor -Ruiz & Pavon	Fascicularia bicolor
	Suberosum Group	Rhodothamnus leachianus	Kalmiopsis leachiana
Rhododendron sutchuense v geraldii	R. x geraldii	Rhodotypos kerrioides	R. scandens
Rhododendron taliense -SBEC 350	R. roxieanum v	Rhodotypos tetrapetala	R. scandens
	cucullatum -SBEC 350	Rhoeo	Tradescantia
Rhododendron tamaense	R. cinnabarinum ssp	Rhoeo discolor	Tradesc. spathacea
	tamaense	Rhoeo spathacea	Tradesc. spathacea
Rhododendron telopeum	R. campylocarpum ssp	Rhoicissus rhombifolia	Cissus rhombifolia
	caloxanthum Telopeum	Rhus arenaria	R. aromatica -Ait.
	Group	Rhus borealis	R. glabra
R. tephropeplum Deleiense Group	R. tephropeplum	Rhus cacodendron	Ailanthus altissima
R. thomsonii v candelabrum	R. x candelabrum	Rhus calophylla	R. glabra
Rhododendron timetum	R. oreotrephes	Rhus canadensis -Marsh.	R. aromatica -Ait.
Rhododendron trichanthum	R. villosum	Rhus carolinianum	R. glabra
R. trichostomum v radinum	R. tric. Radinum Group	Rhus cismontana	R. glabra
R. triflorum Mahogani Group	R. triflorum v triflorum	Rhus cotinoides -Nutt.	Cotinus obovatus -Raf
	Mahogani Group	Rhus cotinus -L.	Cotinus coggygria
Rhododendron triplonaevium	R.alutaceum v russotin	Rhus cotinus v atropurpureus	Cotinus coggygria

Synonym	Current Name	Synonym	Current Name
	Purpureus Group	Robinia frutex -L.	Caragana frutex
Rhus cotinus v purpureus	Cotinus coggygria	Robinia halodendron -Pall.	H. halodendron
	Purpureus Group	Robinia hispida 'Rosea' misapplied	R. hispida
Rhus crenata	R. aromatica	Robinia jubata -Pall.	Caragana jubata
Rhus elegans	R. glabra	Robinia luxurians	R. neomexicana
Rhus glabra 'Laciniata' misapplied	R. x pulvinata Autumn	Robinia pseudoacacia 'Angustifolia'	R. ps. 'Microphylla'
	Lace Group	Robinia pseudoacacia 'Decaisnena'	R. x ambigua
Rhus henryi -Diels.	R. potaninii -Maxim.		'Decaisneana'
Rhus hirta -Sudw. not Engl.	R. typhina -L.	Robinia pseudoacacia 'Erecta'	R. pseudoacacia
Rhus hypselodendrum	R. glabra		'Monophylla Fastigiata'
Rhus javanica -Auct.	R. chinensis	Robinia pseudoacacia 'Fastigiata'	R. ps. 'Pyramidalis'
Rhus occidentalis	R. glabra	Robinia pseudoacacia 'Inermis' h.	R. ps. 'Umbraculifera'
Rhus osbeckii -(DC). Carr.	R. chinensis -Mill.	Robinia pseudoacacia 'Monophylla'	R. ps.'Unifoliola'
Rhus peregrina	Ailanthus altissima	Robinia pseudoacacia 'Twisty Baby'	R. pseudoa. 'Lace Lady'
Rhus semi-alata -Murr.	R. chinensis -Mill.	Robinia pygmaea -L.	Caragana pygmaea
Rhus sinense	Ailanthus altissima	Robinia sinica -Buc'hoz	Caragana sinica
Rhus toxicodendron -many not L.	R. radicans -L.	Robinia spinosa -L.	Caragana spinosa
Rhus trilobata	R. aromatica	Robinia tragacanthoides -Pall.	Caragana tragacanth.
Rhus typhina 'Laciniata' h.	R. typhina 'Dissecta'	Robinia x hillieri	R. x slavinii 'Hillieri'
Rhus venenata -DC.	R. vernix -L.	Robinia x margaretta Casque Rouge	R. x ma. 'Pink Cascade'
Rhus vernicifera -DC.	R. verniciflua -Stokes	Rochea	Crassula
Rhus vernix -Thunb. not L.	R. verniciflua -Stokes	Rochea falcata	Crassula perfoliata v
Rhus x hybrida -Rehd.	R. x pulvinata -Greene		minor
Rhynchelytrum	Melinis	Rodgersia japonica	R. podophylla
Rhynchelytrum roseum	Melinis repens	Rodgersia tabularis	Astilboides tabularis
Rhynchopyle -Engl.	Piptospatha -N. E. Br.	Romanzoffia suksdorfii -Green	R. sitchensis
Rhyncospermum jasminoides -Lindl.	Trachelospermum jas.	Romanzoffia suksdorfii h.	R. californica
Ribes atrosanguineum	R. sanguineum	Romneya trichocalyx	R. coulteri v trichocal.
	'Atrorubens'	Romneya x hybrida	R. coulteri 'White Cloud'
Ribes aureum h.	R. odoratum	Romulea grandiflora	R. bulbocodium
Ribes dioicum	R. alpinum	Romulea longituba	R. macowanii
R. divaricatum 'Worcesterberry'	R. 'Worcesterberry'	Rondelettia speciosa	R. odorata
Ribes floridum	R. americanum	Rooksbya euphorbiodes	Neobuxbaumia euphor.
Ribes glutinosum	R. sanguineum v glutin.	Rorippa armoracia	Armoracia rusticana
Ribes grossularia	R. uva-crispa -L.	Rorippa nasturtium-aquaticum	Nasturtium officinale
Ribes pennsylvanicum	R. americanum	Rorippa rusticanus	Armoracia rusticana
Ribes rubrum White Versailles	R. r. 'Versailles Blanche'	Rosa 'Abbandonata'	R. 'Laure Davoust'
	(White Currant Group)	Rosa 'Alba Semiplena'	R. x alba 'Alba
Ribes sanguineum 'Atrosanguineum'	R. s. 'Atrorubens'		Semiplena'
Ribes sanguineum 'Flore Pleno'	R. sanguineum 'Plenum'	Rosa 'Alfred de Dalmas' misapplied	R. 'Mousseline'
Ribes sanguineum 'Roseum'	R. sang. 'Carneum'	Rosa 'Amelia'	R. 'Celsiana'
Ribes sanguineum double	R. sanguineum 'Plenum'	Rosa 'Apricot Garnet'	R. 'Garnette Apricot'
Ribes sativum -Syme	R. rubrum -L.	Rosa 'Archiduc Joseph' misapplied	R. 'General Schablikine'
Ribes uva-crispa 'Aston Red'	R. u-c. 'Warrington'	Rosa 'Ash Wednesday'	R. 'Aschermittwoch'
Ribes uva-crispa v reclinatum 'Green Gascoigne'		Rosa 'Astra Diamond'	R. 'White Flight'
	R. uva-crispa v reclinatum 'Early Green Hairy'	Rosa 'Autumn Fire'	R. 'Herbstfeuer'
Richardia aethiopica	Zantedeschia aethiopic.	Rosa 'Autumnalis'	R. 'Princesse de
Richardia africana	Zantedeschia aethiopic.		Nassau'
Richardia elliottiana	Zantedeschia elliottiana	Rosa 'Ayrshire Splendens'	R. 'Splendens'
Ricinocarpus virginicus	Acalypha virginica	Rosa 'Baronness Rothschild'	R. 'Baronne Adolph de
Ringentiarum -Nakai	Arisaema -Mart.		Rothschild'
Robertiella robertiana -Hanks	Geranium robertianum	Rosa 'Beauty of Glazenwood'	R. x odorata
Robinia 'Hillieri'	R. x slavinii 'Hillieri'		'Pseudindica'
Robinia altagana v fruticosa -Pall.	Caragana fruticosa	Rosa 'Belle des Jardins' misapplied	R. x centifolia 'Unique
Robinia caragana	Caragana arborescens		Panachee'

Synonym	Current Name	Synonym	Current Name
Rosa 'Black Jack'	R. 'Tour de Malakoff'	Rosa 'Hadvelvet'	R. 'Smooth Velvet'
Rosa 'Blush Noisette'	R. 'Noisette Carnee'	Rosa 'Harisonii'	R. x harisonii
Rosa 'Bouquet Tout Fait' misapplied	R. 'Nastarana'	Rosa 'Jenny Duval' misapplied	R. 'President de Seze'
Rosa 'Bullata'	R. x centifolia 'Bullata'	Rosa 'Josephine Wheatcroft'	R. 'Rosina'
Rosa 'C.F.Meyer'	R. 'Conrad Ferdinand Meyer'	Rosa 'Kazanlik' misapplied	R. 'Professeur Emile Perrot'
Rosa 'Canary Bird'	R. xanthina 'Canary Bird'	Rosa 'Kiftsgate'	R. filipes 'Kiftsgate'
		Rosa 'Kitchener of Khartoum'	R. 'K of K'
Rosa 'Captain Christy'	R. 'Climbing Captain Christy'	Rosa 'L'Ouche' misapplied	R. 'Louise Odier'
		Rosa 'La Belle Sultane'	R. 'Violacea'
Rosa 'Carol'	R. 'Carol Amling'	Rosa 'La Mortola'	R. brunonii 'La Mortola'
Rosa 'Caroline Testout'	R. 'Madame Caroline Testout'	Rosa 'La Reine Victoria'	R. 'Reine Victoria'
		Rosa 'La Rubanee'	R. x centifolia 'Unique Panachee'
Rosa 'Cecile Brunner, White'	R. 'White Cecile Brunner'	Rosa 'Lady Hillingdon' (CIT)	R. 'Climbing Lady Hillingdon' (CIT)
Rosa 'Celestial'	R. 'Celeste'		
Rosa 'Centifolia Variegata'	R. x centifolia 'Unique Panachee'	Rosa 'Lemon Pillar'	R. 'Paul's Lemon Pillar'
		Rosa 'Little White Pet'	R. 'White Pet'
Rosa 'Climbing Little White Pet'	R. 'Felicite Perpetue'	Rosa 'Lubeck'	R. 'Hansestadt Lubeck'
R. 'Climbing Mrs G.A. van Rossem'	R. 'Climbing Mevrouw G.A. van Rossem'	Rosa 'Ludlow Castle'	R. England's Rose
		Rosa 'Lutea Maxima'	R. x harisonii 'Lutea Maxima'
Rosa 'Cloth of Gold'	R. 'Chromatella'		
Rosa 'Columbian'	R. 'Climbing Columbia'	R. 'Madame Eugene Resal' mis.	R. 'Comtesse du Cayla'
R. 'Comte de Chambord' misapplied	R. 'Madame Knorr'	Rosa 'Maiden's Blush, Great'	R. 'Great Maiden's Blush'
R. 'Comtesse de Lacepede' misap.	R. 'Du Maitre d'Ecole'		
Rosa 'Comtesse de Murinais'	R. 'Shailer's White Moss'	Rosa 'Master Hugh'	R. macrophylla 'Master Hugh'
Rosa 'Corylus'	R. 'Hazel le Rougetel'	Rosa 'Matawero Magic'	R. Simply The Best
Rosa 'Cristata'	R. x centifolia 'Cristata'	Rosa 'Max Graf'	R. x jacksonii 'Max Graf'
Rosa 'Daily Mail'	R. 'Climbing Madame Edouard Herriot'	Rosa 'Maxima'	R. x alba 'Alba Maxima'
		Rosa 'Mousseuse du Japon'	R. 'Japonica'
Rosa 'De Meaux, White'	R. 'White de Meaux'	Rosa 'Mutabilis'	R. x odorata 'Mutabilis'
Rosa 'De Meaux'	R. x centifolia 'De Meaux'	Rosa 'Nathalie Nypels'	R. 'Mevrouw Nathalie Nypels'
Rosa 'Devoniensis'	R. 'Climbing Devoniensis'	Rosa 'Oeillet Flamand'	R. 'Oeillet parfait'
		Rosa 'Orpheline de Juillet'	R. 'Ombre Parfaite'
Rosa 'Duchess of Portland'	R. 'Portlandica'	Rosa 'Paul Lede'	R. 'Climbing Paul Lede'
Rosa 'E.H.Morse'	R. 'Ernest H.Morse'	Rosa 'Paulii Alba'	R. 'Paulii'
Rosa 'Empress Josephine'	R. 'Imperatrice Josephine'	Rosa 'Pink Garnette'	R. 'Carol Amling'
		Rosa 'Pompon de Bourgogne'	R. 'Burgundiaca'
Rosa 'F.E.Lester'	R. 'Francis E.Lester'	Rosa 'Pompon de Paris'	R. 'Climbing Pompon de Paris'
Rosa 'Fabvier'	R. 'Colonel Fabvier'		
Rosa 'Fairy Rose'	R. 'The Fairy'	Rosa 'Princesse Marie' misapplied	R. 'Belvedere'
Rosa 'Fulgens'	R. 'Malton'	Rosa 'Prolifera de Redoute' mis.	R. 'Duchesse de Montebello'
Rosa 'Garnette Carol'	R. 'Carol Amling'		
Rosa 'Garnette Golden'	R. 'Golden Garnette'	Rosa 'Queen of Hearts'	R. 'Dame de Coeur'
Rosa 'Garnette Pink'	R. 'Carol Amling'	Rosa 'Red Garnette'	R. 'Garnette'
Rosa 'Garnette Red'	R. 'Garnette'	Rosa 'Red Grootendorst'	R. 'F.J.Grootendorst'
Rosa 'Gold of Ophir'	R. x odorata 'Pseudindica'	Rosa 'Red Wing'	R. 'Red Wing' (hugonis hybrid)
Rosa 'Golden Rambler'	R. 'Alister Stella Gray'	Rosa 'Rescht'	R. 'De Rescht'
Rosa 'Golden Sunblaze'	R. 'Rise n' Shine'	Rosa 'Rose de Meaux White'	R. 'White de Meaux'
Rosa 'Grootendorst'	R. 'F.J.Grootendorst'	Rosa 'Rose de Meaux'	R. x centifolia 'De Meaux'
Rosa 'Hadangel'	R. 'Smooth Angel'		

Synonym	Current Name	Synonym	Current Name
Rosa 'Rose de Rescht'	R. 'De Rescht'		double pink
Rosa 'Rose des Maures' misapplied	R. 'Sissinghurst Castle'	Rosa Burnet, double white	R. pimpin. double white
Rosa 'Rose du Maitre d'Ecole'	R. 'Du Maitre d'Ecole'	Rosa californica 'Plena'	R. nutkana 'Plena'
Rosa 'Rubrotincta'	R. 'Hebe's Lip'	Rosa canina 'Abbotswood'	R. 'Abbotswood'
Rosa 'Sanguinea'	R. x odorata Sanguinea Group		(canina hybrid)
		Rosa canina 'Andersonii'	R. 'Andersonii' (canina)
Rosa 'Scarlet Glow'	R. 'Scharlachglut'	Rosa Chapeau de Napoleon	R. x centif. 'Cristata'
Rosa 'Semiplena'	R. x alba 'Alba Semiplena'	Rosa chinensis 'Minima' h.	R. 'Pompon de Paris'
		Rosa chinensis 'Mutabilis'	R. x odorata 'Mutabilis'
Rosa 'Shailer's White Moss'	R. x centifolia 'Shailer's White Moss'	Rosa chinensis 'Old Blush'	R. x odorata 'Pallida'
		Rosa chinensis 'Viridiflora'	R. x odor. 'Viridiflora'
Rosa 'Snow Dwarf'	R. 'Schneezwerg'	Rosa cinnamomea	R. majalis
Rosa 'Snow Queen'	R. 'Frau Karl Druschki'	Rosa Colibre '80	R. Colibre '79
Rosa 'Souvenir de Brod'	R. 'Erinnerung an Brod'	Rosa Colonial White	R. 'Sombreuil'
R. 'Souvenir de la Malmaison' (ClBb)	R. 'Climbing Souvenir de la Malmaison' (ClBb)	Rosa Common Moss	R. x centif. 'Muscosa'
		Rosa Cooper's Burmese	R. 'Cooperi'
Rosa 'Spanish Beauty'	R. 'Madame Gregoire Staechelin'	Rosa Cottage Maid	R. x centifolia 'Unique Panachee'
Rosa 'Spencer' misapplied	R. 'Enfant de France'	Rosa Crested Moss	R. x centif. 'Cristata'
Rosa 'Spong'	R. x centifolia 'Spong'	Rosa Crimson Damask	R. gallica v officinalis
Rosa 'The Colwyn Rose'	R. Colwyn Bay	Rosa Cuisse de Nymphe	R. 'Great Maiden's Blush'
Rosa 'The New Dawn'	R. 'New Dawn'		
Rosa 'Thoresbyana'	R. 'Bennett's Seedling'	Rosa dumetorum -Thuill.	R. corymbifera
Rosa 'Tipo Ideale'	R. x odorata 'Mutabilis'	Rosa Dwarf King	R. 'Zwergkonig'
Rosa 'Trigintipetala' misapplied	R. 'Professeur Emile Perrot'	Rosa ecae 'Helen Knight'	R. 'Helen Knight' (ecae hybrid)
Rosa 'Unique Blanche'	R. x centifolia 'Unique'	Rosa eglanteria	R. rubiginosa
Rosa 'Village Maid'	R.xc 'Unique Panachee'	Rosa ernestii	R. rubus
Rosa 'Viridiflora'	R. x odorata 'Viridiflora'	Rosa fargesii h.	R. moyesii v fargesii
		Rosa farreri	R. elegantula
Rosa 'White Bath'	R. x centifolia 'Shailer's White Moss'	Rosa farreri v persetosa	R. elegant. 'Persetosa'
		Rosa ferox -Bieb.	R. biebersteinii
Rosa 'Williams' Double Yellow'	R. x harisonii 'Williams' Double Yellow'	Rosa filipes 'Brenda Colvin'	R. 'Brenda Colvin'
		Rosa Fortune's Double Yellow	R. x od. 'Pseudindica'
Rosa 'Woolverstone Church Rose'	R. 'Surpassing Beauty of Woolverstone'	Rosa gallica 'Complicata'	R. 'Complicata'
		Rosa gallica 'Conditorum'	R. 'Conditorum'
Rosa 'Yellow cecile Brunner'	R. 'Perle d'Or'	Rosa gentilliana H. lev. &Vaniot	R. multiflora v cathayensis
Rosa Agatha'	R. x francofurtana 'Agatha'	Rosa gigantea 'Cooperi'	R. 'Cooperi'
Rosa alpina	R. pendulina	Rosa Gipsy Boy	R. 'Zigeunerknabe'
Rosa altaica h.	R. pimpinellifolia 'Grandiflora'	Rosa glaucophylla -Ehrh	R. hemisphaerica
		Rosa glutinosa	R. pulverulenta
Rosa anemoniflora	R. x beanii	Rosa Gold Crown	R. 'Goldkrone'
Rosa anemonoides	R. 'Anemone'	Rosa Gypsy Boy	R. 'Zigeunerknabe'
Rosa anemonoides 'Ramona'	R. 'Ramona'	Rosa haematodes -Crep.	R. pendulina v oxyodon
Rosa Anvil Sparks	R. 'Ambossfunken'	Rosa hispida	R. pimpinellifolia v hispida
Rosa apothecary's rose	R. gallica v officinalis		
Rosa Austrian copper rose	R. foetida 'Bicolor'	Rosa holodonta	R. moyesii f rosea
Rosa Austrian yellow	R. foetida	Rosa Holy Rose	R. x richardii
Rosa Awakening	R. 'Probuzeni'	Rosa Honeymoon	R. 'Honigmond'
Rosa banksiae 'Purezza'	R. 'Purezza'	Rosa horrida	R. biebersteinii
Rosa banksiae alba	R. banksiae v banksiae	Rosa hugonis	R. xanthina f hugonis
Rosa berberifolia -Pall.	R. persica	Rosa hugonis 'Plenissima'	R. xanthina f hugonis
Rosa Burgundian rose	R. 'Burgundiaca'	Rosa Hume's Blush	R. x odorata 'Odorata'
Rosa Burnet, double pink	R. pimpinellifolia	Rosa indica -Ait.	R. chinensis

Synonym	Current Name	Synonym	Current Name
Rosa Jacobite Rose	R. x alba 'Alba Maxima'	Rosa parvifolia	R. 'Burgundiaca'
Rosa Jacpico	R. 'Pristine'	Rosa Peace Sunblaze	R. Lady Meillandina
Rosa Jacques Cartier h.	R. 'Marchesa Boccella'	Rosa pendulina 'Morlettii'	R. 'Morlettii'
Rosa Jazz	R. That's Jazz	Rosa Persian yellow	R. foetida 'Persiana'
Rosa laevigata 'Anemonoides'	R. 'Anemone'	Rosa persica	Hulthemia persica
Rosa laevigata 'Cooperi'	R. 'Cooperi'	Rosa Phoebe	R. 'Fimbriata'
Rosa longicuspis misapplied	R. mulliganii	Rosa pimpinellifolia 'Altaica'	R. pimpin. 'Grandiflora'
Rosa lucens -Rolfe	R. longicuspis -Bertol.	Rosa pimpinellifolia 'Harisonii'	R. x harisonii
Rosa lucida	R. virginiana		'Harison's Yellow'
Rosa lutea -Mill.	R. foetida	Rosa pimpinellifolia 'Lutea'	R. x ha. 'Lutea Maxima'
Rosa lutea v hoggii -D.Don	R. x harisonii	R. pimpinellifolia 'Stanwell Perpetual'	R. 'Stanwell Perpetual'
Rosa Macartney Rose	R. bracteata	Rosa pimpinellifolia double yellow	R. x harisonii 'Williams'
Rosa macrophylla 'Doncasteri'	R. 'Doncasteri'		Double Yellow'
Rosa Maltese Rose	R. 'Cecile Brunner'	Rosa pimpinellifolia v altaica -Rehd.	R. pimpin. 'Grandiflora'
Rosa marginata -Auct.	R. jundizillii	Rosa pimpinellifolia x pendulina	R. x reversa
Rosa Meicobius	R. Terracotta	Rosa pink moss	R. x centif. 'Muscosa'
Rosa microphylla	R. roxburghii	Rosa polyantha -Sieb & Zucc.	R. multiflora
Rosa Millenium Rose 2000	R. Rose 2000	Rosa polyantha grandiflora	R. gentiliana
Rosa mirifica stellata	R. stellata v mirifica	Rosa pomifera	R. villosa
Rosa moschata 'Autumnalis'	R. 'Princesse de	Rosa pomifera 'Duplex'	R. 'Wolley-Dod'
	Nassau'	Rosa Portland rose	R. 'Portlandica'
Rosa moschata h.	R. brunonii	Rosa Prairie rose	R. setigera
Rosa moschata v nastarana	R. 'Nastarana'	Rosa Quatre Saisons	R. x damascena v
Rosa moschata v nepalensis	R. brunonii		semperflorens
Rosa moschata v nivea	R. 'Dupontii'	Rosa Queen Elizabeth	R. 'The Queen Elizabeth'
Rosa Mother's Day	R. 'Moersdag'	Rosa Queen of Denmark	R. 'Konigin von
Rosa moyesii 'Geranium'	R. 'Geranium' (moyesii		Danemark'
	hybrid)	Rosa Queen of the Belgians	R. 'Reine des Belges'
Rosa moyesii 'Highdownensis'	R. 'Highdownensis'	Rosa red moss	R. 'Henri Martin'
	(moyesii hybrid)	Rosa Red New Dawn	R. 'Etendard'
Rosa moyesii 'Hillieri'	R. 'Hillieri'	Rosa red rose of Lancaster	R. gallica v officinalis
Rosa moyesii 'Sealing Wax'	R. 'Sealing wax'	Rosa Rosenprofessor Sieber	R. Halcyon Days Rose
	(moyesii hybrid)	Rosa roxburghii 'Plena'	R. roxburghii f roxb.
Rosa moyesii holodonta	R. moyesii f rosea	Rosa rubra	R. gallica
Rosa multiflora 'Platyphylla'	R. multiflora 'Grevillei'	Rosa rubrifolia	R. glauca
Rosa multiflora v watsoniana	R. watsoniana	Rosa rubrifolia 'Carmenetta'	R. 'Carmenetta'
Rosa Mummy	R. Newly Wed	Rosa rugosa 'Scabrosa'	R. 'Scabrosa'
Rosa mundi	R. gallica 'Versicolor'	Rosa rugosa v kamtschatica	R. rugosa v
Rosa mundi 'Versicolor'	R. gallica 'Versicolor'		ventenatiana
Rosa muscosa -Ait.	R. x centif. 'Muscosa'	Rosa Saint John's rose	R. x richardii
Rosa New Arrival	R. 'Red Patio'	Rosa Saint Mark's rose	R. 'Rose d'Amour'
Rosa odorata v gigantea	R. gigantea	Rosa sancta	R. x richardii
Rosa officinalis	R. gallica v officinalis	Rosa Scarlet Fire	R. 'Scharlachglut'
Rosa old blush China	R. x odorata 'Pallida'	Rosa Scotch rose	R. pimpinellifolia
Rosa old cabbage	R. x centifolia	Rosa Scotch yellow	R. x harisonii
Rosa old pink moss rose	R. x centif. 'Muscosa'		'Williams' Double
Rosa old red moss	R. 'Henri Martin'		Yellow'
Rosa old red moss	R. 'Lanei'	Rosa Sea of Fire	R. 'Feuermeer'
Rosa old velvet moss	R. 'William Lobb'	Rosa sericea 'Heather Muir'	R. 'Heather Muir'
Rosa old yellow Scotch	R. x harisonii 'Williams'		(sericea hybrid)
	Double Yellow'	Rosa seven sisters rose	R. multiflora 'Grevillei'
Rosa omeiensis	R. sericea ssp omeien.	Rosa sinica -Ait.	R. laevigata
Rosa oxyodon -Boiss.	R. pendulina v oxyodon	Rosa sinowilsonii	R. longicuspis v sinow.
Rosa Park's yellow China	R. x od. 'Ochroleuca'	Rosa spaldingii	R. nutkana v hispida
Rosa Parson's pink China	R. x odorata 'Pallida'	Rosa spinosissima	R. pimpinellifolia

Synonym	Current Name	Synonym	Current Name
Rosa suffulta	R. arkansana v suffulta	R. officinalis 'Collingwood Ingram'	R. o. v angustissimus
Rosa sulphurea -Ait.	R. hemisphaerica		'Benenden Blue'
Rosa Tapis Jaune	R. 'Golden Penny'	Rosmarinus officinalis 'Erectus'	R. officinalis 'Miss
Rosa Thousand Beauties	R. 'Tausendschon'		Jessopp's Upright'
Rosa threepenny bit rose	R. elegantula	Rosmarinus officinalis 'Fastigiatus'	R. officinalis 'Miss
	'Persetosa'		Jessopp's Upright'
Rosa triphylla	R. x beanii	Rosmarinus officinalis 'Frimley Blue'	R. o. 'Primley Blue'
Rosa versicolor	R. gallica 'Versicolor'	Rosmarinus officinalis 'Gilded'	R. officinalis 'Aureus'
Rosa villosa 'Duplex'	R. 'Wolley-Dod'	Rosmarinus officinalis 'Golden Rain'	R. o. 'Joyce DeBaggio'
Rosa villosa misapplied	R. mollis	R. officinalis 'Lockwood Variey'	R. o. 'Lockwood de
Rosa virginiana 'Plena'	R. 'Rose d'Amour'		Forest' (Prostr. Gr.)
Rosa vosagiaca	R. caesia ssp glauca	Rosmarinus officinalis 'Prostratus'	R. o. Prostratus Group
Rosa white moss	R. 'Comtesse de	R. officinalis 'Roseus-Cozart'	R. o. 'Majorca Pink'
	Murinais'	Rosmarinus officinalis 'Variegatus'	R. officinalis 'Aureus'
Rosa white moss	R. x centifolia	Rosmarinus officinalis f pyramidalis	R. officinalis 'Miss
	'Shailer's White Moss'		Jessopp's Upright'
Rosa white Provence	R. x centifolia 'Unique'	R. officinalis lavandulaceus	R. o. Prostratus Group
Rosa white rose of York	R. x alba 'Alba	Rosmarinus officinalis repens	R. o. Prostratus Group
	Semiplena'	Rosmarinus repens	R. o. Prostratus Group
Rosa willmottiae	R. gymnocarpa v willm.	Rosmarinus x lavandulaceus -Noe	R. eriocalyx
Rosa woodsii v fendleri	R. woodsii	Rosmarinus x lavandulaceus h.	R. o. Prostratus Group
Rosa x alba 'Maxima'	R. x alba 'Alba Maxima'	Rosularia acuminata	R. alpestris ssp
Rosa x alba Celestial	R. 'Celeste'		alpestris
Rosa x centifolia 'Parvifolia'	R. 'Burgundiaca'	Rosularia alba	R. sedoides
R. x damascena 'Trigintipetala' mis.	R. 'Professeur Emile	Rosularia crassipes	Rhodiola wallichiana
	Perrot'	Rosularia pallida -A.Berger	R. chrysantha
Rosa x damascena v bifera	R.x d. v semperflorens	Rosularia pallida -Stapf	R. aizoon
Rosa x francofurtana misapplied	R. 'Imperatrice	Rosularia platyphylla h.	R. muratdaghensis
	Josephine'	Rosularia spatulata h.	R. sempervivum ssp
Rosa x macrantha 'Raubritter'	R. 'Raubritter'		glaucophylla
	('Macrantha' hybrid)	Rottlera japonica -(Thunb.) Spreng.	Mallotus japonicus
R. x od. 'Fortune's Double Yellow'	R. x odorata	Roulinia karwinskiana -Brongiart	Nolina longifolia
	'Pseudindica'	Roupellia grata	Strophanthus gratus
Rosa x penzanceana	R. 'Lady Penzance'	Roxburghia gloriosa	Stemona tuberosa
Rosa x pruhonica 'Hillieri'	R. 'Hillieri'	Roystonea caribaea	R. borinquena
Rosa xanthina 'Flore Pleno'	R. xanthina	Rubia manjith	R. cordifolia
Rosa yellow Scotch	R. x harisonii 'Williams'	Rubus Japanese wineberry	R. phoenicolasius
	Double Yellow'	Rubus 'Tridel'	R. 'Benenden'
Rosa York and Lancaster	R. x dam. v versicolor	Rubus bambusarum -Focke	R. henryi v bambus.
Roscoea capitata h.	R. scillifolia	Rubus calycinoides -Hayata	R. pentalobus
Roscoea cautleoides	R. cautleyoides	Rubus cissoides v pauperatus -Kirk	R. squarrosus
Roscoea chamaeleon	R. cautleyoides	Rubus fockeanus h.	R. pentalobus
Roscoea procera	R. purpurea	Rubus fruticosus 'Himalayan Berry'	R. discolor
Roscoea purpurea v procera	R. purpurea	Rubus fruticosus v laciniatus	R. laciniatus
Roscoea purpurea v purpurea	R. purpurea	Rubus japonicus -L.	Kerria japonica
Roscoea yunnanensis	R. cautleyoides	Rubus nutans	R. nepalensis
Roscoea yunnanensis purpurata	R. cautleyoides	Rubus nutkanus -Mocino ex Ser.	R. nepalensis
Roseocactus fissuratus	Ariocarpus fissuratus	Rubus polytrichus -Franch.	R. tricolor
Rosmarinus corsicus 'Prostratus'	R. officinalis	Rubus pseudochamaemorus -Tolm.	R. chamaemorus -L.
	Prostratus Group	Rubus spectabilis 'Flore Pleno'	R. sp. 'Olympic Double'
Rosmarinus eriocalyx h.	R. officinalis	Rubus thibetanus 'Silver Fern'	R. thibetanus
	Prostratus Group	Rubus thyrsoideus 'Plenus'	R. linkianus
Rosmarinus lavandulaceus -Noe	R. erioclayx	Rubus veitchii -Rolfe	R. thibetanus
Rosmarinus lavandulaceus misap.	R. off. Prostratus Gr.	Rubus x tridel 'Benenden'	R. 'Benenden'
R. officinalis 'Aureovariegatus'	R. officinalis 'Aureus'	Rudbeckia Autumn Sun	R. 'Herbstsonne'

Synonym	Current Name	Synonym	Current Name
Rudbeckia columnifera	Ratibida columnifera	Salix 'Caerulea'	S. alba ssp caerulea
Rudbeckia deamii	R. fulgida v deamii	Salix 'Chrysocoma'	S. x sepulcralis v
Rudbeckia echinacea purpurea	Echinacea purpurea		chrysocoma
Rudbeckia gloriosa	R. hirta	Salix 'Decipiens'	S. fragilis v decipiens
Rudbeckia hirta 'Green Eyes'	R. hirta 'Irish Eyes'	Salix 'E.A.Bowles'	S. 'Bowles' Hybrid'
Rudbeckia July Gold	R. 'Juligold'	Salix 'Elegantissima'	S. pendulina v
Rudbeckia laciniata 'Golden Fountain'	R. 'Goldquelle'		elegantissima
Rudbeckia laciniata 'Golden Glow'	R. laciniata 'Hortensia'	Salix 'Fuiri-koriyanagi'	S. integra 'Hakuro-
Rudbeckia newmannii	R. fulgida v speciosa		nishiki'
Rudbeckia pinnata	Ratibida pinnata	Salix 'Ginme'	S. x tsugaluensis
Rudbeckia purpurea	Echinacea purpurea		'Ginme'
Rudbeckia speciosa	R. fulgida v speciosa	Salix 'Golden Curls'	S. 'Erythroflexuosa'
Rudbeckia sullivantii	R. fulgida v sullivantii	Salix 'Hagensis'	S. 'The Hague'
Ruellia amoena	R. graecizans	Salix 'Hippophaifolia'	S. x mollisima v
Rumex acetosa 'Redleaf'	R. acet. ssp vineatus		hippophaeifolia
Rumex acidus	R. acetosa	Salix 'Jacquinii'	S. alpina
Rumex acuminatus	R. acetosa	Salix 'Kishu'	S. kinuyanagi
Rumex agrestis	R. acetosa	Salix 'Kureneko'	S. gracilistyla
Rumex fontanopaludosus	R. acetosa		'Melanostachys'
Rumex hortensis	R. acetosa	Salix 'Kuro-me'	S. gr. 'Melanostachys'
Rumex intermedius	R. acetosa	Salix 'Kuroyanagi'	S. gr. 'Melanostachys'
Rumex montanus 'Ruber'	R. alpestris 'Ruber'	Salix 'Melanostachys'	S. gr. 'Melanostachys'
Rumex platyphyllus	R. acetosa	Salix 'Setsuka'	S. udensis 'Sekka'
Rumohra adiantiformis	Lastreopsis calantha	Salix 'Yelverton'	S. alba ssp vitellina
Rumohra simplicior	Arachnoides simplicior		'Yelverton'
Ruschia derenbergiana	Ebracteola derenberg.	Salix adenophylla -Hook.	S. cordata
Ruscus racemosus -L.	Danae racemosa	Salix alba 'Caerulea'	S. alba ssp caerulea
Russelia juncea	R. equisetiformis	Salix alba 'Chermesina' h.	S. alba ssp vitellina
Ruta albiflora -Hook.	Boenninghausenia albif.		'Britzensis'
Ruta chalepensis prostrate form	R. chalepensis	Salix alba 'Regalis'	S. alba v sericea
	'Dimension Two'	Salix alba 'Sericea'	S. alba v sericea
Ruta prostrata	R. c. 'Dimension Two'	Salix alba 'Splendens'	S. alba v sericea
Rydbergia grandiflora	Tetraneuris grandiflo.	Salix alba 'Tristis' misapplied	S. humilis
Rylstonea darwinioides	Homoranthus darwini.	Salix alba 'Tristis' misapplied	S. x sepulcralis v
Sabal glabra	S. minor		chrysochoma
Sabal guatemalensis	S. mexicana	Salix alba 'Vitellina Pendula'	S. alba 'Tristis'
Sabal minima	S. minor	Salix alba 'Vitellina Tristis'	S. alba 'Tristis'
Sabal princeps	S. bermudana	Salix alba f argentea -Wimm.	S. alba v sericea
Sabal pumila	S. minor	Salix alniformis	S. caprea -L.
Sabal texana	S. mexicana	Salix amygdalina	S. triandra
Sabina	Juniperus	Salix aquatica -L.	S. caprea -L.
Saccharum strictum -Ell ex Nutt.	S. baldwinii	Salix arbuscula 'Erecta'	S. waldsteiniana
Sageretia theezans	S. thea	Salix arenaria	S. repens v argentea
Sagina glabra 'Aurea'	S. subulata 'Aurea'	Salix arenaria -L.	S. repens v argentea
Sagittaria japonica	S. sagittifolia	Salix atrocinerea	S. cinerea ssp oleifolia
Sagittaria pubesccens	S. latifolia	Salix babylonica 'Annularis'	S. babylonica 'Crispa'
Sagmen jaceoides	Centaurea scabiosa	Salix babylonica 'Ramulis Aureis'	S. x sepulcralis v
Sagmen scabiosa	Centaurea scabiosa		chrysocoma
Saintpaulia 'Granger's Wonderland'	S. 'Wonderland'	Salix babylonica 'Tortuosa'	S. babylonica v
Saintpaulia 'Optimara Colorado'	S. 'Colorado'		pekinensis 'Tortuosa'
Saintpaulia 'Rococo Pink'	S. 'Rococo Anna'	Salix bigemmis	S. daphnoides
Salicornia fruticosa	Arthrocnemum frutico.	Salix cantoniensis	S. babylonica -L.
Salisburia adiantifolia -Sm.	Ginkgo biloba -L.	Salix caprea v pendula (f)	S. cap. 'Weeping Sally'
Salix 'Axukime'	S. integra	Salix caprea v pendula (m)	S. caprea 'Kilmarnock'
Salix 'Basfordiana'	S. 'Basfordiana'	Salix cardiobasis	S. caprea -L.

Synonym	Current Name	Synonym	Current Name
Salix chinensis -Burm. f.	S. babylonica -L.	Salix repens v subopposita	S. subopposita
Salix cinerea 'Variegata'	S. cinerea 'Tricolor'	Salix rosmarinifolia h.	S. elaeagnos ssp angustifolia
Salix cinerea ssp atrocinerea	S. cinerea ssp oleifolia		
Salix compressa	S. daphnoides	Salix sachalinensis	S. udensis
Salix daphnoides v acutifolia	S. acutifolia	Salix salviifolia -Link.	S. x seringeana
Salix decipiens	S. fragilis	Salix saskatchavana	S. arbusculoides
Salix eucalyptoides	S. arbutifolia -Pall.	Salix schraderiana -Willdenow	S. bicolor -Willdenow
Salix fallacina	S. caprea -L.	Salix serpyllum	S. fruticulosa
Salix formosa -Willd.	S. arbuscula	Salix syrticola	S. cordata
Salix furcata	S. fruticulosa	Salix tristis	S. humilis
Salix ganderi	S. caprea -L.	Salix viminalis 'Bowles' Hybrid'	S. 'Bowles' Hybrid'
Salix hibernica	S. phylicifolia	Salix vitellina	S. alba ssp vitallina
Salix humillima	S. arbusculoides	Salix vitellina 'Pendula'	S. alba 'Tristis'
Salix hylematica	S. fruticulosa	Salix wehrhahnii -Bonst.	S. hastata 'Wehrhahnii'
Salix incana	S. elaeagnos	Salix wrightii	S. amygdaloides
Salix integra 'Albomaculata'	S. integra 'Hakuro-nishiki'	Salix x blanda	S. x pendulina 'Blanda'
		Salix x caerulea -Sm.	S. alba ssp caerulea
Salix japonica h.	S. babylonica 'Lavelleei'	Salix x chrysocoma	S. x sepulcralis v chrysocoma
Salix lanata 'Mark Postill'	S. 'Mark Postill'	Salix x erythroflexuosa	S. 'Erythroflexuosa'
Salix lanata 'Stuartii'	S. 'Stuartii'	Salix x gillotii -h.	S. x cottetii
Salix liliputa	S. turczaninowii	Salix x mollissima	S. trevirani
Salix livida -Vahl.	S. starkeana	Salix x moorei -F.B.White	S. x grahamii 'Moorei'
Salix longiramea	S. daphnoides	Salix x myricoides	S. x bebbii
Salix magnolioides	S. caprea -L.	Salix x pontederiana	S. x sordida
Salix matsudana	S. babylonica v pekinensis	Salix x salamonii	S. x sepulchralis 'Salamonii'
S. mats. 'Tortuosa Aureopendula'	S. 'Erythroflexuosa'	Salix x sepulcralis 'Erythroflexuosa'	S. 'Erythroflexuosa'
Salix matsudana 'Tortuosa'	S. babylonica v pekinensis 'Tortuosa'	Salix x smithiana	S. x stipularis
		Salix x viridis	S. x rubens
Salix medemii	S. aegyptiaca	Salvia 'Dear Anja'	S. x superba 'Dear Anja'
Salix medemii -Boiss.	S. aegyptica		
Salix melanostachys -Mak.	S. gracilistyla 'Melanostachys'	Salvia 'Maraschino'	S. x jamensis 'Maraschino'
Salix missouriensis -Bebb	S. eriocephala	Salvia 'Trebah'	S. x jamensis 'Trebah'
Salix muscina h.	S. aegyptica	Salvia 'Trenance'	S. x jam. 'Trenance'
Salix myrsinites v jacquiniana	S. alpina	Salvia 'Van-Houttei'	S. splendens 'Van-Houttei'
Salix myrtilloides x repens	S. x finnmarchica		
Salix nepalensis	S. lindleyana	Salvia 'Vatican City'	S. sclarea 'Vatican White'
Salix nigricans	S. myrsinifolia		
Salix nitida	S. repens v argentea	Salvia acetabulosa	S. multicaulis
Salix nivalis	S. reticulata ssp niv.	Salvia africana-caerulea	S. africana
Salix occidentalis	S. humilis	Salvia africana-lutea	S. aurea
Salix persicifolia	S. fragilis -L.	Salvia ambigens	S. guaranitica 'Blue Enigma'
Salix platystachya	S. caprea -L.		
Salix procumbens	S. myrsinites	Salvia angustifolia -Cavanilles	S. reptans
Salix pruinosa -Bess.	S. acutifolia	Salvia angustifolia -Michaux	S. azurea
Salix prunifolia	S. arbuscula	Salvia aurea	S. africana-lutea
Salix purpurea 'Eugenei'	S. x rubra 'Eugenei'	Salvia azurea h.	S. uliginosa
Salix purpurea 'Helix'	S. purpurea	Salvia bacheriana	S. buchananii
Salix purpurea f gracilis	S. purpurea 'Nana'	Salvia bertolonii	S. pratensis Bertolonii Group
Salix purpurea v japonica -Nakai	S. koriyanagi		
Salix purpurea v multinervis	S. integra	Salvia bethellii	S. involucrata 'Bethellii'
Salix repens pendula	S. 'Boyd's Pendulous'		
Salix repens v nitida -Wenderoth	S. repens v argentea	Salvia bicolor -Desfontaines	S. barrelieri

Synonym	Current Name	Synonym	Current Name
Salvia brachycalyx	S. indica	Salvia muelleri misapplied	S.greggii x serpyllifolia
Salvia bulleyana misapplied	S. flava v megalantha	Salvia nemerosa 'Plumosa'	S. n. 'Pusztflamme'
Salvia caerulea -L.	S. africana	Salvia nemerosa East Friesland	S. n. 'Ostfriesland'
Salvia caerulea misapplied	S. guaranitica 'Black and Blue'	Salvia neurepia	S. microphylla v micro.
		Salvia odorata	S. candidissima
Salvia calycina	S. pomifera	Salvia officinalis 'Alba'	S. officinalis 'Albiflora'
Salvia cardinalis	S. fulgens	S. officinalis 'Aurea' gold variegated	S. officinalis 'Icterina'
Salvia chinensis	S. japonica	Salvia officinalis 'Variegata'	S. officinalis 'Icterina'
Salvia chromatica	S. officinalis	Salvia officinalis latifolia	S. off. broad-leaved
Salvia cleistogamma misapplied	S. glutinosa	Salvia officinalis narrow-leaved	S. lavandulifolia
Salvia coahuilensis misapplied	S. greggii x S. serpyllifolia	Salvia officinalis prostrata	S. lavandulifolia
		Salvia papillosa	S. officinalis
Salvia coccinea 'Indigo'	S. guaranitica 'Indigo Blue'	Salvia patens 'Alba' misapplied	S. pat. 'White Trophy'
		Salvia patens 'Oxford Blue'	S. patens
Salvia concolor misapplied	S. guaranitica	Salvia patens 'Royal Blue'	S. patens
Salvia cristata	S. officinalis 'Crispa'	Salvia pratensis 'Rhapsody in Blue'	S. x sylvestris 'Rhapsody in Blue'
Salvia darcyi misapplied	S. roemeriana		
Salvia deserta	S. x sylvestris	Salvia puberula	S. involucrata v puber.
Salvia flava v megalantha	S. bulleyana	Salvia regeliana misapplied	S. virgata -Jacq.
Salvia forskaohlei	S. forsskaolii	Salvia riparia misapplied	S. rypara
Salvia grahamii	S. microphylla v microphylla	Salvia rutilans	S. elegans 'Scarlet Pineapple'
Salvia grandiflora -Etl. HH&K 210	S. tomentosa -Etl.	Salvia semiatrata misapplied	S. chamaedryoides
Salvia greggii 'Blush Pink'	S. microp. 'Pink Blush'	Salvia souliei	S. brevilabra
Salvia greggii 'Dark Dancer'	S. x jamensis 'Dark Dancer'	Salvia splendens Fireball	S. splen. 'Blaze of Fire'
		Salvia splendens Ryco	S. splen. 'Red Riches'
Salvia greggii 'Desert Blaze'	S. jam. 'Desert Blaze'	Salvia tachiei h.	S. forsskaolii
Salvia greggii 'Devon Cream'	S. gregii 'Sungold'	Salvia tesquicola	S. nemerosa ssp tesq.
Salvia greggii 'Peach' misapplied	S. x jam. 'Pat Vlasto'	Salvia transcaucasica	S. staminea
Salvia greggii 'Plum Wine'	S. x jam. 'Plum Wine'	Salvia triloba	S. fruticosa
Salvia greggii 'Raspberry Royal'	S. 'Raspberry Royale'	Salvia verticillata 'White Rain'	S. verticillata 'Alba'
Salvia greggii 'San Isidro Moon'	S. x jamensis 'San isidro Moon'	Salvia villicaulis	S. amplexicaulis
		Salvia viridis 'Monarch Bouquet'	S. viridis 'Bouquet'
Salvia greggii 'Sierra San Antonio'	S. x jamensis 'Sierra San Antonio'	Salvia viscosa -Sesse & Moc.	S. riparia
		Salvia x sylvestris Blue Mound	S. x syl. 'Blauhugel'
Salvia greggii lycioides	S. gregii x serpyllifolia	Salvia x sylvestris Blue Queen	S. x sylv. 'Blaukonigin'
Salvia haematodes	S. pratensis Haematodes Group	Salvia x sylvestris May Night	S. x sylv. 'Mainacht'
		Sambucus arborescens	S. nigra
Salvia hispanica misapplied	S. lavandulifolia	Sambucus caerulea	S. nigra ssp caerulea
Salvia horminum	S. viridis v comata	Sambucus coraensis	S. williamsii ssp corea.
Salvia involucrata 'Mrs.Pope'	S. invol. 'Hadspen'	Sambucus florida	S. nigra
Salvia lanceolata	S. reflexa	Sambucus japonica -Thunb.	Euscaphis japonica
Salvia lemmonii	S. microphylla v wislizenii	Sambucus nigra 'Albomarginata'	S. nigra 'Marginata'
		Sambucus nigra 'Albovariegata'	S. nigra 'Marginata'
Salvia leptophylla	S. reptans	S. nigra 'Argenteomarginata'	S. nigra 'Marginata'
Salvia lycioides misapplied	S.greggii x serpyllifolia	Sambucus nigra 'Black Beauty'	S. nigra f porphyro phylla 'Gerda'
Salvia macellaria misapplied	S. microphylla		
Salvia microphylla 'Red Velvet'	S. x jam. 'Red Velvet'	Sambucus nigra 'Black Lace'	S. nigra f porphyrop hylla 'Eva'
S. microphylla 'Trebah Lilac White'	S. x jamensis 'Trebah'		
S. microp. 'Trelawney Rose Pink'	S. 'Trelawney'	Sambucus nigra 'Foliis Pupureis'	S. ni. 'Guincho Purple'
S. mic. 'Trelissick Creamy Yellow'	S. 'Trelisick'	Sambucus nigra 'Guincho Purple'	S. nigra f porphyro phylla 'Guincho Purple'
S. microphylla 'Trenance Lilac Pink'	S. x jam. 'Trenance'		
S. microphylla 'Trewithen Cerise'	S. 'Trewithen'	Sambucus nigra 'Heterophylla'	S. nigra 'Linearis'
S. microphylla 'Variegata' splashed	S. micr. 'Ruth Stungo'	Sambucus nigra 'Purpurea'	S. nigra f porphyro phylla 'Guincho Purple'
Salvia microphylla v neurepia	S. microphylla v micro.		

Synonym	Current Name	Synonym	Current Name
Sambucus nigra 'Variegata'	S. nigra 'Marginata'	Sarracenia x farnhamii	S. x readii 'Farnhamii'
Sambucus pyramidata	S. nigra	Sasa albomarginata -Miq.	S. veitchii
S. racemosa 'Serratifolia Aurea'	S. ra. 'Plumosa Aurea'	Sasa auricoma -(Mitf.) E.G.Camus	Pleioblastus auricomus
Sambucus sieboldiana	S. rac. v sieboldiana	Sasa borealis	Sasamorpha borealis
Sambucus virescens	S. nigra	Sasa chrysantha h.	Pleiobastus chino
Sambucus wightiana	S. javanica	Sasa disticha -(Mitf.) E.G.Camus	Pleiobastus pygmaeus
Samuela faxoniana -Trelease	Y. faxoniana -Sarg.		v distichus
Sanchezia glaucophylla	S. speciosa	Sasa disticha 'Mirrezuzume'	Pleiobastus pygmaeus
Sanchezia nobilis h.	S. speciosa		'Mirrezuzume'
Sanchezia spectabilis	S. speciosa	Sasa fastuosa -(Mitf.) E.G.Camus	Semiarundinaria fastu.
Sanguinaria acaulis	S. canadensis	Sasa glabra f albostriata	Sasaella masamuneana
Sanguinaria australis	S. canadensis		f albostriata
S. canadensis 'Flore Pleno'	S. canadensis 'Plena'	Sasa humilis	Pleioblastus humilis
Sanguinaria dilleniana	S. canadensis	Sasa japonica	Pseudosasa japonica
Sanguinaria grandiflora	S. canadensis	Sasa kurilensis 'Shimofuri'	S. k. 'Shima-shimofuri'
Sanguinaria rotundifolia	S. canadensis	Sasa nana	S. veitchii f minor
Sanguinaria stenopetala	S. canadensis	Sasa paniculata	S. senanensis
Sanguisorba magnifica alba	S. albiflora	Sasa pumila	Pleioblastus argen
Sanguisorba obtusa v albiflora	S. albiflora		teostriatus f pumilus
Sanguisorba parviflora	S. tenuifolia v parviflo.	Sasa pygmaea	Pleioblastus pygmaeus
Sanguisorba pimpinella	S. minor	Sasa ramosa	Sasaella ramosa
Sanguisorba sitchensis	S. stipulata	Sasa ruscifolia	Shibataea kumasasa
Sanguisorba vallistellinae	S. dodecandra	Sasa tessellata	Indocalamus tessellat.
Sanicula gregaria	S. odorata	Sasa variegata -(Miq.) E.G.Camus	Pleioblastus variegatus
Sansevieria sessiliflora	Reineckia carnea	Sasaella glabra	S. masamuneana
Santolina chamaecyparissus ssp tomentosa S. pinnata		Sasamorpha borealis	Sasa borealis
S. chamaecyparissus v corsica	S. chamaecyp. v nana	Sasamorpha migoi	Indocalamus migoi
Santolina incana -L.	S. chamaecyparissus	Sasamorpha nubigena	Indocalamus wilsonii
Santolina neapolitana	S. pinnata ssp neapolit.	Sasamorpha purpurascens	Sasa borealis
Santolina pectinata	S. rosmarinifolia ssp	Sasamorpha sinica	Sasa sinica
	canescens	Sasamorpha tesselata	Indocalamus tesselatus
S. pinnata ssp neapolitana cream	S. pinnata ssp neapolit.	Sassafras officinale	S. albidum
	'Edward Bowles'	Sassafras triloba	S. albidum
Santolina tomentosa	S. pinnata ssp neapolit.	Satureja acinos	Acinos arvensis
Santolina virens -Mill.	S. rosmarinifolia ssp r.	Satureja alpina	Acinos alpinus
Santolina viridis -Willd.	S. r. ssp rosmarinifolia	Satureja arkansana	Calamintha arkansana
Saponaria 'Bressingham Hybrid'	S. 'Bressingham'	Satureja capitata	Thymus capitatus
Saponaria officinalis 'Taff's Dazzler'	S. officinalis 'Dazzler'	Satureja glabella	Calamintha arkansana
Saponaria officinalis 'Variegata'	S. officinalis 'Dazzler'	Satureja glabra	Calamintha arkansana
Saponaria pulvinaris	S. pumilio	Satureja grandiflora	Calamintha grandiflora
Saponaria pumila	S. pumilio	Satureja montana 'Coerulea'	S. coerulea
Saponaria zawadskii	Silene zawadskii	Satureja montana subspicata	S. montana ssp illyrica
Sarauja vaniotii -Levl	Celastrus vaniotii	Satureja nepeta	Calamintha nepeta ssp
Sarcococca 'Roy Lancaster'	S. ruscifolia 'Dragon		nepeta
	Gate'	Satureja repanda	S. spicigera
Sarcococca humilis	S. hookeriana v humilis	Satureja reptans	S. spicigera
Sarcococca pruniformis	S. saligna	Satureja rupestris	Micromeria thymifolia
Sarmienta scandens	S. repens	Satureja vulgaris	Clinopodium vulgare
Sarothamnus grandiflorus	Cytisus grandiflorus	Sauromatum guttatum	S. venosum
Sarothamnus scoparius -(L.) K.Koch	Cytisus scoparius	Saussurea costus	S. lappa
S. scoparius ssp maritimus	Cytisus sc. ssp marit.	Saxifraga 'Alba' (sempervivum)	S. 'Zita'
Sarracenia alata x purpurea	S. x exornata	Saxifraga 'Alba' (x arco-valleyi)	S. 'Ophelia' (x arco-
Sarracenia drummondii	S. leucophylla		valleyi)
Sarracenia flava all green giant	S. flava v maxima	Saxifraga 'Albertii' (callosa)	S. 'Albida'
Sarracenia minor 'Okefenokee Giant'	S. minor 'Okee Giant'	S. 'Aphrodite' (sempervivum)	S. 'Afrodite'

196

Synonym	Current Name	Synonym	Current Name
S. 'Aurea Maculata' (cuneifolia)	S. 'Aureopunctata'	Saxifraga 'Silver Mound'	S. 'Silver Cushion'
Saxifraga 'Balcana'	S. paniculata v orientalis	Saxifraga 'Stormonth's Variety'	S. 'Stella' (x stormont)
		Saxifraga 'Unique'	S. 'Bodensee' (x hofm)
Saxifraga 'Baldensis'	S. panic. v baldensis	Saxifraga 'Valborg'	S. 'Cranbourne' (x ang)
Saxifraga 'Birch Yellow'	S. 'Pseudoborisii' (x borisii)	Saxifraga 'Valentine'	S. 'Cranbourne' (x ang)
		Saxifraga 'Valerie Finnis'	S. 'Aretiastrum' (x bo)
Saxifraga 'Carmen'	S. 'Carmen' (x elisabethae)	Saxifraga 'Variegata' (umbrosa)	S. 'Aureopunctata' (x urbium)
Saxifraga 'Chambers' Pink Pride'	S. 'Miss Chambers' (x urbium)	Saxifraga 'Winter Fire'	S. 'Winterfeuer' (call.)
		Saxifraga 'Wisley Primrose'	S. 'Kolbiana' (x paulin.)
S. 'Crimson Rose' (paniculata)	S. 'Rosea'	Saxifraga aizoon	S. paniculata
Saxifraga 'Dentata' (x geum)	S. 'Dentata' (x polita)	Saxifraga angustifolia	S. hypnoides
Saxifraga 'Dentata' (x urbium)	S. 'Dentata' (x polita)	Saxifraga bronchialis v vespertina	S. verspertina
Saxifraga 'Elizabethae'	S. 'Carmen' (x elisabethae)	Saxifraga brunoniana	S. brunonis
		Saxifraga caesia h. (x fritschiana)	S. 'Krain'
Saxifraga 'Flowers of Sulphur'	S. 'Schwefelblute'	Saxifraga callosa lingulata	S. callosa
Saxifraga 'General Joffre'	S. 'Marechal Joffre'	Saxifraga callosa v bellardii	S. callosa
Saxifraga 'Geoides'	S. hirsuta ssp paucicrenata	Saxifraga callosa v lantoscana	S. c. ssp c. v australis
		Saxifraga callosa x cochlearis	S. Silver Farreri Group
S. 'Gertie Pritchard'	S. 'Mrs Gertie Pritchard' (x megaseif)	Saxifraga carolinica	S. 'Carniolica'
		Saxifraga catalaunica	S. callosa ssp catalau.
S. 'Glauca' (paniculata v brevifolia)	S. 'Labradorica'	Saxifraga caucasica v desoulavyi	S. desoulavyi
Saxifraga 'Gloriana'	S. 'Godiva' (x gloriana)	Saxifraga chrysospleniifolia	S. rotundifolia ssp chrysospleniifolia
Saxifraga 'Gloriosa' (x gloriana)	S. 'Godiva' (x gloriana)		
Saxifraga 'Grace' (x arendsii)	S. 'Seaspray'	Saxifraga ciliata	Bergenia ciliata
Saxifraga 'Gracilis' (x geum)	S. 'Gracilis' (x polita)	Saxifraga corbariensis	S. fragilis
Saxifraga 'Hirsuta' (x geum)	S. x geum	Saxifraga cortusifolia v fortunei	S. fortunei
Saxifraga 'Irvingii'	S. 'Walter Irving' (x irvingii)	Saxifraga crassifolia	Bergenia crassifolia
		Saxifraga crustata v vochinensis	S. crustata
Saxifraga 'Joy'	S. 'Kaspar Maria Stern berg' (x petraschii)	Saxifraga cuneifolia v capillipes	S. cuneifolia ssp cunei.
		Saxifraga cuscutiformis	S. 'Cuscutiformis' (stolonifera)
Saxifraga 'Juliet'	S. 'Riverslea' (x hornibrookii)	Saxifraga dahurica	S. cuneifolia
		Saxifraga densa	S. cherlerioides
Saxifraga 'Kingii'	S. hypnoides v egemmulosa	Saxifraga exarata pyrenaica	S. androsacea
		Saxifraga Fair Maids of France	S. 'Flore Pleno' (granulata)
S. 'Labradorica' (paniculata)	S. paniculata neogaea		
Saxifraga 'Lady Beatrix Stanley'	S. 'Beatrix Stanley' (x anglica)	Saxifraga federici-augusti	S. frederici-augusti
		S. ferdinandi-coburgi v pravislavii	S.f-coburgi v rhodopea
Saxifraga 'Lutea' (diapensioides)	S. 'Primulina'	S. ferdinandi-coburgi v radoslavoffii	S.f-coburgi v rhodopea
Saxifraga 'Lutea' (diapensioides)	S. 'William Tell'	Saxifraga florulenta	S. callosa
Saxifraga 'Lutea' (marginata)	S. 'Faust' (x borisii)	S. Golden Prague (x pragensis)	S. 'Zlata Praha' (x pragensis)
Saxifraga 'Major Lutea'	S. 'Luteola' (x boydii)		
Saxifraga 'Marshall Joffre'	S. 'Marechal Joffre'	Saxifraga granulata 'Flore Pleno'	S. 'Flore Pleno'
S. 'Minor Glauca' (paniculata)	S. 'Labradorica'	Saxifraga grisebachii	S. frederici-augusta ssp grisebachii
S. 'Minor' (paniculata)	S. paniculata v brevifo.		
S. 'Moonlight Sonata' (x boydii)	S. 'Mondscheinsonate' (x boydii)	Saxifraga grisebachii montenegrina	S. frederici-augusta
		Saxifraga juniperifolia ssp sancta	S. sancta
Saxifraga 'Moonlight'	S. 'Sulphurea' (x boyd.)	S. juniperifolia v macedonica	S. juniperifolia
Saxifraga 'Pixie Alba'	S. 'White Pixie'	Saxifraga latina	S. oppositifolia ssp lati.
Saxifraga 'Plena' (granulata)	S. 'Flore Pleno' (gran.)	Saxifraga lingulata	S. callosa
Saxifraga 'Primulaize'	S. x primulaize	S. longifolia 'Tumbling Waters'	S. 'Tumbling Waters'
Saxifraga 'Purpurea' (fortunei)	S. 'Rubrifolia' (fortun)	Saxifraga Love Me	S. 'Miluj Mne' (x polua.)
Saxifraga 'Sartorii'	S. 'Pygmalion' (x web)	Saxifraga luteoviridis	S. corymbosa
Saxifraga 'Schelleri' (x petraschii)	S. 'White Star' (x petr)	Saxifraga macedonica	S. juniperifolia
Saxifraga 'Schleicheri' (x kellereri)	S. 'Schleicheri' (x land)		

Synonym	Current Name	Synonym	Current Name
Saxifraga marginata v balcanica	S. marg. v rocheliana	Saxifraga Your Kiss	S. 'Tvuj Polibek' (x pol.)
S. marginata v karadzicensis	S. karadzicensis	Saxifraga Your Smile	S. 'Tvuj Usmev' (x pol.)
Saxifraga moschata	S. exarata ssp mosch.	Saxifraga Your Song	S. 'Tvuj Pisen' (x polu.)
Saxifraga oppositifolia x biflora	S. x kochii	Saxifraga Your Success	S. 'Tvuj Uspech' (x pol.)
S. paniculata ssp kolenatiana	S. pa. ssp cartilaginea	Scabiosa 'Butterfly Pink'	S. 'Pink Mist'
Saxifraga paniculata ssp neogaea	S. 'Labradorica'	Scabiosa 'Chile Black'	S. atropurpurea 'Chile Black'
Saxifraga pectinata -Pursh	Luetkia pectinata		
Saxifraga peltata	Darmera peltata	Scabiosa 'Chile Pepper'	S. atropurpurea 'Chilli Pepper'
Saxifraga porophylla v thessalica	S. sempervivum f stenophylla	Scabiosa 'Chile Red'	S. atropurpurea 'Chilli Red'
Saxifraga primuloides	S. 'Primuloides' (umbrosa)	Scabiosa 'Chile Sauce'	S. atropurpurea 'Chilli Sauce'
Saxifraga punctata	S. nelsoniana	Scabiosa alpina -L.	Cephalaria alpina
Saxifraga sancta ssp pseudosancta	S. juniperifolia	Scabiosa arvensis	Knautia arvensis
S. sancta ssp pseud. v macedonica	S. juniperifolia	Scabiosa banatica	S. columbaria
Saxifraga sarmentosa	S. stolonifera	S. caucasica 'Crimson Cushion'	Knautia macedonica 'Crimson Cushion'
Saxifraga sarmentosa 'Tricolor'	S. 'Tricolor' (stolonifera)		
Saxifraga scardica v dalmatica	S. obtusa	Scabiosa gigantea	Cephalaria gigantea
Saxifraga scardica v obtusa	S. obtusa	Scabiosa hirsuta	Knautia arvensis
S. stenophylla ssp stenophylla	S. flagellaris	Scabiosa maritima	S. atropurpurea ssp maritima
Saxifraga thysanodes	Bergenia ciliata		
Saxifraga umbrosa 'Aurea'	S. 'Aureopunctata'	Scabiosa montana	Knautia arvensis
Saxifraga umbrosa 'Primuloides'	S. 'Primuloides' (umb.)	Scabiosa ochroleuca	S. columbaria v ochr.
Saxifraga umbrosa v primuloides	S. 'Primuloides' (umb.)	Scabiosa odora	S. atropurpurea
Saxifraga x apiculata	S. 'Gregor Mendel' (x apiculata)	Scabiosa parnassi	Pterocephalus perennis
Saxifraga x arco-valleyi	S. 'Arco' (x arco-valleyi)	Scabiosa perennis ssp parnassi	Pteroceph. perennis
Saxifraga x biasolettoi	S. 'Phoenix' (x biasolettoi)	Scabiosa polymorpha	Knautia arvensis
		Scabiosa pterocephala	Pteroceph. perennis
Saxifraga x borissii h.	S. 'Sofia'	Scabiosa pyrenaica	S. holosericea
Saxifraga x elegantissima	S. x clibranii	Scabiosa rumelica	Knautia macedonica
Saxifraga x elisabethae h.	S. 'Carmen' (x elisabethae)	Scabiosa succisa	Succisa pratensis
		Scabiosa syriaca	Cephalaria syriaca
Saxifraga x fritschiana h.	S. 'Krain'	Scabiosa tatarica	Cephalaria gigantea
Saxifraga x geuderi	S. 'Eulenspiegel' (x geuderi)	Scadoxus 'Konig Albert'	Haemanthus 'Konig Albert'
Saxifraga x heinrichii h.	S. 'Ernst Heinrich'	Scadoxus natalensis	S. puniceus
Saxifraga x irvingii	S. 'Walter Irving' (x irvingii)	Scaevola 'Blue Wonder'	S. aemula 'Blue Wonder'
Saxifraga x kellereri h.	S. 'Johann Kellerer' (x kellereri)	Scaevola aemula 'Blue Fan'	S. aem. 'Blue Wonder'
		Scaevola arenaria	S. humifusa
Saxifraga x landaueri h.	S. 'Leonore' (x land.)	Scaevola attenuata	S. nitida
Saxifraga x megaseiflora	S.'Robin Hood' (x meg.)	Scaevola brooksiana	S. brookeana
Saxifraga x pectinata	S. 'Krain'	Scaevola decipiens	S. amblyantha
Saxifraga x prosenii h.	S. 'Regina' (x pross.)	Scaevola densevestita	S. ovalifolia
Saxifraga x pseudokotschyi h.	S. 'Denisa' (x pseud.)	Scaevola depressa	S. humifusa
Saxifraga x salmonica h.	S. 'Salomonii'	Scaevola dielsii	S. thesioides
Saxifraga x semmleri	S. 'Martha' (x semml.)	Scaevola fasciculata	Goodenia fasciculata
S. x u. primuloides 'Elliott's Variety'	S. 'Clarence Elloitt'	Scaevola frutescens	S. taccada
Saxifraga Your Day	S. 'Tvuj Den' (x poluanglica)	Scaevola helmsii	Goodenia helmsii
		Scaevola holosericea	S. anchusifolia
		Scaevola koenigii	S. taccada
Saxifraga Your Friend	S. 'Tvuj Pritel' (x polu.)	Scaevola pallida	S. albida
Saxifraga Your Good Fortune	S. 'Tvuj Uspech' (x pol.)	Scaevola repens misapplied	S. paludosa

Synonym	Current Name	Synonym	Current Name
Scaevola saligna	S. aemula	Scirpus acicularis	Eleocharis acicularis
Scaevola scaberula	Coopernookia barbata	Scirpus albomarginatus	Eleoch. quadrangulata
Scaevola sericea	S. taccada	Scirpus caldwellii	Bolboschoenus caldw.
Scaevola striata v depauperata	S. striata	Scirpus capitatus	Eleocharis elliptica
Scaevola suaveolens	S. calendulacea	Scirpus cernuus	Isolepis cernua
Scandix cerefolium	Anthriscus cerefolium	Scirpus cespitosus	Trichophorum cespit.
Scandix nemerosa	Anthriscus sylvestris	Scirpus flavescens	Eleocharis flavescens
Schefflera octophylla	S. heptaphylla	Scirpus holoschoenus	Scirpoides holosch.
Schima argentea	S. wallichii ssp noron hae v superba	Scirpus intermedius -Muhl.	Eleocharis intermedia
		Scirpus kamtschaticus	Eleocharis kamtschati.
Schima khasiana	S. wallichii ssp wallichii v khasiana	Scirpus lacustris	Schoenoplectus lacus.
		Scirpus lacustris 'Spiralis'	Juncus effusus f spir.
Schinus dependens -Ort.	S. polygamus	Scirpus marginatus	Eleocharis quadrangul.
Schisandra grandifl. v cathayensis	S. sphaerandra	Scirpus maritimus	Bolboschoenus marit.
Schisandra grandiflora v rubriflora	S. rubriflora	Scirpus mitratus	Eleocharis kamtschati.
Schivereckia bornmuelleri	S. doerfleri	Scirpus nitidus	Eleocharis nitida
Schizocasia -Schott ex Engl.	Alocasia	Scirpus obtusus	Eleocharis obtusa
Schizocentron	Heterocentron	Scirpus ovatus	Eleocharis ovata
Schizocodon	Shortia	Scirpus palustris	Eleocharis palustris
Schizophragma hydrangeoides 'Brookside Litteleaf'		Scirpus pauciflorus	Eleocharis quinqueflora
Hydrangea anomala ssp petiolaris v cordifolia		Scirpus quadrangulatus	Eleocharis quadrangul.
Schizophragma viburnoides	Pileostegia viburnoides	Scirpus quinqueflorus	Eleocharis quinqueflora
Schizostylis coccinea 'Gigantea'	S. coccinea 'Major'	Scirpus rostellatus	Eleocharis rostellata
Schizostylis coccinea 'Grandiflora'	S. coccinea 'Major'	Scirpus sachalinensis	Eleoch. kamtschatica
Schizostylis coccinea 'Sunset'	S. coccinea 'Sunrise'	Scirpus tabernaemontani	Schoenoplectus lacus tris ssp tabernaemont.
Schizotheca littoralis	Atriplex littoralis		
Schizotheca patula	Atriplex patula	Scirpus tenuis	Eleocharis tenuis
Schlumbergera bridgesii	S. x buckleyi	Scirpus uniglumis	Eleocharis uniglumis
Schmaltzia	Rhus	Sclerotium cocos	Wolfporia cocos
Schollera hispidula	Gaultheria hispidula	Scoliopus bigelovii	S. bigelowii
Scilla 'Tubergeniana'	S. mischtschenkoana	Scolopendrium	Asplenium
Scilla adlamii	Ledebouria cooperi	Scolopendrium officinarum	Asplen. scolopendrium
Scilla amethystina	S. litardierei	Scolopendrium phyllitis	Asplenium scolopendr.
Scilla campanulata	Hyacinthoides hispanica	Scolopendrium scolopendrium	Asplenium scolopendr.
		Scolopendrium vulgare	Asplenium scolopendr.
Scilla chinensis	S. scilloides	Scolymus	Cynara
Scilla cooperi	Ledebouria cooperi	Scopiola sinensis	Atropanthe sinensis
Scilla hispanica	Hyacinthoides hispanic.	Scopolia atropoides	S. carniolica
Scilla italica	Hyacinthoides italica	Scopolia carniolica ssp hladnikiana	S. carn. v brevifolia
Scilla japonica	S. scilloides	Scopolia lucida -J.R. & G.Forst.	Anisodus luridus
Scilla libanotica	Puschkinia scilloides v libanotica	Scopolia sinensis	Atropanthe sinensis
		Scrophularia aquatica	S. auriculata
Scilla non-scripta	Hyacinthoides n-scrip.	S.buergeriana 'Lemon and Lime'mis.	Teucrium viscidum 'Lemon and Lime'
Scilla nutans	Hyacinthoides n-scrip.		
Scilla ovalifolia	Ledebouria ovalifolia	Scrophularia nodosa variegata	S. auriculata 'Variegata'
Scilla pratensis	S. litardierei		
Scilla siberica 'Atrocoerulea'	S. sib. 'Spring Beauty'	Scutellaria canescens	S. incana
Scilla socialis	Ledebouria socialis	Scutellaria epilobiifolia	S. galericulata
Scilla vicentina	Hyacinthoides vicentina	Scutellaria hastata	S. hastifolia
Scilla violacea	Ledebouria socialis	Scutellaria indica v japonica	S. indica v parvifolia
Scilla x allenii	x Chionoscilla allenii	Scutellaria macrantha	S. baicalensis
Scindapsus aureus	Epipremnum aureum	Scutellaria supina	S. alpina
Scindapsus pictus	Epipremnum pictum	Seaforthia elegans	Ptychosperma elegans
Scindapsus pictus 'Argyraeus'	Epipremnum pictum 'Argyraeum'	Securigera	Coronilla
		Securigera varia	Coronilla varia

199

Synonym	Current Name	Synonym	Current Name
Securinega ramiflora	S. suffruticosa		Group
Sedastrum	Sedum	Sedum himalense	Rhodiola 'Keston'
Sedirea japonica	Aerides japonica	Sedum hispanicum glaucum	S. hispanicum v minus
Sedum 'Bronze Queen'	S. lydium	Sedum integrifolium	Rhodiola rosea ssp
Sedum 'Eleanor Fisher'	S. telephium ssp		integrifolia
	ruprechtii	Sedum ishidae	Rhodiola ishidae
Sedum 'Matrona'	S. telephium 'Matrona'	Sedum jaeschkei	S. oreades
Sedum 'Washfield Purple'	S. 'Purple Emperor'	S. kamtschaticum v middendorff.	S. middendorffianum
Sedum 'Weihenstephaner Gold'	S. kamtschaticum v	Sedum kirilovii	Rhodiola kirilovii
	floriferum	Sedum kostovii	S. grisebachii ssp kos.
	'Weihenstephaner Gold'	Sedum lydium 'Aureum'	S. hispanicum v minus
Sedum aggregatum	Orostachys aggregata		'Aureum'
Sedum aizoon 'Aurantiacum'	S. aizoon	Sedum lydium 'Bronze Queen'	S. lydium
	'Euphorbioides'	Sedum maweanum	S. acre v majus
Sedum albescens	S. rupestre f	Sedum maximowiczii	S. aizoon
	purpureum	Sedum murale	S. album ssp
Sedum alboroseum	S. erythrostictum		teretifolium 'Murale'
Sedum album ssp clusianum	S. gypsicola	Sedum nicaeense	S. sediforme
	glanduliferum	Sedum oppositifolium	S. spurium v album
Sedum album v macranthum	S. album 'Chloriticum'	Sedum oreganum 'Procumbens'	S. oreganum ssp tenue
Sedum algidum	S. alsium	Sedum pachyclados	Rhodiola pachyclados
Sedum altissimum	S. sediforme	Sedum pluricaule Rose Carpet	S. plu. 'Rosenteppich'
Sedum amplexicaule	S. tenuifolium	Sedum polytrichoides	Rhodiola komarovii
Sedum anopetalum	S. ochroleucum	Sedum primuloides	Rhodiola primuloides
Sedum anopetalum alpine form	S. ochroleucum ssp	Sedum pruinosum	S. spathulifolium ssp
	montanum		pruinosum
Sedum asiaticum	Rhodiola wallichiana	Sedum quadrifidum	Rhodiola quadrifida
Sedum athoum	S. album	Sedum quinquefarium	S. brevifolium v quinqu.
Sedum atlanticum	S. dasyphyllum ssp	Sedum ramosissimum	Villadia ramosissima
	dasy. v mesatlanticum	Sedum reflexum -L.	S. rupestre -L.
Sedum Autumn Joy	S. 'Herbstfreude'	Sedum retusum	S. obtusatum ssp ret.
Sedum batesii	S. hemsleyanum	Sedum rhodiola	Rhodiola rosea
Sedum beyrichianum h.	S. glaucophyllum	Sedum rosea	Rhodiola rosea
Sedum bithynicum 'Aureum'	S. hispanicum v minus	Sedum rosea v heterodontum	Rhodiola heterodonta
	'Aureum'	Sedum rubroglaucum -Praeger	S. obtusatum
Sedum ciliare	S. spurium	Sedum rubroglaucum mispplied	S. oregonense
Sedum clusianum	S. gypsicola	Sedum ruprechtii	S. telephium ssp rupr.
	glanduliferum	Sedum sarocaule h.	Crassula sarocaulis
Sedum crassipes	Rhodiola wallichiana	Sedum sediforme nicaeense	S. sediforme
Sedum crassularia	Crassula milfordiae	Sedum sibiricum	S. hybridum
Sedum cyaneum h.	S. ewersii v	S. sieboldii 'Foliis Mediovariegatis'	S. sieboldii
	homophylium		'Mediovariegatum'
Sedum dasyphyllum mucronatis	S. dasyphyllum ssp	Sedum sieboldii 'Variegatum'	S. sieboldii
	das. v mesatalanticum		'Mediovariegatum'
Sedum douglasii	S. stenopetalum	Sedum spectabile 'Variegatum'	S. erythrostictum
	'Douglasii'		'Mediovariegatum'
Sedum ellacombeanum	S. kamtschaticum v el.	Sedum spectabile September Glow	S. sp. 'Septemberglut'
Sedum elrodi	S. acre	Sedum spinosum	Orostachys spinosa
Sedum erythrostichum	S. alboroseum	Sedum spurium 'Tricolor'	S. s. 'Variegatum'
Sedum fastigiatum	Rhodiola fastigiata	Sedum spurium Dragon's Blood	S. s. 'Schorbuser Blut'
Sedum floriferum	S. kamtschaticum	Sedum spurium Purple Carpet	S. s. 'Purpurteppich'
Sedum glaucum	S. hispanicum v minus	Sedum stephanii	Rhodiola crassipes v
Sedum hayersii	S. ewersii		stephanii
Sedum heterodontum	Rhodiola heterodonta	Sedum stribrnyi	S. urvillei Stribrnyi Gr.
Sedum hillebrandtii	S. urvillei Hillebrandtii	Sedum telephium 'Abbeydore'	S. fabaria

Synonym	Current Name	Synonym	Current Name
Sedum telephium ssp fabaria	S. fabaria		'White Christmas'
Sedum trollii	Rhodiola trollii	Sempervivum acuminatum	S. tectorum v glaucum
Sedum wallichianum	Rhodiola wallichiana	Sempervivum allionii	Jovibarba allionii
Sedum weinbergii	Graptopetalum	Sempervivum arachnoideum 'Kappa'	S. 'kappa'
	paraguayense	S. arachnoideum 'Laggeri'	S. ar. ssp tomentosum
Sedum yezoense	S. pluricaule	S. arachnoideum ssp doellianum	S. arachnoideum v
Sedum yunnanense	Rhodiola yunnanensis		glabrescens
Seemannia	Gloxinia	S. arachnoideum ssp tomentosum m.	S. x barbulatum
Seguinum -Raf.	Dieffenbachia -Schott		'Hookeri'
Selaginella emmeliana	S. pallescens	Sempervivum arboreum	Aeonium arboreum
Selenicereus chrysocardium	Epiphyllum chrysoc.	Sempervivum arenarium	Jovibarba arenaria
Selinum anethum	Anethum graveolens	Sempervivum arvernense	S. tectorum
Selinum anisum	Pimpinella anisum	Sempervivum balsamiferum	Aeonium balsamiferum
Selinum benthami -not Kurtz	Conioselinum chinense	Sempervivum borisii	S. ciliosum v borisii
Selinum canadense	Conioselinum chinense	S. calcareum 'Monstrosum'	S. c. 'Grigg's Surprise'
Selinum carvi	Carum carvi	S. cantabricum spp guadarramense	S. vicentei ssp paui
Selinum chinense	Conioselinum chinense	Sempervivum comollii	S. x calcaratum
Selinum cicutaria	Anthriscus sylvestris	Sempervivum complanatum	Aeonium tabuliforme
Selinum coriandrum	Coriandrum sativum	Sempervivum densum	S. tectorum
Selinum foeniculum	Foeniculum vulgare	Sempervivum fimbriatum	S. x barbulatum
Selinum graveolens	Apium graveolens	Sempervivum haworthii	Aeonium haworthii
Selinum hookeri	Conioselinum chinense	Sempervivum helveticum	S. montanum
Selinum levisticum	Levisticum officinale	Sempervivum hirtum	Jovibarba hirta
Selinum pacificum	Conioselinum chinense	Sempervivum hueffelii	Jovibarba hueffelii
Selinum petroselinum	Petroselinum cripsum	Sempervivum imbricatum	S. x barbulatum
Selinum podagraria	Aegopodium podagr.	Sempervivum masferreri	Aeonium sedifolium
Selinum sisarum	Sium sisarum	Sempervivum montanum 'Rubrum'	S. 'Red Mountain'
Selinum sphondylium	Heracleum sphondyli.	Sempervivum nobile	Aeonium nobile
Selinum tenuifolium	S. wallichianum	Sempervivum patens	Jovibarba heuffelii
Selinum virosum	Cicuta virosa -L.	Sempervivum reginae	S. reginae-amaliae
Semiaquilegia simulatrix	S. ecalcarata	Sempervivum schlehanii	S. marmoreum
Semiarundinaria murielae	Fargesia murielae	Sempervivum soboliferum	Jovibarba sobolifera
Semiarundinaria nitida	Fargesia nitida	Sempervivum stansfieldii	S. arachnoideum ssp
Semiarundinaria villosa	S. okuboi		tomentosum
Semnanthe	Erepsia		'Stansfieldii'
Sempervivella	Rosularia	Sempervivum webbianum	S. arachnoideum ssp
Sempervivum 'Aureum'	Greenovia aurea		tomentosum
Sempervivum 'Boisseri'	S. tectorum ssp tecto	Senebiera didyma	Coronopus didymus
	rum 'Boisseri'	Senecio 'Gregynog Gold'	Ligularia 'Gregynog
Sempervivum 'Cherry Glow'	Jovibarba hueffelii		Gold'
	'Cherry Glow'	Senecio 'Leonard Cockayne'	Brachyglottis 'Leonard
Sempervivum 'Correvons'	S. 'Aymon Correvon'		Cockayne'
Sempervivum 'Hookeri'	S. x barbulatum	Senecio 'Moira Reid'	Brachyglottis 'Moira
	'Hookeri'		Reid' (Dunedin Group)
Sempervivum 'Lennick's Glory'	S. 'Crispyn'	Senecio 'Sunshine'	Brachyglottis
Sempervivum 'Lloyd Praeger'	S. montanum ssp stiri		'Sunshine' (Dunedin Gr)
	acum 'Lloyd Praeger'	Senecio abrotanifolius v tiroliensis	S. abrotanifolius
Sempervivum 'Malby's Hybrid'	S. 'Reginald Malby'	Senecio angustifolius	S. australis
Sempervivum 'Nigrum'	S. tectorum 'Nigrum'	Senecio angustilobus	S. anethifolius ssp ane.
Sempervivum 'Queen Amalia'	S. reginae-amaliae	Senecio argentinus	S. viravira
Sempervivum 'Rubrifolium'	S. marmoreum ssp	Senecio arguta -(A. Rich.) DC.	S. glomeratus ssp gl.
	marm. 'Rubrifolium'	Senecio argutus	S. glomeratus ssp gl.
S. 'Silberkarneol' misapplied	S. 'Silver Jubilee'	Senecio argutus -A. Rich.	S. evansianus
Sempervivum 'Simonkaianum'	Jovibarba hirta	Senecio atkinsoniae	S. bipinnatrisectus
Sempervivum 'White Christmas'	S. arachnoideum	Senecio aureus	Packera aurea

Synonym	Current Name	Synonym	Current Name
Senecio australis v macrodontus	S. linearifolius v macr.		'Sunshine' (Dunedin Gr)
Senecio bedfordii	Bedfordia arborescens	Senecio ledebourii	Ligularia macrophylla
Senecio bicolor ssp cineraria	S. cineraria	Senecio lessonianus	S. glomeratus
Senecio bidwillii	Brachyglottis bidwillii	Senecio leucostachys	S. viravira
Senecio billardieri	Bedfordia linearis	Senecio ligularia	Ligularia sibirica
Senecio brachyglossus	S. glossanthus	Senecio maritimus	S. cineraria
Senecio brachyglossus v major	S. halophilus	Senecio mikanioides	Delairea odorata
Senecio brevilingueus	S. glossanthus	Senecio minimus v picridioides	S. picridioides
Senecio brunonis	Brachyglottis brunonis	Senecio monroi	Brachyglottis monroi
Senecio buchananii	Brachyglottis buchan.	Senecio muelleri	S. minimus
Senecio cahillii	S. diaschides	Senecio odoratus v longifolius	S. odoratus
Senecio candicans	S. cineraria	Senecio odoratus v obtusifolius	S. odoratus
Senecio capillifolius	S. pinnatifolius v capill.	Senecio odoratus v petiolata	S. hypoleucus
S. carnulentus v angustissimus	S. pinnatifolius v latilobus	Senecio pectinatus v ochroleucus	S. albogilvus
		Senecio pectinatus v pleiocephalus	S. leptocarpus
Senecio chrysanthemoides	Euryops chrysanthem.	Senecio persicifolius	S. linearifolius v macrodontus
Senecio cinerarioides	S. linearifolius v macrodontus	Senecio populifolius	Pericallis appendiculata
Senecio clivorum	Ligularia dentata		
Senecio compactus	Brachyglottis compact.	Senecio przewalskii	Ligularia przewalskii
Senecio cruentus	Pericallis x hybrida	Senecio pusillus	S. glomeratus
Senecio cunninghamii v serratus	S. lanibracteus	Senecio pusillus	S. multicaulis ssp mult.
Senecio dryadeus -Ewart	S. garlandii	Senecio reinholdii	Brachyglottis rotundifolia
Senecio dryadeus -Sieb. ex Spreng.	S. garlandii		
Senecio dryadeus v garlandii	S. garlandii	Senecio richardianus	S. linearifolius v macrodontus
Senecio dryadeus v macrodontus	S. linearifolius v macr.		
Senecio Dunedin Hybrids	Brachyglottis Dunedin Group	Senecio rotundifolia	Brachyglottis rotundif.
		Senecio scapiger	Brachyscome scapige.
Senecio elaeagnifolius	Brachyglottis elaeagni.	Senecio spedenii	Brachyglottis spedenii
Senecio flaccidus	S. biserratus	Senecio stenocephalus	Ligularia stenocephala
Senecio forsteri	Brachyglottis repanda	Senecio takedanus	Tephroseris takedanus
Senecio georgianus	S. helichrysoides	Senecio tanguticus	Sinacalia tangutica
Senecio georgianus v latifolius	S. gawlerensis	Senecio veitchianus	Ligularia veitchiana
Senecio glabrescens	S. quadrirentatus	Senecio werneriifolius	Packera werneriifolius
Senecio glandulosa	S. campylocarpus	Senecio x hybridus	Pericallis x hybridus
Senecio glandulosus	S. quadrirentatus	Senna arborescens	S. surattensis ssp sulfurea
Senecio gracilis	Packera aurea		
Senecio greyi -Hooker	Brachyglottis greyi	Senna artemisoides ssp circinnata	S. circinnata
Senecio greyi misapplied	Brachyglottis 'Sunshine' (Dunedin Gr)	Senna artemisoides ssp glaucifolia	S. glaucifolia
		S. artemisoides ssp hamersleyensis	S. hamersleyensis
Senecio hectoris	Brachyglottis hectoris	Senna artemisoides ssp stricta	S. stricta
Senecio heritieri	Pericallis lanata	Senna artemisoides ssp symonii	S. symonii
Senecio hispidulus v dissectus	S. bathurstianus	S. cardiosperma ssp cuthbertsonii	S. cuthbertsonii
Senecio huntii	Brachyglottis huntii	Senna cardiosperma ssp flexuosa	S. flexuosa
Senecio japonicus	Ligularia japonica	Senna cardiosperma ssp manicula	S. manicula
Senecio kirkii	Brachyglottis kirkii	Senna cardiosperma ssp pilocarina	S. pilocarina
Senecio lautus	S. australis	Senna cardiosperma ssp stowardii	S. stowardii
Senecio lautus ssp alpinus	S. pinnatifolius v alpin.	Senna glauca	S. timorensis
Senecio lautus ssp dissectifolius	S. spanomerus	Senna glutinosa ssp charlesiana	S. charlesiana
Senecio lautus ssp lanceolatus	S. pinnatifolius v serratus	Senna glutinosa ssp ferraria	S. ferraria
		Senna obtusa -Clos	S. candolleana
Senecio lautus ssp maritimus	S. pinnatifolius v mar.	Senna odorata	S. barronfieldii
Senecio lautus v capillifolius	S. pinnatifolius v capil.	Senna speciosa	S. surattensis
Senecio laxifolius - Buchanan	Brachyglottis laxifolia	Senna sulfurea	S. surattensis ssp sulf.
Senecio laxifolius h.	Brachyglottis	Senna surattensis ssp retusa	S. gaudichaudii

Synonym	Current Name	Synonym	Current Name
Senna tomentosa	S. multiglandulosa	Sieversia triflora	Geum triflorum
Senniella spongiosa	Atriplex spongiosa	Sigmatostalix radicans	Ornithophora radicans
Senniella spongiosa f microcarpa	Atriplex holocarpa	Silene acaulis 'Pedunculata'	S. acaulis ssp acaulis
Senniella spongiosa v amoena	Atriplex spongiosa	Silene acaulis ssp elongata	S. acaulis ssp acaulis
Senniella spongiosa v xylocarpa	Atriplex holocarpa	Silene acaulis ssp exscapa	S. acaulis ssp bryoides
Sequoia gigantea -(Lindl). Decne.	Sequoiadendron gigant.	Silene alba	S. latifolia
Sequoia glyptostroboides	Metasequoia glyptos.	Silene atropurpurea	Lychnis viscaria ssp
Sequoia sempervirens 'Albospica'	Sequoia s. 'Adpressa'		atropurpurea
Sequoia wellingtonia -Seem.	Sequoiadendron gigant.	Silene dioica 'Compacta'	S. dioica 'Minikin'
Serangium -Wood ex Salisb.	Monstera -Adans.	Silene dioica 'Rubra Plena'	S. dioica 'Flore Pleno'
Serapias helleborine	Epipactis helleborine	Silene dioica 'Variegata'	S. d. 'Graham's Delight'
Serapias latifolia	Epipactis helleborine	Silene diurna	S. dioica
Serenoa serrulata	S. repens	Silene githago	Agrostemma githago
Serissa foetida	S. japonica	Silene inflata	S. vulgaris
Serjania australis	Dodonaea pinnata	Silene ingramii	S. hookeri Ingramii Gr.
Serpicula canadensis	Elodea canadensis	Silene maritima	S. uniflora
Serpicula occidentalis	Elodea nuttallii	Silene maritima 'Flore Pleno'	S. uniflora 'Robin
Serpicula verticillata	Elodea nuttallii		Whitebreast'
Serratula arvensis	Cirsium arvense	Silene multifida	S. fimbriata
Serratula ciliata	Cirsium arvense	Silene orientalis	S. compacta
Serratula incana	Cirsium arvense	Silene pumilio	Saponaria pumilio
Serratula lanata	Cirsium arvense	Silene quadrifida	S. pusilla
Serratula setosa	Cirsium setosum	Silene rubra	S. dioica
Serratula shawii	S. seoanei	Silene rubra 'Flore Pleno'	S. dioica 'Flore Pleno'
Seseli aegopodium	Aegopodium	Silene schafta 'Abbotswood'	Lychnis x walkeri
	podagraria		'Abbotswood Rose'
Seseli carvi	Carum carvi	Silene sieboldii	Lychnis coronata v sie.
Seseli foeniculum	Foeniculum vulgare	Silene uniflora 'Alba Plena'	S.u.'Robin Whitebreast'
Seseli graveolens	Apium graveolens	Silene uniflora 'Flore Pleno'	S.u.'Robin Whitebreast'
Seseli podagraria	Aegopodium podagr.	Silene uniflora 'Variegata'	S. uniflora 'Druett's
Seseli sisarum	Sium sisarum		Variegated'
Sesleria caerulea ssp calcarea	S. albicans	Silene uniflora Weisskehlchen	S.u.'Robin Whitebreast'
Sesleria cylindrica	S. argentea	Silene vulgaris ssp alpina	S. u. ssp prostrata
Setachna cyanus	Centaurea cyanus	Silene vulgaris ssp maritima	S. uniflora
Setachna fimbriata	Centaurea jacea	S. v. ssp maritima 'Flore Pleno'	S.u.'Robin Whitebreast'
Setachna montana	Centaurea montana	Silene wallichiana	S. vulgaris
Setachna nigra	Centaurea nigra	Silene x arkwrightii	Lychnis x arkwrightii
Setcreasea	Tradescantia	Silphiodsperma perpusillum	Brachyscome perpusil.
Setcreasea purpurea	Tradescantia pallida	Silphiosperma glandulosum	Brachyscome glandul.
	'Purpurea'	Silphium solidaginoides	Heliopsis helianthoides
Setcreasea striata	Callisia elegans	Simaba quassioides -D.Don	Picrasma quassioides
Shawia avicennifolia -Raoul	Oleria avicennifolia	Simmondsia californica	S. chinensis
Shawia hygrophila	Olearia hygrophila	Simplocarpus -Ledeb.	Symplocarpus
Shawia paniculata -J.R. & G.Forst.	Olearia paniculata	Sinapsis juncea	Brassica juncea
Sibiraea altaiensis	S. laevigata	Sinapsis muralis	Diplotaxis muralis
Sida abutilon	Abutilon theophrasti	Sinapsis nigra	Brassica nigra
Sida picta	Abutilon pictum	Sinarundinaria anceps	Yushania anceps
Sida vitifolia -Cav.	Abutilon vitifolium	Sinarundinaria jaunsarensis	Yushania anceps
Sideritis taurica	S. syriaca	Sinarundinaria maling	Yushania maling
Sideroxylon lanuginosum	Bumelia lanuginosa	Sinarundinaria murieliae	Fargesia murieliae
Sideroxylon lycioides -L.	Bumelia lycioides	Sinarundinaria nitida -(Mitf.) Nakai	Fargesia nitida
Sieversia ciliata	Geum triflorum	Sinningia leucotricha	S. canescens
Sieversia grisea	Geum triflorum	Sinobambusa tootsik 'Variegata'	S. tootsik 'Albostriata'
Sieversia paradoxa -D.Don	Fallugia paradoxa	Sinocalamus giganteus	Dendrocalamus gigant.
Sieversia pentapetala	Geum pentapetalum	Siphonosmanthus delavayi	Osmanthus delavayi

Synonym	Current Name	Synonym	Current Name
Siphonosmanthus suavis	Osmanthus suavis	Skimmia rubella	S. japonica 'Rubella'
Sison ammi	Trachyspermum ammi	Skimmia x foremannii h.	S. japonica 'Veitchii'
Sison anisum	Pimpinella anisum	Smilacina alpina	Clintonia udensis
Sison podagraria	Aegopodium podagr.	Smilacina borealis	Clintonia borealis
Sison ruta	Apium graveolens	Smilax asparagoides 'Nanus'	Asparagus aspar.
Sison sisarum	Sium siarum		'Myrtifolius'
Sisymbrium alliaria	Alliaria petiolata	Smilax officinalis	S. regelii
Sisymbrium barbarea	Barbarea vulgaris	Smilax ornata	S. regelii
Sisymbrium erucastrum	Diplotaxis muralis	Smyrnium laterale	Apium graveolens
Sisymbrium murale	Diplotaxis muralis	Solandra grandiflora misapplied	S. maxima
Sisymbrium tanacetifolium	Huguennia tanacetifolia	Solandra hartwegii	S. maxima
Sisymbrium thalianum	Arabidopsis thalianum	Solandra nitida	S. maxima
Sisyrinchium 'Ball's Mauve'	S. 'E.K.Balls'	Solanum assimile	S. dulcamara
Sisyrinchium 'May Snow'	S. idahoense 'Album'	Solanum coronopus	Chamaesaracha coron.
Sisyrinchium 'North Star'	S. 'Pole Star'	Solanum crispum 'Autumnale'	S. crispum 'Glasnevin'
Sisyrinchium bellum h.	S. idahoense v bellum	Solanum jasminoides	S. laxum
Sisyrinchium bermudianum -L.	S. angustifolium -Mill.	Solanum topiro	S. sessiliflorum
Sisyrinchium bermudianum 'Album'	S. graminoides 'Album'	Soldanella montana ssp hungarica	S. hungarica
Sisyrinchium birameun	S. graminoides	Soldiago axillaris	S. caesia
Sisyrinchium boreale	S. californicum	Soleirolia soleirolii 'Argentea'	S. soleirolii 'Variegata'
Sisyrinchium brachypus	S. cal. Brachypus Gr.	Soleirolia soleirolii 'Golden Queen'	S. soleirolii 'Aurea'
Sisyrinchium coeruleum	Gelasine coerulea	Soleirolia soleirolii 'Silver Queen'	S. soleirolii 'Variegata'
Sisyrinchium cuspidatum	S. arenarium	Solenomelus chilensis	S. pedunculatus
Sisyrinchium douglasii	Olsynium douglasii	Solenopsis axillaris	Isotoma axillaris
Sisyrinchium filifolium	Olsynium filifolium	Solenostemon thyrsoideus	Plectranthus thyrsoid.
Sisyrinchium grandiflorum	Olsynium douglasii	Solidago 'Golden Fleece'	S. sphacelata 'Golden
Sisyrinchium hieraciifolium	Erysimum hieraciifoli.		Fleece'
Sisyrinchium idahoense 'May Snow'	S. idahoense 'Album'	Solidago 'Golden Rays'	S. 'Goldstrahl'
Sisyrinchium iridifolium	S. micranthum	Solidago 'Golden Thumb'	S. 'Queenie'
Sisyrinchium junceum	Olsynium junceum	Solidago 'Lemore'	x Solidaster luteus
Sisyrinchium lutescens	S. striatum		'Lemore'
Sisyrinchium macounii	S. idahoense	Solidago altissima	S. canadensis v scabra
Sisyrinchium scabrum	S. chilense	Solidago Babygold	S. 'Goldkind'
Sisyrinchium striatum 'Variegatum'	S. striatum 'Aunt May'	Solidago brachystachys	S. cutleri
Sisyrinchium x anceps	S. angustifolium -Miller	Solidago dumetorum	S. gigantea
Sium angustifolium	Berula erecta	Solidago Golden Baby	S. 'Goldkind'
Sium apium	Apium graveolens	Solidago Goldzwerg	S. 'Golden Dwarf'
Sium carum	Carum carvi	Solidago hybrida	x Solidaster luteus
Sium carvi	Carum carvi	Solidago latifolia	S. canadensis
Sium cicuta	Cicuta virosa -L.	Solidago latifolia	S. flexicaulis
Sium erectum	Berula erecta	Solidago minutissima	S. virgaurea ssp
Sium graveolens	Apium graveolens		alpestris v minutissima
Sium podagraria	Aegopodium podagr.	Solidago pitcheri	S. gigantea
Sium triternatum	Angelica acutiloba	Solidago Strahlenkrone	S. 'Crown of Rays'
Skimmia 'Fisheri'	S. japonica 'Veitchii'	Solidago virgaurea v cambrica	S. virgaurea v minuta
Skimmia fortunei	S. jap. ssp reevesiana	Solidago vulgaris 'Variegata'	S. virg. 'Variegata'
Skimmia japonica 'Alba'	S. j. 'Wakehurst White'	Solidaster luteus	x Solidaster luteus
Skimmia japonica 'Foremannii'	S. japonica 'Veitchii'	Sollya drummondii -Morr.	Billardiera drummondii
Skimmia japonica 'Fragrant Cloud'	S. japonica 'Fragrans'	Sollya erecta	Billardiera heterohylla
Skimmia japonica 'Fructu Albo'	S. j. 'Wakehurst White'	Sollya fusiformis -Payer	Billardiera fusiformis
Skimmia japonica v repens	S. jap. v intermedia	Sollya heterophylla	Billardiera heterohylla
Skimmia laureola 'Fragrant Cloud'	S. japonica 'Fragrans'	Sollya linearis	Billardiera fusiformis
Skimmia melanocarpa h.	S. x confusa	Sollya parviflora	Billardiera drummondii
Skimmia reevesiana	S. jap. ssp reevesiana	Sollya salicifolia	Billardiera fusiformis
Skimmia rogersii	S. jap.Rogersii Group	Sonchus alpinus	Cicerbita alpina

Synonym	Current Name	Synonym	Current Name
Sonchus biennis	Lactuca biennis	Sorbus hybrida v meinichii	S. meinichii
Sonchus canadensis	Lactuca canadensis	Sorbus lanata h.	S. vestita
Sophora kentukea	Cladastris kentukea	Sorbus matsumurana misapplied	S. commixta
Sophora platycarpa -Maxim.	Cladrastis platycarpa	Sorbus microcarpa	S. americana
Sophora prostrata misapplied	S. 'Little Baby'	Sorbus moravica 'Laciniata'	S. aucup. 'Beissneri'
Sophora tetraptera v microphylla	S. microphylla	Sorbus pekinensis	S. reticulata ssp pekin.
Sophora tetraptera v prostrata	S. prostrata -Buch.	Sorbus pinnatifida 'Gibbsii'	S. hybrida 'Gibbsii'
Sophora viciifolia -Hance	S. davidii	Sorbus pohuashanensis misapplied	S. x kewensis
Sophronitis grandiflora	S. coccinea	Sorbus poteriifolia h.	S. sp McLaren D84
Sorbaria aitchisonii	S. tomentosa v angustifolia	Sorbus prattii f subarachnoidea	S. prattii
		Sorbus prattii misapplied	S. munda
Sorbaria arborea	S. kirilowii	Sorbus prattii v tatsienensis	S. prattii
Sorbaria lindleyana	S. tomentosa	Sorbus pygmaea h.	S. poterifolia
Sorbus 'Embley'	S. commixta 'Embley'	Sorbus reflexipetala	S. commixta
Sorbus 'Fastigiata'	S. aucuparia 'Fastigiata'	Sorbus rehderiana misapplied	S. aucuparia
		Sorbus rufoferruginea	S. commixta v rufofer.
Sorbus 'Fastigiata'	S. thuringiaca 'Fastigiata'	Sorbus salicifolia -(Myrin) Hedl.	S. rupicola
		Sorbus sargentiana warleyensis h.	S. pohuashanensis
Sorbus 'Golden Wonder'	S. 'Lombarts Golden Wonder'	Sorbus scopulina misapplied	S. aucup. 'Fastigiata'
		Sorbus sp. KW 21127	S. wardii
Sorbus 'Mitchellii'	S. thibetica 'John Mitchell'	Sorbus sp. Lowndes	S. ursina
		Sorbus umbellata v cretica	S. graeca
Sorbus americana 'Nana'	S. aucup. 'Fastigiata'	Sorbus ursina	S. foliolosa
Sorbus americana erecta	S. decora	Sorbus vilmorinii	S. 'Pink Pearl'
Sorbus aria 'Decaisneana'	S. aria 'Majestica'	Sorbus x confusa	S. x vagensis
Sorbus aria 'Mitchellii'	S. thibetica 'John Mitchell'	Sorbus zahlbruckneri h.	S. alnifolia
		Sorghastrum avenaceum	S. nutans
Sorbus aria v salicifolia	S. rupicola	Sorghum saccaratum	S. bicolor
Sorbus arionioides	S. caloneura	Sorghum vulgare	S. bicolor
Sorbus aucuparia 'Dulcis'	S. aucuparia 'Edulis'	Souliea	Actaea
Sorbus aucuparia 'Fifeana'	S. auc. 'Fructo Luteo'		S. fragrans ssp grand.
Sorbus aucuparia 'Laciniata'	S. auc. 'Aspleniifolia'	Sparaxis grandiflora	Dierama pulcherrimum
Sorbus aucuparia 'Moravica'	S. aucuparia 'Edulis'	Sparaxis pulcherrima	
Sorbus aucuparia 'Rossica'	S. aucuparia v edulis 'Rossica Major'	Sparganium minimum	S. natans
		Sparganium ramosum	S. erectum
Sorbus aucuparia 'Xanthocarpa'	S. auc. v xanthocarpa	Sparmannia	Sparrmannia
Sorbus aucuparia pluripinnata	S. scalaris	Sparmannia africana 'Plena'	Sparrmannia africana 'Flore Pleno'
Sorbus conradinae -Koehne	S. esserteauana		
Sorbus conradinae misapplied	S. pohuashanensis	Sparrmannia palmata	S. ricinocarpa
Sorbus cuspidata	S. vestita	Spartina cynosuroides	S. pectinata
Sorbus decora v nana	S. aucup. 'Fastigiata'	Spartina michauxiana	S. pectinata
Sorbus decurrens	S. x thuringiaca 'Decurrens'	Spartina michauxii	S. pectinata
		Spartina pectinata 'Aureovariegata'	S. pectinata 'Aureomarginata'
Sorbus discolor misapplied	S. commixta		
Sorbus domestica 'Maliformis'	S. dom. v pomifera	Spartium aetnense -Bivona	Genista aetnensis
Sorbus domestica 'Pyriformis'	S. dom. v pyrifera	Spartium cinereum -Vill.	Genista cinerea
Sorbus fenneca -(Klam) Fries	S. hybrida -L.	Spartium complicatum -L.	Adenocarpus complic.
Sorbus fruticosa 'Koehneana'	S. koehneana	Spartium decumbens -Durande	Cytisus decumbens
Sorbus glabra -(Thunb.) Zab.	Photinia glabra	Spartium grandiflorum -Brot.	Cytisus grandiflorus
Sorbus glabrescens	S. hupehensis	Spartium horridum -Vahl	Genista horrida
Sorbus hupehensis 'November Pink'	S. hup. 'Pink Pagoda'	Spartium monospermum -L.	Retama monosperma
Sorbus hupehensis 'Rosea'	S. hupehensis v obtusa	Spartium multiflorum -Ait.	Cytisus multiflorus
Sorbus hybrida 'Fastigiata'	S. x thuringiaca 'Fastigiata'	Spartium radiatum -L.	Genista radiata
		Spartium scoparium -L.	Cytisus scoparius
Sorbus hybrida misapplied	S. x thuringiaca	Spartium sphaerocarpon -L.	Genista sphaerocarpa
		Spartium supranubium -L.f.	C. supranubius

Synonym	Current Name	Synonym	Current Name
Spartium virgatum -Ait.	Genista tenera	Spiraea laevigata -L.	Sibiraea laevigata
Spartocytisus	Cytisus	Spiraea lancifolia	S. decumbens ssp
Spartocytisus nubigenus	Cytisus supranubius		tomentosa
Spathipapppus	Tanacetum	Spiraea lindleyana	Sorbaria tomentosa
Spathiphyllopsis -Tijsm. & Binn.	Spathiphyllum -Schott	Spiraea menziesii	S. douglasii ssp menz.
Spathocarpus -Post & Kuntze	Spathicarpa -Hook.	Spiraea menziesii 'Triumphans'	S. x billardii
Spathodea nilotica	S. africana		'Triumphans'
Spathyema foetida	Symplocarpus foetidus	Spiraea millefolium -Torr.	Chamaebatiaria millef.
Spathyema-Raf.	Symplocarpus	S. nipponica v tosaensis misapplied	S. nip. 'Snowmound'
Specularia americana	Campanula americana	Spiraea opulifolia -L.	Physocarpus opulif.
Specularia speculum-veneris	Legousia speculum-ve.	Spiraea palmata	Filipendula palmata
Speirantha gardenii	S. convallarioides	Spiraea palmata elegans	Filipendula purpurea
Sphacele	Lepechinia		'Elegans'
Sphacele campanulata	Lepechinia	Spiraea pectinata	Luetkea pectinata
	chamaedryoides	Spiraea prunifolia 'Plena'	S. prunifolia
Sphaeralcea umbellata	Phymosia umbellata	Spiraea prunifolia f simplicilora	S. prunifolia
Sphaerium lacryma	Coix lacryma-jobi	Spiraea reevesiana -Lindl.	S. cantoniensis
Sphaeromeria argentea	Tanacetum nuttallii	Spiraea roseata	S. douglasii
Sphaeropteris	Cyathea	Spiraea salicifolia v latifolia -Ait.	S. latifolia
Sphaeropteris excelsa	Cyathea brownii	Spiraea sorbifolia	Sorbaria sorbifolia
Sphincterostigma -Schott	Philodendron -Schott	Spiraea splendens -Baumann	S. densiflora v splend.
Spicanta acuminata	Blechnum norfolkianum	Spiraea thunbergii 'Mellow Yellow'	S. thunbergii 'Ogon'
Spilanthes acmella	Acmella oleraccea	Spiraea trichicarpa 'Snow White'	S. 'Snow White'
Spilanthes oleracea	Acmella oleraccea	Spiraea trifoliata	Gillenia trifoliata
Spiloxene capensis	Hypoxis capensis	Spiraea ulmaria	Filipendula ulmaria
Spinovitis davidii -Carr.	Vitis davidii	Spiraea venusta 'Magnifica'	Filipendula rubra
Spiraea 'Superba'	S. x foxii		'Venusta'
Spiraea aitchisonii	Sorbaria tomentosa v	Spiraea x arguta 'Bridal Wreath'	S. 'Arguta'
	angustifolia	Spiraea x arguta 'Compacta'	S. x cinerea
Spiraea albiflora	S. japonica v albiflora	Spiraea x arguta 'Nana'	S. x cinerea
Spiraea arborea	Sorbaria kirilowii	Spiraea x billardii 'Triumphans'	S. x pseudosalicifolia
Spiraea ariaefolia -Sm.	Holodiscus discolor v		'Triumphans'
	ariifolius	Spiraea x bumalda	S. japonica 'Bumalda'
Spiraea aruncus	Aruncus dioicus	S. x bumalda 'Anthony Waterer'	S. j. 'Anthony Waterer'
Spiraea bracteata -Zab.	S. nipponica	Spiraea x bumalda 'Goldflame'	S. japonica 'Goldflame'
Spiraea bullata	S. japonica 'Bullata'	Spiraea x bumalda 'Wulfenii'	S. japonica 'Walluf'
Spiraea caespitosa	Petrophytum caespito.	Spiraea x margaritae -Zab.	S. 'Margaritae'
Spiraea callosa 'Alba'	S. japonica v albiflora	Spiraea x nobleana -Hook.	S. x sanssouciana
Spiraea camtschatica	Filipendula palmata		'Nobleana'
Spiraea cantoniensis 'Lanceata'	S. canton. 'Flore Pleno'	Spiraea x syringiflora -Lemoine	S. x semperflorens
Spiraea confusa -Reg. & Koernicke	S. media		'Syringiflora'
Spiraea crispifolia	S. japonica 'Bullata'	Spiranthes constricta	S. cernua
Spiraea discolor -Pursh	Holodiscus discolor	Spironema fragrans	Callisia fragrans
Spiraea dumosa -Nutt.	Holodiscus dumosus	Spirospatha -Raf.	Homalomena -Schott
Spiraea filipendula	Filipendula vulgaris	Sponia occidentalis	Celtis occidentalis
Spiraea gigantea h.	Filipendula palmata	Sportella atalantioides -Hance	Pyracantha atalant.
Spiraea grandiflora -not Sweet	Exochorda racemosa	Spraguea multiceps	S. umbellata
Spiraea hacquetii -Fenzl & K.Koch	S. decumbens ssp	Spyridium rotundifolium	Pomaderris rotundifo.
	tomentosa	Stachyrus lancifolius -Koidz	S. praecox v
Spiraea hendersonii -(Canby) Piper	Petrophytum henders.		matsuzakii
Spiraea japonica 'Alba'	S. japonica v albiflora	Stachys 'Primrose Heron'	S. byzantina 'Primrose
Spiraea japonica 'Alpina'	S. japonica 'Nana'		Heron'
Spiraea japonica 'Nyewoods'	S. japonica 'Nana'	Stachys 'Silver Carpet'	S. byz. 'Silver Carpet'
Spiraea japonica 'Shiburi'	S. japonica v albiflora	Stachys aethiopica 'Danielle'	S. thunbergii 'Danielle'
Spiraea japonica 'Shirobana'	S. japonica v albiflora	Stachys betonica	S. officinalis

Synonym	Current Name	Synonym	Current Name
S. byz.a 'Countess Helen von Stein'	S. byzantina 'Big Ears'	Stenolobium stans	Tecoma stans
Stachys byzantina 'Sheila McQueen'	S. byz. 'Cotton Boll'	Stenomesson incarnatum	S. variegatum
Stachys byzantina 'Variegata'	S. b. 'Striped Phantom'	Stenophragma thaliana	Arabidopsis thalianum
Stachys byzantina gold-leaved	S. b. 'Primrose Heron'	Stenurus -Salisb.	Biarum -Schott
Stachys byzantina large-leaved	S. byzantina 'Big Ears'	Stephanandra flexuosa	S. incisa 'Crispa'
Stachys densiflora	S. monieri	Stephanandra incisa 'Prostrata'	S. incisa 'Crispa'
Stachys foeniculum	Agastache foeniculum	Stephanotis jasminoides	S. floribunda
Stachys grandiflora	S. macrantha	Sterculia acerifolia	Brachychiton acericif.
Stachys italica	S. cretica	Sterculia caudata	Brachyc. diversifolia
Stachys lanata	S. byzantina	Sterculia decipiens	Brachychiton diversif.
Stachys macrantha 'Hummelo'	S. monieri 'Hummelo'	Sterculia discolor	Brachychiton discolor
Stachys maeotica	S. palustris -L.	Sterculia diversifolia	Brachyc. populneus
Stachys mexicana misapplied	S. thunbergii	Sterculia diversifolia v occidentalis	Brachychiton gregorii
Stachys monieri 'Hummelo'	S. officinalis	Sterculia garrawayae	Brachyc. garrawayae
Stachys monieri 'Saharan Pink'	S. off. 'Saharan Pink'	Sterculia gregorii	Brachychiton gregorii
Stachys monieri misapplied	S. officinalis	Sterculia incana	Brachychiton incana
Stachys nivea	S. discolor	Sterculia lurida	Brachychiton discolor
Stachys olympica	S. byzantina	Sterculia paradoxa	Brachychiton parado.
Stachys spicata	S. macrantha	Sterculia platanifolia -L.f.	Firmiana simplex
Stachys tuberifera	S. affinis	Sterculia ramiflora	Brachychiton parad.
Stachys x ambigua	S. officinalis	Sterculia tuberculata	Brachychiton tuberc.
Stachyurus japonicus -Steud	S. praecox	Sterculia viridiflora	Brachychiton viridif.
Stapelia europaea	Caralluma europaea	Sterculia viscidula	Brachychiton viscidul.
Stapelia flavirostris	S. grandiflora	Sterculia vitifolia	Brachychiton vitifolius
Stapelia nobilis	S. gigantea	Stereoxylon pulverulentum	Escallonia pulverulenta
Stapelia variegata	Orbea variegata	Stereoxylon revolutum	Escallonia revoluta
Staphylea 'Hessei'	S. colchica 'Hessei'	Sterioglossa humilis	Brachyscome
Staphylea colchica 'Coulombieri'	S. x coulombieri		diversifolia
Staphylea trifoliata -Marsh.	S. trifolia -L.	Sternbergia macrantha	S. clusiana
Staphylea x elegans -Zab.	S. x coulombieri	Steroglossa rigidula	Brachyscome rigidula
Statice	Limonium	Stewartia 'Korean Splendor'	S. pseudocamellia
Statice armeria	Armeria maritima		Koreana Group
Statice bellidifolia	Limonium bellidifolium	Stewartia gemmata -Chien & Cheng	S. sinensis
Statice maritima	Armeria maritima	Stewartia koreana	S. pseudocamellia
Statice minuta	Limonium minutum		Koreana Group
Statice spicata	Psylliostachys spicata	Stewartia pentagyna -L'Herit	S. ovata
Statice suworowii	Psylliostachys suwor.	S. pseudocamellia v koreana	S. pseudocamellia
Stauntonia latifolia -(Wall). Wall	Holboellia latifolia		Koreana Group
Stauromatum -Endl.	Typhonium -Schott	Stipa arundinacea	Calamagrostis arundin.
Steetzia pannosa	Olearia pannosa	Stipa brachytricha	Calamagrostis brachy.
Stegania fluviatilis	Blechnum fluviatile	Stipa hymenoides	Achnatherum hymenoi.
Stegania lanceolata	Blechnum norfolkianum	Stipa lasiagrostis	S. calamagrostis
Stegania minor	Blechnum minus	Stipa pulcherrima f nudicostata	S. barbata
Steironema ciliata	Lysimachia ciliata	Stipa splendens misapplied	S. calamagrostis
Stellaria aquatica	Myosoton aquaticum	Stipa stenophylla	S. tirsa
Stellaria serpyllifolia	Arenaria serpyllifolia	Stipa tenuifolia misapplied	S. tenuissima
Stellaria tomentosa	Cerastium tomentosum	Stizolobium pruriens	Mucuna pruriens
Stenanthium angustifolium	S. gramineum	Stobaea purpurea	Berkheya purpurea
Stenocarpus 'Top End'	S. verticis	Stoechas dentata -(L.) Mill.	Lavendula denata -L.
Stenocarpus concolor	S. salignus	Stokesia cyanea	S. laevis
Stenocarpus cunninghamii -Hook.	S. sinuatus	Stransvaesia	Photinia
Stenocarpus cunninghamii -R. Br.	S. acacioides	Stranvaesia davidiana	Photinia davidiana
Stenocarpus moorei	S. sinuatus	Stranvaesia davidiana v salicifolia	Photinia davidiana
Stenocarpus salignus v acacioides	S. acacioides		Salicifolia Group
Stenochilus denticulatus	Eremophila denticulata	Stranvaesia davidiana v undulata	Photinia d. v undulata

Synonym	Current Name	Synonym	Current Name
Stranvaesia nussia -(D.Don) Decne.	Photinia nussia	Swida monbeigii -(Hemsl.) Sojak	Cornus monbeigii
Stranvaesia undulata -Decne.	Photinia d. v undulata	Swida oblonga -(Wall.) Sojak	Cornus oblonga - Wall.
Strelitzia reginae 'Pygmaea'	S. reginae 'Humilis'	Swida paucinervis -(Hance) Sojak	Cornus paucinervis
Strelitzia reginae v juncea	S. juncea	Swida racemosa -(Lam.) Moldenke	Cornus racemosa
Strepsanthera -Raf.	Anthurium -Schott	Swida rugosa -(Lam.) Rydb.	Cornus rugosa -Lam.
Streptanthera cuprea	Sparaxis elegans	Swida sanguinea -(L.) Opiz	Cornus sanguinea -L.
Streptanthera elegans	Sparaxis elegans	Swida stolonifera -(Michx.) Rydb.	Cornus stolonifera
Streptocarpella	Streptocarpus	Swida walteri -(Wanger.) Sojak	Cornus walteri
Streptocarpus 'Upstart'	S. 'Blue Upstart'	Syagrus weddelliana	Lytocaryum weddelian.
Strobilanthes atropurpurea -Nees	S. wallichii	Sycopsis orbiculatus 'Variegatus'	S. o. 'Foliis Variegatis'
St. atropurpurea misapplied	S. attenuata	Sycopsis rivularis	S. albus v laevigatus
Strobilanthes cusia	Baphicacanthus cusia	Sycopsis tutcheri	Distylium racemosum
Strobilanthes flaccidifolius	Baphicacanthus cusia		tutcheri
Stromanthe amabilis	Ctenanthe amabilis	Symphoria albus	Symphoricarpos albus
Stromanthe lutea	S. jacquinii	Symphoria conglomerata	Symphoric. orbiculatus
Strophocaulos arvensis	Convolvulus arvensis	Symphoria elongata	Symphoricarpos albus
Struthiopteris germanica	Matteuccia	Symphoria glomerata	Symphoric. orbiculatus
	struthiopteris	Symphoria heterophylla	Symphoricarpos albus
Struthiopteris niponica	Blechnum niponicum	Symphoria parviflora	Symphoric. orbiculatus
Struthiopteris pennsylvanica	Matteuccia struthiopt.	Symphoria racemosa	Symphoricarpos albus
Struthiopteris pensylvanica	Matt. struthiopteris	Symphoricarpos albus 'Variegatus'	S. albus 'Taff's White'
Struthiopteris spicant	Blechnum spicant	Symphoricarpos humilis	S. albus
Stuartia	Stewartia	S. orbiculatus 'Albovariegatus'	S. orbiculatus 'Taff's
Styluris banksii	Grevillea banksii		Silver Edge'
Styphelia colensoi	Leucopogon colensoi	S. orbiculatus 'Argenteovariegatus'	S. orbiculatus 'Taff's
Styrax japonicus 'Roseus'	S. jap. Benibana Group		Silver Edge'
Styrax serrulata	S. dasyantha v	Symphoricarpos orbiculatus 'Bowles'	Golden Variegated'
	cinerascens		S. o. 'Foliis Variegatis'
Suaeda fruticosa -Auct.	S. vera	S. orbiculatus 'Variegatus'	S. o. 'Foliis Variegatis'
Suaeda heteroptera	S. salsa	Symphoricarpos pauciflorus	S. albus
Suaeda ramosissima	S. nigra	Symphoricarpos racemosus	S. albus
Suaeda suffrutescens	S. nigra	Symphoricarpos racemosus -Michx	S. albus
Submatucana aurantiaca	Cleistocactus aurantia.	Symphoricarpos rivularis	S. albus v laevigatus
Sulcorebutia	Rebutia	Symphoricarpos vulgaris -Michx	S. orbiculatus
Sulcorebutia arenacea	Rebutia arenacea	Symphyandra asiatica	Hanabusaya asiatica
Sulcorebutia rauschii	Rebutia rauschii	Symphyandra pendula alba	S. pendula
Sulcorebutia tiraquensis	Rebutia tiraquensis	Symphyotrichum	Aster
Sutera jurassica	Jamesbrittenia jurass.	Symphytum 'Jubilee'	S. 'Goldsmith'
Suttonia australis -A.Rich	Myrsine australis	Symphytum 'Mereworth'	S. uplandicum
Suttonia chathmanica	Myrsine chathmanica		'Mereworth'
Suttonia nummularia -(Hook.f.) Mez	Myrsine nummularia	Symphytum 'Roseum'	S. 'Hidcote Pink'
Swainsonia	Swainsona	Symphytum armeniacum	S. asperum
Swammerdamia antennaria -DC.	Ozothamnus antennaria	Symphytum asperrimum	S. x uplandicum
Swida alba -(L.) Opiz	Cornus alba -L.	Symphytum bohemicum	S. officinale
Swida alternifolia -(L. f.) Small	Cornus alternifolia -L.f.	Symphytum elatum	S. officinale
Swida amomum -(Mill.) Small	Cornus amomum -Mill.	Symphytum grandiflorum	S. ibericum
Swida australis	Cornus australis	Symphytum ibericum 'Jubilee'	S. 'Goldsmith'
Swida baileyi -(Coult & Evans) Rydb.	Cornus stolonifera	Symphytum ibericum 'Variegatum'	S. 'Goldsmith'
	'Baileyi'	Symphytum microcalyx	S. officinale
Swida controversa -(Hemsl.) Sojak	Cornus controversa	Symphytum patens	S. officinale
Swida glabrata -(Benth.) Heller	Cornus glabrata -Benth	Symphytum peregrinum	S. x uplandicum
Swida hemsleyi	Cornus hemsleyi	Symphytum uligonosum	S. officinale
Swida hessei -(Koehne) Sojak	Cornus hemsleyi	Symplocarpos -Schult. & Schult.f.	Symplocarpus
Swida macrophylla -(Wall.) Sojak	Cornus macrophylla	Symplocos crataegoides	S. paniculata
Swida microcarpa -(Nash) Small	Cornus asperifolia	Symptocarpus -A. Rich.	Symplocarpus

Synonym	Current Name	Synonym	Current Name
Synadenium grantii 'Rubrum'	S.compactum v rubrum	Tagetes signata	T. tenuifolia
Synadenium grantii v rubrum	S.compactum v rubrum	Talauma coco	Magnolia coco
Synandriospadix -Engl.	Synandrospadix -Engl.	Tamarix altaica	T. ramosissima
Synantherias -Schott	Amorphophallus	Tamarix anglica -Webb	T. gallica
Syndesmon thalictroides	Anemonella thalictr.	Tamarix caspica h.	T. tetrandra
Synnotia	Sparaxis	Tamarix eversmanni	T. ramosissima
Syringa 'Isabella'	S. x prestoniae 'Isabella'	Tamarix eversmannii	T. ramosissima
Syringa affinis	S. oblata v alba	Tamarix gallica v micrantha	T. ramosissima
Syringa afghanica misapplied	S. protolaciniata	Tamarix germanica	Myricaria germanica
Syringa amurensis	S. reticulata v amuren.	Tamarix japonica h. ex Dipp.	T. chinensis
Syringa amurensis v japonica	S. reticulata	Tamarix juniperina -Bunge	T. chinensis
Syringa bretschneideri -Lemoine	S. villosa -Vahl	Tamarix odessana -Stev. ex Bunge	T. ramosissima
Syringa correlata	S. x chinensis	Tamarix pentandra	T. ramosissima
Syringa dubia	S. x chinensis	Tamarix plumosa h. ex Carr.	T. chinensis
Syringa formosissima -Nakai	S. wolfii	T. ramosissima 'Summer Glow'	T. ramosissima 'Rubra'
Syringa japonica	S. reticulata	Tamarix tetrandra v purpurea	T. parviflora
Syringa julianae	S. pubescens ssp jul.	Tanacetum arcticum	Arctanthemum arct.
Syringa microphylla	S. pubescens ssp mic.	Tanacetum audiberti -DC.	T. vulgare -L.
Syringa microphylla 'Superba'	S. pubescens ssp microphylla 'Superba'	Tanacetum balsamita tomentosum	T. balsamita ssp balsametoides
Syringa palibiniana	S. meyeri 'Palibin'	Tanacetum balsamita v tanacetoides	T. balsamita ssp balsamita
Syringa patula -(Palibin) Nakai	S. pubescens ssp patu.		
Syringa patula misapplied	S. meyeri 'Palibin'	Tanacetum capitatum	Sphaeromeria capitata
Syringa pekinensis	S. reticulata ssp pek.	Tanacetum herderi	Hippolytia herderi
Syringa reflexa	S. komarovii ssp refl.	Tanacetum leucanthemum	Leucanthemum vulgare
Syringa reticulata v mandschurica	S. ret. ssp amurensis	Tanacetum macrophyllum mis.	Achillea grandifolia
Syringa sargentiana -Schneid.	S. komarowii	Tanacetum maximum	Leucanthemum x superbum
Syringa sempervirens -Franch.	Ligustrum sempervir.		
Syringa suspensa -Thunb.	Forsythia suspensa	Tanacetum nubigenum	Dendranthema nubige.
Syringa velutina	S. pubescens ssp patula	Tanacetum pallidum	Leucanthemopsis palli.
		Tanacetum parthenium 'Flore Pleno'	T. parthenium 'Plenum'
S. vulgaris 'Christopher Columbus'	S. vulgaris 'Christophe Colomb'	T. parthenium 'Sissinghurst White'	T. par. 'Rowallane'
		Tanacetum serotinum	Leucanthemella seroti.
S. vulgaris 'Glory of Horstenstein'	S. vulgaris 'Ruhm von Horstenstein'	Tanacetum sibiricum	Artemisia sibirica
		Tanacetum simplicifolium	T. balsamita -L.
Syringa vulgaris 'Lavanensis'	S. v. 'Lavaliensis'	Tanakea	Tanakaea
S. vul. 'Souvenir de Louis Spaeth'	S. vulgaris 'Andenken an Ludwig Spath'	Tarachia multicaulis	Asplenium ruta-muraria
		Tarachia platyneura	Asplenium platyneuron
Syringa vulgaris Beauty of Moscow	S. vulgaris 'Krasavitsa Moskvy'	Tarachia ruta-muraria	Asple. ruta-muraria
		Taraktogenos kurzii	Hydnocarpus kurzii
Syringa wilsonii -Schneid.	S. tomentella	Taraxacum dens-leonis	T. officinale
Syringa x persica v laciniata	S. x laciniata -Miller	Taraxacum vagans	T. officinale
Syzygium jambos	S. malaccense	Taraxacum vulgare	T. officinale
Tabebuia avellanedae	T. impetiginosa	Tasmannia aromatica -R.Br.	Drimys lanceolata
Tabebuia donnell-smithii	Cybistax donnell-smit.	Tassenia canadensis	Conyza canadensis
Tabebuia flavescens	T. serratifolia	Taxodium ascendens	T. distichum v imbricatum
Tabebuia pentaphylla h.	T. rosea		
Tabernaemontana coronaria	T. divaricata	Taxodium australis	Pandorea pandoreana ssp autrocaledonica
Tacitus	Graptopetalum		
Tacitus bellus	Graptopetalum bellum	Taxodium austrocaledonica	Pandorea pandoreana ssp austrocaledonica
Tacsonia mollissima	Passiflora mollissima		
Tacsonia umbilicata -Griseb.	Passiflora umbilicata	Taxodium sempervirens -D.Don	Sequoia sempervirens
Tacsonia vanvolxemii -Lem.	Passif. antioquiensis	Taxus baccata 'Argentea Minor'	T. bac. 'Dwarf White'
Tacsonia x exoniensis	Passiflora x exoniensis	T. bac. 'Dovastonii Aurea Pendula'	T. b. 'Dovastonii Aurea'
Tagetes rotundifolia	Tithonia rotundifolia	Taxus baccata 'Fastigiata Standishii'	T. baccata 'Standishii'

Synonym	Current Name	Synonym	Current Name
Taxus baccata 'Hibernica'	T. baccata 'Fastigiata'	Thalictrum corynellum	T. pubescens
Taxus baccata 'Variegata'	T. bac. Aurea Group	T. dipterocarpum misapplied	T. delavayi
Taxus baccata f aurea	T. bac. Aurea Group	Thalictrum flavum 'Chollerton'	T. sp Afghanistan
Taxus harringtonia -Forbes	Cephalotaxus harring.	Thalictrum flexuosum	T. minus ssp minus
Taxus macrophylla -Thunb.	Podocarpus macrop.	Thalictrum glaucodeum	T. pubescens
Tecoma australis	Pandorea pandorana	Thalictrum hypoglaucum	T. dasycarpum
Tecoma chinensis v aurantiaca	Campsis x tagliabuana	Thalictrum japonicum	Coptis japonica
Tecoma grandiflora -(Thunb.) Loisel.	Campsis grandiflora -	Thalictrum koreanum	T. ichangense
Tecoma grandiflora v princei -Dipp.	Campsis x tagliabuana	Thalictrum labradoricum	T. pubescens
Tecoma hybrida -Dipp.	Campsis x tagliabuana	Thalictrum minus ssp saxatile	T. min. ssp olympicum
Tecoma radicans -(L.) Juss.	Campsis radicans	Thalictrum perelegans	T. pubescens
Tecoma ricasoliana	Podranea ricasoliana	Thalictrum polyganum	T. pubescens
Tecoma tagliabuana -Vis.	Campsis x tagliabuana	Thalictrum rugosum	T. flavum ssp glaucum
Tecomaria	Tecoma	Thalictrum speciosissimum	T. flavum ssp glaucum
Tecomaria petersii	Tecoma capensis	Thalictrum zibellinum	T. pubescens
Tecophilaea cyanocrocus 'Purpurea'	T. cy. 'Violacea'	Thamnocalamus falcatus	Drepanostachyum falc.
Tectaria aculeata	Polystichum aculeatum	Thamnocalamus falconeri	Himalayacalamus falc.
Tectaria filix-mas	Dryopteris filix-mas	Thamnocalamus funghomii	Schizostachyum fungh.
Telesonix	Boykinia	Thamnocalamus khasianus	Drepanostachyum khasianum
Teline	Genista		
Telipodus -Raf.	Philodendron -Schott	Thamnocalamus maling	Yushania maling
Tellima grandiflora 'Purpurea'	T. grand. Rubra Group	Th. spathaceus misapplied	Fargesia murieliae
Teloxys botrys	Chenopodium botrys	Thapsia decipiens	Melanoselinum decipi.
Templetonia biloba	Cristonis biloba	Thaspium	Zizia
Templetonia regina	Leptosema aphyllum	Thea assamica -Mast.	Camellia sinensis
Tenoria romana	Foeniculum vulgare	Thea biflora	Camellia biflora
Ternstroemia gymnanthera	T. japonica	Thea bohea	Camellia sinensis
Terrellia curvata	Elymus curvatus	Thea cuspidata -Kochs	Camellia cuspidata
Testudinaria elephantipes	Dioscorea elephantipes	Thea sinensis -L.	Camellia sinensis
Tetradium officinalis	T. ruticarpum	Thea taliensis -W.W.Sm.	Camellia taliensis
Tetragonocalamus quadrangularis	Chimonobambusa quadrangularis	Thea viridis	Camellia sinensis
		Theleophyton bllardierei	Atriplex billardierei
Tetragonolobus	Lotus	Thelycrania	Cornus
Tetranema mexicanum	T. roseum	Thelypteris clintoniana	Dryopteris clintoniana
Tetrapanax papyriferus	T. payrifer	Thelypteris decursive-pinnata	Phegopteris de-pinnata
Tetrapathaea	Passiflora	Thelypteris dilatata	Dryopteris dilatata
Teucrium arduinii	T. arduinoi	Thelypteris dryopteris	Gymnocarpium dryopt.
Teucrium aroanum	T. aroanium	Thelypteris filix-mas	Dryopteris filix-mas
Teucrium aureum	T. polium aureum	Thelypteris goldiana	Dryopteris erythrosora
Teucrium chamaedrys misapplied	T. x lucidrys	Thelypteris hexagonoptera	Phegopteris hexago.
Teucrium majoricum	T. polium f pii-fontii	Thelypteris limbosperma	Oreopteris limbosper.
Teucrium massiliense misapplied	T. x lucidrys	Thelypteris marginalis	Dryopteris marginale
Teucrium officinale	T. chamaedrys	Thelypteris oreopteris	Oreopteris limbosper.
Teucrium pulverulentum	T. cossonii	Thelypteris phegopteris	Phegopteris connectilis
Teucrium reptans	Ajuga reptans	Thelypteris robertiana	Gymnocarpium robert.
Teucrium rosmarinifolum	T. creticum	Thelypteris spinulosa	Dryopteris carthusiana
Teucrium sinuatum	T. chamaedrys	Thelypteris thelypteroides	Thelypteris palustris
Teutiopsis patula	Atriplex patula	Themeda japonica	T. triandra v japonica
Thacla natans	Caltha natans	Thermia rhombifolia	Thermospis rhombifol.
Thalictrum adiantifolium	T. minus 'Adiantifolium'	Thermopsis annulocarpa	T. rhombifolia
Thalictrum anemonoides	Anemonella thalictroides	Thermopsis arenosa	T. rhombifolia
		Thermopsis caroliniana	T. villosa
Thalictrum angustifolium	T. lucidum	Thermopsis fabacea	T. lupinoides
T. aquilegiifolium Purple Cloud	T. aquil. 'Thundercloud'	Thermopsis laburnifolia -D.Don	Piptanthus nepalensis
Thalictrum coreanum	T. ichangense	Thermopsis montana	T. rhombifolia v mont.

Synonym	Current Name	Synonym	Current Name
Therorhodion camtschaticum	R. camtschaticum	Thuja occidentalis 'Mastersii Aurea'	T. occidentalis 'Aurea'
Thesium umbellatum	Comandra umbellata ssp umbellata	T. occidentalis 'Mastersii Pygmaea'	T. oc. 'Pygmaea'
		T. o. 'Orientalis Semperaurescens'	Platycladus orientalis 'Semperaurea'
Thevetia neriifolia	T. peruviana		
Thlaspi alpestre	T. alpinum	Thuja occidentalis 'Plicata Pygmaea'	T. oc.'Pygmaea'
Thlaspi biebersteinii	Pachyphragma macrophyllum	Thuja occidentalis 'Pyramidalis'	T. oc. 'Fastigiata'
		Thuja occidentalis 'Robusta'	T. oc. 'Wareana'
Thlaspi bursa-pastoris	Capsella bursa-past.	Thuja occidentalis 'Spaethii'	T. oc. 'Ohlendorfii'
Thlaspi burseta	Capsella bursa-past.	Thuja occidentalis 'Stricta'	T. oc. 'Fastigiata'
Thlaspi campestre	Lepidium campestre	Thuja occidentalis 'Wareana Aurea'	T. occidentalis 'Wareana Lutescens'
Thlaspi cuneatum	Capsella bursa-past.		
Thlaspi hirtum	Capsella bursa-past.	Thuja orientalis	Platycladus orientalis
Thlaspi incanum	Lepidium campestre	Thuja orientalis 'Compacta'	Platyclad. o. 'Sieboldii'
Thlaspi infestum	Capsella bursa-past.	Thuja orientalis 'Decussata'	Pla. o. 'Juniperoides'
Thlaspi macrophyllum	Pachyphragma macro.	Thuja orientalis 'Miller's Gold'	Platycladus orientalis 'Aurea Nana'
Thlaspi rotundifolium	T. cepaeifolium ssp rotundifolium	Thuja orientalis 'Nana'	Platycladus orientalis 'Sieboldii'
Thlaspi schrankii	Capsella bursa-past.		
Thlaspi umbellatum	Iberis umbellata	T. orientalis 'Rosedalis Compacta'	Platycladus orientalis 'Rosedalis'
Thlaspi vulgatum	Lepidium campestre		
Thomasia hexandra	Lysiopetalum hexand.	Thuja pensilis -Staunton	Glyptostrobus pensilis
Thomasia involucrata	Lysiopetalum involuc.	Thuja pisifera	Chamaecyparis pisife.
Thompsonia -Steudl.	Amorphophallus	Thuja plicata 'Aurea Rogersii'	T. occ. 'Rogersii'
Thomsonia -Wall.	Amorphophallus	Thuja plicata 'Aureovariegata'	T. occ. 'Zebrina'
Thouinia adenophora	Dodonaea adenophora	Thuja plicata 'Nana'	T. occ. 'Hillieri'
Thrinax bahamensis	T. morrisii	Thuja plicata 'Stolwijk's Gold'	T. occ. 'Stolwijk'
Thrinax ponceana	T. morrisii	Thuja plicata 'Stricta'	T. occ. 'Fastigiata'
Thryallis glauca	Galphimia glauca	Thuja sphaeroides -Spreng.	Chamaecyparis thyoides
Thryptomene davisiae	T. mucronulata		
Thryptomene dielsiana	T. mucronulata	Thuja tetragona -Hook.	Libocedrus uvifera
Thryptomene hexamera	Micromyrtus hexam.	Thujopsis borealis	Chamaecyparis nootkatensis
Thryptomene leptocalyx	Micromyrtus leptoca.		
Thryptomene minutiflora	Micromyrtus minutiflo.	Thujopsis dolabrata 'Laetevirens'	T. dolabrata 'Nana'
Thryptomene prolifera	T. mucronulata	Thujopsis koraiensis	Thuja koraiensis
Thuja 'Extra Gold'	T. plicata 'Irish Gold'	Thujopsis standishii	Thuja standishii
Thuja acuta	Platycladus orientalis	Thunbergia gibsonii	T. gregorii
Thuja andina -Poepp. & Endl.	Austrocedrus chilensis	Thuyopsis	Thujopsis
Thuja bodmeri h. ex Beissn.	T. occidentalis	Thuyopsis borealis -Carr.	Chamaecyparis nootkatensis
Thuja chilensis -D.Don	Austrocedrus chilensis		
Thuja compacta	T. occidentalis	Thymus 'Anderson's Gold'	T. x pulegioides 'Bertram Anderson'
Thuja dolabrata -L.	Thujopsis dolabrata		
Thuja doniana -Hook.	Libocedrus plumosa	Thymus 'Coccineus'	T. Coccineus Group
Thuja gigantea -Carr. not Nutt.	Calocedrus decurrens	Thymus 'E.B.Anderson'	T. pulegioides 'Bertram Anderson'
Thuja gigantea -Nutt.	T. plicata		
Thuja japonica -Maxim.	T. x standishii	Thymus 'Hardstoft Red'	T. 'Hardstoft Red' (Coccineus Group)
Thuja lineata -Poir.	Glyptostrobus pensilis		
Thuja lobbii h.	T. plicata	Thymus 'Highland Cream'	T. 'Hartington Silver'
Thuja obtusa	Chamaecyparis obtusa	Thymus 'Lemon Caraway'	T. herba-barona 'Lemon-scented'
Thuja occidentalis 'Columnaris'	T. oc. 'Fastigiata'		
Thuja occidentalis 'Emerald'	T. oc. 'Smaragd'	Thymus 'Silver Posie'	T. vulgaris 'Silver Posie'
Thuja occidentalis 'Holmstrupensis'	T. oc. 'Holmstrup'		
Thuja occidentalis 'Holmstrupii'	T. oc.'Holmstrup'	Thymus acinoides	T. caespititius
T. occ. 'Lombarts' Wintergreen'	T. oc. 'Wintergreen'	Thymus acinos	T. caespititius
Thuja occidentalis 'Lutescens'	T. occidentalis 'Wareana Lutescens'	Thymus arvensis	T. caespititius
		Thymus azoricus	T. caespititius

Synonym	Current Name	Synonym	Current Name
Thymus carnosus misapplied	T. vulgaris 'Erectus'	Tiarella collina	T. wherryi
Thymus clinopodium	Clinopodium vulgare	Tiarella cordifolia 'Rosalie'	x Heucherella alba 'Rosalie'
Thymus drucei	T. polytrichus		
Thymus erectus	T. vulgaris 'Erectus'	Tiarella cordifolia v collina	T. wherryi
Thymus herba-barona citrata	T. herba-barona 'Lemon-scented'	Tiarella menziesii	Tolmiea menziesii
		Tibouchina semidecandra h.	T. urvilleana
Thymus lanuginosus misapplied	T. pseudolanuginosus	T. semidecandra ssp floribunda h.	T. organensis
Thymus marschallianus	T. pannonicus	Tilia 'Euchlora'	T. x euchlora
Thymus micans	T. caespititius	Tilia 'Hillieri'	T. 'Harold Hillier'
Thymus minus	Calamintha nepeta	Tilia affinis	T. platyphyllos
Thymus montanus	T. pulegioides	Tilia alba -Ait. in part	T. tomentosa
Thymus murcicus	T. membranaceus	Tilia argentea	T. tomentosa
Thymus nitidus	T. richardii ssp nitidus	Tilia begoniifolia	T. dasystyla
Thymus odoratissimus	T. pallasianus ssp pall.	Tilia cordata 'Erecta'	T. cordata 'Bohlje'
Thymus polytrichus misapplied	T. praecox	Tilia dasystyla -Rehd. in part	T. caucasica
Thymus praecox 'Coccineus'	T. serpyllum v coccineus	Tilia dasystyla h.	T. x euchlora
		Tilia floridana	T. caroliniana ssp flori.
Thymus praecox ssp arcticus	T. polytrichus ssp britannicus	Tilia glabra	T. americana
		Tilia grandifolia	T. platyphyllos
T. praecox ssp arcticus v albus	T. polytrichus ssp britannicus v albus	Tilia grandifolia 'Aurantia'	T. platyphyllos 'Aurea'
		Tilia monticola	T. heterophylla
Thymus richardii ssp nitidus 'Compactus Albus'		Tilia neglecta	T. americana
	T. vulg. 'Snow White'	Tilia parvifolia	T. cordata
T. serpyllum 'Albus Variegatus'	T. 'Hartington Silver'	Tilia petiolaris	T. 'Petiolaris'
Thymus serpyllum 'Atropurpureus'	T. 'Atropurpureus' misapplied (Coccin. Gr)	Tilia platyphyllos 'Aurantiaca'	T. platyphyllos 'Aurea'
		Tilia platyphyllos 'Corallina'	T. platyphyllos 'Rubra'
Thymus serpyllum 'Lavender Sea'	T. 'Lavender Sea'	Tilia platyphyllos 'Erecta'	T. platyp. 'Fastigiata'
Thymus serpyllum 'Minimus'	T. serp. 'Minimalist'	Tilia platyphyllos 'Pyramidalis'	T. platyphyllos 'Aurea'
Thymus serpyllum 'Minus'	T. serpyllum 'Minor'	Tilia tomentosa 'Petiolaris'	T. 'Petiolaris'
Thymus serpyllum 'Pink Ripple'	T. 'Pink Ripple'	Tilia x euchlora 'Redmond'	T. americana 'Redmond'
Thymus serpyllum 'Purple Beauty'	T. 'Purple Beauty' (Coccineus Group)		
		Tilia x intermedia -DC.	T. x europaea
Thymus serpyllum 'Purpurteppich'	T. 'Purple Beauty' (Coccineus Group)	Tilia x moltkei	T. 'Moltkei'
		Tilia x orbicularis -(Carr.) Jouin	T. 'Orbicularis'
Thymus serpyllum 'Red Elf'	T. 'Red Elf' (Cocc. Gr.)	Tilia x spectabilis	T. 'Moltkei'
Thymus serpyllum 'Ruby Glow'	T. 'Ruby Glow'	Tilia x vulgaris	T. x europaea
Thymus serpyllum 'Variegatus'	T. 'Hartington Silver'	Tillaea	Crassula
T. serpyllum coccineus 'Minor'	T. 'Alan Bloom'	Tillandsia benthamiana	T. erubescens
T. ser. coccineus 'Minor' misapplied	T. Coccineus Group	Tillandsia dianthoidea	T. aeranthos
Thymus serpyllum ssp lanuginosus	T. pseudolanuginosus	Tillandsia ionantha v scaposa	T. kolbii
Thymus silvaticus	Clinopodium vulgare	Tillandsia tenuifolia v surinamensis	T. tenuifolia v tenuifolia
Thymus vulgaris 'Aureus' h.	T. pulegioides 'Goldentime'	Tillandsia valenzueliana	T. variabilis
		Tillandsia velickiana	T. matudae
T. x citriodorus 'Anderson's Gold'	T. pulegioides 'Bertram Anderson'	Tiniaria baldschuanica	Fallopia baldschuanica
		Tiniaria japonica	Fallopia japonica
T. x citriodorus 'Archer's Gold'	T. pulegioides 'Archer's Gold'	Tiniaria sachalinensis	Fallopia sachalinensis
		Tipuana speciosa	T. rotundifolia
Thymus x citriodorus 'Aureus'	T. pulegioides 'Aureus'	Tipuana speciosa	T. tipu
T. x citr. 'Golden Lemon' misapplied	T. pulegioides 'Aureus'	Tithymalus cyparissias	Euphorbia cyparissias
Thymus x citriodorus 'Silver Posie'	T. vulg. 'Silver Posie'	Tithymalus esula	Euphorbia esula
T. x citr. 'Variegatus' misapplied	T. x citr. 'Golden King'	Tithymalus helioscopia	Euphorbia helioscopia
Thymus x citriodorus repandus	T. 'Rosemary's Lemon Carpet'	Tium alpinum	Astragalus alpinus
		Tnaria aubertii	Fallopia baldschuanica
Tiarella 'Viking Ship'	x Heucherella 'Viking Ship'	Tofieldia borealis	T. pusilla
		Tofieldia minima	T. pusilla

Synonym	Current Name	Synonym	Current Name
Tolmiea 'Goldsplash'	T. menziesii 'Taff's Gold'	Trichocereus candicans	Echinopsis candicans
		Trichocereus chiloensis	Echinopsis chiloensis
Tolmiea menziesii 'Maculata'	T. menz. 'Taff's Gold'	Trichocereus grandiflorus	Echinopsis huascha
Tolmiea menziesii 'Variegata'	T. menz. 'Taff's Gold'	Trichocereus huascha	Echinopsis huascha
Torilis anthriscus	T. japonica	Trichocereus pasacana	Echinopsis pasacana
Tornelia -Gut. ex Schott	Monstera -Adans.	Trichocereus shaferi	Echinopsis schickendantzii
Tovara	Persicaria		
Townsendia montana	T. alpigena v alpigena	Trichocereus spachianus	Echinopsis spachianus
Townsendia sericea	T. exscapa	Trichocereus terscheckii	Echinopsis terscheckii
Townsendia wilcoxiana h.	T. rothrockii	Tricholaena repens	Melinis repens
Toxicodendron altissimum -Mill.	Ailanthus altissima	Trichomanes ebeneum	Asplenium playneuron
Toxicodendron crenatum -Mill.	Rhus aromatica -Ait.	Trichomanes ruta-muraria	Asplenium ruta-mura.
Toxicodendron succedaneum	Rhus trichocarpa	Trichophyllum aciculare	Eleocharis acicularis
Toxicodendron trichocarpum	Rhus trichocarpa -Miq.	Trichophyllum capitatum	Eleocharis elliptica
Toxicodendron vernicifluum	Rhus verniciflua	Trichophyllum intermedium	Eleocharis intermedia
Trachelospermum crocostemon	T. asiaticum	Trichophyllum obtusum	Eleocharis obtusa
Trachelospermum divaricatum	T. asiaticum	Trichophyllum palustre	Eleocharis palustris
Trachelospermum japonicum	T. jasminoides 'Japonicum'	Trichophyllum robbinsii	Eleocharis robbinsii
		Trichophyllum rostellatum	Eleocharis rostellata
Trachelospermum majus -Nakai	T. asiaticum	Trichophyllum tenue	Eleocharis tenuis
Trachelospermum majus misapplied	T. jasminoides 'Japonicum'	Trichosanthes anguina	T. cucumerina v angu.
		Trichosanthes japonica	T. kirilowii v japonica
Trachomitum venetum	Apocynum venetum	Trichosiphon	Brachychiton
Trachycarpus excelsus -H.Wendl.	T. fortunei	Trichostigma arguta -Sieb. & Zucc.	Actinidia arguta
Trachypoa vulgaris	Dactylis glomerata	Trichostigma polygama	Actinidia
Trachyspermum copticum	T. ammi	Tricondylus	Lomatia
Tradescantia 'Purple Heart'	T. pallida 'Purpurea'	Tricuspidaria	Crinodendron
Tradescantia 'Purple Sabre'	T. pallida 'Purpurea'	Tricuspidaria dependens -h.	Crinodendron hookerianum -Gay
Tradescantia albiflora	T. fluminensis		
Tradescantia blossfeldiana	T. cerinthoides	Tricuspidaria dependens	Crinodendron patagua
Tradescantia canaliculata	T. ohiensis	Tricuspidaria lanceolata -Miq.	Crinodendron hookeri.
Tradescantia multiflora	Tripogandra multiflora	Tricyrtis affinis 'Variegata'	T. latifolia
Tradescantia navicularis	Callisia navicularis	Tricyrtis bakeri	T. latifolia
Tradescantia pendula	T. zebrina	Tricyrtis dilatata	T. macropoda
Tradescantia pexata	T. sillamontana	Tricyrtis flava ssp ohsumiensis	T. ohsumiensis
Tradescantia purpurea	T.pallida 'Purpurea'	Tricyrtis japonica	T. hirta
Tradescantia tricolor	T. zebrina	Tricyrtis macranthopsis	T. macrantha ssp macranthopsis
Tradescantia velutina	T. sillamontana		
T. x andersoniana 'Caerulea Plena'	T. virginiana 'Caerulea Plena'	Tricyrtis stolonifera	T. formosana Stolonifera Group
T. x andersoniana Carmine Glow	T. x and. 'Karminglut'	Trifllidium	Trillium
Tradescantia zebrina pendula	T. zebrina	Trifolium 'Dark Dancer'	T. repens 'Purpur ascens Quadrifolium'
Tragacantha alpina	Astragalus alpinus		
Tragacantha massiliensis -Mill.	Astragalus massilien.	Trifolium melilotus-officinalis	Melilotus officinalis
Tragium anisum	Pimpinella anisum	Trifolium pratense 'Chocolate'	T. prat. 'Purple Velvet'
Tragopogon leiocarpos	T. pratensis	Trifolium pratense 'Dolly North'	T. prat. 'Susan Smith'
Tragopogon roseus	T. ruber	Trifolium pratense 'Ice Cool'	T. repens 'Green Ice'
Tragopogon shuttleworthii	T. pratensis	Trifolium repens 'Gold Net'	T. prat. 'Susan Smith'
Tragopogon undulatus	T. pratensis	Trifolium repens 'Pentaphyllum'	T. r. 'Quinquefolium'
Trautvetteria palmata	T. caroliniensis	Trifolium repens 'Tetraphyllum Purpureum'	T. repens ' Purpur ascens Quadrifolium'
Tricercandra japonica	Chloranthus japonicus		
Tricercandra quadrifolia	Chloranthus japonicus	Triglochin concinna	T. maritimum
Trichocalyx	Calytrix	Triglochin elata	T. maritimum
Trichocereus bridgesii	Echinopsis lageniformis	Trillium chloropetalum v rubrum	T. chloro. v giganteum
Trichocereus camarguensis	Echinopsis camarguen.	Trillium foetidum	T. erectum

Synonym	Current Name	Synonym	Current Name
	caerulea Oculata Gr.	Ulmus elliptica -Koehne	U. rubra
Tulipa pulchella humilis	T. humilis	Ulmus exoniensis	U. glabra 'Exoniensis'
Tulipa rhodopea	T. urumoffii	Ulmus floridana	U. americana
Tulipa stellata	T. clusiana v stellata	Ulmus foliacea -Gilib.	U. minor
Tulipa stellata v chrysantha	T. clusiana v chrysan.	Ulmus fulva -Michx.	U. rubra
Tulipa violacea	T. humilis Violacea Gr.	Ulmus glabra 'Aspleniifolia'	U. glabra 'Crispa'
Tulipa whittallii	T. orphanidea Whittallii	Ulmus glabra 'Fastigiata'	U. glabra 'Exoniensis'
	Group	Ulmus glabra 'Horizontalis'	U. glabra 'Pendula'
Tulipa wilsoniana	T. montana	Ulmus glabra 'Pendula'	U. glabra 'Horizontalis'
Tulipastrum accuminatum	Magnolia acuminata	Ulmus glabra 'Urticifolia'	U. glabra 'Crispa'
Tulipifera liriodendron -Mill.	Liriodendron tulipifera	Ulmus glabra 'Vegeta'	U. x hollandica 'Vegeta'
Tunica	Petrorhagia	Ulmus major -Smith	U. x hollandica 'Major'
Turbinicarpus schmiedickeanus	Neolloydia schmiedick.	Ulmus minor 'Jacqueline Hillier'	U. x hollandica
Tussaca pulchella	Chrysothemis pulchella		'Jacqueline Hillier'
Tussilago ruderalis	T. farfara	Ulmus minor 'Van Houttei'	U.m. 'Louis van Houttei'
Tussilago rupestriis	T. farfara	Ulmus minor v sarniensis	U. minor 'Sarniensis'
Tussilago vulgaris	T. farfara	Ulmus mollifolia	U. americana
Tylecodon wallichii	T. papillaris ssp wall.	Ulmus montana	U. glabra
Typha stenophylla	T. laxmannii	Ulmus nitens -Moench	U. minor
Typhoides arundinacea	Phalaris arundinacea	Ulmus parvifolia 'Pygmaea'	U. parvifolia 'Hokkaido'
Udora canadensis	Elodea canadensis	Ulmus pedunculata -Foug.	U. laevis
Udora occidentalis	Elodea canadensis	Ulmus pendula 'Camperdownii'	U. glabra
Udora verticillata	Elodea nuttallii		'Camperdownii'
Ulex europaeus 'Fastigiatus'	U. europaeus 'Strictus'	Ulmus plotii -Druce	U. minor v lockii
Ulex europaeus 'Hibernicus'	U. europaeus 'Strictus'	Ulmus procera 'Australis'	U. x hollandica
Ulex europaeus 'Plenus'	U. europ. 'Flore Pleno'		'Australis'
Ulex nanus	U. minor	Ulmus pumila v arborea h.	U. 'Pinnatoramosa'
Ulmaria rubra	Filipendula rubra	Ulmus racemosa	U. thomasii
Ulmus 'Camperdownii'	U. glabra	Ulmus sarniensis -(Loud). Bancroft	U. minor 'Sarniensis'
	'Camperdownii'	Ulmus sarniensis 'Aurea'	U. minor 'Dicksonii'
Ulmus 'Commelin'	U. x hollandica	Ulmus sarniensis 'Dicksonii'	U. minor 'Dicksonii'
	'Commelin'	Ulmus sarniensis 'Purpurea'	U. minor 'Purpurea'
Ulmus 'Dicksonii'	U. minor 'Dicksonii'	Ulmus scabra 'Pyramidalis'	U. glabra 'Exoniensis'
Ulmus 'Jacqueline Hillier'	U. x hollandica	Ulmus sieboldii	U. parvifolia
	'Jacqueline Hillier'	Ulmus stricta -(Ait.) Lindl.	U. minor
Ulmus 'Vegeta'	U. x hollandica 'Vegeta'	Ulmus vegeta -(Loud.) Ley	U. x hollandica 'Vegeta'
Ulmus 'Wheatleyi Aurea'	U. minor 'Dicksonii'	Ulmus viminalis 'Argentea'	U. minor 'Viminalis
Ulmus angustifolia	U. minor ssp angustifo.		Marginata'
Ulmus angustifolia -West	U. minor	Ulmus viminalis 'Aurea'	U. minor 'Viminalis
Ulmus angustifolia v cornubiensis	U. minor 'Cornubiensis'		Aurea'
Ulmus belgica -West.	U. x hollandica 'Belgica'	Ulmus viminalis 'Marginata'	U. minor 'Viminalis
Ulmus campestris -L.	U. procera (mainly)		Marginata'
Ulmus campestris 'Aurea'	U. minor 'Viminalis	U.s x eleg. 'Jacqueline Hillier'	U. x hollandica
	Aurea'		'Jacqueline Hillier'
Ulmus campestris 'Rosseelsii'	U. mi. 'Viminalis Aurea'	Ulmus x hollandica 'Dampieri Aurea'	U. m. 'Dampieri Aurea'
Ulmus carpinifolia -Gleditsch	U. minor	Ulmus x hollandica 'Pendula'	U. x hollanica 'Smithii'
Ulmus carpinifolia 'Dicksonii'	U. minor 'Dicksonii'	Ulmus x hollandica 'Wredei Aurea'	U. m. 'Dampieri Aurea'
Ulmus carpinifolia 'Italica'	U. x holl. 'Australis'	Ulmus x hollandica 'Wredei'	U. x hollandica
Ulmus carpinifolia 'Variegata'	U. minor 'Variegata'		'Dampieri Aurea'
Ulmus carpinifolia v cornubiensis	U. minor 'Cornubiensis'	Uncasia perfoliata	Eupatorium perfoliatum
Ulmus carpinifolia v sarniensis	U. minor 'Sarniensis'	Uncasia truncata	Eupatorium perfoliatum
Ulmus chinensis	U. parvifolia	Unifolium canadense	Maianthemum canad.
Ulmus davidiana v japonica	U. japonica	Uniola latifolia	Chasmanthium latifoli.
Ulmus effusa	U. laevis	Uniola palmeri	Chasmanth. latifolium
Ulmus elegantissima -Horwood	U. minor	Urceolina longipetala	Hymenocallis longipeta.

215

Synonym	Current Name	Synonym	Current Name
Urceolina miniata	Stenomesson miniatum	Vagnera stellata	Smilacina stellata
Urceolina pendula	Stenomesson miniatum	Valeriana 'Alba'	Centranthus ruber '
Urceolina peruviana	Stenomesson miniatum		Albus'
Urechites	Pentalinon	Valeriana 'Coccinea'	Centranthus ruber
Urginea maritima	Drimia maritima	Valeriana ruber	Centranthus ruber
Urophyllum -K. Koch	Urospatha -Schott	Valerianella olitoria	V. locusta
Ursinia geyeri	U. chrysanthemoides v geyeri	Vallisneria verticillata	Elodea nuttallii
		Vallota speciosa	Cyrtanthus elatus
Urtica cylindrica	Boehmeria cylindrica	Valoradia plumbaginoides	Ceratostigma
Urtica iners	U. urens		plumbaginoides
Urtica intermedia	U. urens	Vanda sanderiana	Euanthe sanderiana
Urtica monoica	U. urens	Vania	Thlapsi
Urtica ovalifolia	U. urens	Vellozia elegans	Talbotia elegans
Urtica parvula	U. urens	Veltheimia glauca	V. capensis
Urtica quadristipulata	U. urens	Veltheimia roodiae	V. capensis
Urtica spicata	Boehmeria spicata	Veltheimia undulata	V. bracteata
Urtica verticillata	U. urens	Veltheimia viridifolia -Jacquin	V. bracteata
Utricularia biflora	U. intermedia	Veltheimia viridifolia misapplied	V. capensis
Utricularia exoleta	U. gibba	Venidium	Arctotis
Uva-ursi alpina	Arctous alpina	Veratrum luteum	Chamaelirium luteum
Uva-ursi buxifolia	Arctostaphylos uva-ursi	Verbascum 'Arctic Summer'	V. bombyciferum 'Polarsommer'
Uva-ursi procumbens	Arctostap. uva-ursi	Verbascum 'Broussa'	V. bombyciferum
Uva-ursi uva-ursi	Arctostap. uva-ursi	Verbascum alatum	V. thapsus
Uvaria japonica -Thunb.	Kadsura japonica	Verbascum angustius	V. thapsus
Uvularia pudica	U. caroliniana	Verbascum blattariforium	V. blattaria
Vaccaria grandiflora	V. hispanica	Verbascum blattariforme -Griseb.	V. blattaria
Vaccaria pyramidata	V. hispanica	Verbascum canescens	V. thapsus
Vaccaria segetalis	V. hispanica	Verbascum carduifolium	V. blattaria
Vaccaria vulgaris	V. hispanica	Verbascum claytonii	V. blattaria
Vaccinium brachycerum -Michx.	Gaylussacia brachyce.	Verbascum decurrens	V. thapsus
Vaccinium buxifolium -Salisb.	Gayluss. brachycera	Verbascum indicum	V. thapsus
Vaccinium cantabricum -Huds.	Daboecia cantabrica	Verbascum lanatum	V. thapsus
Vaccinium dacamerocarpon	Gaylussacia baccata	Verbascum leptophyllum	V. blattaria
Vaccinium donianum	V. sprengelii	Verbascum longifolium v pannosum	V. olympicum
Vaccinium dumosum -Andr.	Gaylussacia baccata	Verbascum luridum	V. blattaria
Vaccinium frondosum -L.	Gaylussacia baccata	Verbascum majus	V. thapsus
Vaccinium hispidulum	Gaultheria hispidula	Verbascum mas	V. thapsus
Vaccinium hispidulum -L.	Gaultheria hispidula	Verbascum neglectum	V. thapsus
Vaccinium humifusum -Graham	Gaultheria humifusa	Verbascum nitidum	V. blattaria
Vaccinium ligustrinum -L.	Lyonia ligustrina	Verbascum officinarum	V. thapsus
Vaccinium longiflorum -Wikstr.	V. cylindraceum	Verbascum pallidum	V. thapsus
Vaccinium mortinia	V. floribundum	Verbascum plantagineum	V. thapsus
V. oxycoccus v microcarpum	V. oxycoccus	Verbascum pseudothapsiforme	V. thapsus
Vaccinium palustre	V. oxycoccus	Verbascum ramosissimum	V. blattaria
Vaccinium palustre	V. oxycoccus -L.	Verbascum repandum	V. blattaria
Vaccinium parviflorum	Gaylussacia baccata	Verbascum rhinanthifolium	V. blattaria
Vaccinium pensylvanicum -Lam.	V. angustifolium v laevifolium	Verbascum salgirensis	V. thapsus
		Verbascum schraderi	V. thapsus
Vaccinium resinosum -Ait.	Gaylussacia baccata	Verbascum simplex	V. thapsus
Vaccinium ursinum -M.A.Curtis	Gaylussacia ursina	Verbascum spectabile	V. thapsus
Vaccinium venustum -Ait.	Gaylussacia frondosa	Verbascum subalpinum	V. thapsus
Vaccinium vitis-idaea 'Nana'	V. vitis-idaea ssp minus	Verbascum tapsus -Neck.	V. thapsus
Vaccinium yunnanense -Franch.	Gaultheria yunnanensis	Verbascum thapsiforme	V. densiflorum
Vagnera racemosa	Smilacina racemosa	Verbascum thapsiforme	V. thapsus

Synonym	Current Name	Synonym	Current Name
Verbascum visianianum	V. thapsus	V. decussata h. in part not Ait.	Hebe x franciscana
Verbena 'Lois' Ruby'	V. 'Claret'	Veronica dieffenbachii -Benth.	Hebe dieffenbachii
Verbena 'Mahonettii'	V. x maonettii	Veronica diffusa -Hook. f.	Parahebe catarractae
Verbena 'Pink Bouquet'	V. 'Silver Anne'	Veronica diosmifolia -A.Cunn.	Hebe diosmifolia
Verbena 'Tenerife'	V. 'Sissinghurst'	Veronica diosmifolia v trisepala	Hebe diosmifolia
Verbena alpina h.	V. x maonettii	Veronica elliptica -Forst. f.	Hebe elliptica
Verbena chamaedrifolia	V. peruviana	Veronica elliptica h. not Forst. f.	Hebe x franciscana
Verbena chamaedrioides	V. peruviana	Veronica epacridea -Hook.f.	Hebe epacridea
Verbena citriodora	Aloysia tripylla	Veronica formosa	Parahebe formosa
Verbena juncea -Gill. & Hook.	Diostea juncea	Veronica franciscana -Eastw.	Hebe x franciscana
Verbena paniculata	V. hastata	Veronica gibbsii -T.Kirk	Hebe gibbsii
Verbena patagonica	V. bonariensis	Veronica gigantea -Ckn.	Hebe gigantea
Verbena pinnatifida	V. hastata	Veronica glaucocaerulea h.	Hebe pimeleoides
Verbena pulchella	V. tenera		'Glaucocaerulea'
Verbena scaberrima	V. rigida	Veronica glaucophylla -Ckn.	Hebe glaucophylla
Verbena triphylla	Aloysia tripylla	V. gracillima -(Kirk) Cheesem.	Hebe gracillima
Verbena triphylla -L'Herit.	Aloysia triphylla	Veronica haastii -Hook.f.	Hebe haastii
Verbena venosa	V. rigida	Veronica hectori -Hook. f.	Hebe hectorii
Vernonia arkansana	V. crinita	Veronica hendersonii	V. subsessilis henders.
Veronica 'White Icicle'	V. spicata 'Icicle'	Veronica hulkeana -F.V.Muell.	Hebe hulkeana
Veronica albicans -Petrie	Hebe albicans	Veronica incana	V. spicata ssp incana
Veronica amethystina	V. spuria	Veronica jasminoides h.	Hebe diosmifolia
Veronica amplexicaulis -J.B.Armstr.	Hebe amplexicaulis	Veronica kellereri	V. spicata
V. angustifolia -not Fisch. & Link.	Hebe parviflora v	Veronica kirkii -J.B.Armstr.	Hebe 'Kirkii'
	angustifolia	Veronica laevis -Benth. not Lam.	Hebe venustula
Veronica anomala -Armstr.	Hebe odora	Veronica laevis v carnosula -Hook. f.	Hebe carnosula
Veronica aoira h.	Hebe recurva 'Aoira'	Veronica lanceolata -Benth.	Parahebe catarractae
Veronica arborea -Buchan.	Hebe parviflora v	Veronica latisepala -Kirk	Hebe macrocarpa v
	arborea		latisepala
V.armstrongii -h. in part not Armst.	Hebe ochracea	Veronica lavaudiana -Raoul	Hebe lavaudiana
Veronica austriaca ssp teucrium 'Shirley Blue'		Veronica leiophylla -Cheesem.	Hebe leiophylla
	V. 'Shirley Blue'	Veronica ligustrifolia -A.Cunn.	Hebe ligustrifolia
Veronica austriaca v dubia	V. prostrata	Veronica ligustrifolia v gracillima	Hebe gracillima
Veronica barkeri -Ckn.	Hebe barkeri	Veronica linifolia -Hook. f.	Parahebe linifolia
Veronica bidwillii -Hook.	Parahebe x bidwillii	V. lobelioides -Anders. Henry	Hebe x franciscana
Veronica bidwillii -of most authors	Parahebe decora	V. lobelioides -Anders. Henry	Hebe x franciscana
Veronica Blue Bouquet	V. longifolia	Veronica longifolia 'Foerster's Blue'	V. longifolia 'Blauriesin'
	'Blaubundel'	Veronica longifolia Blue Giantess	V. longifolia 'Blauriesin'
Veronica bonarota	Paederota bonarota	Veronica longifolia subsessilis	V. subses. hendersonii
Veronica brachysiphon	Hebe brachysiphom	Veronica lutea	Paederota lutea
Veronica buchananii -Hook.f.	Hebe buchananii	Veronica lyallii -Hook. f.	Parahebe lyallii
Veronica buxifolia -Benth.	Hebe buxifolia	Veronica lycopioides -Hook. f.	Hebe lycopiodes
Veronica candida	V. spicata ssp incana	Veronica macrantha -Hook. f.	Hebe macrantha
Veronica canescens	Parahebe canescens	Veronica macrocarpa -Vahl	Hebe macrocarpa
Veronica canterburiensis	Hebe canterburiensis	Veronica macroura	Hebe stricta v macr.
Veronica carnosula	Hebe carnosula	Veronica magellanica -Gmelin	Hebe elliptica
Veronica catarractae -Forst. f.	Parahebe catarractae	Veronica matthewsii -Cheesem.	Hebe matthewsii
Veronica chamaedrys 'Variegata'	V. cham. 'Miffy Brute'	Veronica nummarifolia	V. nummularia
Veronica colensoi -Hook. f.	Hebe colensoi	Veronica nummularioides	V. nummularia
Veronica cupressoides -Hook.	Hebe cupressoides	Veronica odora -Hook. f.	Hebe odora
Veronica cupressoides v variabilis	Hebe propinqua	Veronica pageana h.	Hebe pinguifolia 'Pagei'
Veronica darwiniana -sensu Cheesem., Col. in part		Veronica parviflora -Vahl	Hebe parviflora v
	Hebe glaucophylla		angustifolia
Veronica decumbens -J.B.Armstr.	Hebe decumbens	Veronica parviflora v phillyraefolia	Hebe leiophylla
Veronica decussata -Ait.	Hebe elliptica	Veronica peduncularis 'Oxford Blue'	V. peduncularis

Synonym	Current Name	Synonym	Current Name
	'Georgia Blue'	Verticordia demissa	V. oxylepis
Veronica perfoliata	Parahebe perfoliata	Verticordia drummondii v lindleyi	V. lindleyi
Veronica pimeleoides -Hook.f.	Hebe pimeleoides	Verticordia fontanesii	V. plumosa
V. pimeleoides v glaucocaerulea h.	Hebe pimeleoides	Verticordia fontanesii v parviflora	V. minutiflora
	'Glaucocaerulea'	Verticordia gilbertii	V. chrysantha
Veronica pinguifolia -Hook. f.	Hebe pinguifolia	Verticordia hirta	V. endlicheriana
Veronica prenja	V. austriaca	Verticordia pectinata	V. plumosa v
Veronica propinqua -Cheesem.	Hebe propinqua		grandiflora
Veronica prostrata 'Miss Willmott'	V. pr. 'Warley Blue'	Verticordia pentandra	V. picta
Veronica prostrata Blue Mirror	V. pr. 'Blauspiegel'	Verticordia preissii	V. acerosa v preissii
Veronica pulvinaris	Chionhebe pulvinaris	Verticordia setigera	V. pennigera
Veronica rakaiensis -J.B.Armstr.	Hebe rakaiensis	Verticordia stelluligera	V. densiflora v stell.
Veronica raoulii -Hook. f.	Hebe raoulii	Verticordia stylosa	V. huegelii v stylosa
Veronica repens	V. reptans	Verticordia stylotricha	V. brachypoda
Veronica rupestris	V. prostrata	Verticordia umbellata	V. habrantha
Veronica salicifolia -Forst. f.	Hebe salicifolia	Verticordia wilhelmii	Homoranthus wilhelmii
Veronica salicifolia v atkinsonii	Hebe stricta v atkins.	Vesicaria graeca	Alyssoides utriculata v
Veronica salicifolia v egmontiana	Hebe stricta v egmon.		graeca
Veronica salicifolia v gigantea	Hebe gigantea Veronica	Vestia lycioides	V. foetida
salicifolia v kirkii	Hebe 'Kirkii'	Viburnum 'Anne Russell'	V. x burkwoodii 'Anne
Veronica salicifolia v kirkii	Hebe 'Kirkii'		Russell'
Veronica salicifolia v stricta	Hebe stricta	Viburnum 'Chenaultii'	V. x burkw. 'Chenaultii'
Veronica salicornioides -Hook.f.	Hebe salicornioides	Viburnum 'Fulbrook'	V. x burkw. 'Fulbrook'
V. salicornioides h. not Hook. f.	Hebe propinqua	Viburnum alnifolium	V. lantanoides
Veronica saxatilis	V. fruticans	Viburnum americanum -Auct.	V. trilobum
Veronica scott-thomsonii -Allan	Hebe rakaiensis	Viburnum aragonense -Pau	V. lantana -L.
Veronica selleri	V. wormskjoldii	Viburnum canbyi	V. dentatum
Veronica speciosa -A.Cunn.	Hebe speciosa	Viburnum ceanothoides	V. foetidum v ceanoth.
V. speciosa h. in part not A.Cunn.	Hebe x franciscana	Viburnum coriaceum -Blume	V. cylindricum
Veronica speciosa v brevifolia	Hebe macrocarpa v	Viburnum densiflorum -Chapm.	V. acerifolium -L.
	brevifolia	Viburnum farinosum	V. lantana -L.
Veronica spicata 'Royal Candles'	V. spicata 'Glory'	Viburnum farreri 'Album'	V. farreri
Veronica spicata Blue Fox	V. spicata 'Blaufuchs'		'Candidissimum'
Veronica spicata Red Fox	V. spicata 'Rotfuchs'	Viburnum farreri 'Compactum'	V. farreri 'Nanum'
Veronica spicata rosea	V. spicata 'Erika'	Viburnum foetans	V. grandiflorum f
Veronica squalida -Kirk	Hebe parviflora v		foetans
	angustifolia	Viburnum fragrans -Bunge	V. farreri
Veronica stelleri	V. wormskjoldii	Viburnum grandifolium -Ait.	V. lantanoides -Michx.
Veronica stricta -Benth.	Hebe stricta	Viburnum hessei	V. wrightii v hessei
Veronica subalpina -Ckn.	Hebe subalpina	Viburnum lantana 'Auratum'	V. lantana 'Aureum'
V. subalpina -h. not (Ckn.)Ckn.& All.	Hebe rakaiensis	Viburnum macrophyllum -Blume	V. japonicum
Veronica tetrasticha -Hook. f.	Hebe tetrasticha	Viburnum macrophyllum -Thunb.	Hydrangea macrophyl.
Veronica teucrium	V. austriaca ssp teuc.	Viburnum maculatum -Pantoczek	V. lantana v discolor
Veronica traversii -Hook. f.	Hebe traversii Veronica	Viburnum mariesii	V. plicatum f
traversii h. not Hook. f.	Hebe brachysiphom		tomentosum 'Mariesii'
Veronica venustula -Col.	Hebe venustula	Viburnum nervosum -Auct.	V. grandiflorum
Veronica vernicosa -Hook. f.	Hebe vernicosa	Viburnum nitidum -Ait.	V. cassinoides -L.
Veronica virginica	Veronicastrum virgin.	V. odoratissimum 'Emerald Lustre'	V. awabuki 'Emerald
Veronicastrum virginicum roseum	V. virg. v incarnatum		Lustre'
Verticordia adenocalyx	V. helmsii	Viburnum opulus 'Snowball'	V. opulus 'Roseum'
Verticordia callitricha	V. monadelpha v call.	Viburnum opulus 'Sterile'	V. opulus 'Roseum'
Verticordia cespitosa	V. densiflora v cespit.	Viburnum opulus 'Watanabe'	V. plicatum 'Nanum
Verticordia compta	V. insignis ssp compta		Semperflorens'
Verticordia conferta	V. fastigiata	Viburnum pallidum	V. lantana -L.
Verticordia darwinioides	Homoranthus darwin.	Viburnum pauciflorum	V. edule

Synonym	Current Name	Synonym	Current Name
Viburnum plicatum 'Nanum'	V. plic. f tomentosum 'Nanum Semperflorens'	Vinca minor 'Caerulea Plena'	V. minor 'Azurea Flore Pleno'
Viburnum plicatum 'Sterile'	V. plicatum f plicatum	Vinca minor 'Dartington Star'	V. major v oxyloba
Viburnum plicatum 'Watanabe'	V. plic. f tomentosum 'Nanum Semperflorens'	Vinca minor 'Double Burgundy'	V. minor 'Multiplex'
		Vinca minor 'Purpurea'	V. m. 'Atropurpurea'
Viburnum plicatum f tomentosum	V. plicatum	Vinca minor 'Rubra'	V. m. 'Atropurpurea'
Viburnum pubescens -(Ait). Pursh	V. dentatum v pubesc.	Vinca minor 'Variegata Aurea'	V. m. 'Aureovariegata'
Viburnum pubescens v canbyi	V. dentatum v pubesc.	Vinca minor 'Variegata'	V. minor 'Argenteovariegata'
Viburnum recognitum -Fern.	V. dentatum v lucidum		
Viburnum rigidum	V. tinus ssp rigidum	Vinca minor Green Carpet	V. m. 'Gruner Teppich'
Viburnum sandankwa -Hassk.	V. suspensum	Vinca rosea	Catharanthus roseus
Viburnum sargentii 'Fructuluteo'	V. sargentii f flavum	Vincetoxicum officinale	V. hirundinaria
Viburnum scandens -L. f.	Hydrangea scandens	Viola 'Admiral Avellan'	V. 'Amiral Avellan'
Viburnum schneiderianum	V. calvum	Viola 'Boughton Blue'	V. 'Belmont Blue'
Viburnum semperflorens	V. plic. f tomentosum ' Nanum Semperflorens'	Viola 'Czar'	V. 'The Czar'
		Viola 'E.A.Bowles'	V. 'Bowles' Black'
Viburnum serratum -Thunb.	Hydrangea serrata	Viola 'Freckles'	V. soraria 'Freckles'
Viburnum theiferum -Rehd.	V. setigerum	Viola 'Haslemere'	V. 'Nellie Britton'
Viburnum tinus 'Pyramidale'	V. tinus 'Strictum'	Viola 'Irish Elegance'	V. 'Sulfurea'
Viburnum tinus f hirtum h.	V. tinus hirtellum	Viola 'Johnnny Jump Up'	V. cornuta
Viburnum tinus ssp rigidum	V. rigidum	Viola 'Johnny Jump Up'	V. 'Helen Mount'
Viburnum tomentosum	V. plicatum	Viola 'Lady Saville'	V. 'Sissinghurst'
Viburnum trilobum	V. opulus v americanum	Viola 'Neapolitan'	V. 'Pallida Plena'
		Viola 'Netta Statham'	V. 'Belmont Blue'
Viburnum virens -Thunb.	Hydrangea scandens	Viola 'Princess of Wales'	V. 'Princesse de Galles'
Viburnum watanabei	V. plicatum 'Nanum Semperflorens'	Viola 'Queen Charlotte'	V. 'Koningin Charlotte'
		Viola 'Queen Victoria'	V. 'Victoria Regina'
Viburnum x pragense	V. 'Pragense'	Viola 'Swanley White'	V. 'Conte di Brazza'
Vicia angustifolia	V. sativa ssp nigra	Viola 'Victoria'	V. 'Czar Bleu'
Victoria regia	V. amazonica	Viola 'White Ladies'	V. cucullata 'Alba'
Victoria trickeri	V. cruziana	Viola adunca v minor	V. labradorica
Vigiera laevis -Vell.	Escallonia laevis	Viola aduncoides	V. adunca
Vilfa heterolepis	Sporobolus heterolepis	Viola aetolica saxatilis	V. aetolica
Villadia hemsleyana	Sedum hemsleyanum	Viola albanica	V. magellensis
Villaresia	Citronella	Viola albertina	V. adunca
Villarsia bennettii	Nymphoides peltata 'Bennettii'	Viola arenaria	V. rupestris
		Viola bellidifolia	V. adunca
Villarsia crista-galli	Nephrophyllidium c-gal	Viola borealis	V. selkirkii
Villarsia nymphoides	Nymphoides peltata 'Bennettii'	Viola bosniaca	V. elegantula bosniaca
		Viola carnosula	V. selkirkii
Vinca 'Hidcote Purple'	V. major v oxyloba	Viola cascadensis	V. adunca
Vinca ellipticifolia	V. minor -L.	Viola chaerophylloides	V. dissecta v chaerop.
Vinca herbacea 'Hidcote Purple'	V. major v oxyloba	Viola consimilis	V. odorata
Vinca hirsuta h.	V. major v oxyloba	Viola cornuta 'Minor Alba'	V. cornuta 'Alba Minor'
Vinca humilis	V. minor -L.	Viola crassicornis	V. selkirkii
Vinca intermedia	V. minor -L.	Viola curtisii	V. tricolor ssp curtisii
Vinca major 'Dartington Star'	V. major v oxyloba	Viola dissecta v chaerophylloides f eizanensis	V. eizanensis
Vinca major 'Elegantissima'	V. major 'Variegata'		
Vinca major 'Surrey Marble'	V. major 'Maculata'	Viola dissecta v sieboldiana	V. chaerophylloides v sieboldiana
Vinca major hirsuta h.	V. major v oxyloba		
Vinca major v pubescens	V. major ssp hirsuta	Viola dumetorum	V. odorata
Vinca media -Hoffmans & Link	V. difformis	Viola erecta	V. elatior
Vinca minor 'Alba Aureavariegata'	V. min. 'Alba Variegata'	Viola floribunda	V. odorata
Vinca minor 'Bowles' Blue'	V. minor 'La Grave'	Viola gonzaloi	V. odorata
Vinca minor 'Bowles' Variety'	V. minor 'La Grave'	Viola hederacea v sieberi	V. sieberiana

Synonym	Current Name	Synonym	Current Name
Viola heterophylla ssp epirota	V. bertolonii	Virgilia lutea -Michx	Cladrastis kentukea
Viola hortensis	V. odorata	Virgilia secundiflora	Sophora secundiflora
Viola imberbis	V. selkirkii	Viscaria alpina	Lychnis alpina
Viola incompta	V. odorata	Viscaria elegans	Silene coeli-rosa
Viola inornata	V. pedata	Viscaria viscosa	Lychnis viscaria
Viola jucunda	V. odorata	Viscaria viscosa alpina	Lychnis viscaria
Viola kamtschatica	V. selkirkii	Viscaria vulgaris	Lychnis viscaria
Viola koreana	V. grypoceras v exilis	Vitadenia triloba	Erigeron karvinskianus
Viola labradorica h.	V. riviniana Purpurea Group	Vitex incisa	V. negundo v heterophylla
V. labradorica purpurea misapplied	V. riviniana Purp. Gr.	Vitex macrophylla h.	V. agnus-castus v latifolia
Viola lejeunei	V. tricolor		
Viola longipes	V. adunca	Vitis 'Cascade'	V. Seibel 13053
Viola lutea ssp elegans	V. lutea	Vitis 'Trollinger'	V. vinifera 'Schiava Grossa'
Viola macedonica	V. tricolor ssp maced.		
Viola montanensis	V. adunca	Vitis aconitifolia -(Bunge) Hance	Ampelopsis aconitifolia
Viola obliqua	V. cucullata	Vitis alemannica	V. vinifera
Viola odorata 'Sulphurea'	V. 'Sulfurea'	Vitis antiquorum	V. vinifera
Viola odorata apricot	V. 'Sulfurea'	Vitis arborea -L.	Ampelopsis arborea
Viola odorata pink	V. odorata Rosea Gr.	Vitis armata -Diels & Gilg	V. davidii
Viola odorata rosea	V. odorata Rosea Gr.	Vitis Black Hamburgh	V.vin. 'Schiava Grossa'
Viola odorata v dumetorum	V. alba	Vitis blanda	V. labrusca
Viola oreophila	V. adunca	Vitis bodinieri -Levl. & Vant.	Ampelopsis bodinieri
Viola papilionacea	V. sororia	Vitis bryoniifolia	V. vinifera
Viola pensylvanica	V. pubescens v eriocarpa	Vitis byzantina	V. vinifera
		Vitis capensis	Rhoicissus capensis
Viola prionosepala	V. cucullata	Vitis chaffanjonii -Levl.	Ampelopsis chaffonjonii
Viola propinqua	V. odorata	Vitis columbina	V. riparia
Viola puberula	V. adunca	Vitis corinthiaca	V. vinifera
Viola purpurea misapplied	V. riviniana Purp. Gr.	Vitis cylindrica	V. vinifera
Viola ranunculifolia	V. pedata	Vitis davidiana -(Carr.) Nichols.	Ampelopsis humulifolia
Viola reniforme	V. hederacea	Vitis delavayana -Franch. ex Bean	Ampelopsis delavayana
Viola rolandii	V. cornuta	Vitis deliciosa	V. vinifera
Viola rugulosa	V. canadensis v rugul.	Vitis dimidiata	V. riparia
Viola rydbergii	V. canadensis	Vitis engelmannii -Dieck	Parthenocissus quin quefolia v engelmannii
Viola sarmentosa	V. odorata		
Viola saxatilis	V. tricolor ssp subalpina	Vitis ferruginea	V. labrusca
		Vitis ficifolia	V. thunbergii
Viola septentrionalis	V. sororia	Vitis flexuosa major h.	V. pulchra
Viola septentrionalis 'Alba'	V. sororia 'Albiflora'	Vitis hederacea	Parthenocissus quinquefolia
Viola stolonifera	V. odorata		
Viola suavissima	V. odorata	Vitis henryana -Hemsl.	Parthenocissus henry.
Viola subcarnea	V. odorata	Vitis heterophylla	Ampelopsis glandulosa v brevipedunculata
Viola subvestitia	V. adunca		
Viola sulphurea	V. odorata	Vitis heterophylla v cordata -Reg.	Ampelopsis glandulosa v brevipedunculata
Viola tenerrima	V. odorata		
Viola umbrosa	V. selkirkii	Vitis heterophylla v humulifolia	A. glandulosa v brevipedunculata
Viola uncinulata	V. adunca		
Viola variata	V. tricolor	Vitis heterophylla v maximowiczii	A. glandulosa v maxim.
Viola velutina	V. gracilis	Vitis himalayana -Brandis	Parthenocissus him.
Viola versicolor	V. tricolor	Vitis himalayana v semicordata	Parthenocissus him.
Viola wiedemannii	V. odorata	Vitis incisa	V. riparia
Viola yakusimana	V. verecunda v yakusi.	Vitis inconstans -Miq.	Parthenocissus tricuspidata
Viola zoysii	V. calcarata ssp zoysii		
Virgilia capensis	V. oroboides	Vitis inconstans 'Purpurea'	Parthenocissus

Synonym	Current Name	Synonym	Current Name
	tricuspidata 'Veitchii'	Vitis vulpina h.	V. riparia
Vitis indivisa -Willd.	Ampelopsis cordata	Vittadenia triloba	Erigeron karvinskianus
Vitis inserta -Kerner	Parthenocissus insert.	Vittadinia cuneata	V. australis
Vitis laciniosa	V. vinifera	Vleckia anethiodora	Agastache foeniculum
Vitis lubruscoides	V. labrusca	Vleckia foeniculum	Agastache foeniculum
Vitis luteola	V. labrusca	Wahlenbergia pumilio	Edraianthus pumilio
Vitis meditterranea	V. vinifera	Wahlenbergia serpyllifolia	Edraianthus serpyllif.
Vitis megaphylla -Veitch	Ampelopsis	Wahlenbergia tasmanica	W. saxicola
	megalophyla	Waldheimia	Allardia
Vitis micans -(Rehd.) Bean	Ampelopsis bodinieri	Waldsteinia ternata 'Variegata'	W. ternata 'Mozaick'
Vitis montana	V. riparia	Waldsteinia trifolia	W. ternata
Vitis obovata	V. labrusca	Wallia cinerea	Juglans cinerea
Vitis occidentalis	V. labrusca	Wallia nigra	Juglans nigra
Vitis odoratisiima -Donn	V. riparia	Washingtonia filamentosa	W. filifera
Vitis odoratissima	V. riparia	Watsonia ardernei	W. borbonica ssp ard.
Vitis orientalis	Ampelopsis orientalis		'Arderne's White'
Vitis parsley-leaved	V. vinifera 'Ciotat'	Watsonia beatricis	W. pillansii
Vitis persica -Boiss.	Ampelopsis vitifolia	Watsonia borbonica ssp ardernei	W. borbonica ssp ard.
Vitis populifolia	V. riparia		'Arderne's White'
Vitis prolifera	V. labrusca	Watsonia brevifolia	W. laccata
Vitis quinquefolia -(L). Lam.	Parthenocissus quinq.	Watsonia bulbillifera	W. meriana
Vitis quinquefolia v macrophylla	Parthenocissus quinq.	Watsonia coccinea -Baker	W. spectabilis
Vitis quinquefolia v major h.	Parthenocissus quinq.	Watsonia pyrimadata	W. borbonica
Vitis rhombifolia	Cissus rhombifolia	Watsonia roseoalba	W. humilis
Vitis Seibel 5455	V. 'Plantet'	Wattakaka	Dregea
Vitis semicordata -Wall.	Parthenocissus	Wattakaka sinensis -(Hemsl.) Stapf	Dregea sinensis
	himalayana	Weigela 'Avalanche' -Lemoine	W. praecox 'Avalanche'
Vitis serjanaefolia -(Bunge) K.Koch	V. japonica	Weigela 'Avalanche' h.	W. 'Candida'
Vitis Seyve Villard 12.375	V. 'Villard Blanc'	Weigela 'Bristol Snowflake'	W. 'Snowflake'
Vitis Seyve Villard 5276	V. 'Seyval Blanc'	Weigela 'Vanicek'	W. 'Newport Red'
Vitis striata -(Ruiz & Pavon) Miq.	Cissus striata	Weigela floribunda	W. japonica
Vitis taurina	V. labrusca	Weigela florida 'Variegata Aurea'	W. florida
Vitis thomsonii -M.A.Laws.	Cayratia thomsonii		'Aureovariegata'
Vitis vinifera 'Apiifolia'	V. vinifera 'Ciotat'	Weigela grandiflora	W. coraeensis
Vitis vinifera 'Black Alicante'	V. vinifera 'Alicante'	Weigela nikoensis -Nakai	W. decora
Vitis vinifera 'Black Hamburgh'	V. vi. 'Schiava Grossa'	Weigela pauciflora	W. florida
Vitis vinifera 'Blue Portuguese'	V. vinifera	Weigela rosea -Lindl.	W. florida
	'Portugieser'	Weigela sessilifolia	Diervilla sessilifolia
Vitis vinifera 'Bouviertraube'	V. vinifera 'Bouvier'	Weigela splendens -Carr.	Diervilla x splendens
Vitis vinifera 'Brant'	V. 'Brant'	Weingartia neocumingii	Rebutia neocumingii
Vitis vinifera 'Chasselas d'Or'	V. vinifera 'Chasselas'	Weinmannia paniculata -Cav.	Caldcluvia paniculata
Vitis vinifera 'Glory of Boskoop'	V. 'Boskoop Glory'	Wellingtonia gigantea	Sequoiadendron gigant.
Vitis vinifera 'Golden Chasselas'	V. vinifera 'Chasselas'	Welwitschia bainesii	W. mirabilis
Vitis vinifera 'Malbec'	V. vinifera 'Cot'	Werckleocereus glaber	Weberocereus glaber
Vitis vinifera 'Muscadet'	V. vinifera 'Melon de	Westringia cinerea	W. dampieri
	Bourgogne'	Westringia eremicola v quatema	W. eremicola
Vitis vinifera 'Royal Muscadine'	V. vinifera 'Chasselas'	Westringia grevillina	W. dampieri
Vitis vinifera 'Schwarzriesling'	V. vinifera 'Meunier'	Westringia raleighii	W. brevifolia v raleighii
Vitis vinifera 'Spatburgunder'	V. vinifera 'Pinot Noir'	Westringia rosmariniformis	W. fruticosa
Vitis vinifera 'Thompson Seedless'	V. vinifera 'Sultana'	Westringia violacea v violacea	W. glabra
Vitis vinifera Riesling-Silvaner	V. v. 'Muller-Thurgau'	Widdringtonia cupressoides	W. nodiflora
Vitis vinifera Strawberry Grape	V. 'Fragola'	Widdringtonia juniperoides -Endl.	W. cedarbergensis
Vitis vitacea -(Knerr) Bean	Parthenocissus inserta	Widdringtonia whytei -Rendle	W. nodiflora
Vitis voinieriana	Tetrastigma voinieri.	Wigandia macrophylla	W. caracasana
Vitis vulgaris	V. labrusca	Wigginsia	Parodia

Synonym	Current Name	Synonym	Current Name
Wigginsia vorwerkiana	Parodia vorwerkiana	Wittiocactus amazonicus	Disocactus amazonicus
Wilcoxia albiflora	Echinocereus leucanthus	Woodsia bellii	Woodsia alpina
		Woodsia brantii	Woodsia intermedia
Wilcoxia schmollii	Echinocereus schmollii	Woodsia perriniana	Woodsia obtusa
Wintera aromatica -(Murr.)	D. winteri	Woodsia subintermedia	Woodsia intermedia
Winteriana lanceolata -(Poir.)	D. lanceolata	Woodwardia angustifolia	W. areolata
Wisteria brachybotrys 'Alba Plena'	W. brachybotrys 'Shiro Kapitan'	Woodwardia banisteriana	W. virginica
		Woodwardia thelypteroides	W. virginica
Wisteria brachybotrys 'Alba'	W. brachybotrys 'Shiro Kapitan'	Wormia suffruticosa	Dillenia suffruticosa
		Worsleya procera	W. rayneri
Wisteria brachybotrys f alba	W. brachybotrys 'Shiro Kapitan'	x Achimenantha 'Cerulean Mink'	x Smithicodonia 'Cerulean Mink'
Wisteria brachybotrys f plena	W. b. 'Shiro Kapitan'	x Amarcrinum howardii	x A. memoria-corsii 'Howardii'
Wisteria chinensis	W. sinensis		
Wisteria floribunda 'Black Dragon'	W. x formosa 'Yae-kokuryu' (d)	x Aporoheliocereus mallisonii	x Aporoheliocereus smithii
Wisteria floribunda 'Burford'	W. 'Burford'	x Brunsdonna	x Amarygia
W. fl. 'Double Black Dragon' misap.	W. fl. 'Violacea Plena'	x Carmispartium astens	x C. hutchinsii
Wisteria floribunda 'Hichirimen'	W. floribunda 'Asagi'	x Citrofortunella Limequat	C. x floridana
Wisteria floribunda 'Hon-beni'	W. floribunda 'Rosea'	x Citrofort. microcarpa 'Variegata'	C. microcarpa 'Tiger'
Wisteria floribunda 'Honey Bee Pink'	W. floribunda 'Rosea'	x Citrofortunella mitis	C. microcarpa
Wisteria floribunda 'Honko'	W. floribunda 'Rosea'	x Citrofortunella mitis	x Citrofortunella microcarpa
Wisteria floribunda 'Jakohn-fuji'	W. sinensis 'Jako'		
Wisteria floribunda 'Lipstick'	W. fl. 'Kuchi-beni'	x Crinodonna	x Amarcrinum
W. floribunda 'Longissima Alba'	W. floribunda 'Alba'	x Crinodonna corsii	x Amarcrinum memoria-corsii
Wisteria floribunda 'Longissima'	W. fl. 'Multijuga'		
Wisteria floribunda 'Macrobotrys'	W. fl. 'Multijuga'	x Cupressocyparis 'Galway Gold'	x C. leylandii 'Castlewellan'
W. floribunda 'Peaches and Cream'	W. fl. 'Kuchi-beni'		
Wisteria floribunda 'Pink Ice'	W. floribunda 'Rosea'	x Cupressocyparis 'Variegata'	x C. ley. 'Harlequin'
Wisteria floribunda 'Shiro-noda'	W. floribunda 'Alba'	x Ericalluna bealeana 'W.G. Notley'	E. cinerea 'W.G. Notley'
Wisteria floribunda 'Snow Showers'	W. floribunda 'Alba'	x Fatshedera lizei 'Aureopicta'	x F. lizei 'Aurea'
Wisteria floribunda Murasaki-naga	W. fl. 'Purple Patches'	x Fatshedera lizei 'Lemon and Lime'	x F. lizei 'Annemieke'
Wisteria floribunda Reindeer	W. sinensis 'Jako'	x Fatshedera lizei 'Maculata'	x F. lizei 'Annemieke'
Wisteria floribunda Shiro-naga	W. floribunda 'Alba'	x Gaulnettya	Gaultheria
Wisteria frutescens 'Alba'	W. frutescens 'Nivea'	x Gaulthettya -Camp	Gaultheria
Wisteria frutescens 'Magnifica'	W. macrostachys 'Magnifica'	x Halimiocistus 'Susan'	Halimium 'Susan'
		x Halimiocistus algarvensis	Halimium ocymoides
Wisteria Kapitan-fuji	W. brachybotrys	x Halimiocistus ingwersenii	x H. 'Ingwersenii'
Wisteria multijuga	W. floribunda 'Multijuga'	x Halimiocistus revolii h.	x H. sahucii
		x Hulthemosa hardii -(Cels) Rowley	R. x hardii
Wisteria multijuga 'Alba'	W. floribunda 'Alba'	x Malosorbus florentina	Malus florentina
Wisteria multijuga 'Rosea'	W. floribunda 'Rosea'	x Osmarea burkwoodii	Osmanthus x burkwo.
Wisteria sinensis 'Consequa'	W. sinensis 'Prolific'	x Solidaster hybridus	x S. luteus
Wisteria sinensis 'Prematura Alba'	W. brachybotrys 'Shior-kapitan'	x Stranvinia 'Redstart'	Photinia 'Redstart'
		x Stranvinia 'Redstart'	Photinia x fraseri 'Redstart'
Wisteria sinensis 'Prematura'	W. floribunda 'Domino'		
Wisteria sinensis Shiro-capital	W. sinensis 'Alba'	x Stravinia	Photinia
Wisteria venusta	W. b. 'Shiro Kapitan'	x Venidioarctotis	Arctotis
Wisteria venusta 'Alba Plena'	W. brachybotrys 'Shiro Kapitan'	Xanthium sibiricum	X. strumarium
		Xanthorhiza apiifolia -L'Herit.	X. simpliciissima
Wisteria venusta v violacea	W. brachybotrys Murasaki-kapitan	Xanthosoma lindenii	Caladium lindenii
		Xanthoxylum	Zanthoxylum
Wisteria x formosa Black Dragon	W. x f. 'Yae-kokuryu'	Xanthoxylum daniellii -Benn.	Tetradium daniellii
Wisteria x formosa Domino	W. floribunda 'Domino'	Xenophya -Schott	Alocasia
Wittia amazonica	Disocactus amazonicus	Xeranthemum bracteatum	Xerochrysum bractea.

Synonym	Current Name	Synonym	Current Name
Xerotes	Lomandra	Zantedeschia 'Edge of Night'	Z. 'Black Star'
Xiphium latifolium	Iris latifolium	Zantedeschia africana	Z. aethiopica
Xolisma ligustrina -(L.) Britt.	Lyonia ligustrina	Zantedeschia black	Z. 'Schwarzwalder'
Xolisma lucida -(Lam.) Rehd.	Lyonia lucida	Zantedeschia melanoleuca	Z. albomaculata
Xolisma ovalifolia -(Wall.) Rehd.	Lyonia ovalifolia	Zantedeschia pentlandii	Z. angustiloba
Xylomelum pyriforme v salicinum	X. benthamii	Zanthorhiza	Xanthorhiza
Xylomelum salicinum	X. cunninghamianum	Zanthoxylum alatum v planispinum	Z. planispinum
Xylomelum salicinum	X. scottianum	Zanthoxylum bungei -Planch.	Z. simulans
Xylorhiza	Machaeranthera	Zanthoxylum fraxinifolium	Z. americanum
Xylosma congestum	Xylosma japonica	Zanthoxylum oppositifolium	Boronia alata
Xylosma racemosa	X. japonica	Zapania citriodora	Aloysia citriodora
Xylosma racemosum	X. japonica	Zauschneria arizonica	Z. californica ssp latifolia
Xylosteum	Lonicera		
Yucca angustifolia -Pursh	Y. glauca -Nutt.	Zauschneria californica 'Glasnevin'	Z. californica 'Dublin'
Yucca angustifolia v elata -Engelm.	Y. elata	Zauschneria californica microphylla	Z. californica ssp cana
Y. angustifolia v radiosa -Engelm.	Y. elata	Zauschneria cana villosa	Z. californica ssp mexicana
Yucca argospatha -Verlot	Y. treculeana -Carr.		
Yucca aspera -Reg.	Y. treculeana -Carr.	Zauschneria canescens -Eastw.	Z. californica ssplat.
Yucca baccata v macrocarpa -Torr.	Y. torreyi -Schafer	Zauschneria microphylla	Z. californica ssp cana
Yucca californica -Lemmon	Y. whipplei -Torr.	Zebrina pendula	Tradescantia zebrina
Yucca californica -Nutt. ex Baker	Y. schidigera	Zelkova acuminata -(Lindl.) Planch.	Z. serrata
Yucca carnerosana	Y. faxoniana -Sarg.	Zelkova crenata	Z. carpinifolia
Yucca concava -Haworth	Y. filamentosa -L.	Zelkova cretica -Spach	Z. abelicea
Yucca contorta h.	Y. treculeana -Carr.	Zelkova davidii -(Hance) Hemsl.	Hemiptelea davidii
Yucca cornuta h.	Y. treculeana -Carr.	Zelkova formosana	Z. serrata
Yucca crassifolia -Engelm.	Y. torreyi -Schafer	Zelkova hirta	Z. serrata
Yucca filifera 'Ivory'	Y. flaccida 'Ivory'	Zelkova keaki	Z. serrata
Yucca funifera -K.Koch	Hesperaloe funifera	Zelkova keaki (Sieb.) Maxim.	Z. serrata
Yucca gloriosa 'Aureovariegata'	Y. gloriosa 'Variegata'	Zenobia pulverulenta v nuda	Z. pulverulenta f nitida
Yucca gloriosa v mollis -Carr.	Y. recurvifolia -Salis.	Zephyranthes andersonii	Habranthus tubispathus
Yucca gloriosa v recurvifolia -	Y. recurvifolia -Salis.		
Yucca graminifolia -Wood	Y. whipplei -Torr.	Zephyranthes carinata	Z. grandiflora
Yucca guatemalensis -Baker	Y. elephantipes -Reg.	Zephyranthes robusta	Habranthus robustus
Yucca longifolia -Buckley	Y. treculeana -Carr.	Zerna canadensis	Bromus ciliatus
Yucca longifolia -Schultes	Nolina longifolia	Zerna ciliata	Bromus ciliatus
Yucca macrocarpa	Y. torreyi -Schafer	Zerna inermis	Bromus inermis
Yucca mohavensis -Sarg.	Y. schidigera	Zexmenia hispida	Wedelia texana
Yucca newberryi -McKelvey	Y. whipplei -Torr.	Zichya glabrata	Kennedia glabrata
Yucca nitida -C.Wright ex W.Watson	Y. whipplei -Torr.	Zinnia angustifolia	Z. haageana
Yucca parviflora -Torr.	Hesperaloe parviflora	Zinnia angustifolia	Z. linearis
Yucca parviflora v engelmannii	Hesperaloe parviflora v engelmannii	Zinnia angustifolia h.	Z. haageana
		Zinnia haageana 'Classic'	Z. haag. 'Orange Star'
Yucca parvifolia -Hemsley	Hesperaloe parviflora	Zinnia mexicana	Z. haageana
Yucca pendula -Groen.	Y. recurvifolia -Salis.	Zizania caducifolia	Z. latifolia
Yucca radiosa	Y. elata	Ziziphora glabella	Calamintha arkansana
Yucca recurva -Haworth	Y. recurvifolia -Salis.	Ziziphus flavescens	Berchemia flavescens
Yucca rupicola v rigida -Engelm.	Y. rigida	Ziziphus sativa	Z. jujuba
Yucca smalliana -Fernald	Y. filamentosa -L.	Ziziphus vulgaris	Z. jujuba
Yucca torreyi f parviflora -McKelvey	Y. torreyi -Schafer	Zygocactus truncatus	Schlumbergera trunca.
Yucca tortifolia -Lind. ex Engelm.	Y. rupicola -Scheele	Zygopetalum mackayi	Z. mackaii
Yucca vandervinniana -Koch	Y. treculeana -Carr.		
Zabelia triflora	Abelia triflora		
Zantedeschia 'Best Gold'	Z. 'Florex Gold'		
Zantedeschia 'Black Forest'	Z. 'Shwarzwalder'		
Zantedeschia 'Black Pearl'	Z. 'Schwarzwalder'		

Abbreviation of Authors' Names

Abbr.	Name	Abbr.	Name	Abbr.	Name	Abbr.	Name
A. Cunn	A. Cunningham	Franch.	Franchet	Muell.	Mueller	Vent.	Ventenat
Adans.	Adanson	Gaertn.	J. Gaertner	Muhl.	Muhlenberg	Vis.	R.de Visiani
A. Gr	A. Gray	Gardn.	Gardner	N. E. Br.	N. E. Brown	Wald.	Walden
All.	Allioni	G. Don	George Don	Newm.	Newman	Waldst.	Waldstein
A. Murr.	A. Murray	Gilib.	Gilibert	Nutt.	Thomas Nuttall	Wall.	Wallich
Andr.	Andreanszky	Godr.	D. A. Godron	Orph.	Orphanides	Walt.	Walter
Arn.	G. A. W. Arnott	Gord.	Gordon	Pall.	Pallas	Waganh.	Wangenheim
Bartl.	F. G. Bartling	Graebn.	Graebner	Pav.	Pavon	Wanger.	Wangerin
Batal.	Batalin	Gren.	J. C. M. Grenier	Paxt.	Paxton	Wats.	Watson
Benth.	Bentham	Griff.	W. Griffith	Pers.	Persoon	Weng.	Wengmayr
Bercht.	Berchtold	Guin.	Guinochet	Phil.	Philippi	Willd.	Willdenow
Bertol.	Bertoloni	Hacq.	Hacquet	Poepp.	Poeppig	Wils.	Wilson
Bge.	Bunge	Hand.Mazz.	Handel-Mazzetti	Poit.	Poitier	W.W. Sm.	W. W. Smith
Bl.	Blume	Handl.	Handley	Raf.	Rafinesque	Zucc.	Zuccarini
Blake.	Blakely	Hartw.	Hartweg	R. Br.	Robert Brown		
Boiss.	Boissier	HBK	H B Kane	Reg.	Regel		
Bong.	Bongard	Heist.	Heister	Rehd.	Rehder		
Borkh.	Borkhausen	Hemsl.	Hemsley	Reichb.	Reichenbach		
Britt.	Britten	Herd.	Herder	Roem.	Roemer		
Brongn.	Brongniart	H. Karst.	H. Karsten	Roxb.	W. Roxburgh		
Brot.	Brotero	Hook.	Hooker	Rubr.	Rubrizius		
B urb.	Burbidge	Houtt.	Houttuyn	Rupr.	Ruprecht		
Burgsdf.	Burgsdorff	Huds.	Hudson	Rusb.	Rusby		
Cambess.	Cambessedes	Jacks.	G. Jackson	Rydb.	P. A. Rydberg		
C. A. Mey	Meyer	Jacq.	N. von Jacquin	Salis.	Salisbury		
Carr.	Carriere	Juss.	Jussieu	Sarg.	Sargent		
Cav.	Cavaliere	Kirchn.	Kirchner	Sart.	Sartorelli		
C. B. Cl.	C. B. Clarke	Kit.	Kitaibel	Sav.	Savatier		
Cheesem.	Cheeseman	L.	Linnaeus	Schltr.	Schlechter		
Chev.	Chevalier	l'Herit.	L'Heritier	Scheid.	Scheidegger		
Chois.	Choisy	Labill.	Labillardiere	Schlect.	Schlecter		
Ckn.	Cockayne	Lam.	Lamarck	Schneid.	Schneider		
Coss.	Cosson	Lemm.	Lemmens	Schult.	J. A. Schultes		
Coult.	T. Coulter	Less.	Lessing	Scop.	G A Scopoli		
Dallim.	Dallimore	Lev.	Leveille	Seem.	Seemann		
DC.	De Candolle	Lind.	Lindley	Ser.	Seringe		
D. Don	David Don	Lingelsh.	Lingelsheim	Seraf.	Serafimov		
Decne.	Decaisne	Loisel.	Loiseleur	Sm.	Smith		
Delarb.	Delarbre	Loud.	Louden	Spreng.	Sprengel		
Desf.	Desfontaine	Mak.	Makino	Standl.	Standley		
Dipp.	Dippel	Marsh.	Marshall	Steud.	Steudel		
Dougl.	Douglas	Mast.	Masters	Sw.	Swartz		
E. Desv.	E. Desvaux	Matsum.	Matsumae	Szyssz.	Szyszylowicz		
Ehrh.	Ehrhardt	Maxim.	Maximowicz	Targ. Tozz.	Targioni Tozzetti		
Endl.	Endlicher	Med.	Medeiros	Ten.	Tenore		
Engel.	Engelmann	Meissn.	Meissner	Thell.	A. Thellung		
Facc.	Facchini	Michx.	Michaux	Thunb.	Thunberg		
Fisch.	F. E. L. von Fischer	Mill.	Miller	Torr.	John Torrey		
Forst.	W. Forster	Miq.	Miquel	Tratt.	Trattinnick		
Forstn.	Forstner	Mitf.	Mitford	Trautv.	Trautvetter		
		Moq.	Moquin-Tandon	Turc.	Turczaninow		